HANDBOOK OF NATURAL RESOURCE AND ENERGY ECONOMICS

VOLUME I

HANDBOOKS
IN
ECONOMICS
6

Series Editors

KENNETH J. ARROW
MICHAEL D. INTRILIGATOR

NORTH-HOLLAND
AMSTERDAM · NEW YORK · OXFORD

HANDBOOK OF NATURAL RESOURCE AND ENERGY ECONOMICS

VOLUME I

Edited by

ALLEN V. KNEESE

Resources for the Future, Inc.

and

JAMES L. SWEENEY

Stanford University

1985

NORTH-HOLLAND
AMSTERDAM · NEW YORK · OXFORD

ISBN North-Holland for this set 0 444 87646 4
ISBN North-Holland for this volume 0 444 87644 8

Publishers
ELSEVIER SCIENCE PUBLISHERS B.V.
P.O. Box 1991
1000BZ Amsterdam
The Netherlands

Sole distributors for the U.S.A. and Canada
ELSEVIER SCIENCE PUBLISHING COMPANY, INC.
52 Vanderbilt Avenue
New York, N.Y. 10017
U.S.A.

Library of Congress Cataloging in Publication Data

Main entry under title:

Handbook of natural resource and energy economics.

   (Handbooks in economics ; v. 6)
   Includes bibliographies.
   1. Energy industries. 2. Natural resources.
3. Conservation of natural resources. 4. Power resources.
5. Environmental protection. I. Kneese, Allen V.
II. Sweeney, James L. III. Series: Handbooks in
economics ; bk. 6.
HD9502.A2H257 1985   333.7   85-10322
ISBN 0-444-87646-4 (set)

PRINTED IN THE NETHERLANDS

INTRODUCTION TO THE SERIES

The aim of the *Handbooks in Economics* series is to produce Handbooks for various branches of economics, each of which is a definitive source, reference, and teaching supplement for use by professional researchers and advanced graduate students. Each Handbook provides self-contained surveys of the current state of a branch of economics in the form of chapters prepared by leading specialists on various aspects of this branch of economics. These surveys summarize not only received results but also newer developments, from recent journal articles and discussion papers. Some original material is also included, but the main goal is to provide comprehensive and accessible surveys. The Handbooks are intended to provide not only useful reference volumes for professional collections but also possible supplementary readings for advanced courses for graduate students in economics.

CONTENTS OF THE HANDBOOK

PART 6 – ENVIRONMENT AND RENEWABLE RESOURCES IN SOCIALIST SYSTEMS

VOLUME III

PART 1 – SOME BASIC CONCEPTS

PART 2 – ANALYTICAL TOOLS

PREFACE TO THE HANDBOOK

Natural resources have been studied by economists from the earliest days of the profession. They have been seen as providing a basis for national prosperity, power, and wealth. The ability to harness energy in new ways has been recognized as a major, if not the major, factor underlying the industrial revolution. Because forests, fisheries, and agricultural land are fundamental to food supplies, these resources have been long studied.

Yet only relatively recently have there been developed broad theories specific to the fields of natural resources and energy economics. Previously, examination of these fields relied upon the general economic theories being utilized for analysis of other commodities. More recently, however, it has been recognized by economists that certain special characteristics of natural resources have required theories which explicitly accounted for these characteristics.

Agricultural land, forest, and fisheries have been seen only in the last generation to be usefully described as renewable resources. Such resources are self-renewing at a limited rate which may itself depend upon the size of the stock in existence at any given time and upon the extent and nature of human intervention into the stock dynamics.

Minerals and many energy commodities are now seen as depletable or nonrenewable resources. These are resources for which only a limited concentrated stock exists for allocation over all time. For these resources, a central issue involves *when* they should be extracted, since a decision to utilize a given portion of the stock at one moment of time precludes the opportunity of using that portion at another time.

Even more recently have the environmental resources – air, water, open space – been also seen as renewable or even in some cases depletable resources. The image of environmental resources, fisheries, and wild animal stocks as common property resources owned by everyone and hence by no one is also of relatively recent development. And even more recently, economists have systematically incorporated concepts of materials balance into theories of the flow of physical materials from the natural environment, through the economy, and back into the natural environment.

And it has been only since the early 1970s that energy resources have been given particular attention as a matter for theorizing, empirical testing, and policy-making.

Thus, there now exists a set of concepts which unite the field of natural resource economics. While these concepts are also finding application in other branches of economics, their formalization has been motivated by the need to better understand natural resource issues.

Also uniting the study of natural resource issues is the growing realization that most important energy and natural resource issue are inherently interdisciplinary. The interdisciplinary nature requires applied work to integrate information from some combination of physics, engineering, chemistry, biology, ecology, political science, and law.

To a lesser extent the current theories also reflect this interdisciplinary reality. Materials balance concepts from physics are now fundamental to economic theories of the environment. Population dynamics concepts from biology and ecology are intertwined with economic concepts in renewable resources theories. Thermodynamic concepts and concepts of energy conservation are fundamental to theoretical work on energy economics. Legal concepts of property rights and ownership greatly influence analysis of environmental economics.

The study of resource economics has thus required and motivated researchers to reach out beyond their own disciplines and to integrate ideas from other fields into their own disciplines. Presumably this integration will influence not only resource economics but also other areas within economics.

The three volume comprising the *Handbook of Natural Resource and Energy Economics* examine the current theory and sample current application methods for natural resource and energy economics. Volumes I and II deal with the economics of environmental and renewable resources. Volume III, which is still in preparation and whose outline is included in this volume, will deal with the economics of energy and minerals.

Volumes I and II are divided into six parts. Part 1, which deals with basic concepts, consists of five chapters. The first chapter discusses environmental issues and welfare economics. Among the more penetrating developments in the short history of environmental economics is a wedding of the concepts of economic general equilibrium, materials balance, and common property resources into a single unified theory. This model offers a systematic explanation of the occurrence of pollution-type environmental problems and an opportunity to explore the welfare economics of suggested remedies. In Chapter 1, Karl-Göran Mäler uses a version of this model to provide a general theoretical framework for the field of environmental economics.

Chapter 2 attests to the interdisciplinary character of both environmental and renewable resource economics. In it James Wilen explains the bioeconomic models pertinent to these fields. The response of biological systems both to insults and to management actions is a central concern in many natural resource problems. Often, models simulating these responses are an integral part of the economic analysis of such problems.

In much of economics the spatial relationships among economic activities can be safely ignored. In environmental economics these relationships can rarely be ignored. Environmental effects of human action occur in and through space; neglect of this fact can lead to serious error. Space is involved in such matters as the degradation of residuals in the environment, the effects of airborne residuals on visibility, and the efficiency of alternative environmental policies. Moreover, environmental economics must address problems of interregional and international trade. In Chapter 3, Horst Siebert explores the spatial aspects of environmental economics.

Conservation of natural resources is a long-standing human concern. But in the last two decades there has been active economics research addressing the problems related not to scarcity of resource commodities, but rather to the protection of natural areas. This research has concerned itself with such issues as irreversibility, option values, and asymmetric technological change. In Chapter 4, Anthony Fisher and John Krutilla address these new conservation issues.

The final chapter in Part 1 deals with ethics and environmental economics. The theoretical underpinning of benefit–cost analysis, one of the basic tools of natural resource economics, is welfare economics. Welfare economics, in turn, can be viewed as an enormous elaboration and adaptation of an ethical theory: classical utilitarianism. But there are other valid ethical systems. And these other systems might imply quite different outcomes if applied to natural resources problems. For example, issues such as the long-term storage of nuclear waste and changes in climate resulting from resource use raise ethical issues perhaps more strongly than is usual in economics. These concerns are addressed in Chapter 5 by William Schulze and Allen Kneese.

Part 2 deals with methods and applications of economics to environmental problems. In Chapter 6, A. Myrick Freeman reviews methods for assessing the benefits of environmental programs. One of the most challenging areas of environmental economics, development of methods for estimating benefits of environmental improvements, has also been one of the most active areas of research in recent years. The interest results, in part at least, from increased pressure to demonstrate benefits from the costly environmental improvement and protection programs put into place by governments of industrialized countries in recent years.

Another major area of environmental economics, pursued especially actively in the 1970s, is the application of quantitative (usually linear) economic models to environmental questions. Such models have been applied to analyze effects of alternative policies on residuals generation and on control cost at both the industrial and regional level of detail. For regional analysis transfer functions which translate emissions at various points into ambient concentration at other receptor points – are often embedded directly into economic models. David James reviews both industrial and regional models and their applications in Chapter 7.

An important class of linear models applied to environmental problems is that of national input–output models. When outfitted with residuals generation coefficients and residuals control options such models can be utilized to analyze indirect, as well as direct, effects on the environment of economic growth, changes in product mix, and alteration of other variables of interest. In Chapter 8, Finn Førsund describes the use of national input–output models, with special application to the economy of Norway.

Part 3 of the Handbook includes two chapters on the economics of environmental policy. Chapter 9, by Gregory Christainsen and Tom Tietenberg, reviews what is known about the distributional and macroeconomic consequences of environmental policy. How, if at all, does environmental policy contribute to inflation or to unemployment? How are the costs and benefits of environmental policy distributed among income groups? This chapter describes methods of addressing such questions and offers a set of conclusions.

Chapter 10, by Peter Bohm and Clifford Russell, provides a comparative analysis of environmental policy instruments. While the idea of effluent fees as a policy instrument flows naturally from abstract economic reasoning, most governments have chosen not to follow economists' advice and have resorted to command and control strategies. Also advocated by some economists, and partially implemented, are tradeable permits to emit residuals. Deposit-and-return systems are also applied to some environmental problems and may have potential for dealing with others. This chapter reviews what the last twenty years of economic research have shown about the strength and weaknesses of these various approaches.

Part 4 deals with uses of renewable resources other than simply as recipients of residuals. Water resource development and use has probably received more attention from economists than any other natural resources subject except agriculture. There are at least three reasons for this attention. Because federal water resources agencies have long practiced benefit–cost analysis in the evaluation of water resources, there has been much opportunity for economists to develop and use theoretical concepts, methods, and data for such evaluations. Second, the development of river systems for multiple purposes has provided interesting opportunities for the application of systems analysis, that close relative of microeconomics. Third, market processes have played some role in the allocation of scarce western water. Chapter 11, by Robert Young and Robert Haveman, reviews economic and institutional aspects of water development.

The remaining two chapters in this part, Chapter 12 by Michael Bowes and John Krutilla, and Chapter 13 by Alan Randall and Emery Castle, deal with land use, although not in the traditional manner as a factor of production in agriculture or yielder of a single product, wood, in forestry.

Chapter 12 deals with the management of wildlands. Recognizing that wildlands yield not only timber but also recreational and aesthetic values, this chapter integrates theory derived from the forestry literature with that from the multipurpose firm literature. Chapter 13 also departs from the conventional view of land, using an asset pricing model to analyze land markets. The chapter includes an in-depth study of rent determination, examining influences of macroeconomic changes and of growing alternative demand for land on land prices, and in turn examines the reaction of land prices to increasing rents. The chapter also explores implications for land use planning and regulation and examines the role of land in the evolution of economic thinking.

Part 5 deals with the economics of renewable resource goods or services provision. Chapter 14, by Anthony Scott and Gordon Munro, treats commercial fishery economics. Commercial fishing has fascinated natural resources economists because this activity uses a common property resource as an essential input. The common property nature of the resource in a free market leads to decisions which produce economic inefficiency. Free access can lead to excessive depletion of the resource and to excess investment, both phenomena eliminating any net economic returns that would, under optimal management, be available from this resource. The chapter reviews these issues and spells out implications for public policy and international cooperation.

Chapter 15, the final one in this part, by Kenneth McConnell, treats the economics of outdoor recreation. It surveys conceptual and empirical approaches, problems, and solutions encountered in applying economics to the provision of natural resources for recreational purposes. It also shows how the evolution of the economics of outdoor recreation was influenced by the distinctive nature of markets for outdoor recreation.

Part 6 concludes Volumes I and II with two case studies dealing with environment and renewable resources in socialist systems. The first, by Marshall Goldman, focuses upon the Soviet Union, and the second, dealing with China, is by Shigeto Tsuru.

Since in socialist states all means of production are owned by the state, a superficial view might suggest that all externalities would be internalized and that, therefore, there would be no incentive to generate excessive residuals or overuse renewable resources. Goldman, in his study, shows that for the Soviet Union this impression is very far from the truth. He argues that the incentives for abusing resources are at least as large as in market economies and, possibly, much larger. Tsuru's study of China suggests that the situation may be somewhat different there. China is a developing economy and resources for environmental protection are accordingly limited. There is, however, explicit recognition of the environmental problem, and there is a public policy aimed at the comprehensive recycling of wastes. Presumably, this recycling is motivated by the scarcity of resource inputs as well as by a desire for control of residuals.

ALLEN V. KNEESE
Resources for the Future, Inc.

JAMES L. SWEENEY
Stanford University

CONTENTS OF VOLUME I

PART 1

SOME BASIC CONCEPTS

Chapter 1

WELFARE ECONOMICS AND THE ENVIRONMENT

KARL-GÖRAN MÄLER*

The Stockholm School of Economics, Stockholm

1. Introduction

The purpose of this chapter is to survey environmental economics as seen from the standpoint of neoclassical welfare economics. As a survey, no attempts have been made to go into operational aspects of the theory. However, a kind of theoretical framework for measurements of welfare effects of changes in the environment is offered in the latter part of this chapter. This framework is founded on a "general equilibrium approach" to environmental problems. That approach is presented in the first part of the chapter. The same approach can be and has been used as a framework for a discussion of the choice of environmental policy instruments. We will not go into that, however, in this chapter (Chapter 10 of this Handbook deals with environmental policy).

The basic aim of this chapter is thus to give a conceptual theoretical framework for environmental economics. This framework will be presented in mathematical form. Although this may deter some readers, the conveniences of a mathematical approach are obvious in this case. First, it is possible to develop the theory in a logical way (assuming of course that the mathematics used is correct). Second, it gives a way of showing that the concepts that are constructed are not void but do theoretically exist. This is important in particular in connection with the discussion of the concept of a Lindahl equilibrium and the Coase controversy. Third, most of the models to be presented are too complex to admit simple verbal analysis, which means that a mathematical discussion is necessary.

The basic concept in the presentation is the concept of a "Lindahl equilibrium". It is the most natural correspondence in an economy with public goods to the

*In writing this chapter I have benefited substantially from discussions with many colleagues. Above all I would like to mention the advice I got from Lars Bergman, Clas Bergström, Peter Englund, Stefan Lundgren and Mats Persson, all at the Stockholm School of Economics, and Allen Kneese at Resources for the Future. My debt to them is substantial. Of course, I absolve them from any responsibility for mistakes and faults that still probably remain. Finally, Marianne Widing has in a wonderful way translated my illegible handwriting into typed pages, a feat I appreciate very much.

Handbook of Natural Resource and Energy Economics, vol. I, edited by A.V. Kneese and J.L. Sweeney
© *Elsevier Science Publishers B.V., 1985*

"competitive equilibrium" in an economy without public goods. The traditional general equilibrium models discuss the case where all goods in the model are privately owned and sold and bought on perfect markets. It is well known that the equilibrium in such an economy has some very desirable properties, the most important being that it is Pareto efficient, i.e. that there are no other feasible allocations in the economy which are more desired by some individuals but not less desired by all others. Moreover, it can be shown that every allocation that is Pareto efficient can be accomplished as a competitive equilibrium. Now, these theorems are of course not valid in an economy where environmental effects in the form of public goods exist. But, by using the Lindahl equilibrium concept similar results may be obtained. By a Lindahl equilibrium we mean an equilibrium in an economy with perfect markets for all private goods and in which a special agency (in most cases called a government but in our application an environment protection agency) is responsible for the provision of public goods. All households are assumed to be utility maximizing and all firms are assumed to be profit maximizing. The environment protection agency is also assumed to maximize its profit. This profit results from selling waste disposal services to households and firms (either in the form of charges on emissions of residuals to the environment or by selling pollution rights on an auction market) and from the value of environmental services (net of the cost of providing such services). These services consist of clean air, water, increased productivity due to less pollution, increase in recreational amenities due to clean-ups, etc. The value of these services can be interpreted as a market value if these services are sold on a competitive basis to households and firms. However, there are strong reasons (see Section 4) to doubt that such markets could function and the value of the services must be interpreted in a different way. By assuming that the agency can reveal the preferences of all households (and firms) for environmental services, it follows that the agency can calculate the "equilibrium" prices for such services (i.e. the marginal willingness to pay for them) and the value of the services will henceforth be defined as the value calculated with these prices.

Thus the environment protection agency maximizes its revenues from selling waste disposal services and the total value of the environmental services (net of costs for cleaning up the environment or treatment of wastes). This economy could be interpreted as one in which there are perfect markets for all private goods including waste disposal services and in which the flow of environmental services is determined by cost–benefit analysis, where the marginal willingness to pay for environmental services is used to evaluate the benefits of them. The resulting state of the economy will be called a Lindahl equilibrium. This is, however, unusual usage because there are no markets for the environmental service and thus no equilibrium in a market sense for these services. Instead, one should perhaps call this concept a Lindahl pseudo equilibrium, but we will keep to the simpler terminology.

It can now be proved that under certain conditions there exists a Lindahl equilibrium and that this equilibrium is Pareto efficient. Moreover, every Pareto efficient allocation can be achieved as a Lindahl equilibrium by a suitable redistribution of income. These theorems are proved in Sections 4 and 5. In these sections, a discussion of the assumptions necessary for the theorems is also given, mainly the convexity assumption. The assumption that production sets are convex is necessary in ordinary welfare economics to prove the equivalence of competitive equilibria and Pareto efficient states. Usually convexity is motivated by a reference to infinite divisibility and decreasing marginal productivity of each factor of production. However, these arguments are of no value in the case of the production of environmental services and it is the rule that the production function describing the production of environmental services by reducing the discharge of wastes cannot be assumed to be concave. Still a Lindahl equilibrium may exist but the nonconvexities will cause computational and implementational problems.

These problems in a general equilibrium setting are discussed in Sections 4 and 5. A very brief survey of the foundation of neoclassical welfare economics is given in Section 2, while Section 3 gives the basic ideas used later on the interaction between discharges of wastes into the environment and the resulting flow of environmental services.

One could perhaps summarize the first five sections in the chapter by stating the fundamental results, already referred to above, that there exists a Lindahl equilibrium, that each such equilibrium is Pareto efficient, and conversely that each Pareto efficient state can be achieved by a Lindahl equilibrium. Such an equilibrium is defined as a state in which there are markets for each private good which equilibrate and that there is an agency selling waste disposal services to households and firms and maximizing the resulting revenues together with the imputed value of the flow of the environmental services.

In Section 7 a theoretical discussion is given of various methods that can be and have been used for estimating the value of the flow of environmental services. However, in order to make the chapter self-contained, Section 5 contains a brief survey of the basic consumption theory needed for this discussion. The focal point is the possibility of solving the Slutsky equations in order to derive the utility function from observed demand functions. If one could disregard aggregation problems, it is possible to derive the complete utility function defined on quantities of private goods from the demand functions for these goods. However, as it is not possible to empirically observe demand for environmental services directly, it is not possible to obtain in this way a utility function defined on quantities of private goods *and* the flow of environmental services.

In Section 7, three different approaches to solve this problem, i.e. to obtain that information are discussed. These approaches are: (i) to ask people about their willingness to pay for environmental services; (ii) to make assumptions on preferences which will enable one to derive the utility function over environmental services from the demand functions for private goods; and (iii) to make assumptions that imply that the value of some environmental services is capitalized in the price of some private goods.

These three approaches are discussed at various length in Section 7. The reader should be warned, however, that the number of pages devoted to each approach does not necessarily indicate anything about the opinion of the author about them. The first approach, for example, is very briefly discussed, because it does not seem to be possible to say anything general about it (some additional discussion of this approach is found in Chapter 6 of this Handbook).

In Section 6 the distribution problem is addressed. Who gets the benefits from environmental improvements is a very relevant question which is neglected up to Section 5. In that section the proper choice of welfare measures in view of the fact that distribution matters is discussed.

Finally, some words about the presentation. The chapter is divided into seven sections, most of which are further divided into subsections. The equations are numbered consecutively within each subsection. A list of references appears at the end of the chapter. No attempt has been made to make that list complete. Instead, it only contains such books or articles which directly or indirectly influenced this chapter.

2. Welfare economics

Neoclassical welfare economics[1] deals with the logical implications of various value judgements for the organization of society. Welfare economics is thus normative and aims at giving policy recommendations. As a normative discipline, it is impossible to empirically test the implications that the theory yields. The only way to assert the validity of the theory is to criticaly evaluate all the assumptions the results require and the logic behind the derivations of the implications. All these implications are thus conditional on the underlying value judgements and the assumed functioning of the economy. In order to derive as general implications as possible, it is common in economics to start with a set of very broad value judgements.

The first such judgement is that it is the end states that matter and not the process by which these end states are chosen.[2]

---

[1] The classical presentation of welfare economics in de Graaf (1957). Now, most textbooks on microeconomics include chapters on welfare economics. One modern presentation on which much of the following presentation is based is Sugden (1981).

[2] For a deeper discussion of this and deeper issues consult Sugden (1981) and Nozick (1974) which contains the original contribution.

The end states are typically defined in terms of the allocation of resources between different uses and the distribution of output between different individuals. A certain end state may thus be described by the allocation of factors of production among different production activities and the distribution of the resulting output among the members of society. Such an end state may be achieved in various ways, e.g. as a result of market forces or by administrative decisions. To say that it is the end states that matter means that it is of no concern how the end state is achieved. Of course, the assumption that only end states matter is a rather far-reaching one and not wholly realistic. It certainly matters to me that I have chosen my bundle of consumer goods myself instead of having to consume a bundle prescribed by a dictator, even if it is the same bundle. This remark seems to have special strength in connection with problems of the environment since environmental quality is a collective good. We will later in this chapter come back to a brief discussion of this assumption.

However, the simplifications made possible by this assumption are sufficient to warrant a study of its implications. Moreover, some of the more important implications are also true when the assumption that only end states matter is discarded.

The next three value judgements provide the basis for Paretian welfare economics.[3]

(1) Each individual is the best judge of his own welfare.

(2) The welfare of society depends on the individual welfare of its citizens.

(3) If the welfare of one individual increases and the welfare of no one decreases, the welfare of society increases.

These three assumptions build welfare economics on an individualistic approach. What is relevant is the individual's preferences, which are assumed to be autonomous. There are, of course, several examples when even liberal societies take objection against a complete individualistic approach, drug control being perhaps the best example. However, it seems that these counter examples in no way are pervasive in Western democratic societies. Therefore, it is of considerable interest to find out the implications of an individualistic approach for environmental policy. More problematic is the assumption of autonomous preferences. The preferences of an individual are obviously dependent on his whole environment – his childhood, education, culture and even advertisements.[4] Any change in this environment may change his preferences and therefore society's view of the desirability of that change. Important as this problem may be, we will circumvent it by assuming that the individuals possess stable and autonomous preferences over bundles of produced goods and environmental qualities (in the next section we will discuss the meaning of environmental qualities).

---

[3] This is directly based on Sugden (1981).
[4] For a discussion of related problem, see Arrow and Hahn (1971).

As general as these four assumptions are, they still permit some far-reaching conclusions in welfare economics. One of the aims of this chapter is to find the corresponding conclusions when the theory is applied to an abstract economy where free disposal is not assumed. On the contrary, we will focus on an abstract economy in which one of the main problems is the cost of disposal of nondesired excess supplies. However, the four assumptions yield only a partial ordering of the possible end states, as they are not strong enough to discriminate between changes by which at least one individual is better off and at least one is worse off. In order to be able to say something about the desirability of such changes, value judgements about the inter-personal distribution of welfare are needed, namely:

(4) There exists a social welfare ordering over all possible end states, which is consistent with the first three assumptions.

Such a social welfare ordering is sometimes called a Paretian welfare ordering or a Bergson–Samuelson social welfare ordering.[5]

Nothing has so far been said about who possesses this social welfare ordering. It may represent an arbitrary individual or a benevolent dictator. For the applications in cost–benefit analysis the most reasonable interpretation would be that the social welfare ordering represent the preferences of the government or the relevant decision-maker, whoever that may be. In terms of our first assumption that only end states matter, it is not of prime importance whose welfare ordering we are discussing. The main factor is the properties of the ordering.

3. The environment[6]

When discussing private goods, it is usually assumed that there is a finite number of well-defined goods, the amount of which can be measured in an objective way. There are obviously difficulties because of different quality of goods but these can be overcome, at least in theory, by increasing the number of goods so that each has its own well-defined quality, its own well-defined location, etc. When it comes to a discussion of the natural environment, things are not so simple. It is, for example, not generally possible to attach a number to a scenic view and interpret that number as a measure of the quality of the view. What number should be attached to the view of Grand Canyon of Colorado? The Grand Canyon consists of an infinite number of details, and it is the composition of these details that

---

[5] See de Graaf (1957) and Sugden (1981) for a discussion of the concept of a social welfare function. The concept was first introduced by Bergson (1938). However, it was Samuelson who systematically made use of this concept in order to discuss welfare aspects of different policies.

For the possibility (or rather impossibility) of getting a social welfare function from aggregating individual preferences, see Arrow (1963) and Sen (1970).

[6] This section is based on Mäler (1974).

makes this canyon so overwhelmingly beautiful. This remark leads to the idea that each detail or point in the Grand Canyon can be represented by a vector S, the components of which describe the quality of that point – colour, materials, chemical and physical composition, etc. To each point of the Grand Canyon we can thus associate a vector S which describes the relevant characteristics of that point and it is the aggregate of all these vectors that constitute the particular quality of the Grand Canyon. But this collection of vectors is nothing but a mapping defined on all points in or around the Grand Canyon and with values that describe the qualities of each point. The formal definition of environmental quality would thus go as follows.

Let (x_1, x_2, x_3) be the coordinates of spatial points in the environment and let t be the chronological time. Let E be a subset of R^3 and let F be some set, to be interpreted as a set of environmental characteristics. The quality over time of the region E in the environment is then defined as a mapping f defined on $E\,R$ and with values in F:

$$E : E \times R \ni (X_1, X_2, X_3, t) \to F(X_1, X_2, X_3, t) \in F. \tag{3.1}$$

The environmental quality is thus described as a function and the set of all possible states of the environment will lead to a study of subsets in a function space, i.e. in an infinite dimensional space. However, for most applications a finite dimensional approximation is used, and that is the approximation we shall use in this chapter. We thus assume that there exists a vector $Q \in R^m$, the components of which describe the quality of the environment. One component of Q may measure the dissolved oxygen in a lake at a certain time, another component may measure the dissolved oxygen in another lake, still another component may measure the ground-level ambient concentration of sulfur dioxides at a certain grid point, etc. This vector Q will alternatively be referred to as the vector of environmental quality, the vector of the state of the environment, or the vector of environmental services.

From an economic point of view, environmental services will be regarded as collective or public goods in the sense that a change in one environmental service is of concern for all households and all producers. The valuation of this change may vary between the agents in the economy, but we assume from the onset that all environmental services potentially may be of concern for all agents.

It is easy to find examples of environmental services for which probably only one agent has a concern, e.g. environmental quality limited to a piece of privately owned land. In this case, this quality could be regarded as a characterization of that piece of land and one could argue that it is not a concept for which there is collective concern. In spite of this, it is convenient to include even such cases in our framework of environmental services. In the models to be developed in later sections, these "private" environmental services will have shadow prices that equal the "owner's" marginal valuation of the service. Thus, even if the service is classified as one of collective concern, our results will be so general as to admit the interpretation that only one agent has concern for that service.

The reason that we treat environmental services as public goods is of course that most of these services are of collective concern. Ambient air quality in the down town area of a city will be of concern for all individuals staying there and a change in that quality will consequently affect all these individuals.

The destruction of a scenic landscape is similarly of collective concern, first for all who visit the area but second also for many others who may in the future visit this area (this situation is discussed further in connection with option values). Many agents would also be concerned even if they know they never will visit the area. This concern is called intrinsic value (these types of values are discussed further in Chapters 4 and 6 of this Handbook).

Thus, it seems that no loss in generality is incurred by assuming that the environmental services are of collective concern and in fact most of them have the characteristics of public goods.

The vector of environmental quality depends on the actions of people in many ways. By direct changes in the environment, for example in the form of highway construction, hydropower development, etc., the vector Q is changed. Most of the analysis in this chapter will, however, focus on a more indirect source of environmental changes, namely by pollution. Another way is through using the renewable properties of the environment in the form of agriculture, fisheries, etc. These latter changes are in particular salient for our discussions of general equilibrium, Lindahl equilibria, and Pareto optimality. However, the general principles to be derived for cost–benefit analysis are equally valid for any change in the environment.

The general framework of economic–environmental interactions to be used in this chapter is set out in Figure 1.1. The main purpose of this diagram is to illustrate the circular flow of materials from the extraction of primary resources from the environment through production and consumption activities and back to the environment.

In the diagram, five boxes are shown which correspond to production, capital accumulation, consumption, environmental management, and the environment.

We can now follow the flow of materials in the economy. Before doing that, a brief discussion of the nature of these flows is needed. We assume that there is one all-encompassing list of goods (and bads). Each item on that list represents a commodity or service. These are defined not only with respect to their physical and chemical specifications but also with respect to location and time.[7] We divide this list into two parts. The first contains what are called private commodities and services (i.e. such commodities that are sold and bought on markets) and the second part contains environmental services.

---

[7] For this interpretation of a commodity, see Debreu (1959).

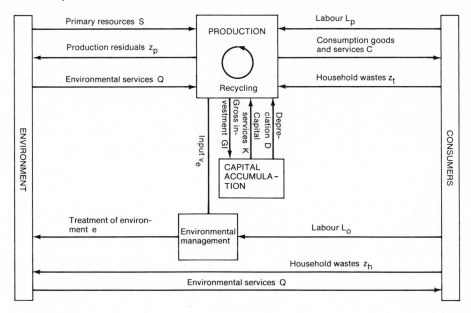

Figure 1.1

We assume there are n different private commodities and services and the flow of these is thus described completely by vectors in R^n. We will use the convention that flows to the environment and the consumers are measured positively and flows in the reverse direction are measured negatively. Flows to the production units (i.e. production inputs) are measured as negative quantities while flows from these units (i.e. outputs and byproducts) are measured as positive quantities.

This means that the flow of discharges into the environment is represented by a vector with the same dimensionality as the vector representing the flow of consumer goods and services. These vectors will in general, however, belong to different subspaces of R^n.

We assume that there are m different environmental services so the flow of environmental services is completely described by a vector in R^m. Each component of such a vector thus describes the location, time and physical and chemical characteristics of a particular environmental service.

When we discuss different flows below, these should thus always be interpreted as vectors belonging either to R^n or R^m, even if the flow is referred to as a flow of labor services or as a flow of depreciation of capital goods. In the upper left corner of Figure 1.1 is an arrow S which corresponds to the extraction of natural or primary renewable and nonrenewable resources from the environment. These resources are used in production as raw materials (and as primary energy commodities). Production also requires labor as an input which is symbolized by the arrow L_p from the Consumption box to the Production box. Similarly, input of capital is symbolized by the arrow denoted Capital services, K, from the Capital Accumulation box to the Production box. The Capital Accumulation box corresponds to the capital stock in the economy. The capital stock is built up by gross investments, i.e. a flow of produced goods, GI, from the Production box to the Capital Accumulation box. That stock is reduced by depreciation which implies a flow of scrapped capital goods, which we, for convenience, assume goes back to the Production box.

From a mass balance point of view[8] the total weight of the flow of investment goods going into the capital stock less the total weight of the scrapped materials must equal the net increase in the weight of the capital stock. A similar identity must of course also hold in monetary terms if we measure in constant prices – the net increase in capital stock equals gross investments less depreciation.

Consumption in this picture of the economy–environment interactions consists of consumption of services, either bought directly from the producers of such services or provided by consumption goods. The consumers thus buy a bundle of consumption goods and services, consume the services that this bundle may yield and are left with wastes equal in weight to what they bought in the form of consumer goods. These wastes or residuals are either discharged directly into the environment represented by the arrow z_h from the Consumption box to the Environment box, or transferred to the Production box where the wastes are treated and raw materials recovered.

The capital stock, represented by the Capital Accumulation box, grows because of gross investments GI, that is, output from the Production box set aside for capital accumulation. Owing to physical wear and tear, the capital stock will depreciate, however, and there is a flow of residuals D generated by this depreciation from the Capital Accumulation box to the Production box. This flow D has two economic effects: first it means a decrease in the capital stock, and second it adds to the flow of residuals generated in the economy. In the Production box raw materials may be extracted from D and the flow may be recycled.

The environmental management agency, a hypothetical collective agency with the objective of managing the environment, buys labor services and input goods, represented by the arrows L_0 and v_e, respectively, and using these inputs treats the environment (cleaning a beach or reclaiming land or landscaping the area surrounding a highway). The size of the treatment is given by the flow e,

---

[8] The mass balance point of view was a major break through in environmental economics and was presented in Ayres and Kneese (1969). Their views were reformulated and presented in a general equilibrium framework in d'Arge, Ayres, and Kneese (1972). Mäler (1974) also includes a general equilibrium model based on mass balances. In this book, the mass balance concept was also used to derive existence of "optimal" taxes and subsidies.

represented by the arrow from the Environmental Management box to the Environment box.

Let us now return to the Production box. Wastes generated in the Consumption and Capital Accumulation boxes enter this box. In the production processes themselves, residuals are also generated, and the total flow of residuals is treated and recycled. This recycling, together with the circular flow of intermediary products, is represented by the circle inside the Production box. It is not in general technologically possible, and it is generally not profitable, to recover all the residuals, so there will be a flow of residuals discharged into the environment from the Production box z_p.

The quality of the environment is affected by the discharge of residuals and by the treatment of the environment. The environment is regarded as a common property asset which yields a flow of services to the consumers, represented by the arrow Q at the bottom of the diagram. This flow consists of such things as recreation possibilities, aesthetic satisfaction, and clean air. An increase in the discharge of residuals will in general decrease this flow, while an increase in the treatment of the environment will in general increase the flow.

If we add the flows (except the flow of environmental services) going out from and in to the environment we get the net flow:

$$z = S + z_p + z_h + e. \tag{3.2}$$

Positive components of the vector z correspond to discharges into the environment (or investments in the environment in order to enhance environmental quality).

The basic idea behind this whole chapter is that the flow of environmental services is related to this net flow into the environment by a production function:

$$F: R^n \ni z \to F(z) = Q \in R^m. \tag{3.3}$$

In most applications it would be natural to assume that F is decreasing monotonically in z. However, it is easy to find examples where F is increasing in a component. If, for example, the discharge of one substance into a watercourse counteracts the bad effects from the discharge of another substance (liming acid lakes), then at least one component of $F(z)$ is increasing in the corresponding component of the z-vector. We do not have to make any assumptions on this, however.

We will, however, make the temporary assumption that F is concave. The primary reason for making this assumption is a technical one, namely to make it possible to outline the correspondence between Pareto efficiency and Lindahl equilibria and also to make it possible to prove the existence of a Lindahl equilibrium. Let z' and z'' be two vectors of net discharges such that

$$z' = (z_1, \ldots, 0, \ldots, z_k, \ldots, z_n)$$

and

$$z'' = (z_1, \ldots, z_i, \ldots, 0, \ldots, z_n).$$

Then the concavity assumption implies that for $0 \leq t \leq 1$:

$$F(tz' + (1-t)z'') \geq tF(z') + (1-t)F(z''), \tag{3.4}$$

i.e. the combined effect of z_i and z_k on the environment is worse than the pure addition of their separate effects. The assumption that F is concave is thus seen to correspond to the idea of synergism between different discharges.

On the other hand, it has been observed that the discharge of municipal effluent may reduce the damaging effects to the environment from acid rains. In this case the F-function would be convex. Thus, the environmental interaction function will not in general be concave. In spite of this, we will for the above-mentioned technical reasons keep the assumption that F is concave. We will return to this very important issue in Section 4.7.

We finally note that $Q_0 = F(0)$ can be interpreted as the flow of environmental services in a virgin state, untouched by human hands. Q_0 could be interpreted as the endowment of nature, similar to initial holdings of goods. However, note that in contrast to private goods, there is no natural scale for the measurement of the components of the vector Q. In particular, the choice of a zero for these scales is purely arbitrary. In some cases Q_0 will be a convenient "zero-vector", i.e. we will study the difference $Q - Q_0$. In order to guarantee that the flow of environmental services always is positive, we assume that $F(z) \geq 0$ for all $z \in R^n$. It will be convenient in what follows to work with the environment interaction set F instead of the function $F(\cdot)$. This set is defined as the convex closure of the graph of $F(\cdot)$, i.e.

$$F = \left\{ (z, Q); (z^i, Q^i), Q^i = F(z^i), i = 1, 2, \ldots, I \right.$$

$$\text{for some integer } I, 0 \leq \mu_i \leq 1, \sum_{i=1}^{I} \mu_i = 1,$$

$$\left. \text{and } (z, Q) = \sum_{i=1}^{I} \mu_i (z^i, Q^i) \right\}. \tag{3.5}$$

Since F is assumed to be concave, it follows that if $Q = F(z)$, (z, Q) is a boundary point of F. The reason is that one could think of Q_0 as an endowment from nature, similar to other initial holdings of goods.

4. A general market equilibrium model

The purpose of this section is to set out a general market equilibrium model for those flows that were described in the previous section except for the flow of environmental services.[9] In a way we will try to construct a model of the Arrow–Debreu type for the private goods while leaving the allocation mechanism for the environmental services open. Such mechanisms will be discussed in the next section.

4.1. Consumers

We assume there are H consumers in the economy, each indexed by h. These consumers have initial holdings of private goods (inherited from the past). They also own shares in firms' profits. In order to simplify the analysis, we will assume that those flows originating or terminating in the natural environment are administered by a special agency and that the possible profits this agency may make are distributed back to the consumers according to some scheme. The wealth W^h of a typical consumer thus consists of the value of his initial holdings w^h, his share in profits of private firms and his share of the profit made by the environmental agency. However, in this section this last component will be disregarded as we are to leave open the mechanism by which environmental services are allocated.

The consumer is assumed to buy and sell goods and services. Let the net demand vector of consumer h be x^h. Then his budget constraint is

$$px^h \leqq W^h, \tag{4.1}$$

where W^h is his wealth as defined above.

In conventional general equilibrium analysis it is assumed that the individual has preferences over different net demand vectors and that these must belong to consumption set X^h, describing the physiological and other physical constraints there are on the individual's consumptions possibilities.[10] In environmental economics it is an advantage to take a slightly different point of view, namely to use the idea of a household production function.[11] We will in a later section dwell more extensively on this. Now it suffices to give two reasons to base the analysis of consumer behavior on household production functions. The first reason is that we want to model the generation of wastes within the household and that can most easily be done by using a household production function. The second has to do with the fact that assuming some simple intuitive structures of the household production functions, it may be possible to estimate the demand for environmental services from observed behavior in markets for private goods.

---

[9] The material in this section is mainly based on Mäler (1974).

[10] For a classical exposition of general equilibrium theory see Debreu (1959). Much of the following discussion is based directly or indirectly on this book.

[11] The concept of a household production function is associated with Lancaster (1966). See also Hori (1975) and Sandmo (1973).

We therefore assume that individuals have preferences over vectors $k \in R^l$, where k_1, k_2, etc. are outputs from household production. k_1 may be recreational experience from visiting a particular skiing site, k_2 may be the experience of TV-watching, etc. These household outputs are produced by using private goods and services and environmental services. Thus, we can think of a production possibility set for the household:

$$K^h = \left\{ \left(k^h, x^h, Q \right) \right\} \subset R^{e+n+m}. \tag{4.1.2}$$

We assume that this set is closed and convex. Define the consumption set X^h by

$$X^h = \left\{ \left(x^h, Q \right) : \text{there exist } k^h \text{ such that } \left(k^h, x^h, Q \right) \in K^h \right\}, \tag{4.1.3}$$

i.e. X^h is the set of possible net demands for private goods and services and for environmental services such that there exist feasible household production plans. As K^h is closed and convex, it follows that X^h also is closed and convex.

In what follows we will mainly represent the production technology by household production functions, i.e.

$$k = f \left(x^h, Q \right). \tag{4.1.4}$$

Because of the convexity of K^h, it follows that the production functions are concave. In the applications in later sections most of these functions are of the form

$$k_i = x_i^2, \tag{4.1.5}$$

except perhaps for one production function containing the environmental service we are interested in as an argument.

The household is assumed to have preferences over the set K^h, i.e. there exists for each h a binary relation $\succsim_h$ defined on K^h such that

(i) $k \succsim_h k$ for all $k \in K^h$;
(ii) for all $k, k^1 \in K^h$, either $k \succsim k^1$ or $k^1 \succsim k$;
(iii) if $k \succsim k^1$ and $k^1 \succsim k^2$, then $k \succsim k^h$; and
(iv) the sets $\{ k \in K^h, k \succsim k^1 \}$ and $\{ k \in K^h, k^1 \succsim k \}$ are closed for all $k^1 \in K^h$.

These four conditions are, however, sufficient for the existence of utility function,[12] i.e. a function $\tilde{u}^h$ with the property that

$$\tilde{u}^h : K^h \rightarrow R,$$

$$\tilde{u}^h(k) \geq \tilde{u}^h(k^1) \text{ if and only if } k \succsim_h k^1.$$

In view of the convenience of using a utility function, we will in what follows always use a utility function as a representation of the preferences.

In addition to the four conditions above, we also assume that

(v) $\tilde{u}^h$ is a quasi concave function defined on K^h; and

---

[12] See Debreu (1959) for a proof of this theorem.

(vi) there does not exist a vector $\bar{k} \in K^h$ such that $k \in K^h$ implies $\tilde{u}^h(k) \leq \tilde{u}^h(\bar{k})$, i.e. the consumer is never satiated.

The utility function $\tilde{u}^h$ on K^h induces a utility function u^h defined on X^h in the natural way:

$$u^h(x^h, Q) = \sup\{\tilde{u}^h(k^h); (k^h, x^h, Q) \in K^h\}. \tag{4.1.6}$$

It is this utility function that will be used in this and the following sections. The original preference structure over household outputs have thus induced a preference structure over goods and environmental services.

Thus, we have a fairly common utility maximization problem as a description of consumer behavior:

$$\begin{aligned} &\max u^h(x^h, Q) \\ &\text{s.t.} \\ &px^h \leq W^h, \\ &(x^h, Q) \in X^h. \end{aligned} \tag{4.1.7}$$

However, in view of the fact that we admit negative prices this maximization problem may not have a solution because the budget set is unbounded. It will turn out that there is a solution (or rather set of solutions because we have not assumed that the utility function is strictly quasi concave), so we will not for the moment worry about the existence of utility maximizing commodity vectors.

It is worth studying the role of negative prices in more detail. If the price of an always desired commodity (i.e. the utility function is strictly increasing in the corresponding variable) is negative, no solution to the utility maximization problem would exist since it would be advantageous to increase the consumption of that commodity without bounds. Thus, for desired commodities prices must be non-negative. On the other hand, for residuals, i.e. commodities obtained as byproducts and not desired in themselves in the sense that the utility function is decreasing in the corresponding variable, price must be nonpositive. The only value of household wastes to the household is of course coming from the consumption giving rise to the wastes.[13]

The utility maximization problem as formulated above treats the supply of environmental services as a parameter. The demand for private goods and services will thus become a function of the actual supply of such services. This is the formulation that we will mainly rely on when we in later sections discuss welfare measurements and methods for estimating demand for environmental quality improvements. However, for the purpose of the discussions in the next section on allocative mechanisms, another utility maximization problem will be defined.

---

[13] In Mäler (1974) a list of residuals was specified *a priori*. These residuals then had nonpositive prices, while all other commodities and services had nonnegative prices. The present treatment contains substantial generalization as we do not have to specify a list of residuals. That list is itself endogenous in the present model.

We now assume that the environmental agency sells environmental services to the households in such a way that there is an individual price vector for each household for the environmental services. These individual price vectors are chosen so that the demand from each household does not exceed the common supply of the environmental services.

To each household, there is then a specific price vector P_Q^h on the environmental services, so that the budget constraint becomes:

$$px^h + p_Q^h Q \leqq W^h. \tag{4.1.8}$$

Maximizing the utility function subject to this budget constraint and the consumption set yields net demand correspondences for both private goods and services and environmental services:

$$x^h\left(p, p_Q^h, W^h\right), \tag{4.1.9}$$

$$Q^h\left(p, p_Q^h, W^h\right). \tag{4.1.10}$$

The demand for environmental services gives one expression for the consumer preferences between the environment and other goods and services. Equivalent to expressing these preferences in this way is to use the p_Q^h, which can be interpreted as the marginal willingness to pay for environment improvements. In later sections it is this latter approach that will be used. However, in discussing allocation mechanisms it is for the moment more convenient to use the demand correspondence directly.

4.2. Producers

Let there be S different producers. Each producer is characterized by his production possibility set $Y^s \subset R^{n+m}$. A production for this producer is thus a vector $(y^s, Q) \in Y^s$, where y^s is the planned net supply of private goods and services and Q is as before the vector of environmental services. Thus, the production possibilities of the producer are in general affected by the flow of environmental services. However, the producer does not directly affect the quality of the environment, but only through his net supply of private goods and services can he affect the flow on environmental services.

The profit producer s makes when the price on private goods and services is given by the vector p is

$$\tilde{\pi}^s = py^s. \tag{4.2.1}$$

If there is a pseudo market for environmental services with a price vector p_Q^s, the profit is:

$$\pi^s = py^s - p_Q^s Q. \tag{4.2.2}$$

Maximizing profits with regard to the production plan gives the net supply correspondences:

$$y^s(p, p_Q^s),$$ (4.2.3)

$$Q^s(p, p_Q^s).$$ (4.2.4)

4.3. Feasible states

By a feasible state we will mean a $(H + S + m)$ tuple

$$(x^1, \ldots, x^H, y^1, \ldots, y^S, Q),$$

such that

(i) $(x^h, Q) \in X^h, \quad h = 1, \ldots, H,$

(ii) $(y^s, Q) \in Y^s, \quad s = 1, \ldots, S,$

(iii) $\displaystyle\sum_{h=1}^{H} x^h - \sum_{s=1}^{S} y^s - \sum_{h=1}^{H} w^h + z = 0,$

(iv) $Q = F(z).$

A state of the economy thus specifies the consumption of goods and services for each household, the production of each producer and the total net flow of commodities into the environment. In order to be feasible the net flow of commodities into the environment must be such that the resulting flow of environmental services such that consumption of private goods and services and environmental services is feasible, i.e. belongs to the consumption set of each household and such that the production plans of each producer is feasible.

It will turn out to be convenient to introduce a different notation for the state of the economy, a notation that makes it possible to treat the flow of environmental services as private goods and services.[14]

Define the demand for environmental services of household h as

$$Q^{hc}$$

(superscript c stands for consumers), and of producer s as

$$Q^{sp}$$

(superscript p stands for producers).

---

[14] This new notation was used in Mäler (1974) in order to rewrite the model to be identical to an Arrow–Debreu model with free disposal. The present discussion draws heavily on Milleron (1972).

Consider now the set

$$\tilde{X}^h = \left\{ \left(x^h, 0, \ldots, Q^{hc}, \ldots, 0, 0, \ldots, 0 \right); \left(x^h, Q^{hc} \right) \in X^h \right\} \subset R^{n+(H+S)m},$$

$$(4.3.1)$$

$$\tilde{Y}^s = \left\{ \left(y^s, 0, \ldots, 0, 0, \ldots, -Q^{sp}, \ldots, 0 \right); \left(y^s, Q^{sp} \right) \in Y^s \right\} \subset R^{n+(H+S)m}.$$

$$(4.3.2)$$

The net demand of household h is then:

$$\tilde{x}^h = \left(x^h, 0, \ldots, Q^{hc}, \ldots, 0, 0, \ldots, 0 \right),$$

$$(4.3.3)$$

where x^h is as before the net demand for private goods and services and Q^{hc} is the demand for environmental services. The long list of zeros in $\tilde{x}^h$ reflects the fact that the individual household does not demand any environmental services for other households or for any producers.

Similarly, the net supply of producers s is

$$\tilde{y}^s = \left(y^s, 0, \ldots, 0, 0, \ldots, -Q^{sp}, \ldots, 0 \right).$$

$$(4.3.4)$$

The total net demand $\tilde{x}$ is given by

$$\tilde{x} = \sum_{h=1}^{H} \tilde{x}^h = \left(\sum_{h=1}^{H} x^h, Q^{1c}, \ldots, Q^{Hc}, 0, \ldots, 0 \right),$$

$$(4.3.5)$$

and the total net supply of the producers is

$$\tilde{y} = \sum_{s=1}^{S} y^s = \left(\sum_{s=1}^{S} y^s, 0, \ldots, 0, -Q^{1p}, \ldots, -Q^{Sp} \right).$$

$$(4.3.6)$$

The initial holdings are defined by

$$\tilde{w}^{hc} = \left(w^h, 0, \ldots, Q_0^h, \ldots, 0, 0, \ldots, 0 \right) \text{ and } \tilde{w}^{sp} = \left(0, 0, \ldots, 0, 0, \ldots, Q_0^s, \ldots, 0 \right),$$

$$(4.3.7)$$

and total holdings

$$\tilde{w} = \left(\sum_h w^h, Q_0^{1c}, \ldots, Q_0^{Hc}, Q_0^{1p}, \ldots, Q_0^{Hp} \right).$$

$$(4.3.8)$$

Thus $\tilde{w}^h$ includes an initial holding of the virgin environment. Therefore, each household has a legal right to an "unspoiled nature". For technical reasons, we also assume that each producer also has a legal right to an undistorted environment.

The production vector of the environment is defined by

$$\tilde{z} = \left(z, Q - Q_0^{1c}, \ldots, Q - Q_0^{Hc}, Q - Q_0^{1p}, \ldots, Q - Q_0^{Sp} \right).$$

$$(4.3.9)$$

The extended environment interaction set $\tilde{F}$ is defined as

$$\tilde{F} = \{(z, Q - Q_0, \ldots, Q - Q_0); (z, Q) \in F\}. \tag{4.3.10}$$

A state is now defined as

$$(\tilde{x}^1, \ldots, \tilde{x}^H, \tilde{y}^1, \ldots, \tilde{y}^S, Q).$$

A state is feasible if

(i) $\quad \tilde{x}^h \in \tilde{X}^h, \qquad h = 1, 2, \ldots, H,$

(ii) $\quad \tilde{y}^j \in \tilde{Y}^j, \qquad j = 1, \ldots, H,$

(iii) $\quad \displaystyle\sum_{h=1}^{H} \tilde{x}^h - \sum_{j=1}^{S} \tilde{y}^j - \sum_{h=1}^{H} \tilde{w}^h + \tilde{z} = 0,$

(iv) $\quad \tilde{z} \in \tilde{F}.$

State (i) is equivalent to the requirement that $(x^h, Q) \in X^h$ and (ii) is the same as $(y^j, Q) \in Y^j$. $\tilde{z} \in \tilde{F}$ is obviously the same as $(z, Q) \in F$. The interesting feature of this notation lies in (iv). The first component of this vector equation simply demands equality between supply and demand for private goods:

$$\sum_h x^h - \sum_s y^s - \sum_h w^h + z = 0. \tag{4.3.11}$$

The next component in the equation can be written

$$Q^{1c} - Q = 0, \tag{4.3.12}$$

or generally

$$Q^{hc} - Q = 0, \tag{4.3.13}$$

$$Q^{sp} - Q = 0. \tag{4.3.14}$$

Thus, we must have equilibrium, not only for the private goods and services but also for the environmental services in the sense that demanded environmental quality equals the supply of environmental quality.

In this notation there are $(H + S) \cdot m$ different flows of environmental services, one vector flow for each agent. The production technologies as described by $\tilde{F}$ are, however, such that these flows must be jointly supplied to all agents in the economy. Thus, in equilibrium the different agents must consume the same flows.

In this way, we have transformed the original model into one where all goods and services (including environmental services) are private, and we could imagine a private ownership competitive equilibrium for this economy.

4.4. Equilibrium concepts

The model specified in the previous sections explains the net demand from households for private goods and services, the net supply of such goods and services and the resulting net excess demand for private goods and services. However, the model does not specify any allocation mechanisms for the flow of environmental services. The purpose of this section is to discuss three such mechanisms: Pareto efficiency, Nash equilibrium, and Lindahl equilibrium.[15] Pareto efficiency was already discussed in some detail in Section 1 and will be the base case with which the other mechanisms will be compared. Nash equilibrium is defined by individual utility maximization and profit maximization where each agent takes the decision of other agents as given. We can think of two different kinds of Nash equilibria. In the first concept agents take the flow of environmental services as given. Essentially, this means that the Nash equilibrium is a feasible state such that each consumption plan is derived from utility maximization and each production plan is derived from profit maximization. In the second concept, markets for environmental services exist and agents take prices on these markets as given. It is similar to the Lindahl equilibrium which is defined as a feasible state in which each household and producer buys environmental services. Each has to pay an individual price such that their demand is equal to the supply of the services. The total supply of these services is determined in such a way that the total income accruing to the environment from the purchases of the environmental services and the payments for the excess supply is maximized. We will show in the next sections that the Lindahl equilibrium and the Pareto efficiency concepts are equivalent while the first concept of Nash equilibrium leads to quite a different allocation of resources. In fact it may not be true that a Nash equilibrium exists because of detrimental effects on the environment.

4.5. Pareto efficiency

In this section we characterize Pareto efficient states in terms of prices and, in particular, we will show that every Pareto efficient state is a Lindahl equilibrium.

A state $(\bar{x}^1, \ldots, \bar{x}^H, \bar{y}^1, \ldots, \bar{y}^S, \bar{Q})$ is Pareto efficient if

(i) it is feasible, and

(ii) there does not exist any other feasible states $(x^1, \ldots, x^H, y^1, \ldots, y^S, Q)$ such that

$$u^h(x^h, Q) \geqq u^h(\bar{x}^h, \bar{Q}), \qquad h = 1, \ldots, H \tag{4.5.1}$$

---

[15] For an elementary comparison of these equilibrium concepts see Atkinson and Stiglitz (1980) and Dasgupta and Heal (1979).

and for at least one household h'

$$u^{h'}(x^{h'}, Q) > u^{h'}(\bar{x}^{h'}, \bar{Q}). \tag{4.5.2}$$

In order to characterize the set of Pareto efficient states it is necessary to make assumptions on the consumption sets X^h, the production sets Y^s, the environment interaction set F and the preferences.

These assumptions can be summarized in one word – convexity.[16]. We will need convex consumption sets. It is not necessary, however, to assume that each individual production set is convex, it suffices that the aggregate production set is convex. It is meaningless to sum the individual Y^s, however, because then the sum would contain vectors like

$$\left(\sum y^s, \sum Q\right),$$

and the second component is obviously not economically reasonable. Instead, if we use the notation introduced in 3.3 we can form the sum

$$\tilde{Y} = \sum_s \tilde{Y}^s = \left\{ \left(\sum_s y^s, 0, \ldots, 0, -Q^{1\mathrm{p}}, \ldots, -Q^{S\mathrm{p}} \right); \right.$$

$$\left. (y^s, Q^{s\mathrm{p}}) \in Y^s, s = 1, \ldots, S \right\}. \tag{4.5.3}$$

Then we make the following assumptions:
  (i) X^h is a convex for $h = 1, \ldots, H$;
  (ii) $u^h(\cdot, \cdot)$ is quasiconcave and continuous on X^h for $h = 1, \ldots, H$;
  (iii) $\tilde{Y} = \sum_{s=1}^{S} \tilde{Y}^s$ is a convex set;
  (iv) F is a convex set.

Note that (i) is equivalent to assuming $\tilde{X}^h$ is convex and that (iv) is equivalent to assuming that $\tilde{F}$ is convex.[17]

Let $(x^{1*}, \ldots, x^{H*}, y^{1*}, \ldots, y^{N*})$ to a Pareto efficient state. Define

$$\tilde{U}^h_{\tilde{X}^{h*}} = \left\{ \tilde{x}^h \in \tilde{X}^h; \; u^h(x^h, Q^{hc}) \geq u^h(x^{h*}, Q^{hc*}) \right\}, \qquad h = 1, \ldots, H. \tag{4.5.4}$$

Thus, $\tilde{u}^h_{\tilde{X}^{h*}}$ is the set of consumption vectors in $\tilde{\tilde{X}}^h$ that are preferred to the vector $\tilde{x}^{h*} = (x^{h*}, 0, \ldots, Q^{hc*}, 0, \ldots, 0)$. In the same way

$$\tilde{u}^{h1}_{\tilde{X}^{h*}} = \left\{ \tilde{x}^{h'} \in \tilde{X}^{h'}; \; u^{h'}(x^{h'}, Q^{h'c}) > u^{h'}(x^{h'*}, Q^{h'c*}) \right\} \tag{4.5.5}$$

is the set of consumption vectors strictly preferred to $\tilde{x}^{h'*}$.

---

[16] See Koopmans (1957) for a discussion of convexity assumptions in economics.
[17] We will follow Debreu (1959) closely in proving that a Pareto efficient state is a Lindahl equilibrium.

Define the set G as

$$G = U_{\tilde{X}^{h\prime}*}^{h\prime} + \sum_{h \neq h'} U_{X^{h}*}^{h} - \sum_{s=1}^{S} \tilde{Y}^{s} - \tilde{F}. \tag{4.5.6}$$

G can be interpreted as the set of resource vectors w that would make $x^{h}, h = 1, \ldots, H$ feasible, where

$$u^{h}(x^{h}, Q^{hc}) \geqq u^{h}(x^{h*}, Q^{hc*}), \qquad h = 1, \ldots, H, \tag{4.5.7}$$

$$u^{h\prime}(x^{h\prime}Q^{h\prime c}) > u^{h\prime}(x^{h\prime*}, Q^{h\prime c*}). \tag{4.6.8}$$

Since $(\tilde{x}^{1*}, \ldots, \tilde{x}^{H*}, \tilde{y}^{1*}, \ldots, \tilde{y}^{S*})$ is Pareto efficient, it follows that $\sum_{h=1}^{H} w^{h}$ does not belong to G, i.e.

$$w = \sum w^{h} \notin G. \tag{4.5.9}$$

It follows from our convexity assumptions that G is convex. Thus, there exists a hyperplane separating G and w,[18] i.e. a vector $\tilde{p}$ such that

$$\tilde{p}a \geqq \tilde{p}w, \quad \text{for all } a \in G. \tag{4.5.10}$$

Let $\bar{G}$ be the closed hull of G. It is obvious that

$$\tilde{p}a \geqq \tilde{p}w, \quad \text{for all } a \in \bar{G}. \tag{4.5.11}$$

Moreover, it is clear that the set

$$G' = \sum_{1}^{H} \tilde{U}_{\tilde{X}^{h}*}^{h} - \sum_{s=1}^{S} \tilde{Y}^{s} - F \tag{4.5.12}$$

is contained in G. Thus,

$$\tilde{p}a \geqq \tilde{p}w, \quad \text{for all } a \in G'.$$

Moreover, $w \in G'$, so that w minimizes $\tilde{p}a$ on G'. Now

$$w = \sum_{h=1}^{H} \tilde{x}^{h*} - \sum_{s=1}^{S} \tilde{y}^{s*} - \tilde{z}*. \tag{4.5.13}$$

Therefore
  (i) $\tilde{x}^{h*}$ minimizes $\tilde{p}x^{h}$ on $\tilde{U}_{X^{h}*}^{h}$, $h = 1, \ldots, H$;
  (ii) $\tilde{y}^{s*}$ maximizes $\tilde{p}y^{s}$ on $\tilde{Y}^{s}$, $s = 1, \ldots, S$; and
  (iii) $\tilde{z}*$ maximizes $\tilde{p}z$ on $\tilde{F}$.
Let the vector $\tilde{p}$ be decomposed into

$$\tilde{p} = \left(p, p_{Q}^{1c}, \ldots, p_{Q}^{Hc}, p_{Q}^{1p}, \ldots, p_{Q}^{S1p} \right).$$

---

[18] For separating hyperplans, see Koopmans (1957).

Then (i) implies that $pX^h - p^{hc}Q$ is minimized on the set

$$\{(x^h, Q) \in X^h;\ u^h(x^h, Q) \geq u^h(x^{h*}, Q*)\} \text{ by } (x^{h*}, Q*).$$

Now, if

$$w^h = px^{h*} - p_Q^{hc*} \neq \min_{X^h}\left(px^h - p_Q^{hc}Q\right),$$

it can be shown[19] that this implies that $(x^{h*}, Q*)$ maximizes the utility $u^h(x^h, Q)$ s.t.

$$px^h - p_Q^{hc} \leq w^h.$$

(ii) implies that y^{s*}, $Q*$ maximizes

$$py^s - p_Q^{sp}Q \text{ on } y^s.$$

(iii) finally implies that $(z*, Q*)$ maximizes

$$pz + \left(\sum_{h=1}^{H} p_Q^{hc} + \sum_{s=1}^{S} p_Q^{sp}\right)Q \text{ on } F.$$

Thus, the Pareto efficient state can be obtained by the following institutional set-up. For each of the private goods and services there exists a competitive market. Even for such commodities that are of no use, i.e. residuals, there exist competitive markets. However, the prices on these residuals are negative, which means that a consumer or a producer has to pay for the disposal of the residuals. Consumers also demand environmental services for which they have to pay a price, determined in such a way that the demand equals the supply of such services. Producers maximize their profits. They also demand environmental services and the price an individual producer has to pay is set so that his demand equals the actual supply.

Finally, there is an environmental agency, deciding on how much residuals to take care of, partly by treating them and recovering raw materials and partly by discharging them to the environment. The resulting flow of environmental services is sold to consumers and to producers and the agency acts in order to maximize its profit. The profit of the agency comes from selling environmental services, from selling natural resources, and from selling waste disposal services.

This institutional set-up together with the resulting equilibrium will be called a Lindahl equilibrium since it is a straightforward generalization of the mechanism for determining the supply of public goods put forward by Erik Lindahl.[20]

---

[19] See Debreu (1959).

[20] The concept was introduced by Erik Lindahl 1919 in his PhD dissertation "Die Berechtigkeit der Besteuerung". That part of the dissertation that deals with this equilibrium concept has been translated into English and published in Musgrave and Peacock (1967). The Lindahl equilibrium was "rediscovered" by Leif Johansen (1965). Since then many works on this subject have appeared. The most important ones are Foley (1967, 1970) and Milleron (1972).

4.6. Existence of a Lindahl equilibrium

For the sake of references we give a formal definition of a Lindahl equilibrium. A Lindahl equilibrium is a $(H + S + 1)$-tuple

$$\left(x^{1*}, \ldots, x^{H*}, y^{1*}, \ldots, y^{S*}, Q^* \right)$$

and prices

$$\left(p, p_Q^{1c}, \ldots, p_Q^{Hc}, p_Q^{1p}, \ldots, p_Q^{Sp} \right)$$

such that:

(iii) for $h = 1, \ldots, H$, $(x^{h*}, Q^*) \in X^h$ and (x^{h*}, Q^*) maximizes $U^h(x^h, Q)$ on X^h subject to

$$px^h - p_Q^{hc}Q \leq pw^h + \sum_{s=1}^{S} \theta_s^h \pi_s + \alpha^h \pi_F + p_Q^{hc}Q_0,$$

where Q_s^h is household h's share in the profit π_s of the sth firm and α^h is its share in the net revenue π_F of environment agency;

(i) for $s = 1, \ldots, S$, (y^{s*}, Q^*) maximizes

$$\pi_s = py^s - p_Q^{sp}Q + p_Q^{sp}Q_0;$$

(ii) (z^*, Q^*) maximizes

$$\pi_F = pz + \left(\sum_h p^{hc} + \sum_s p^{sc} \right)(Q - Q_0)$$

s.t.

$$(z, Q) \in F,$$

where

$$z^* = \sum_h x^{h*} - \sum_s y^{s*} - \sum_h w^h.$$

We saw in the previous section that a Pareto efficient state is a Lindahl equilibrium. It is also easy to show the converse, i.e. any Lindahl equilibrium must be Pareto efficient. Let

$$\left(x^{1*}, \ldots, x^{H*}, y^{1*}, \ldots, y^{S*}, Q^* \right) \quad \text{and} \quad \left(p, p_Q^{1c}, \ldots, p_Q^{Hc}, p_Q^{1p}, \ldots, p_Q^{Sp} \right)$$

be a Lindahl equilibrium. Assume that it is not Pareto efficient, i.e. assume there exists a feasible state

$$\left(x^1, \ldots, x^H, y^1, \ldots, y^S, Q \right),$$

such that

$$U^h(x^h, Q) \geq U^h(x^{h*}, Q^*), \qquad h = 1, \ldots, H,$$

and   (4.6.1)

$$U^{h\prime}(x^{h\prime}, Q) > U^{h\prime}(x^{h\prime*}, Q^*).$$

Assume no consumer is satiated at the equilibrium. Then we must necessarily have

$$px^h - p_Q^{hc}Q \geqq px^{h*} - p_Q^{hc}Q^*, \tag{4.6.2}$$

because otherwise x^{h*}, Q^* would not maximize utility subject to the budget. We must also have

$$px^{h\prime} - p_Q^{h\prime c}Q > px^{h\prime*} - p_Q^{h\prime c}Q^*. \tag{4.6.3}$$

Adding these inequalities yields:

$$p \sum_{h=1}^{H} x^h + \sum_{h=1}^{H} p_Q^{hc}Q > p \sum_{h=1}^{H} x^{h*} + \sum_{h=1}^{H} p_Q^{hc}Q^*. \tag{4.6.4}$$

We must also have

$$py^s - p_Q^{sp}Q \leqq py^{s*} - p_Q^{sp}Q^*, \quad \text{for } s = 1, \ldots, S, \tag{4.6.5}$$

because (y^{s*}, Q^*) maximizes profit where prices are (p, p_Q^{sp}). Subtracting these inequalities from the former yields:

$$p\left(\sum_h x^h - \sum_s y^s\right) + \left(\sum_h p_Q^{hc} + \sum_s p_Q^{sp}\right)Q > p\left(\sum_h x^{h*} - \sum_s y^{s*}\right)$$

$$+ \left(\sum_h p_Q^{hc} + \sum_s p_Q^{sp}\right)Q. \tag{4.6.6}$$

Now,

$$\sum_h x^h - \sum_s y^s = \sum_h w^h + z \quad \text{and} \quad \sum_h x^{h*} - \sum_s y^{s*} = \sum_h w^h + z^*.$$

Thus,

$$pz + \left(\sum_h p^{hc} + \sum_s p^{sp}\right)Q > pz^* + \left(\sum_h p^{hc} + \sum_s p^{SP}\right)Q^*, \quad \text{for all } (z, Q) \in F.$$

But this is impossible since (x^*, Q^*) maximizes the net revenue of the environment agency. Thus, our assumption that $(x^{1*}, \ldots, x^{H*}, y^{1*}, \ldots, y^{S*}, Q^*)$ is not Pareto efficient must be wrong.

Note that we had to make only two assumptions for this result, that households are not satiated and that there exists a Lindahl equilibrium. Let us now turn to the question of existence of such an equilibrium.[21]

Let us first rewrite the definition of Lindahl equilibrium in terms of the extended notations from eq. (3.3).

---

[21] The concept of a quasi equilibrium is due to Debreu (1962). It is also used by Milleron (1972).

Let us define the utility function $\tilde{U}^h$ on $\tilde{X}^h$ [note that $\tilde{U}^h$ is not the same function as the one discussed in eq. (3.1)] by

$$\tilde{U}^h(\tilde{x}^h) = U^h(x^h, Q^{hc}).\tag{4.6.7}$$

Then a Lindahl equilibrium is defined as a state $(\tilde{x}, \ldots, \tilde{x}^H, \tilde{y}^1, \ldots, \tilde{y}^S)$ and a price vector p such that:

(i) For $h = 1, \ldots, H\tilde{x}^h$ maximizes $\tilde{U}^h$ on $\tilde{X}^h$ s.t. to the budget constraint

$$\tilde{p}\tilde{x}^h \leq \tilde{p}\tilde{w}^h + \sum_{s=1}^{S} \theta_s^h \pi_s + \alpha^h \pi_F.$$

(ii) For $s = 1, \ldots, S$ y^s maximizes profits on Y^s, i.e. y^s maximizes

$$\tilde{p}\tilde{y}^s + \tilde{p}\tilde{w}^{s\mathrm{P}} = \pi_s.$$
s.t.

$$\tilde{y}^s \in \tilde{Y}^s.$$

(iii)

$$\bar{z} = \sum_s \tilde{y}^s + \sum_h w^{hc} + \sum_s w^{s\mathrm{P}} - \sum_h \tilde{x}^h.$$

(iv) $\bar{z}$ maximizes

$$\tilde{p}\tilde{z} = \pi_F$$
s.t.

$$\tilde{z} \in \tilde{F}.$$

It is apparent that the definition of a Lindahl equilibrium can be interpreted as a competitive equilibrium for a private ownership economy. In order to prove the existence of a Lindahl equilibrium one can therefore rely on existing proof for the existence of a competitive equilibrium in economies without free disposal. The most general such proof has been given by Debreu.[22] However, Debreu's existence theorem is quite complicated and even to write down the assumptions he makes would require new notation and a quite long detour. Instead we will be satisfied by referring to an existence proof given by Hart and Kuhn.[23]

Assume:

(A) For $h = 1, \ldots, H$:

  (i) $\tilde{X}^h$ is closed, convex and bounded below;
  (ii) $\tilde{U}^h$ is continuous and quasi-concave;
  (iii) there is no saturation point $\tilde{x}^h$; and
  (iv) household h has an initial endowment $\tilde{w}^h$ which is interior to $\tilde{X}^h$.

---

[22] These notations are all from Debreu (1962).
[23] Debreu (1962) and Milleron (1972).

(B) For $s = 1, \ldots, S$:
   (i) the production set $\tilde{Y}^s$ is convex and closed and contains the origin;
   (ii) F is closed and convex and contains the origin;
   (iii) the aggregate production set,

$$\tilde{Y} = \sum_{s=1}^{S} + \tilde{F},$$

satisfies $(\tilde{Y} \cap - \tilde{Y}) \subset \{0\}$ and $\tilde{Y} \cap \{\tilde{y} : \tilde{y} \geqq 0\} = \{0\}$; and
   (iv) $\sum_{h=1}^{H} Q_s^h = 1$ and $\sum_{h=1}^{H} \alpha^h = 1$. Then there exists a Lindahl equilibrium.

The troublesome assumption is, of course, (A, iv) requiring initial holdings of each commodity the household demands. One reason for defining $Q^0 = F(0)$ is that Q^0 is certainly contained in the interior of the intersection of X with that subspace representing environmental services.

In the theorem of Debreu referred to above this assumption is generalized substantially. For an analysis of existence of a Lindahl equilibrium based on Debreu's theorem, the reader is referred to Milleron.[24]

4.7. Interpretation of a Lindahl equilibrium and the Coase theorem

The concept of a Lindahl equilibrium as defined in the previous sections relies on a specific agency, the environmental agency, which in a sense has a legal right to manage the environment. It decides on how much can be extracted from the environment as raw materials. It decides on how much of different residuals will be allowed to be dumped in the environment and it can also decide on modifications of the environment. However, the model as it has been developed in this paper gives the households and the producers a legal right to an unspoiled natural environment. This assumption is of a formal nature, and was made to facilitate the use of Debreu's theorem for proving the existence of an equilibrium. We will later show, in connection with a discussion of Coase's theorem, the role of this assumption. By allowing discharges of residuals or by allowing extraction of natural resources, the flow of environmental services will change. In most cases we would agree that the environment deteriorates from the virgin state, but in some respects (or for certain households or producers) environmental quality may improve. In any case, the environmental agency must compensate those who experience a net deterioration of environmental quality (and charge those who are experiencing an improved environment). Thus, there is a kind of market for the flow of environmental services where each household has its own initial holding of environmental resources which it can supply. The environment agency, thus, has to offer each household a price which makes all the individual supplies equal.

[24] See Milleron (1972).

The idea that the environment agency maximizes its profits or net income implies that it makes a social cost–benefit analysis of the use of the environment.[25] The income from selling waste disposal services to households and producers reflects the value of these services to households and producers and is compared with the value of the deterioration of the environment caused by using these services, reflected in the payment of compensations.

The model has been constructed in such a way that the most obvious interpretation is that the agency's purchases of rights to change environmental quality from the households and the producers are carried out on competitive markets. There are at least three very important aspects that should be assessed before such an interpretation is accepted.

(1) On each market there is one buyer – the environment agency – and one seller – a household or a producer. This market is thus not a competitive market but a bilateral monopoly.[26] Unfortunately, we do not have any useful theories for this kind of bargaining situation. The only thing we could be quite certain about is that the resulting equilibrium will not be the same as would have been the case if both parties had been price takers. Thus, it does not seem to be realistic to interpret the prices p_Q as competitive prices determined on markets.

(2) Next we have the problem of incentives compatibility.[27] Each household and producer knows that the flow of environmental services has the characteristics of a flow of collective goods. In negotiating with the agency, the household knows that other households may accept a certain degradation of the environment and that its own decision will scarcely influence the final outcome. It will therefore have incentives to negotiate a much higher price than would correspond to its true valuation of the environment. Thus, we have the problem of the free rider, in this case in a reverse situation compared with the common example in the literature. If we had distributed the initial rights differently so that the agency would have the legal right to the virgin environment, then each household would have to pay the agency for improving the environment. For the same reason as given above, each household would have incentives to negotiate as low a price as possible in the hope that the other households and producers will pay for the desired environmental improvement.

Thus, if we interpret the Lindahl equilibrium in this market sense, we have a mechanism which is not compatible with the incentives households and producers have when negotiating the prices on the flow of environmental services.

---

[25] See Mäler (1974) for a more detailed discussion of this issue.

[26] This was first observed by Arrow in Haveman, Margolis (1970).

[27] The problems of incentives in determining the supply of public goods is an old one in economics. It was observed by Wicksell (1896), translated to English and published in Musgrave and Peacock (1967). Samuelson (1954) and (1969) also discussed this problem. For a penetrating discussion of incentives competibility see Laffont and Green (1980). Mäler (1974) offers some observations in the environmental field.

(3) The third aspect has to do with our assumption that the total extended production set of the economy is convex. It has been argued forcefully that the presence of detrimental externalities necessarily will cause nonconvexities in the total production possibility set.[28] Now, if that set $\tilde{Y}$ is nonconvex, our proof that a Pareto optimum is a Lindahl equilibrium breaks down and the concept of a Lindahl equilibrium looses much of its interest.

We have already encountered arguments that the environment interaction function F is not concave, i.e. the environment interaction set is not convex. These arguments were based on some intuitive reasoning about the effects of discharges of wastes into the environment. But even if the environment interaction set could be assumed to be convex, there are some strong economic arguments that have been raised against the assumption that the set Y should be convex.[29]

Baumol, Baumol and Bradford, and Starret have argued forcefully that the existence of negative externalities imply necessarily that the aggregate production set is nonconvex. A most illuminating example of this is offered by Starret and we quote:

> To illustrate the basic nonconvexity, consider a single product firm affected by an externality, and plot its output (b) as a function of the externality (z), holding all inputs at fixed levels. The resulting function must be downward sloping, since z is a diseconomy; but it must also be nonnegative, since the firm could always choose to produce nothing regardless of the externality level. Such a curve clearly cannot be concave over the entire z axis. Two possible shapes for the curve are shown below. In case (1) marginal losses to z increases right up to the point where the firm quits, after which they are zero; in case (2) they increase up to a point, and then decrease toward zero as the affected firm becomes "saturated" in z. Once nonconvexities are introduced, the arguments of Section 1 (arguments showing the existence of a Lindahl equilibrium) naturally breaks down. Indeed, we can easily see that there will be (in general) no equilibria on artificial markets. At any price for externality rights, the pollutee will seek to sell an arbitrarily large number of rights (since this will increase his profits without bound). Intuitively speaking, the firm is being offered a positive price for accepting externalities; and since (under the assumption of competitive behavior) he believes that he can purchase whatever amounts he likes at the quoted prices, he has (theoretically) an infinite supply of rights.

Thus, Starret gives quite a strong argument against assuming that the aggregate production set is convex. Moreover, one could also argue that the assumption that

---

[28] Starret (1972), Baumol (1964), Baumol and Bradford (1972), and Portes (1970).
[29] Baumol and Bradford (1972).

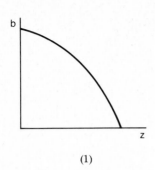

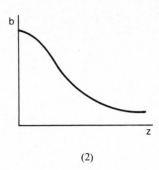

(1)   (2)

the utility function U^h is quasi-concave. If a river becomes so polluted that it turns into an open sewer, the benefits for households or producers from a marginal improvement may be zero because the river is still an open sewer. With convex preferences and production possibilities we would, however, expect a very high benefit from a marginal improvement if the river is very polluted.

In conclusion, we may say that there are very strong reasons for not believing in the possibility of creating some pseudo markets for environmental services in which the environment agency buys and sells the right to such services. We will soon give another interpretation of the model which avoids this and also avoids some of the problems connected with nonconvexity. Before discussing that alternative interpretation, we will briefly look at Coase's theorem.[30]

Coase's theorem roughly states that

(1) given well defined legal property rights,

(2) given that there are no transaction costs, and

(3) given that we can neglect any income effects, then the final allocation is independent of the initial distribution of property rights and that this outcome will be Pareto efficient.

Coase proved this theorem for the case where there are two parties, one of which causes an externality on the other. Because of the absence of any transaction costs, the two parties will negotiate a solution which Coase claims to be Pareto efficient.

Now, this is obviously a case of bilateral monopoly and there are no convincing theoretical arguments that the resulting agreement will be Pareto efficient. That may depend on the parties' bargaining strength, etc. But abstracting from this, Coase theorem is correct for a two-party externality.

The problems we are discussing in connection with the environment have typically a large number of agents involved. There may be thousands of households and producers affected by an environmental deterioration and there may

---

[30] The theorem is presented in Coase (1960). It has been the subject of very intensive debate. A good summary is given in *Natural Resources Journal* (1973).

even be many households and producers creating the undesired environmental change. All these agents must negotiate with each other in order to reach an efficient state. By assuming that all agents take the other agents' decisions as given, we get the concept of a Nash equilibrium for this economy. But then the problem of incentives compatibility will again be a major obstacle for the achievement of an efficient outcome. Exactly as in our discussion of the market interpretation of a Lindahl equilibrium, the free rider problem will appear.

One could say that the Coase solution to this environment problem corresponds to our Lindahl equilibrium without an environment agency as an intermediate agency. But without the environment agency, the dimensionality of the model is reduced and arguments for nonconvex social production sets are valid. Thus, even after abstracting from transaction costs and incentives compatibility, the Coase theorem is not applicable to environment problems because of the fundamental nonconvexities that are created by the environmental problems. Thus, it should be clear that the Nash equilibrium in this sense (if one exists) cannot be Pareto efficient. Moreover, it is at least theoretically possible, that there is no Nash equilibrium because the resulting degradation of the environment will make the consumption plans unfeasible.

In the usual interpretation of Coase's theorem, property rights are distributed among the different agents who are then supposed to negotiate with each other. In the present framework, that would correspond for example to a situation where households and producers would have initial rights to the waste disposal capacity of the environment but those who are damaged by the consequential environmental degradations would pay the polluters to reduce pollution. In this case, without an intermediate agency, nonconvexities will create an obstacle to efficiency.

However, in a more general interpretation, legal rights to the environment are given over to the environment agency, and the Lindahl equilibrium would coincide with the Coase outcome. A change in initial property rights, i.e. a change in Q_0 can easily be included in the model. Q_0 has been defined by $Q_0 = F(0)$, i.e. the flow of environmental services in a virgin environment. However, nothing in our previous discussions (except perhaps the existence proof) prevents Q_0 being defined by $Q_0 = F(z)$, where z is any vector of excess supply. Quite independent of the choice of Q_0 [subject to the requirement given in the existence theorem in (3.6) on initial holdings] the resulting Lindahl equilibrium will be efficient. Thus, the Coase solution may, with suitable extensions, be interpreted as a Lindahl equilibrium. However, the previous criticisms against this concept are still valid.

Let us now, finally, try to interpret the concept of a Lindahl equilibrium in a more reasonable way. Instead of assuming markets for environmental services, let us assume that the environment agency has some methods by which it can reveal the marginal willingness to pay for environmental service, i.e. the prices p_Q^{hc} and p_Q^{sp}. To some extent, such an assumption is to neglect the whole question of incentives compatibility. However, we are now going to use these prices, not as payments for actual transfers on a market, but for evaluating the benefits from environmental improvements. We will later in this chapter see some examples in which such revelations, at least in theory, are possible.

The role of the agency is then to evaluate the " value" of the environment using these prices and determine the amount of residuals discharged and the amount of natural resources extracted in such a way that the value of the environment plus the incomes from selling waste disposal services and resource extraction rights is maximized. Thus, the agency has either to establish a market for discharging residuals or to tax the discharge in such a way that the social value of the environment is maximized.

However, this interpretation relies very much on the basic assumption that only end states matter. Our discussion has been completely based on this assumption. From a liberal point of view, the concept of a Lindahl equilibrium in which there are "markets" for environmental services may as an additional merit have the property of being based on "liberal" mechanisms. This latter interpretation violates that property in a substantial way. Now, there is an agency determining the "optimal" environmental quality for each and every household and the individual can do nothing about the decision of the agency. Even if the decision on environmental quality is based on household preferences, a single household may object to the decision simply because it is not permitted to take part of the decision.

Now this is not a serious criticism of the concept if markets for environmental services are impossible to implement. Thus, we will maintain our interpretation of a Lindahl equilibrium and that view will characterize the rest of this chapter. We will in what follows attack two problems: how to estimate the benefits from environmental improvements, and how to choose between different Lindahl equilibria which differ from each other in the distribution of initial rights.

5. Consumer theory

5.1. Introduction

Since welfare statements will be made with respect to the preferences of individuals, the economic theory of consumer behavior is fundamental to welfare economics. There are several excellent self-contained surveys of consumer theory avail able.[31] However, environmental economics often has particular features that make a special survey warrented. The first is the fact, already observed in the previous sections, that environmental quality is in general a public good, and the consumer theory should take that into account. The second has to do with the

---

[31] See Deaton and Muellbauer (1980) which also contains empirical observations, and Barten and Böhm (1982).

necessity of explaining the generation of wastes or residuals within the house-holds. This calls for an explicit treatment of consumer technology. Finally, in attempts to measure consumers' valuation of environmental changes, it is in general necessary to make some *a priori* assumptions on the structure of the demand for environmental improvements.[32] Such assumptions may be formalized in household production functions as discussed in Section 4.1.

However, we will in this section continue to discuss consumer behavior with respect to vectors of goods and services and the flow of environmental services. Thus, the household production function approach will not be used explicitly.

The main purpose of the following discussion is to define measures of individual welfare changes and relate these to observable quantities. In Section 6 we will look at social welfare changes. Section 5.2 contains a very brief summary of the needed elementary facts from consumer theory.

5.2. Utility maximization

Consumer behavior is described as if he maximizes
$$U(x, Q)$$
s.t.
$$px \leq W, \tag{5.2.1}$$
$$(x, Q) \in X,$$
where x is his net demand for private goods, p the corresponding price vector, W his wealth, Q the supply of environmental services, and X his consumption set.

As prices are allowed to be negative, the budget constraint does not necessarily define a compact subset of X, which could be used to motivate the existence of a solution to the maximization problem above. The existence theorem in Section 4.6 guarantees, however, such a solution. Because of the strict quasi-concavity of the utility function, the solution must be unique.[33]

Moreover, it can be shown that the commodity bundle x satisfying the budget constraint and maximizing utility in X is a continuous function of prices, wealth, and the vector of environmental services, i.e. the function
$$x = g(p, W, Q)$$
is continuous for all (p, W, Q) for which an optimum exists. We will, in addition, assume that this demand function is continuously differentiable. Thus we have the description of consumer behavior in terms of the demand function g.

It is easily proved that the following properties hold for the demand function:
(i) g is homogeneous of degree zero in (p, W),
(ii) $pg(p, W, Q) \equiv W,$

---

[32] See, for example, Varian (1984).
[33] See Nikaido (1968).

(iii)

$$\frac{\partial g_i}{\partial p_j} + x_j \frac{\partial g_i}{\partial W} = \frac{\partial g_i}{\partial p_i} + x_i \frac{\partial g_i}{\partial W}, \quad \text{all } i, j$$

(iv)

$$\left[\frac{g_i}{p_j} + x_j \frac{\partial g_i}{\partial W} \right]$$

is nonpositive semi-definite.

The compensated demand function and the expenditure function is defined from the cost minimization problem

$$\begin{aligned}
&\min px \\
&\text{s.t.} \\
&U(x, Q) \geq \bar{U}, \\
&(x, Q) X.
\end{aligned} \tag{5.2.2}$$

The cost minimization vector x deforms the compensating demand function:

$$x = h(p, \bar{U}, Q), \tag{5.2.3}$$

and the least cost defines the expenditure function m:

$$m(p, \bar{U}, Q) \equiv ph(p, \bar{U}, Q).$$

It can be shown that

$$h_i(p, \bar{U}, Q) = \frac{\partial m(p, \bar{U}, Q)}{\partial p_i}. \tag{5.2.4}$$

It can also be shown that if the demand function $g(p, W, Q)$ satisfies properties (i)–(iv) above, the following system of equations:

$$\frac{\partial m}{\partial p_i} = q_i(p, m, Q), \tag{5.2.5}$$

has a solution:

$$m = \xi(p, A, Q), \tag{5.2.6}$$

where A is a constant of i negations satisfying the initial condition:

$$W^0 = \xi(p^0, A, Q), \tag{5.2.7}$$

where (p^0, W^0) is the price–wealth combination in the initial situation.

By solving for A we get

$$A = \varphi(p^0, W^0, Q), \tag{5.2.8}$$

where φ can be interpreted as an indirect utility function v, i.e.

$$v(p, W, Q) = U(g(p, W, Q)). \tag{5.2.9}$$

Note, however, that this holds only for a given Q. Although, we can in this way recover the indirect utility function for private goods for the demand function, we cannot in general recover the preferences for environmental services.

Finally, Roy's theorem, i.e.

$$g(p, W, Q) = -\frac{\partial v}{\partial p_i} \bigg/ \frac{\partial v}{\partial W}, \tag{5.2.10}$$

can easily be proved as well as

$$\delta_j = \frac{\partial v}{\partial Q_j} \bigg/ \frac{\partial v}{\partial W}, \tag{5.2.11}$$

where δ_j is the marginal willingness to pay for Q_j.

Given demand functions $g(p, W, Q)$ satisfying these four properties, one can construct a utility function generating these demand functions. A heuristic proof of this assertion goes as follows.

Consider the system of partial differential equations,

$$\frac{\partial m}{\partial p_i} = g(p, m, Q), \qquad i = 1, 2, \ldots, n.$$

From Frobenius' theorem[34] it follows that this system has a unique solution:

$$m = \varphi(p, p^0, W^0, Q).$$

Now, knowledge of the expenditure function φ is almost the same as knowledge of the utility function U. However, the φ function does not carry all information on the demand for Q, unless one makes *a priori* assumptions on U.

5.3. Compensating and equivalent variation

We will in this section use the notation of the previous section to discuss operational welfare measures.

The expenditure function in m is strictly increasing in U which means that for given $\bar{p}, \bar{Q}$,

$$m(\bar{p}, \bar{Q}, U(x, Q)) \tag{5.3.1}$$

is a strictly increasing transformation of the utility function. With fixed $\bar{p}$ and fixed $\bar{Q}$, the expenditure function is thus a valid utility function. This representation of the preferences gives the least expenditures at prices $\bar{p}$ and public goods supply $\bar{Q}$ necessary to achieve the same utility level as given by (x, Q), where $U = U(x, Q)$.[35]

Let us consider two situations, A and B, such that at A the price vector is p', the public goods supply is Q' and the income of the individual W', and at B we have p'', Q'', and W''. Let the utility level at A be U' and at B be U''.

[34] See Debreu (1959).
[35] See Dieudonné (1960) and Chipman, Hurwicz, Richter and Sonnenschein (1971).

If we consider A as the present situation and B an alternative, we can define the compensating (resp. the equivalent) variation in the following way:

$$CV = m(p', Q', U') - m(p'', Q'', U') + W'' - W'. \tag{5.3.2}$$

This definition is equivalent to the classical definition of CV except that we have assumed that the net wealth may change and included that change in the definition.[36] As

$$W' = m(p', Q', U') \quad \text{and} \quad W'' = m(p'', Q'', U'')$$

it follows that

$$CV = m(p'', Q'', U'') - m(p'', Q'', U'). \tag{5.3.3}$$

Thus, CV is the change in the utility function (5.3.1) when we choose $\bar{p} = p''$ and $\bar{Q} = Q''$.

In the same way the equivalent variation is defined as:

$$EV = m(p', Q', U'') - m(p'', Q'', U'') + W'' - W', \tag{5.3.4}$$

which also can be written:

$$EV = m(p', Q', U'') - m(p', Q', U'). \tag{5.3.5}$$

EV is then the change in the utility function (5.3.1) when we choose $\bar{p} = p'$ and $\bar{Q} = Q'$.

Both representations of the preferences are of course equally valid and it is not possible on the basis of this discussion to discriminate between the two concepts.

But let us now assume that there are at least three alternatives which we want to compare simultaneously. Let the variables in the three states be separated by a' in the initial state A, a'' in one alternative state B, and a''' in the second alternative state C.

One possible representation of the preferences of the individual would be

$$m(p', Q', U).$$

The utility differences between the different states with this utility function correspond to as we have seen the equivalent variations. If we let EV'' be the EV for the change from A to B, and EV''' for the change from A to C, we have:

$$EV'' = m(p', Q', U'') - m(p', Q', U'), \tag{5.3.6}$$

$$EV''' = m(p', Q', U''') - m(p', Q', U'). \tag{5.3.7}$$

If we know EV'' and EV''' we know the complete ranking of the three states. Thus, if $EV''' > EV''$, then C is preferred to B, and if $EV'' > 0$, then B is

---

[36] See Hurwicz and Uzawa in Chipman et al. (1971).

preferred to A. Note, however, that $EV''' - EV''$ is not the equivalent variation of going from B to C.

If, instead of knowing the equivalent variations we only know the compensating variations of going from A to B and from A to C, i.e.

$$CV'' = m(p'', Q'', U'') - m(p'', Q'', U'),$$ (5.3.8)

$$CV''' = m(p''', Q''', U''') - m(p''', Q''', U'),$$ (5.3.9)

we do not know the complete ranking. The reason is of course that we are using two different utility functions when we compute the change from A to B and when we compute the change from A to C. Therefore, CV'' is not comparable with CV'''.

Thus, if we have to consider more than two alternatives, the compensating variation is not as useful as the equivalent variation.

Finally, Willig[37] has shown that unless the income elasticity for a commodity is very high, the equivalent and compensating variations for a price change will not differ considerably. That this does not necessarily hold for changes in the flow of environmental services is easy to prove by way of an example. Consider an old man who has been living in a valley for a lifetime. The valley is threatened by a hydropower development project, which would force the man to move to an urban area. His equivalent variation, i.e. the loss of income equivalent to be moved out, is bounded by his budget, while his compensating variation is not so bounded and can take arbitrary high values. Thus, it may make a substantial difference whether the compensating or the equivalent variation is used, although both are perfectly valid representations of the preferences of the old man. We will discuss this problem in some detail in Section 6.3.

6. Social welfare functions

6.1. Social indirect utility functions

In order to be able to make welfare statements, some ethical values must be given by which interpersonal comparisons can be made. Such values were discussed in Section 1 in terms of a social welfare function. There is an enormous literature on social welfare representations in terms of social welfare functions. There is no need for us to go into that in order to construct a theoretical base for evaluating environmental changes. We will simply postulate the existence of social preferences over different states of the economy. In order to make that postulate as concrete as possible, we assume there is a body – government, parliament,

---

[37] Willig (1976).

environment agency – which has preferences over the states and these preferences will be identified with social preferences.

Let us then assume that this body is concerned with prices p, wealth distribution $I^1,\ldots,I^H$, and environmental quality Q (note that because the letter W will now be used for welfare, we have in this section changed the notation for wealth to I).

These preferences are assumed to be such that they can be represented by a continuously differentiable function V:

$$W = V(p, I', \ldots, I^H, Q).$$

This function will be called the indirect social welfare function.[38]

We assume that it is increasing in each individual wealth, i.e.

$$\frac{\partial V}{\partial I^h} > 0, \qquad h = 1, \ldots, H.$$

We also assume that the preferences for price changes are such that it is only the effects on the real incomes of the households that count. This means in particular that

$$\frac{\partial V}{\partial p_i} = -\sum_{h=1}^{H} x_i^h \frac{\partial V}{\partial w^h}, \qquad i = 1, \ldots, n. \tag{6.1.1}$$

We make a similar assumption concerning environmental services, i.e. that

$$\frac{\partial V}{\partial Q_m} = \sum_{h=1}^{H} \delta_m^h \frac{\partial V}{\partial w^h}, \qquad m = 1, \ldots, M, \tag{6.1.2}$$

where δ_m^h is the marginal willingness to pay for the mth environmental service in the hth household.

Let $v^h(p, W^h, Q)$ be the indirect utility function of household h. We can now prove that there exists a function $W: R^H \to R$ with the following property:

$$W(v'(p, W', Q), \ldots, v^H(p, W^H, Q)) \equiv V(p, W^1, \ldots, W^H, Q) \tag{6.1.3}$$

Let $v^h(p, W^h, Q)$ be the indirect utility function and $m^h(p, u^h, Q)$ the expenditure function of household h. Then

$$W^h \equiv m^h(p, u^h, Q)$$

and

$$V(p, m^1(p, u^1, Q), \ldots, m^H(p, u^H, Q), Q)$$

$$\equiv \varphi(p, u^1, \ldots, u^H, Q) \tag{6.1.4}$$

---

[38] This approach to the social welfare function was first discussed in Mäler (1974) on which most of the following is based.

Now

$$\frac{\partial \varphi}{\partial p_i} = \frac{\partial V}{\partial p_i} + \sum_{h=1}^{H} \frac{\partial V}{\partial I^h} \frac{\partial m^h}{\partial p_i}$$

$$= \frac{\partial V}{\partial p_i} + \sum_{h=1}^{H} x_i^h \frac{\partial V}{\partial I^h} = 0 \qquad (6.1.5)$$

and

$$\frac{\partial \varphi}{\partial Q_m} = \sum_{h=1}^{H} \frac{\partial V}{\partial I^h} \frac{\partial m^h}{\partial Q_m} + \frac{\partial V}{\partial Q_m}$$

$$= \sum_{h=1}^{H} \delta_m^h \frac{\partial V}{\partial I^h} + \frac{\partial V}{\partial Q_m} = 0. \qquad (6.1.6)$$

φ is thus not a function of p and Q but only of $u', \ldots, u^H$. Then define

$$W(u', \ldots, u^H) \equiv \varphi(p, u', \ldots, u^H, Q),$$

and W is the desired function.

We have started with social preferences over income distribution, prices and environmental services and proved that if these preferences are such that they are consistent with consumer sovereignty in the sense that social preferences over prices are only over their effects on real income, and social preferences over environmental services are also only over their real income effects, then these preferences can be represented by a social welfare function:

$$W(u', \ldots, u^H).$$

Ordinarily, one starts with the W-function and defines the indirect welfare function in terms of the W-function. The reason we have reversed that process is that the indirect function is defined on directly observable variables: prices, household incomes, and environmental quality measurements. It is therefore easier to assume that a body has preferences over these variables than over the more abstract utility levels.

The drawback is, of course, the two assumptions made. The first can easily be defended, i.e. that it is only the real income effects of prices that matter from a social point of view, but the second is more doubtful. However, these assumptions can, of course, be proved if we start with the W-function.

If we do not make the assumption (6.1.2), the derived social welfare function would be

$$W = W(U^1, \ldots, U^H, Q),$$

i.e. the agency would have direct preferences for environmental services besides the effects through the individual utility functions.

6.2. Welfare criteria

Consider two states A and B. These states can either be characterized by the allocation of resources and the distribution of goods among households or by the price vectors and the distribution of wealth. In this section we will characterize the states by the price vector p on private goods, the vector of the flow of environmental services Q, and the distribution of wealth $W'', \ldots, W^H$.

Let the state A then be characterized by $(p', Q', W^{1'}, \ldots, W^{H'})$ and state B by $(p'', Q'', W^{1''}, \ldots, W^{H''})$. Then the utility levels are, respectively:

$$u^{u'} = v^h(p', W^{h'}, Q') \tag{6.2.1}$$

and

$$u^{u''} = v^h(p'', W^{h''}, Q'') \tag{6.2.2}$$

Given the indirect utility function $V(p, W', \ldots, W^H, Q)$ the welfare change in going from A to B is

$$\Delta W = V(p'', W^{1''}, \ldots, W^{H''}, Q'') - V(p', W^{1'}, \ldots, W^{H'}, Q')$$
$$\equiv W(v'(p'', W^{1''}, Q''), \ldots, v^H(p'', W^{H''}, Q''))$$
$$- W(v'(p', W^{1''}, Q''), \ldots, v^H(p', W^{H'}, Q')). \tag{6.2.3}$$

Let $\bar{p}, \bar{Q}, \bar{W}^h$ be given and let us use

$$\tilde{u}^h = m^h(\bar{p}, u^h, \bar{Q}) \tag{6.2.4}$$

as a representation of the preferences of household h. By solving u^h we get

$$u^h = v^h(\bar{p}, \tilde{u}^h, \bar{Q}^v), \tag{6.2.5}$$

so that

$$v^h(\bar{p}, m^h(\bar{p}, u^h, \bar{Q}), \bar{Q}) \equiv u^h. \tag{6.2.6}$$

Then social welfare can be written

$$W = W(v^1(\bar{p}, m^1(\bar{p}, u^1, \bar{Q}), \bar{Q}), \ldots, v^H(\bar{p}, m^H(\bar{p}, u^H, \bar{Q}), \bar{Q}))$$
$$\equiv V(\bar{p}, m^1(\bar{p}, \bar{Q}, u'), \ldots, m^H(\bar{p}, \bar{Q}, u^H), \bar{Q}). \tag{6.2.7}$$

The change in social welfare of going from A to B is, with this representation:

$$\Delta W = V(\bar{p}, m^1(\bar{p}, \bar{Q}, u^{1''}), \ldots, m^H(\bar{p}, \bar{Q}, u^{H''}), \bar{Q})$$
$$- V(\bar{p}, m^1(\bar{p}, \bar{Q}, u^{1'}), \ldots, m^H(p, Q, u^{H'}), \bar{Q}). \tag{6.2.8}$$

Let us set $\bar{p} = p'$ and $\overline{Q} = Q'$

$$\Delta W = V\left(p', m^1\left(p', Q', u^{1'}\right) + EV^1, \ldots, m^H\left(p', Q', Q^{H'}\right) + EV^H, Q'\right)$$
$$- V\left(P', m^1\left(p', Q', u^{1'}\right), \ldots, m^H\left(p', Q', u^{H'}\right)Q'\right)$$
$$= \sum_h \frac{V\left(p', \alpha', \alpha^1, \ldots, \alpha^H, Q'\right)}{\partial W^h} EV^h, \tag{6.2.9}$$

$$m^h\left(p', Q', u^{h'}\right) \leq \alpha^h \leq m^h\left(p', Q', u^{h'}\right) + EV^h,$$

or

$$m^h\left(p', Q', u^{h'}\right) \geq \alpha^h \geq m^h\left(p', Q', u^{h'}\right) + EV^h.$$

Let us then set $\bar{p} = p''$ and $\overline{Q} = Q''$. We then get as an equally valid representation of the welfare change:

$$\Delta W = \sum_h \frac{\partial V\left(p'', \beta^1, \ldots, \beta^H, Q''\right)}{\partial W^h} CV^h, \tag{6.2.10}$$

where

$$m^h\left(p'', Q'', u^{h'}\right) \leq \beta^h \leq m^h\left(p'', Q'', u^{h'}\right) + CV^h$$

or

$$m^h\left(p'', Q'', u^{h'}\right) \geq \beta^h \geq m^h\left(p'', Q'', u^{h'}\right) + CV^h.$$

The welfare change is thus a weighted sum of the individual compensating variations or a weighted sum of the individual equivalent variations. The weights are of course different in the two situations but from a theoretical point of view both are equally valid as representations of the welfare change.

In applied cost–benefit analysis one very seldom finds examples where the individual compensating variations or equivalent variations have been weighted. Instead, the applied researcher assumes that all individuals carry the same weight. Now if we assume that in the representation (6.2.9) all weights are the same it follows that the weights must differ in the representation (6.2.10) and vice versa. Therefore it is a legitimate question to ask whether it is more "reasonable" to assume constant weights for the CV representation or if it is more "reasonable" to assume constant weights for the EV representation.

The main justifications for assuming identical weights for all individuals seem to be the following:

(a) we are in general indifferent to income distribution;

(b) the income distribution is optimal with respect to the welfare function; and

(c) distributional matters are taken care of by a special distributional branch of the government and are therefore of no concern in a cost–benefit analysis.

Let us discuss the relevance of these different justifications for the choice between compensating and equivalent variation.

Let us start out by trying to make precise the statement that society is indifferent to income distribution. One very natural way of making that statement precise would be to assume that the indirect social welfare function is specified as

$$V\left(p, Q, \sum_h W^h\right). \tag{6.2.11}$$

This specification guarantees that it does not matter who gets the income. The only interesting variable is the total income $W = \sum_h W^h$. This specification is, however, not in general consistent with the idea of a direct social welfare function. In Mäler[39] it is shown that the following two conditions on the indirect social welfare function are both necessary and sufficient for the indirect welfare function to be derived from a direct welfare function:

$$\frac{\partial V}{\partial p_i} = -\sum_h X_i^h \frac{\partial V}{\partial W^h}, \qquad i = 1, 2, \ldots, n,$$

$$\frac{\partial V}{\partial Q_j} = \sum_h \frac{\partial m^h}{\partial Q_j} \frac{\partial V}{\partial W^h}, \qquad j = 1, 2, \ldots, m.$$

In view of the specification (6.2.11) the first of these conditions can be written as

$$\frac{\partial V}{\partial p_i} = -\frac{\partial V}{\partial W} \sum_h X_i^h$$

or

$$\frac{\partial V}{\partial p_i} \bigg/ \frac{\partial V}{\partial W} = -\sum_h X_i^h, \qquad i, 2, \ldots, n.$$

The left-hand side is obviously independent of income distribution. In order that the right-hand side also should be independent of income distribution it is necessary that the individuals have identical and homothetic preferences. If not, the total demand for a good will depend on income distribution. Thus, unless one is willing to make quite strong assumption on individual preferences (such strong assumptions that there would be no difference between compensating and equivalent variations), it is not possible use the specification given in (6.2.11) as a definition of indifference to income distribution.

Another possible assumption would be to assume that initially society is indifferent to marginal changes in income distribution. That is equivalent to the

[39] Mäler (1974).

assumption that

$$\frac{\partial V\left(p', Q', W^{1'}, \ldots, W^{H'}\right)}{\partial W^h} = \lambda, \qquad h = 1, 2, \ldots, H.$$

If we assume that the V-function is approximately linear in I^h, we can compute the welfare change as

$$\Delta W = V\left(p', Q', m^1\left(p', Q', u^{1'}\right) + EV^1, \ldots, m^H\left(p', Q', u^{H'}\right) + EV^H\right)$$

$$- V\left(p', Q', m^1\left(p', Q', u^{1'}\right), \ldots, m^H\left(p', Q', u^{H'}\right)\right)$$

$$\approx \lambda \sum_h EV^h.$$

Thus, in this case it is the equivalent variation that is relevant. It may be worth while to spell out this result in some detail. If the initial situation is such that on the margin a redistribution of net wealth does not affect welfare and if the proposed change is such that the real income of the individuals will not change "too much" (too much is defined with respect to the rate at which the marginal social welfare of individual income decreases), then it is appropriate to use the equivalent variation as a welfare measure. If, however, the change means large increases or decreases in real income for some individuals, then this assumption is of no use.

On the other hand, if we assume that the income distribution after the change is such that a marginal change in income distribution would not affect social welfare, i.e. that

$$\frac{\partial V\left(p'', Q'', W^{1''}, \ldots, W^{H''}\right)}{\partial W^h} = \lambda, \qquad h = 1, \ldots, H,$$

it follows in the same way that it is the compensating variation that should be used. Thus, by using the compensating variation we will in fact filter out projects that would give as a result wide disparity between the weights $\partial V / \partial I^h$ in the final situation, although such projects may in fact increase welfare.

It seems from this discussion that it is not possible to give a strict theoretical justification for either compensating or equivalent variation. And this result should come as no surprise. It has been known for quite a long time now that it is impossible to separate distributional issues from allocative issues, and in carrying out cost–benefit analysis we should always bear in mind the necessity of using specific value judgements on distributional questions. But as soon as we do that the compensating and equivalent variations are really equivalent.

In most cases the cost–benefit analysis does not have available a set of distributional weights. One way to overcome the problems arising from that lack of information might be to use an average of the compensating and the equivalent variation. By doing that, we essentially assume that somewhere in between the two states is another state at which all individuals carry the same weight. The advantage of such a procedure would be that the assumption that the present income distribution is such that all individuals can be treated equally (i.e. the same weights) is combined with the idea of screening out those projects that would cause great changes in income distribution.

As a final point, if there is a special distributional branch of the government which can carry out lump-sum redistributions the distinction between compensating and equivalent variations disappear, because then the whole society behaves as if there is only one person, and for one individual we know that CV and EV give the same criterion.

7. Measuring the preferences for environmental services

Since we have discarded the idea of markets for environmental services (Section 4.7), there are no markets on which households' preferences for these services can be revealed. We will in this section look into some other ways by which it may be possible to get some information about those preferences.

There are basically two approaches that can be used: asking people, or making sufficiently strong assumptions on the households' preferences or technology or market mechanisms in order to enable indirect estimates of the preferences.[40]

7.1. Direct methods

The direct methods can conveniently be divided into two different classes. The first class encompasses those methods that can be used directly in decision-making, while the second class contains methods that can be used in purely hypothetical situations.

We will in this section consider a change in the flow of a certain environmental source, say Q, from Q'_1 to Q''_1. We know the cost of making that change, i.e. $p(z'' - z')$ (assuming prices do not change in response to the environment quality change). In order to make a decision compatible with a given welfare function we must have information on the individuals' preferences for the change. Let us assume for simplicity that we are interested in their willingness to pay for the change (if the change is an improvement, this is equal to the compensating variation).

---

[40] The following discussion will necessarily be very brief and will only give a sketch of a theoretical structure of the most practised methods of estimating the value of environmental services. For more penetrating surveys, see Mäler and Wyzga (1976), Freeman (1979), and Hufschmidt et al. (1982).

7.1.1. Groves–Ledyard mechanisms

The first class contains procedures such that the individuals know that their answers to the questions on the amount they are willing to pay will determine the final decision. In this case the households have in general incentives to misrepresent their preferences. If they know they have to pay the sum they have responded with, they have incentives to respond with very small amounts, in the hope that others will state sufficient amounts to ensure that the desired change comes about.

On the other hand, if the change is financed in some other way, the households have incentives to state a too high willingness to pay.

If, however, the households are uncertain on how the cost of the change will be distributed, Mäler has shown that correct revelation of preferences is a max–min strategy.[41] Unfortunately, the max–min strategy is not unique, so the result is not very useful.

Some mechanisms with such payments have been shown to be free of incentives to misrepresent preferences. These Groves–Ledyard[42] procedures involve such payments to the households that in an ingenious way depend on other households' responses in such a way that the individual household has no incentives to misrepresent preferences. These mechanisms, although theoretically very elegant, are quite complicated and not to my knowledge empirically tested. They will also require an unbalanced budget because the payments from the households to the government or payments in the other direction will not add to zero. Green and Laffont have, however, proved that the deviations from a balanced budget are likely to be small. Finally, even if the mechanisms yield incentives to true preference revelation on the individual level, coalitions of households may still be able to benefit from strategic behavior. Green and Laffont proved that these benefits in all likelihood for large economies are small and that therefore the creation of such coalitions is not likely.

7.1.2. Bidding games

A very common approach to eliciting preferences about the environment is to ask purely hypothetical questions about willingness to pay. Those who are asked then know that their responses will be of no consequence for the ultimate decision and they lack for that reason incentives to behave strategically.

On the other hand, in purely hypothetical situations the response may not be thoroughly considered and it may be difficult to interpret the stated willingness to pay. Moreover, it seems that the responses in these cases are very sensitive to who

---

[41] Mäler (1974).
[42] Groves (1974), Groves and Ledyard (1975), and Green and Laffont (1980).

is asking the questions and the procedure that is followed. This, of course, follows from the fact that the response is of no consequence for the respondent.

However, empirical experiments with various forms of hypothetical questioning have been in general successful and the theoretical problems outlined above may just be theoretical problems.[43]

7.2. Indirect methods

Indirect methods are based on the fact that a change in the flow of environmental services may change the behavior of households and sometimes therefore prices on private goods. By relating these changes to the change in environmental quality, it may sometimes be possible to determine the willingness to pay.

Changes in household behavior due to changes in environmental quality are described by the demand functions for private goods:

$$x^h = g^h(p, W^h, Q).$$

If we can estimate such functions from empirical data and if we have made sufficiently strong assumptions about the household production functions, we can in general recover the utility function as a function not only of private goods and services but also the flow of environmental services.

7.2.1. Aggregation

In general, it is in practice not possible to estimate the demand functions of individual households, but only for large groups of households. Thus, instead of estimating

$$x^h(p, W^h, Q), \tag{7.2.1.1}$$

we are forced to estimate

$$\sum_{h=1}^{H} x^h(p, W^h, Q), \tag{7.2.1.2}$$

or rather a function of the type

$$x(p, \sum W^h, Q). \tag{7.2.1.3}$$

It is obvious that if the individual demand functions have the four properties derived in Section 4, then the aggregate demand function will satisfy the two first, i.e. it will be homogeneous of degree zero in prices and wealth and it will satisfy the budget constraint. However, it will not necessarily have the remaining two

---

[43] Freeman (1979) and Desvouges, Smith and McGivney (1983) give good surveys of these techniques.

properties. In fact, even to write the aggregate function as a function of total income $\sum W^h$ instead of the income distribution $(W^1, \ldots, W^H)$ requires quite strong assumptions.

In view of the fact that we need properties (iii) and (iv) in order to calculate the willingness to pay from information on individual behavior, we are more or less forced to make assumptions that ensure consistent aggregation over individuals. One set of such assumptions is:

(i) all households have identical utility functions and production functions; and

(ii) utility functions and production functions are homothetic, i.e. monotone transformations of linearly homogeneous functions.

The second assumption implies that changes in the wealth of a household do not change the budget shares. The first assumption then implies that an income redistribution does not change the budget share in the aggregate.

These are quite restrictive assumptions which seem to make aggregate analysis more or less meaningless. Some preliminary results of the author indicate, however, that the situation is not as bad as that. In some simulation experiments, when it is assumed that households have quite different preferences (which do not need to be homothetic), the error committed when one uses aggregate functions seems to be small.

7.2.2. *The problem*

In order to facilitate the presentation we will make some very simplifying assumptions. First, we will, according to the discussion in the previous section, only consider one individual. Second, we will only consider one flow of environment services, so the symbol Q now is a scalar. Similarly, x is the demand for a private good (or rather an aggregate of private goods). κ is, as before, a measure of the output of some service or good that is being produced within the household. Let the utility function of the representative household or individual be

$$U = u(x, \kappa). \tag{7.2.2.1}$$

We assume that κ is produced according to the production function[44]

$$\kappa = \varphi(y, Q), \tag{7.2.2.2}$$

where y is the input of some private good and Q the input of the public good. We also assume that φ is the same for all individuals.

There are many examples of this kind of production, for example the private good, vehicles, and the public good, highways, produce transport services. Fishing expenditures and water quality produce fishing experience.

---

[44] On household production functions and public goods, see Hori (1975) and Sandmo (1973).

The budget constraint is

$$P_x x + P_y y \leqq W, \tag{7.2.2.3}$$

where P_x and P_y are prices on x and y, respectively, and W is the lump-sum income.

Utility maximization subject to the budget constraint yields the Lagrangian:

$$L = u(x, \varphi(y, Q)) - \lambda(P_x x + P_y y - W'),$$

and the necessary conditions:

$$u_x - \lambda P_x = 0, \tag{7.2.2.4}$$

$$u_z \varphi_y - \lambda P_y = 0. \tag{7.2.2.5}$$

The solution to the constrained utility maximization problem defines the demand functions for the private goods:

$$x = x(P_x, P_y, W, Q), \tag{7.2.2.6}$$

$$y = y(P_x, P_y, W, Q). \tag{7.2.2.7}$$

The demand for the public good is defined by the marginal willingness to pay δ for Q, i.e.

$$\delta = P_x \frac{u_z \varphi_Q}{u_x} = P_y \frac{\varphi_Q}{\varphi_y}. \tag{7.2.2.8}$$

Our problem is whether it is possible to estimate (7.2.2.8) from information on (7.2.2.6) and (7.2.2.7).

This is not in general possible. In order to make such inference possible some *a priori* assumptions on the household production function φ are needed.

We have, however, seen in Section 5 that information on the demand functions are sufficient to recover the utility function as a function of private goods, by first solving for the expenditure function m as a function of prices. Our problem is to find out how to obtain m as a function of Q also.[45]

If we know the production function φ, it is straightforward to show that δ can be calculated given information on the demand for private goods. This is, however, to neglect the question. The problem of estimating the demand for a public good exists because we simply do not know how the public good enters the utility functions. Let us, in spite of this, assume that the production function is of the Cobb-Douglas type:

$$\varphi = y^\alpha Q^\beta.$$

---

[45] This problem was stated in Mäler (1974) and the results that follows can be found in that book. However, most of the proofs are much simpler in this presentation.

It is obviously no loss of generality to assume that $\alpha + \beta = 1$. From (7.2.2.8), (7.2.2.4) and (7.2.2.3) we see that

$$\delta = P_x \cdot \frac{u_z \cdot \varphi_Q}{u_x} = P_y \frac{\beta \cdot z/Q \cdot u_z}{\alpha \cdot z/y \cdot u_z} = \frac{\beta}{\alpha} \cdot \frac{P_y y}{Q}$$

or

$$\delta Q = \frac{\beta}{\alpha} P_y y.$$

If there is reason to believe that $\alpha = \beta$, we have

$$\delta Q = P_y y,$$

i.e. the value of the public good evaluated at a price equal to the marginal willingness to pay is equal to the expenditure on the private good y. There are many studies where indeed the value of a public good has been estimated as the expenditure on a private good, for example the value of recreation facilities has been estimated as the expenditures on recreation equipment. This approach is supported by the argument above *if* one can make it plausible that the household production function is of Cobb–Douglas type and that the exponents are equal.

In general, however, there is no information available that would enable the researcher to specify either the functional form of the production function or its numerical structure. However, it is sometimes possible to make assumptions about some broad characteristics of the productions functions, such as whether one input is essential or not or whether the two inputs are substitutes or complements.

We will review the following three types of assumptions:
(a) weak complementarity between the inputs;
(b) the inputs are perfect substitutes; and
(c) the inputs are separable.

7.2.3. Weak complementarity

One quite general specification of the production function is weak complementarity.[46] This is defined as the requirement that the private good input to the production function is essential, i.e.

$$\phi(0, Q) = 0, \qquad \frac{\partial \varphi(0, Q)}{\partial Q} = 0, \qquad (7.2.3.1)$$

---

[46] This concept was introduced by Mäler (1971). See also Bradford and Hildebrandt (1977).

which implies

$$\frac{\partial u(y, \varphi(0, Q))}{\partial Q} = 0. \tag{7.2.3.2}$$

This seems to be a most reasonable assumption in many cases.

If, for example, Q stands for highways and y for motor cars, it seems quite realistic to assume that the individual is not concerned when a highway development is discussed if he does not have a car. Another example is given by interpreting Q as water quality in a lake and y as private expenditures for recreation in that same lake.

The Slutsky equation can be written:

$$\frac{\partial m}{\partial P_x} = x(P_x, P_y, m, Q), \tag{7.2.3.3}$$

$$\frac{\partial m}{\partial P_y} = y(P_x, P_y, m, Q). \tag{7.2.3.4}$$

The solution can be written:

$$m = \xi(P_x, P_y, Q, A(Q)), \tag{7.2.3.5}$$

where A is an unknown function of Q.

The compensated demand for y is given by

$$y(P_x, P_y, m, Q) \equiv \frac{\partial \xi}{\partial P_y}.$$

From $\partial \xi / \partial P_y = 0$ we can solve for P_y:

$$P_y = \Psi(P_x, Q, A(Q)).$$

If $P_y \geq \Psi(P_x, Q, A(Q))$, it follows that $y = 0$ because the price elasticity of the compensated demand is always nonpositive.

When $P_y \geq \Psi(P_x, Q, A(Q))$ the expenditure function becomes $m = \xi(P_x, \Psi(P_x, Q, A(Q)), Q, A(Q))$ and it follows from (7.2.3.1) and (7.2.3.2) that

$$\frac{\partial m}{\partial Q} = \frac{\partial \xi}{\partial P_y}\left(\frac{\partial \Psi}{\partial Q} + \frac{\partial \Psi}{\partial A}\frac{dA}{dQ}\right) + \frac{\partial \xi}{\partial Q} + \frac{\partial \xi}{\partial A}\frac{dA}{dQ} = 0$$

or

$$\frac{dA}{dQ} = -\frac{\dfrac{\partial \Psi}{\partial Q}\dfrac{\partial \xi}{\partial P_y} + \dfrac{\partial \xi}{\partial Q}}{\dfrac{\partial \xi}{\partial P_y}\dfrac{\partial \Psi}{\partial A} + \dfrac{\partial \xi}{\partial A}}. \tag{7.2.3.6}$$

We know that

$$\xi = P_x \frac{\partial \xi}{\partial P_x} + P_y \frac{\partial \xi}{\partial P_y}.$$

Since $\partial \xi / \partial P_y = 0$ when $P_y = \Psi(P_x, Q, A)$, it follows that

$$\xi(P_x, \Psi(P_x, Q, A), Q, A) = P_x \frac{\partial \xi(P_x, \Psi(P_x, Q, A), Q, A)}{\partial P_x}.$$

This entails

$$\frac{\partial \xi}{\partial A} = P_x \left\{ \frac{\partial^2 \xi}{\partial P_y \partial P_x} \frac{\partial \Psi}{\partial A} + \frac{\partial^2 \xi}{\partial A \partial P_x} \right\} \tag{7.2.3.7}$$

and

$$\frac{\partial \xi}{\partial Q} = P_x \left\{ \frac{\partial^2 \xi}{\partial P_y \partial P_x} \frac{\partial \Psi}{\partial Q} + \frac{\partial^2 \xi}{\partial Q \partial P_x} \right\}, \tag{7.2.3.8}$$

where all derivatives are evaluated at $(P_x, \Psi(P_x, Q, A), Q, A)$.

From the definition of the Ψ-function we have:

$$\frac{\partial \Psi}{\partial P_x} = - \frac{\partial^2 \xi}{\partial P_x \partial P_y} \bigg/ \frac{\partial^2 \xi}{\partial P_y^2}, \tag{7.2.3.9}$$

$$\frac{\partial \Psi}{\partial Q} = - \frac{\partial^2 \xi}{\partial Q \partial P_y} \bigg/ \frac{\partial^2 \xi}{\partial P_y^2}, \tag{7.2.3.10}$$

$$\frac{\partial \Psi}{\partial A} = - \frac{\partial^2 \xi}{\partial A \partial P_y} \bigg/ \frac{\partial^2 \xi}{\partial P_y^2}. \tag{7.2.3.11}$$

We can now prove that the right-hand side (RHS) of (7.2.3.6) is independent of P_x.

Remember that $\partial \xi / \partial P_y = 0$. It then follows that [$N$ denotes the denominator in (7.2.3.6)]:

$$\frac{\partial \text{RHS}}{\partial P_x} = - \frac{1}{N^2} \left[\frac{\partial \xi}{\partial A} \left\{ \frac{\partial \Psi}{\partial Q} \left(\frac{\partial^2 \xi}{\partial P_x \partial P_y} + \frac{\partial^2 \xi}{\partial P_y^2} \frac{\partial \Psi}{\partial P_x} \right) \right. \right.$$

$$\left. + \frac{\partial^2 \xi}{\partial P_x \partial Q} + \frac{\partial^2 \xi}{\partial P_y \partial Q} \frac{\partial \Psi}{\partial P_x} \right\} - \frac{\partial \xi}{\partial Q} \left\{ \frac{\partial \Psi}{\partial A} \left(\frac{\partial^2 \xi}{\partial P_x \partial P_y} + \frac{\partial^2 \xi}{\partial P_y^2} \frac{\partial \Psi}{\partial P_x} \right) \right.$$

$$\left. \left. + \frac{\partial^2 \xi}{\partial P_x \partial A} + \frac{\partial^2 \xi}{\partial P_y \partial A} \frac{\partial \Psi}{\partial P_x} \right\} \right] = [\text{because of } (7.2.3.3), (7.2.3.5)]$$

$$= -\frac{1}{N^2}\left[\frac{\partial \xi}{\partial A}\left(\frac{\partial^2 \xi}{\partial P_x \partial Q} + \frac{\partial^2 \xi}{\partial P_y \partial Q}\frac{\partial \Psi}{\partial P_x}\right) - \frac{\partial \xi}{\partial Q}\left(\frac{\partial^2 \xi}{\partial P_x \partial A} + \frac{\partial \xi}{\partial P_x \partial A}\frac{\partial \Psi}{\partial P_x}\right)\right]$$

$$= [\text{because of } (7.2.3.7), (7.2.3.8), (7.2.3.10), (7.2.3.11)]$$

$$= -\frac{P_x}{N^2\left(\partial^2 \xi/\partial P_y^2\right)}\left[\left(-\frac{\partial^2 \xi}{\partial P_y \partial P_x}\frac{\partial^2 \xi}{\partial A \partial P_y} + \frac{\partial^2 \xi}{\partial A \partial P_x}\frac{\partial^2 \xi}{\partial P_y^2}\right)\right.$$

$$\times \left(\frac{\partial^2 \xi}{\partial P_x \partial Q}\frac{\partial^2 \xi}{\partial P_y^2} - \frac{\partial^2 \xi}{\partial P_y \partial Q}\frac{\partial^2 \xi}{\partial P_x \partial P_y}\right)$$

$$-\left(-\frac{\partial^2 \xi}{\partial P_y \partial P_x}\frac{\partial^2 \xi}{\partial Q \partial P_y} + \frac{\partial^2 \xi}{\partial Q \partial P_x}\frac{\partial^2 \xi}{\partial P_y^2}\right)$$

$$\times \left.\left(\frac{\partial^2 \xi}{\partial P_x \partial A}\frac{\partial^2 \xi}{\partial P_y^2} - \frac{\partial^2 \xi}{\partial P_y \partial A}\frac{\partial^2 \xi}{\partial P_x \partial P_y}\right)\right] = 0.$$

RHS is thus independent of P_x and (7.2.3.6) is an ordinary differential equation in the unknown function $A(Q)$. Let the solution be

$$A = \alpha(Q, C),$$

where C is an integration constant. C can be determined from the initial condition:

$$\xi\left(P_x, P_y, Q, \Psi(Q, C)\right) = W.$$

Thus, we have been able to reconstruct the expenditure function from the demand functions assuming that weak complementarity prevails.

7.2.4. Perfect substitutes

If the inputs are perfect substitutes, then the production function can be written:

$$\phi = y + BQ, \tag{7.2.4.1}$$

where B is a constant.
It follows that

$$\delta = P_y\frac{u_z B}{u_z} = BP_y, \tag{7.2.4.2}$$

where B can be interpreted as determined by the scale with which Q is measured. B can be determined in the following way.

The necessary conditions for utility maximization are, in this case,

$$u_x - \lambda p_x = 0,$$
$$u_z - \lambda p_y = 0, \qquad\qquad (7.2.4.3)$$
$$-p_x x - p_y y = -W.$$

Differentiating these equations with respect to I and Q yields:

$$\begin{bmatrix} u_{xx} & u_{xz} & -p_x \\ u_{xz} & u_{zz} & -p_y \\ -p_x & -p_y & 0 \end{bmatrix} \begin{bmatrix} dx \\ dy \\ d\lambda \end{bmatrix} = \begin{bmatrix} -Bu_{xz} & dQ \\ -Bu_{zz} & dQ \\ -dW \end{bmatrix}. \qquad (7.2.4.4)$$

The solution to this linear system includes

$$\frac{\partial x}{\partial Q} = B\frac{p_y u_{xz} - p_x u_{zz}}{D} - p_y \qquad\qquad (7.2.4.5)$$

and

$$\frac{\partial x}{\partial I} = \frac{p_y u_{xz} - p_x u_{zz}}{D}, \qquad\qquad (7.2.4.6)$$

where D is the determinant of the matrix in the left-hand side of (7.2.4.4).

Dividing (7.2.4.5) by (7.2.4.6) yields:

$$p_y B = \frac{\partial x}{\partial Q} \bigg/ \frac{\partial x}{\partial W}.$$

If $y > 0$, we then have:

$$\delta = p_y B = \frac{\partial x}{\partial Q} \bigg/ \frac{\partial X}{\partial W}. \qquad\qquad (7.2.4.7)$$

However,

$$p_x \frac{\partial x}{\partial Q} + p_y \frac{\partial y}{\partial Q} = 0$$

so that

$$\delta = -p_y \frac{\partial y}{\partial Q} \bigg/ p_x \frac{\partial x}{\partial W}. \qquad\qquad (7.2.4.8)$$

The numerator, $-p_y(\partial y/\partial Q)$, is simply the cost reduction made possible by an increase in Q. That cost reduction has also an income effect, so we have to divide by $p_x(\partial x/\partial I)$ to take that into account.

This result has been used in numerous studies on pollution damage. The damage of corrosion has been estimated by the cost of repainting, assuming that pollution control and paint are perfect substitutes. Cleaning and pollution control give another example.

By estimating the demand function for x we can thus estimate the marginal willingness to pay for the public good.

7.2.5. Separability

It is interesting to note that (7.2.4.8) is valid under more general conditions than that the two inputs are perfect substitutes. In order to deduce the most general conditions under which (7.2.4.8) is valid, let us return to the general specification of the household production function $\phi(y, Q)$.

The first-order necessary conditions for utility maximization are restated for convenience:

$$u_x - \lambda p_x = 0,$$
$$u_z \phi_y - \lambda p_y = 0,$$
$$-p_x x - p_y y = -W.$$

Differentiating with respect to Q and I yields:

$$\begin{bmatrix} u_{xx} & u_{xz}\phi_y & -p_x \\ u_{xz}\phi_y & u_{zz}\phi_y^2 + u_z\phi_{yy} & -p_y \\ -p_x & -p_y & 0 \end{bmatrix} \begin{bmatrix} dx \\ dy \\ d\lambda \end{bmatrix} = \begin{bmatrix} -u_{xz}\phi_Q \, dQ \\ (-u_{zz}\phi_y\phi_Q - u_z\phi_{yQ}) \, dQ \\ -dW \end{bmatrix}.$$

The solutions for $\partial x/\partial I$ and $\partial x/\partial Q$ are, respectively:

$$\frac{\partial x}{\partial W} = \frac{\phi_y}{D}\left(p_y u_{xz} - p_x u_{zz}\phi_y - p_x u_z \frac{\phi_{yy}}{\phi_y} \right)$$

and

$$\frac{\partial x}{\partial Q} = \frac{P_y \phi_Q}{D}\left(p_y u_{xz} - p_x u_{zz}\phi_y - p_x u_z \frac{\phi_{yQ}}{\phi_y} \right).$$

Thus,

$$\frac{\partial x}{\partial Q} \bigg/ \frac{\partial x}{\partial W} = P_y \frac{\phi_Q}{\phi_y}$$

if and only if

$$\frac{\phi_{yy}}{\phi_y} = \frac{\phi_{yQ}}{\phi_Q}$$

or

$$\frac{\partial}{\partial_y} \log \phi_y = \frac{\partial}{\partial_y} \log \phi_Q.$$

that is

$$\phi_y = A\phi_Q,$$

where A is an arbitrary function of Q: $A(Q)$. The partial differential equation,

$$\phi_y - A(Q)\phi_Q = 0,$$

has as the general solution:

$$\phi = f(y + B(Q)Q),$$

where f is arbitrary.

Thus (7.2.4.8) is valid if and only if the marginal rate of substitution between the two inputs depends only on the amount of the public good input and not on the private good input. Then the production function must be separable in private goods and environmental services, and the marginal productivity of the private goods must be constant.[47]

7.3. Property values

Since demand for private goods may be affected by changes in environmental quality, prices on these goods may also change. A natural candidate is land and one would intuitively expect that differences in environmental quality between different regions will be capitalized in property values. We will in this section construct a simple model in order to analyze that issue.[48]

Let us assume we have a region of fixed size. For simplicity, assume the region is one-dimensional so that different points can be represented by a single coordinate t. Each point in the region is characterized by its environmental quality Q, its transportation costs T, and other amenities or variables K.

Let the transportation cost T be given as a function

$$T = \tau(t),$$

where the transportation cost is assumed to be a fixed cost, not dependent on household consumption but only on where the household has chosen to live.

Consider a household planning to buy a piece of land in this region. Let its utility function be

$$u^h(C^h, S^h, Q, K),$$

---

[47] This result has not been published elsewhere.

[48] The model to be constructed is extremely simple. For more complicated models and critical assessment see Mäler (1977), Mäler and Wyzga (1976), Freeman (1979), Lind (1966), Rosen (1974) and Strotz (1966).

where C is private consumption and S is land holdings. Note that this specification implicitly makes an assumption of weak complementarity. Only environmental quality on the piece of land a household rents is of concern to them. We assume that the household only holds a connected piece of land which is small in relation to the total area of the region.

The budget constraint of the household is

$$pC^h + rS^h \le W^h, \tag{7.3.1}$$

where W^h is the wealth, p is the price index on consumer goods, and r is the land rental. Now r will vary over the region and thus be a function of the space coordinate, as well as of environmental quality and of other amenities.

The price index for consumption goods may also be a function of these variables. Thus:

$$p = p(t, Q, K). \tag{7.3.2}$$

Utility maximization yields (with λ a Lagrangian multiplier):

$$\frac{\partial U^h}{\partial C} = \lambda^h p, \tag{7.3.3}$$

$$\frac{\partial U^h}{\partial S} = \lambda^h r, \tag{7.3.4}$$

$$\frac{\partial U^h}{\partial Q} = \lambda^h \left(\frac{\partial p}{\partial Q} C^h + \frac{\partial r}{\partial Q} S^h \right), \tag{7.3.5}$$

$$\frac{\partial U^h}{\partial K} = \lambda^h \left(\frac{\partial p}{\partial K} C^h + \frac{\partial r}{\partial K} S^h \right), \tag{7.3.6}$$

$$\frac{\partial p}{\partial t} C^h + \frac{\partial r}{\partial t} S^h + \tau' = 0. \tag{7.3.7}$$

Now, the marginal willingness to pay, δ^h, for environmental services is easily seen to be

$$\delta^h = p \frac{\partial U^h}{\partial Q} \bigg/ \frac{\partial U^h}{\partial C} = \frac{\partial p}{\partial Q} C^h + \frac{\partial r}{\partial Q} S^h. \tag{7.3.8}$$

If we assume that environmental quality only capitalizes in land rents and not in any other prices (wages, restaurant prices, sport rentals, cost of cleaning equipment, etc.), then

$$\frac{\partial p}{\partial Q} = 0 \tag{7.3.9}$$

and

$$\delta^h = S^h \frac{\partial r}{\partial Q}. \tag{7.3.10}$$

This also requires that there are sufficiently many subdistricts within the region so that the environment quality can be described as a continuous variable over the whole region.[49]

Now, if we can estimate the function $r(t, Q, K)$ from data on land rents and the distribution of amenities and environmental quality, we have an obvious way of estimating δ^h. (A more applied discussion of estimating benefits from environmental improvements is found in Chapter 6 of this Handbook.)

References

D'Arge, R., R. Ayres and A. Kneese (1972) *Economics and the Environment: A Materials Balance Approach* (Baltimore).

Arrow, K. (1963) *Social Choice and Individual Values* (New Haven).

Arrow, K. and F.H. Hahn (1971) *Competitive Analysis* (Oxford).

Arrow, K.J. and A.C. Fisher (1974) "Environmental Preservation Uncertainty and Irreversibility", *The Quarterly Journal of Economics*, May.

Atkinson, A.B. and J.E. Stiglitz (1980) *Lectures on Public Economics* (McGraw-Hill).

Ayres, R. and A. Kneese (1969) "Production, Consumption and Externalities", *American Economic Review*, vol. 59.

Baumol, W.J. (1964) "External Economies and Second-Order Optimality Conditions", *American Economic Review*, vol. 54.

Baumol, W.J. and D.F. Bradford (1972) "Detrimental Externalities and Non-Convexity of the Production Set", *Economica*, May.

Bergson, A. (1938) "A Reformulation of Certain Aspects of Welfare Economics", *Quarterly Journal of Economics*, vol. 52, Feb.

Bohm, P. (1975) "Option Demand and Consumer Surplus: Comment", *The American Economic Review*, Sept.

Bradford and Hildebrandt (1977) "Observable Preferences for Public Goods", *Journal of Political Economy*.

Conrad, J.M. (1980) "Quasi-Option Value and the Expected Value of Information", *The Quarterly Journal of Economics*, June.

Dasgupta, P. (1982) *Control of Resources*.

Dasgupta, P. and G. Heal (1979) *Economic Theory and Exhaustible Resources* (Cambridge).

Debreu, G. (1959) *Theory of Value* (New York).

Debreu, G. (1962) "New Concepts and Techniques for Equilibrium Analysis", *International Economic Review*, vol. 3, Sept.

Debreu, G. (1962) "Existence of Competitive Equilibrium" in: K. Arrow and W. Intriligator (eds.), *Handbook of Mathematical Economics*, vol. II (Amsterdam).

Desvousges, W.H., V.K. Smith and M.P. McGivney (1983) *A Comparison of Alternative Approaches for Estimating Recreation and Related Benefits of Water Quality Improvements*, E.P.A. (Washington D.C.).

Foley, D. (1967) "Resource Allocation and the Public Sector", *Yale Economic Essays* 7.

Foley, D. (1970) "Lindahl's Solution and the Core of an Economy with Public Goods", *Econometrica*, vol. 38.

Freeman III, A.M. (1979) *The Benefits of Environmental Improvement* (Baltimore).

Graaf, J. de (1957) *Theoretical Welfare Economics* (London).

---

[49] The model provides a kind of pseudo market for environmental quality in the form of the market for land. This can be utilized for an analysis of environmental quality and local governments. See Tiebout (1956).

Graham, P.A. (1981) "Cost-Benefit Analysis under Uncertainty", *The American Economic Review*, Sept.

Green, J. and J.-J. Laffont (1980) *Incentives in Public Decision Making* (Amsterdam).

Hart, O.D. and H.W. Kuhn (1975) "A Proof of the Existence of Equilibrium without the Free Disposal Assumption", *Journal of Mathematical Economics* 2.

Haveman, B.H. and I. Margolis (eds.) (1970) *Public Expenditures and Policy Analysis*.

Henry, C. (1974) "Option Values in Economics of Irreplaceable Assets", *Review of Economic Studies*, Symposium, Sept.

Johansen, L. (1965) *Public Economics* (Amsterdam).

Koopmans, T. (1957) *Three Essays on the State of Economic Science* (New York).

Lancaster, K. (1966) "A New Approach to Consumer Theory", *Journal of Political Economy*, vol. 74, April.

Lind, R. (1966) *The Nature of Flood Control Benefits and the Economics of Flood Protection* (Stanford University).

Lind, R.D. (ed.) (1982) *Discounting for Time and Risk in Energy Policy* (Baltimore).

Mäler, K.-G. (1971) "A Method of Estimating Social Benefits from Pollution Control", *Swedish Journal of Economics*, vol. 73.

Mäler, K.-G. (1974) *Environmental Economics, A Theoretical Inquiry* (Baltimore).

Mäler, K.-G. (1977) "A Note on the Use of Property Values in Estimating Marginal Willingness to Pay for Environmental Quality", *Journal of Environmental Economics and Management*, vol. 4.

Milleron, J.-C. (1972) "Theory of Value with Public Goods: A Survey Article", *Journal of Economic Theory*, vol. 5.

Musgrave, R. and A. Peacock (1967) *Classics in the Theory of Public Finance* (New York).

Nozick, R. (1974) *Anarchy, State and Utopia* (New York).

Rosen, S. (1974) "Hedonic Price and Implicit Markets: Product Differentiation in Pure Competition", *Journal of Political Economy*, vol. 87.

Samuelson, P. (1954) "The Pure Theory of Public Expenditures", *Review of Economics and Statistics*, vol. 36.

Samuelson, P. (1969) "The Pure Theory of Public Expenditure and Taxation" in: I. Margolis and H. Guillou (eds.), *Public Economics* (New York).

Sandmo, A. (1973) "Public Goods and the Technology of Consumption", *Review of Economic Studies*, Oct.

Schmalenzee, R. (1972) "Option Demand and Consumer's Surplus: Valuing Price Changes under Uncertainty", *The American Economic Review*, Dec.

Smith, V.K. (1983) "Option Value: A Conceptual Overview", *Southern Economic Journal*, vol. 49, Jan.

Starret, D. (1972) "Fundamental Non-Convexities in the Theory of Externalities", *Journal of Economic Theory*, vol. 4.

Strotz, R. (1966) *Economics of Urban Air Pollution*, Resources for the Future.

Sugden, Robert (1981) "The Political Economy of Public Choice" (Oxford).

Tiebout, C.M. (1956) "A Pure Theory of Local Expenditures", *Journal of Political Economy*, vol. 64.

Varian, H.R. (1984) *Microeconomic Analysis* (New York).

Chapter 2

BIOECONOMICS OF RENEWABLE RESOURCE USE

JAMES E. WILEN

University of California

1. Introduction

One of the characteristics of natural resource economics which makes it both interesting and difficult is its heavy reliance on noneconomic as well as economic concepts. Basic notions from the fields of law, population biology, petroleum engineering, ecology, hydrology, entomology and other fields are increasingly appearing in the literature of the field. Over the past two decades the field has expanded both in breadth of coverage and also in depth of conceptual development so that a well-rounded natural resources economist needs to have considerable knowledge not only about sophisticated techniques in economics but also in several other outside fields.

In light of these facts, the task of writing a survey chapter on something like the bioeconomics of renewable resources runs a risk of ending up looking like the Platte River (a mile wide and an inch deep) or too concentrated in economics to inform the principal readers (economists presumably) much about relevant concepts in the outside discipline. Accordingly, this chapter attempts to walk a fine line of being both compact and comprehensive in discussing relevant concepts from economics and biology. In addition, an attempt has been made to identify unifying threads and areas of potential future development in bioeconomics.

This chapter has four major parts. Section 2 discusses the economic concepts which appear to be central to analyzing biological situations typically encountered. The concepts are drawn from capital theory and cover two classes of problems: a continuous investment/disinvestment problem and a point-input point-output problem where timing of a single action is important. Section 3 then reviews relevant concepts from biology which affect the nature of the corresponding bioeconomic problem. The section is written with most emphasis on the range of population growth mechanisms we see in natural systems and the individual characteristics that have evolved to produce such population mechanisms. Section 4 then draws material from Sections 2 and 3 together in a review of some different bioeconomic models and their conclusions. Section 5 concludes by discussing likely directions of future research.

Handbook of Natural Resource and Energy Economics, vol. I, edited by A.V. Kneese and J.L. Sweeney
© *Elsevier Science Publishers B.V., 1985*

2. Economics and renewable resource use

2.1. *Renewable resources as stocks of capital*

In natural systems with and without the presence of man, evolutionary forces have filled spaces with a diversity of populations of plants, insects, fish, mammals, and birds. Although there is disagreement over where evolution is leading the system in the long run, there is some understanding of the mechanisms of competition and symbiosis between these populations and the elements which act to control given population sizes in their particular patches of space.

From the point of view of man as the ultimate user of these resources, populations of natural organisms are most conveniently viewed as stocks of capital or assets which provide potential flows of services. Determining how to maximize benefits from these resources thus becomes a problem of capital theory – deciding mainly how to utilize this "portfolio" of stocks over time. This view avoids the ethical issues of whether man has "right" to utilize resources for his own good (see discussion in Chapter 5 of this Handbook) but it does admit the possibility that "benign" uses, i.e. leaving the system close to "natural", may be the best from man's perspective also. In addition, such a view requires that a system view be taken in order to account for interrelationships among the populations that make up the portfolio.

The essential questions of modern capital theory are precisely issues of optimal use of stocks over time. While early writers stressed the "intermediateness" or "round-about" nature of capital, the critical characteristics of capital which make it interesting as an economic problem are:

(i)   durability
(ii) sluggishness – capital stocks cannot be instantly adjusted without incurring some adjustment costs.

Durability is a crucial distinguishing characteristic of capital since it links past decisions with current opportunities and also makes future possibilities dependent on today's decision. Inputs that are flows rather than stocks can be treated in a sequential series of static decisions since there is no carryover from past decisions nor impact on the future from current decisions. Hence, durability in relation to decision periods makes it necessary to initiate intertemporal planning and, in particular, to forecast the future in order to make the best decision today. In addition, the fact of capital's durability makes it a store of wealth, i.e. it assumes a value which carries through time, and as a result the stock may be subject to speculative decisions as well as pure production-related decisions involving service flows.

The second characteristic (costly adjustment) is also critical in that it forces the decision-maker to consider the future in order to spread out the costs of altering the capital stock. For example, if a firm is using machinery to produce a product and it can rent or purchase/resell at any moment at some fixed price per unit capital, then it can simply wait for all uncertainty about product prices, etc. to be unveiled and then instantly adjust to meet the desired stock level [Arrow (1964)]. In this case, with no adjustment costs (i.e. costs which rise as the rate of capital stock adjustment increases), determining a capital stock path (or investment plan) is really a sequentially static decision problem, requiring no forecasting or intertemporal planning. On the other hand, if more machines need a larger building, more labor, etc. then there are adjustment costs $C(I)$, where I is the investment level, $C'(I) > 0$ and (critically) $C''(I) \neq 0$. Thus if, for example, $C(I) = I^2$ and the entrepreneur wants to increase the capital stock by 100 units, the costs of investing immediately will be tenfold the costs of adding 10 units each year over a ten-year period. The rapid investment policy, of course, will yield returns earlier and thus we have a classic intertemporal tradeoff problem where one can incur high adjustment costs to get early higher returns or one can adjust slower with a returns penalty. The optimal decision depends in a sometimes complex manner on a balancing of gains from earlier benefits against costs of rapid adjustment.

In summary, these two characteristics of durability and costly adjustment make for a difficult intertemporal planning problem. With durability, it is necessary to know the future profiles of prices, costs, and stock sizes and incorporate them into optimal decisions at any point in time. Thus, even if there are no adjustment costs associated with changing the stock in the future, we are still faced with what we refer to as a *timing problem* of deciding *when* to change the stock level. With positive adjustment costs we face, in addition, an optimal *investment/disinvestment problem* of deciding how *fast* to change the stock, since it may be better to begin increasing or decreasing the stock early in order to spread out adjustment costs.

Biological and other natural resources obviously fit the above characteristics of capital stocks. They are durable in that organisms, or the population, or the species, generally live beyond the interval of the typical planning period. In addition, since all populations have rates of increases limited by their intrinsic population biology, they cannot be instantly and costlessly adjusted upwards so that there are investment adjustment costs (perhaps zero up to certain rates of increase, infinite thereafter). Some stocks which are clustered and easily harvested in total (e.g. schooling fish, forests) may be reduced with virtually no increase in costs but for other resources as stocks thin out it is usually increasingly expensive to harvest remaining units so that reduction adjustment costs may be increasing as well. Thus use of natural systems confronts us with both timing and investment/disinvestment problems generally.

2.2. Capital theory – basic results

In order to understand the nature of intertemporal problems and the complexities introduced by the above characteristics, it will be useful to consider a simple model of a firm. The firm produces a product Q which can be sold at price p each period. The quantity of Q in any period t depends on the quantity of the firm's capital stock K via the production function

$$Q_t = F(K_t), \qquad F' > 0, \; F'' < 0. \tag{1}$$

There are costs $C(I_t)$ of adding to the capital stock where I_t is the investment rate. We will assume that capital depreciates at a constant proportional rate r so that $(\mathrm{d}K/\mathrm{d}t) \equiv \dot{K}_t = I_t - rK_t$. The firm has K_0 units of capital initially and wants to determine the optimal investment plan which maximizes the present value of profits, or

$$\max_{I_t} \int_0^\infty [\, pF(K_t) - C(I_t)\,] \mathrm{e}^{-\delta t} \mathrm{d}t$$
$$\text{s.t.} \tag{2}$$
$$\dot{K}_t = I_t - rK_t,$$

where δ is the discount rate. The solution to this problem depends in an important way on $C(I)$ and particularly on whether $C(I)$ exhibits adjustment costs.[1] Adjustment costs imply that $C(I)$ increases at an increasing rate in I so that marginal costs of adding capital are increasing with the level of addition. A reasonable form for $C(I)$ thus might be something like

$$C(I) = \frac{P_k I^\beta}{\beta}, \tag{3}$$

where P_k is a (minimum) unit price of investment and where $\beta = 1$ implies no adjustment costs and $\beta > 1$ implies positive adjustment costs.

Consider first the case with $\beta = 1$. Then the integrand in (2) becomes

$$\Pi(K, I) = pF(K) - P_k I = \Pi_A(K, \dot{K}) = pF(K) - P_k[\dot{K} + rK].$$

Since it costs nothing extra to rapidly adjust the capital stock compared to a slower adjustment, it obviously is better to adjust it as quickly as possible. The important issue, however, is what level should the stock be adjusted to? The answer to this (and a proof that most rapid adjustment is optimal) is provided in an elegant paper by Spence and Starrett (1975). Let $M(K) = pF(K) - P_k rK$ and let $N(K) = -P_k$. Spence and Starrett show that for *any* problem whose augmented integrand (derived by substituting the dynamic constraint into the original integrand) can be written as

$$\Pi_A(K, \dot{K}) = M(K) + N(K)\dot{K}, \tag{4}$$

the optimal solution reduces to one of simply reaching a steady state level $K = K^*$ as quickly as possible. In the problem considered above, if there are no constraints on I_t, this would be achieved with an initial "impulse control" with $I = \infty$ or $I = -\infty$ that jumps the capital from K_0 to K^*.

---

[1] Time subscripts will be dropped from this point forward where the meaning is obvious.

The optimal level K^* is found as follows. Let

$$S[K(t)] = \int_{K_0}^{K(t)} N(\varepsilon)\,d\varepsilon, \quad \text{so that } \dot{S} = N(K)\dot{K}. \tag{5}$$

Then, the problem in (2) can be written as

$$\max_{K,\dot{K}} \int_0^\infty [M(K) + N(K)\dot{K}]e^{-\delta t}\,dt = \int_0^\infty [M(K) + \dot{S}]e^{-\delta t}\,dt. \tag{6}$$

But the second part of the RHS integral can be integrated by parts to yield:

$$\int_0^\infty \dot{S}e^{-\delta t}\,dt = \delta\int_0^\infty S[K(t)]^{-\delta t}\,dt, \tag{7}$$

so that (6) reduces to

$$\max_K \int_0^\infty [M(K) + \delta S(K)]e^{-\delta t}\,dt = \int_0^\infty V(K)e^{-\delta t}dt. \tag{8}$$

The important thing to note is that the original problem in K and I reduces to a simple problem in K alone. Obviously, (8) is maximized by making K follow a most rapid approach path (MRAP) to $K = K^*$ defined by $V'(K^*) = 0$.[2] Thus, we have an important rule applicable to any capital problem; namely, if by substituting the constraint into the original integrand we have as an augmented integrand $\pi(K, \dot{K})$ which is linear in $\dot{K}$, i.e. as in (4), then the optimal solution is a MRAP to K^* defined by (8).

For the specific problem in (2) with $\beta = 1$, the optimal steady state level of K is given by

$$\frac{pF'(K^*) - rP_k}{\delta} = P_k. \tag{9}$$

The intuition behind this condition is clear: if we happen to be at some level K_0 and contemplate staying there forever, then the present value of future returns will be

$$PV(K_0) = \int_0^\infty [pF(K_0) - P_k I_0]e^{-\delta t}\,dt = \frac{pF(K_0) - P_k rK_0}{\delta}. \tag{10}$$

However, a small change (say ΔK units) away from this level to a new sustained level $K_0 + \Delta K$ would change these profits by

$$\frac{\Delta PV(K_0)}{\Delta K}\Delta K \cong \frac{pF'(K_0) - P_k r}{\delta}\Delta K. \tag{11}$$

The costs of making this change would be $P_k\Delta K$ and hence it pays to make marginal adjustments as long as the gain (loss) in (11) exceeds the cost (benefit from liquidating and selling) of $P_k\Delta K$. At the optimal $K = K^*$, (11) should be equal to $P_k\Delta K$ and hence condition (9) follows.

---

[2] Second-order conditions must be met, of course. If more than one local maximum exists, the solutions must be compared globally, in which case the initial value K_0 may be important.

It should be obvious now that there is a relationship between adjustment costs and the MRAP problem. In particular, if $C(I)$ exhibits adjustment costs so that $\beta > 1$ in (3), then the augmented integrand will no longer be linear in $\dot{K}$ since $C(I)$ will be convex. Thus adjustment costs lead to a more complicated problem where simple impulse controls to a steady state are not the optimal solution. As it turns out, however, the above hueristic of examining the marginal gains and losses associated with moving from a presumed optimal steady-state stock is still valid. In particular, as long as the relevant parameters p, P_k and r are autonomous or invariant with time, the optimal solution involves *approaching* some steady-state stock level K^*. The approach, of course, cannot be MRAP since there are adjustment costs.

Consider, for this more general problem, a situation where we begin with some stock level K_0 and we are considering staying at K_0. Then, since we are committed to this steady state level forever, $I_0 = rK_0$ and

$$PV(K_0) = \int_0^\infty e^{-\delta t} \left[pF(K_0) - C(I_0 = rK_0) \right] dt = \frac{pF(K_0) - C(rK_0)}{\delta}. \quad (12)$$

The characteristic of K^* which makes it the optimal steady-state level is that an incremental increase or decrease to some new level $K^* + \Delta K$ must result in no gains as before. Suppose that we consider a slight increase $\Delta K > 0$ from K_0, i.e. we add ΔK units of capital and move to a new steady state $K = K_0 + \Delta K$. Then the change in the present value of sustained profits will be

$$\frac{\Delta PV(K_0)}{\Delta K} \Delta K \cong \frac{pF'(K_0) - C'(rK_0)r}{\delta} \Delta K. \quad (13)$$

The increase is achieved by purchasing some capital, however, so that we also have a short term acquisition cost of

$$\frac{\Delta C(I_0)}{\Delta I} \Delta I \cong C'(I_0)\Delta I. \quad (14)$$

If we happened to be to the left of the maximum of (12) initially, the acquisition would yield a positive contribution (13) offset by a negative cost (14). As long as the net gain is positive it pays to make the incremental acquisition. Similar reasoning would hold for corresponding marginal liquidations of the capital stock.[3] Thus, K^* can be identified as that level for which a further incremental move results in no net gain or where an equal gain (loss) in *sustained* profits is just matched by the cost (gain) in investment (disinvestment) need to obtain that

---

[3] In this case, it is convenient to assume symmetric adjustment costs so that the marginal cost of adding a unit from the steady-state position is $C'(rK_0)$ and the marginal cost of removing a unit is $-C'(rK_0)$.

move, i.e.

$$\frac{pF'(K^*) - C'(rK^*)r}{\delta} = C'(I^*) = C'(rK^*). \tag{15}$$

The intuition behind this condition is the same as discussed for the linear case in that at the long-run optimal steady-state stock, the present value of the benefits of a marginal change in the steady-state capital stock are just offset by the (current) marginal cost of making that change.

These results can be expressed graphically as follows. Consider the cost function in (3) above with $\beta = 2$ and $\beta = 1$, i.e. alternatively the case with adjustment costs and without them. Figures 2.1(a) and 2.1(b) show the *steady-state* profits per time period for any given long-run K. In the steady state, investment $(I = rK)$ must be just enough to cover depreciation and hence $C(I)$ can be expressed in terms of the stock level or $C(rK)$. The added costs associated with adjustment costs over and above the constant unit investment costs $P_k rK$ imply that steady-state profits will be maximum at a lower stock level with $\beta = 2$ compared with $\beta = 1$. Figure 2.1(c) graphs conditions (9) and (15) above. The optimal steady-state value of $K = K^*$ just balances the marginal gains and losses associated with an incremental change in the long-run steady-state stock level. Note that K^* is *not* where per period sustained profits are largest generally (except when $\delta = 0$). This is because if one happens to be at this point initially, it pays to give up a little of these long run profits in trade for some "liquidation" gains. In fact, the larger the discount rate the more it pays since future losses in steady-state profits become discounted relative to immediate liquidation gains. In contrast, if one starts with a low stock, it pays to invest in stock to increase long-run sustained profits up until K^* is reached. As incremental changes are added in this case, (13) and (14) are both positive but the difference or overall gain is positive until $K = K^*$. Here, again, with a positive discount rate it does not pay to invest up to the point where steady-state profits are maximum since immediate take-home profits must be forgone to do so. The higher the discount rate, the lower are the prospective gains and the more onerous are the present costs.

What role do adjustment costs play in this problem? Generally adjustment costs affect both the steady-state value K^* and the optimal approach to K^* for any arbitrary K_0. The affect on K^* can be seen in Figures 2.1(a)–2.1(c). In particular, if $\beta = 1$, $K^*_{\beta=1}$ is the optimal long-run steady-state stock. In this case, however, as discussed before, the optimal approach to K^* is simply an impulse control which immediately jumps K_0 to K^* with $I = \infty$ (if $K_0 < K^*$) or $I = -\infty$ (if $K_0 > K^*$). In the more interesting case, as adjustment costs increase, K^* decreases because the per period costs of maintaining the stock (i.e. replacing depreciation) are higher.

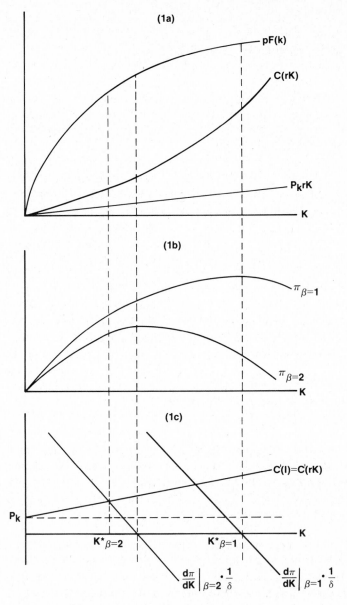

Figure 2.1. Optimal steady-state stock levels – with and without adjustment costs.

The remainder of the optimization problem involves determining how to get to K^* from some arbitrary K_0. The problem of determining the explicit optimal approach is more technically difficult but basically boils down to the condition that K_t^* satisfy

$$C'\left(I_t^*\right) = \int_t^\infty pF'(K)e^{-(\delta+r)(s-t)}\,ds. \tag{16}$$

The expression is basically a non-steady-state version of (15), where I_t and K_t now represent optimal (non-steady-state) values.[4] Eq. (16) is an equation for the optimal path of I_t^* and $\dot{K} + rK$ as well and if differentiated with respect to time, the result will be a (nonlinear generally) second-order differential equation in K whose solution depends upon the end point conditions and the time horizon.[5]

For a well-behaved problem (i.e. with F concave, parameters time invariant, and C convex) with an infinite time horizon, the solution to the differential equation in (16) is qualitatively a smooth asymptotic [see Figure 2.2(a)] approach to the steady-state value of K^*. If a terminal value K_T is to be reached in a finite problem, the solution involves staying "close" to K^* for a time dependent on the horizon length [see Figure 2.2(b)].[6] If $K_0 > K^*$, the optimal path is corresponding

---

[4] This condition is derived as follows. The current valued Hamiltonian for this problem may be written as:
(a) $H = pF(K) - C(I) + \lambda[-rK + I]$.
The optimal investment level I^* satisfies:
(b) $C'(I_t^*) = \lambda_t$,
(c) $\dot{\lambda}_t - \delta\lambda_t = -pF'(K_t) + \lambda r$, and
(d) $\dot{K} = I_t^* - rK_t$.
Integrating (c) directly and evaluating between t and ∞ gives

$$\lambda(t) = \int_t^\infty pF'(K_s)e^{-(\delta+r)(s-t)}\,ds,$$

which when set equal to (b) gives eq. (16) in the text. Note that the assumption of proportional depreciation allows the depreciation costs to be effectively collapsed into a discount factor so that at each point along the optimal trajectory, the marginal cost of adding another unit of investment is just balanced by the future gross marginal benefits, discounted by the augmented discount factor.

[5] To see this, note that differentiating (16) with respect to t gives

$$C''(I) \cdot \dot{I} = (r + \delta)C'(I) - pF'(K).$$

Since $I = \dot{K} + \delta K$, this equation in $\dot{I}$, I, and K can be re-expressed in terms of $\ddot{K}$, $\dot{K}$, and K. With both $F'(K)$ and $C'(\cdot)$ nonlinear, the resulting equation will be a nonlinear second-order differential equation, the solution of which is the optimal time path K_t^*.

[6] This result is the so-called "turnpike" property of the optimal capital accumulation literature, i.e. the optimal savings or investment rate calls for getting the capital stock level close to, and thereby remaining close to, the "turnpike" level [characterized by (15)] and veering off only if an alternate terminal stock must be reached. This makes intuitive sense if it is recalled that K^* is defined as that level for which incremental changes only decrease the present value of corresponding future returns. The rapidity with which one approaches (K^*) and subsequently stays there will, of course, be governed precisely by the onerousness of costs of adjustment. When adjustment costs are zero, it pays to get to K^* as quickly as possible and stay as long as possible. As adjustment costs become positive, one cannot afford to get too close or stay too long, and hence an asymptotic path arises.

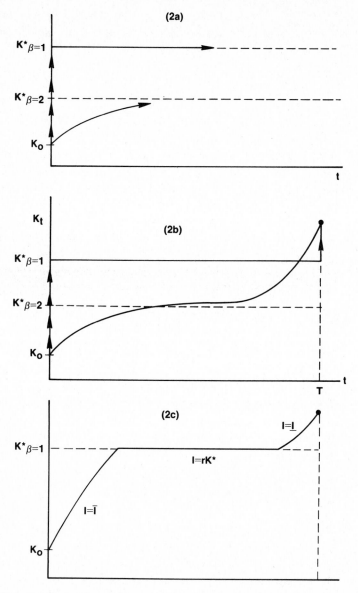

Figure 2.2. Optimal capital accumulation profiles – with and without adjustment costs.

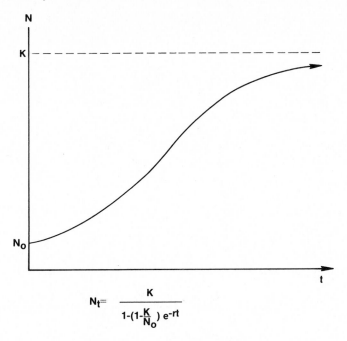

$$N_t = \frac{K}{1-(1-\frac{K}{N_0})\,e^{-rt}}$$

Figure 2.3. Logistic growth model.

asymptotically decreasing. Finally, for a special case of adjustment costs where the investment rate is simply constrained between upper and lower bounds $\underline{I} \leq I_t \leq \bar{I}$, adjustment costs are effectively zero within the range and infinite otherwise, giving rise to the so-called bang-bang solution where investment levels are $\bar{I}$ or $\underline{I}$ until $K^*_{\beta=1}$ is reached.[7] This is illustrated in Figure 2.2(c).

2.3. Optimal use of natural resources – the logistic model

The above introduction to capital theory focusing on a model of the firm provides a useful framework for examining optimal natural resource use since, as discussed earlier, it is convenient to view natural resources essentially as capital goods. Perhaps the most commonly used model of biological populations is the Pearl – Verhulst logistic model [Pearl (1930), Verhulst (1838)] in which the population is assumed to grow as a logistic or S-curve over time (see Figure 2.3). In this model, the numbers or biomass of organisms grows rapidly early as the abundance of food is relatively great and then the growth rate tapers off and the population asymptotically approaches its carrying capacity K. The equation

---

[7] This is the model extensively developed by Clark (1976).

describing the above growth pattern is

$$N(t) = \frac{K}{1 - \left(1 - \dfrac{K}{N(0)}\right) e^{-rt}}. \tag{17}$$

This can be differentiated with respect to t and rearranged to get

$$\dot{N} = rN\left[1 - (N/K)\right] = F(N). \tag{18}$$

This form reveals the interplay between the model's two parameters, r and K. r can be defined as the maximum intrinsic per capita growth rate of the population, i.e. $\lim_{N \to 0}[\dot{N}/N]$. As $N \to K$, the effective per capita increase $r[1 - (N/K)]$ declines linearly towards zero.

The logistic model is actually a flexible model which can represent a variety of growth phenomenon in nature – ranging from the length or mass of a single animal or group to the numbers or biomass of a whole population. We shall use it to introduce two fundamental natural resources using situations – a timing problem and an optimal harvest problem.

Consider first a problem of timing where there are basically no constraints or adjustment costs associated with reducing a given resource. For example, we might have a situation where range animals are placed on a pasture and their total weight gain follows the logistic in (17). If we are deciding when to remove and sell them, we have the problem:

$$\max_{t} PV(t) = e^{-\delta t}V(t) = e^{-\delta t}P(t)N(t), \tag{19}$$

where $P(t)$ is the price per unit biomass at time t. The solution to this problem is found by differentiating (19) t, and setting the result equal to zero. Thus the solution given by

$$\dot{V}(t^*) = \delta V(t^*), \tag{20}$$

where $V(t)$ represents the value at t. The intuition behind this result is that we wait until the increase in value of our capital left "on the hoof" $[\dot{V}(t^*)]$ is just equal to the opportunity cost forgone by *not* removing from the pasture; i.e. the amount we could get by selling and receiving $V(t)$ and reaping a net gain in the bank of $\delta V(t)$ over the same period. If value is growing as in Figure 2.4, the optimal time to harvest is that associated with the highest iso-present value curve PV.[8] Before t^*, it pays to leave one's capital in the natural bank since it is growing in value faster than it would in the commercial bank. Thus, this result is a general one which actually applies to any asset aging problem, whether it be wine kept in storage, paintings or antiques held for value increases, etc.

---

[8] Each of these curves is from the family of iso-present value curves derived by exponentiating some amount PV into a future value V_t, i.e. $V_t = PVe^{\delta t}$. Alternatively, each curve converts some future value V_t into a corresponding present value $PV = V_t e^{-\delta t}$ read off the vertical axis.

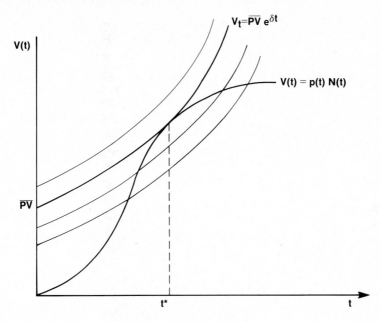

Figure 2.4. Optimal timing problem.

One additional point of interest in this problem is the relationship between costs and prices. If we let C be some fixed costs incurred at harvest time, (20) reduces to

$$\frac{\dot{N}}{N} = \delta \left[1 - \frac{C}{PN} \right] - \left(\frac{\dot{P}}{P} \right). \tag{21}$$

Figure 2.5 plots the "own biological rate of interest" of the species $\dot{N}/N$ against the term in brackets in (21). Note first that if the value per unit biomass is increasing with age (e.g. a larger tree can be cut into more valuable products) then $\dot{P}/P > 0$ and it will pay to wait longer. Note also that unless the maximum intrinsic growth rate r is greater than the discount rate δ, it will not even pay to start the growth process since one can only lose even more money by waiting past $t = 0$ as $r(N)$ declines. Third, if prices are unchanging ($\dot{P} = 0$) and there are no harvesting costs, the optimal timing date is where $\dot{N}/N = \delta$, or where the biological rate of interest just falls to the opportunity cost rate of interest. In this case, interestingly, the price *level* has no impact on the timing date since it impacts both sides of (20) in the same way. Finally, again with $\dot{P} = 0$, the optimal timing date is directly related to the cost/price ratio and as C/P gets larger, the optimal date gets later.

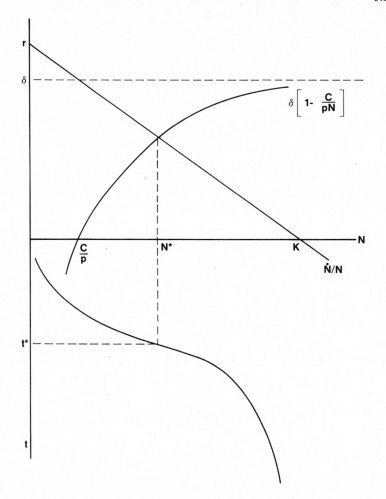

Figure 2.5. Optimal timing problem with costs.

The logistic model is more commonly used to depict populations subject to continuous rather than one-shot harvesting. Let $N(t)$ represent the numbers of organisms in some natural population which grows to a natural equilibrium size (without harvest) of K organisms. By plotting (18) we have the population yield curve in Figure 2.6 which shows the number of organisms or biomass added each period for various levels of N. Thus, if $N = N_0$, the population is below its carrying capacity K and will be producing net surpluses of births over deaths in order to reach K. By choosing an instantaneous harvest rate h, man may cause the stock to decrease, remain at N_0, or increase depending upon whether

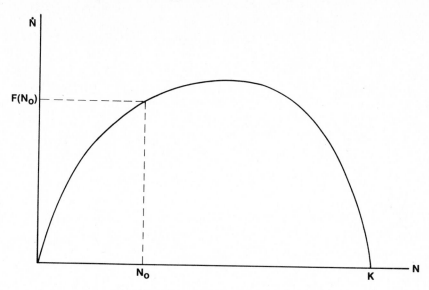

Figure 2.6. Logistic growth model yield curve.

$h \gtreqless F(N_0)$, respectively. It is thus interesting to determine what pattern of harvest rates over time would cause the stock to change in such a way as to maximize the value of the services it provides. The economic problem facing the owner or manager of such as stock would be:[9]

$$\max_{\substack{h \\ \text{s.t.}}} \int_0^\infty e^{-\delta t}[ph - C(N, h)]\, dt$$

$$\dot{N} = F(N) - h. \tag{22}$$

This is different from the timing problem in that a whole profile of harvest rates is to be determined. Note the similarity with the model of the firm presented earlier. Basically in both cases the flow of profits per time period depends upon the stock level and the control variable (or investment/disinvestment rates I or h). In the firm model, $\pi = \pi(K, I)$, where π was concave in K, reflecting concave production as a function of K and convex in I reflecting adjustment costs. In the above model $\pi = \pi(N, h)$ and for an interesting capital adjustment problem we need to specify π as convex in h. This would be the case, for example, if congestion on fishing grounds increased the unit cost of harvesting as h rose. A cost function

[9] Note that this information implicitly assumes that the only values provided by the stock are those obtained by harvesting. Also, by writing the exploited yield curve as an additive function, we are disallowing feedback between the harvest rate and the species biology.

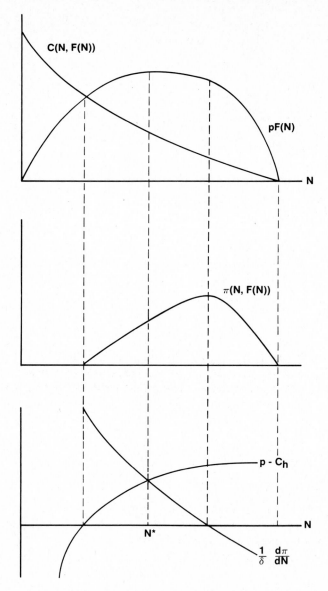

Figure 2.7. Optimal steady-state stock level – harvesting model with adjustment costs.

which reflects congestion and unit costs which decrease as the stock density increases would be

$$C(N, h) = \frac{1}{2} \left(\frac{h}{N} \right)^2. \tag{23}$$

The solution to the above problem can be intuitively determined as before in the investment model of the firm. In particular, there exists an optimal steady state N^* which just balances the present value of a marginal change in sustained rents against the marginal "liquidation" value of reducing the stock further, or

$$\frac{1}{\delta} \frac{\partial}{\partial N} [pF(N) - C(N, F(N))] = \frac{\partial}{\partial h} \left[ph - \frac{1}{2} \left(\frac{h}{N} \right)^2 \right] \Bigg|_{h = F(N)}. \tag{24}$$

With the cost function given in (23), the steady-state N^* solution is as shown in Figure 2.7. The approach is also asymptotic with $h^* \to F(N^*)$ as discussed earlier. If the cost function did not incorporate adjustment costs (i.e. if it were linear in h), the optimal harvest pattern would be a bang-bang control with an initial impulse control if $N_0 > N^*$ or $h^* = 0$ if $N_0 < N^*$ and $h = F(N^*)$ thereafter. In the special case where $0 \le h \le \bar{h} < \infty$, h^* will again be an extreme value control until N^* is reached and $h^* = F(N^*)$ thereafter.

To summarize, this section introduces some fundamental ideas from economic theory that are essential to analyzing optimal use of renewable resources. After pointing out the similarities between economic capital and natural capital, we discuss some fundamental results from capital theory. A distinction is made between timing problems and capital stock adjustment problems and emphasis is placed on the role of adjustment costs in the character of the solution. Finally, to apply the capital theory concepts in an introductory fashion to bioeconomic problems, we use the logistic model in a first look at timing and capital stock adjustment problems. In the next section, we begin to explore more fully underlying mechanisms in nature which give rise to different population processes. The focus of this next section is on the system as a whole, over the evolutionary time frame, with special attention to the way evolutionary forces mold individual natality and mortality characteristics which then impact population processes.

3. Biological mechanisms in natural populations

3.1. r- and K-selection

One of the most important factors guiding evolution of different organisms is stability of the habitat. Semi-arid lands are characteristically unstable habitats, temperate climates more stable, and tropical climates the most stable where "stability" roughly refers to the temporal predictability of nutrient sources.

Within each climatic belt, food supplies vary considerably on a finer spatial scale with variability increasing as the size of the patch decreases. Thus, a given space in a forest (relatively stable overall) may contain patches with decomposing fruits, dung, temporary water sinks, etc. – each its own micro environment offering nutrient sources in various degrees of stability over time. Natural selection has produced a spectrum of organisms presumably best adapted to the spatial and intertemporal habitat variabilities in such a way that efficiently uses nutrients and space. [Southwood (1981)].

When one examines the variety of bacteria, insects, plants, mammals, fish, and birds appearing in natural systems, one of the first regularities which appears is the correlation between size and habitat variability. Relatively smaller organisms generally inhabit areas with higher variability, whereas larger organisms occupy more stable environments. The evolutionary causality is not direct, however, since larger animals can range over larger areas and hence create more stability merely through increasing habitat space [May (1978)]. In fact, evolution has produced a variety of organisms [MacArthur and Wilson (1967)] seemingly designed to make the best use of resources whose temporal and spatial appearance varies greatly. At one end of the spectrum are the so-called K-selected organisms. These organisms must compete with many other organisms in environments with little variation and hence they evolve to be efficient in using resources without overshooting carrying capacity. For these species, "mistakes" created by losing competitive edge to other competitors or by overharvesting have serious evolutionary consequences. Thus, regulatory mechanisms are built into these animals to return to carrying capacity quickly and precisely when perturbations do occur. Generally speaking, K-selected organisms are large in their species (reindeer, elephants, condors) with long generation times, the significance of which will be discussed shortly.

At the other end of the spectrum are r-selected organisms designed to quickly exploit food supplies as they become available in (generally smaller) uncertain environments. These organisms are usually at the small end of the size spectrum and are foragers and opportunists. The r-selected organisms move from one space to another as food supplies are found and utilized. Since there are no substantial evolutionary penalties for overshooting a given area's carrying capacity, they tend to have high reproductive rates and shorter generation times.

How do the basic characteristics of organisms differ among r- and K-selected species? Basically, metabolism, size, generation time, fecundity, mortality, and foraging and competitive behavior are different. Smaller organisms have a higher surface to volume ratio and hence require higher metabolism simply to maintain stasis with their environment. In addition, relatively smaller organisms tend to have high fecundity (hence, large gonad/body weight ratios), reproduce quickly, and undertake high energy foraging activities, and thus their "deterioration rates" are correspondingly high. Lastly, because these organisms have been designed as

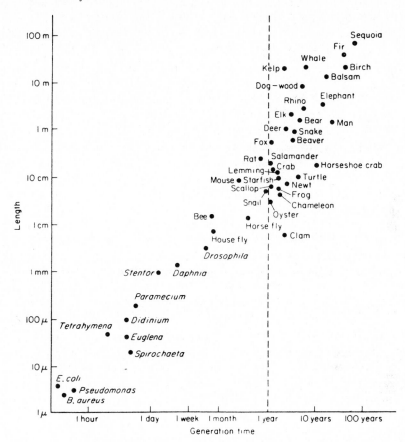

Figure 2.8. Relationship between size and generation time. [From John Tyler Bonner, *Size and Cycle: An Essay on the Structure of Biology* (© 1965 Princeton University Press), Fig. I, p. 17. Reprinted by permission of Princeton University Press.]

exploiters of periodic nutrients, their lifespans have evolved to be relatively brief to fit the intertemporal variation in a manner that reduces energy losses associated with foraging ranges and/or storage. All of these characteristics go hand in hand to produce an observable pattern in nature, whereby length (size) is positively related to generation time τ. Figure 2.8 shows the fit with some organisms. Note that larger organisms are those commonly labeled K-selected and the smaller organisms r-selected. In addition, there are several organisms around the one year generation period. Natural selection has favored these over longer-lived organisms, probably because some natural food supplies vary over one year meteorological cycles and animals whose lifespan is in synchronization do not need as much storage as a species to overwinter [Bonner (1965)].

3.2. Characteristics of organisms and growth processes

The interactions between fecundity, mortality, and generation time are best discussed by developing a population model. The simplest point of departure for considering population processes is to begin at the level of the individual organism. Consider first, the *numbers* of such organisms and growth of such numbers over time. Let $N(0)$ be the initial number of reproductivity-capable units at some time zero (it is often convenient to look simply at females). Suppose that the animals have a lifespan or generation time of exactly τ years (or any other unit of time).[10] Let R represent the *net lifetime replacement* ratio or the number of animals that survive to become reproducers in the next generation, per unit of parent stock. Then population size (or descendants of the $N(0)$) will number

$$N(k\tau) = N(0)R^k. \tag{25}$$

Here, k is an integer indexing the number of generations evolving past the first generation. Note that R is a growth factor similar to the growth factor we might apply to a bank deposit receiving interest – in this case the population "compounds" every τ years and we measure its size at points in time in integers multiples of τ so that $t = k\tau$, where $k = 1, 2, \dots$.

In the above model, population size is measured by numbers of animals at discrete points in calendar time and the critical parameter which determines whether the population grows, stays constant, or declines is obviously R, the net *lifetime* reproductive ratio. We may alternatively express R as a continuous growth rate r by defining

$$r = \frac{\ln R}{\tau}. \tag{26}$$

By taking natural logarithms of (25) and using (26) we then have

$$N(k\tau) = N(0)\exp[rk\tau] \tag{27}$$

as a model whose critical parameter is an instantaneous growth rate r.

In this simple model, the population will grow, remain constant, or decline depending upon whether $r \gtreqless 0$, respectively, or alternatively on whether $R \gtreqless 1$, respectively. The product of r and τ also has an important interpretation that will be explored more fully later. For now, however, it is sufficient to define a system's "characteristic return time" t_c as the time it takes for a system to return to equilibrium following a disturbance. For the logistic model previously examined this characteristic return time t_c is approximately proportional to $1/r$. Thus, if we

---

[10] In the simplest cases, the organism lasts one season and is replaced by some average R offspring. Then season length or lifespan corresponds with generation time. Generally, when organisms overlap in time, the concept of generation time is not so clear cut. One definition is the time that it takes a stable population to increase by the factor R but other definitions are related to the average age of females at reproductive age.

define

$$t_c = 1/r, \tag{28}$$

we can express the parameters above as

$$r = \frac{1}{t_c} = \frac{\ln R}{\tau} \, . \tag{29}$$

This suggests that species with higher lifetime reproduction ratios ($R \gg 1$) may be characterized as having low characteristic return times relative to their generation time τ. As will be discussed later, this has important consequences for the stability of such populations over time [May (1973a)]. Figure 2.9 shows relationships between r, R, and τ for a variety of organisms.

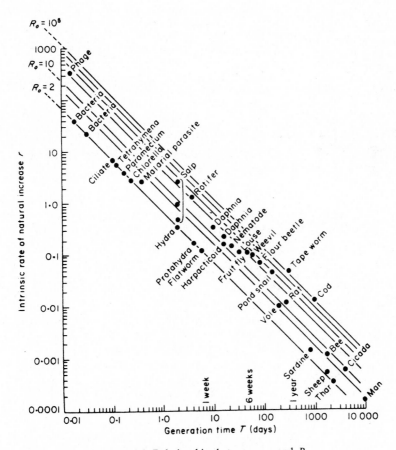

Figure 2.9. Relationships between r, τ and R.

It is obvious that a model such as (27) is an inadequate description of most populations in nature, since most do not explode without limit or crash to extinction as is predicted with values of r greater than or less than zero, respectively. More generally, as the numbers of organisms begin to impinge on their fixed capacity environment, changes in reproductive and mortality rates (R in the above model) and the generation time τ adjust to dampen exponential population growth. Correspondingly, for a declining population, nature has provided stabilizers that work in the direction of increasing r. These mechanisms operate differently depending upon whether the species is r- or K-selected.

Stabilizing mechanisms imply *density dependent growth* of the population, for which a variety of models have been proposed. The characteristics of these models depend upon the strength of the density dependence but a fascinating spectrum exists even for relatively simple forms. In general terms, density dependence implies a relationship between numbers in successive generations such that

$$N_{t+\tau} = F(N_t),\tag{30}$$

where t indexes the generation and F is some nonlinear function. Table 2.1 [May and Oster (1976)] lists some of the forms which have been proposed, each of which depicts numbers growing at levels below some equilibrium defined by the fixed point

$$N^* = F(N^*)\tag{31}$$

and declining for levels above N^*. These models are often referred to as *lumped parameter* models because the size and age-specific information pertinent to the population are collapsed into a single variable N, which may represent numbers, biomass, etc.

The above models are all nonlinear first-order difference equation descriptions of numbers of organisms. The simplest form, and one whose structure lends itself to ready intuitive interpretation is form 1, or

$$N(t+\tau) = N(t)\exp[r(1 - N(t)/K)\tau].\tag{32}$$

Table 2.1

Specific equations for $F(N)$

$$N\exp[r(1 - (N/K))]$$
$$N[1 + r(1 - N/K)]$$
$$\lambda N/(1 + aN)^b$$
$$\lambda N/[1 + \exp(-A(1 - N/B))]$$
$$\lambda N/[1 + (N/B)^b]$$
$$\left.\begin{array}{l} \lambda N \\ \lambda N^{1-b} \end{array}\right\} \text{ as } N \left\{\begin{array}{c} < \\ > \end{array}\right\} K$$
$$N[1/[(a + bN) - \sigma]]$$

In this model K is a measure of the carrying capacity of the environment and r is the maximum intrinsic rate of growth of the population. For values of $N_t \approx 0$ the population increases by some rate close to $r\tau$ and for $N_t \approx K$ the growth rate approaches zero, i.e. the system converges to a steady population size $N^* = K$.

This model is useful because it is capable of expressing the implications of a range of natural selection from r-strategists to K-strategists – referring to the two parameters of the model. As suggested above, the growth parameter and its behavior over a range of population values is critical in determining an organism's adaptability to its environment. In this model we can re-express the r in terms of the lifetime reproduction ratio and τ to get

$$r(N) = \frac{\ln R}{\tau} \left(\frac{K-N}{N} \right) \tag{33}$$

r-selected species have evolved to fill empty ecological niches rapidly and hence have high r's over a wide range of population levels. Thus, evolutionary pressures will tend to make R large and τ small. R can be large by having high fecundity and high immigration rates and/or low mortality and emigration rates. Generally r-strategists have high fecundity levels and spend more energy on foraging and filling spaces than tending young – leading to a gross reproductive ratio R_B that is high and a gross survival ratio R_D that is low, with the product $R = R_B R_D$ relatively large [Southwood et al. (1974)]. In addition, τ is small as discussed before, implying $\ln R/\tau$ is relatively large.

K-selected organisms, on the other hand, evolve to be large to increase their interspecific competition. Thus, τ is relatively large and other things equal $r(N)$ smaller than r-selected species. Since their strategy is one of best adapting to a stable environment, they evolve so that fecundity and mortality are relatively low, with a significant investment in protecting young rather than high R_B values [Pianka (1970), Southwood et al. (1974)]. Thus, with R_B low and R_D high, $\ln R$ will be relatively low, and combined with a high τ, making $r(N)$ low. With $r(N)$ low, however, perturbations will require a long recovery time t_c, and hence these organisms typically have mechanisms which increase R_B when the population is below K (e.g. larger numbers of offspring at birth) or decrease τ (earlier age to maturity) to compensate. Similarly, when the population N nears K, strategies to stabilize so that $R \cong 1$ have evolved, such as territorial behavior and other mating behavior which excludes potential breeders. Thus, K-strategists are designed to stabilize near K, calling for a low r generally. If perturbed globally away from K, the mechanisms that have evolved to handle local perturbations may not be strong enough and the species may be outcompeted for its former space. Typically, these animals require minimum densities to find mates and reproduce (unlike r-strategists, like insects which emit powerful pheromones to attract at low densities) and hence may decline if perturbed below this critical level.

In between the extreme r- and K-strategists are a host of species which mix features of both. For example, certain ungulates such as caribou and deer seem adapted to swings in available vegetation longer than the yearly cycle. They have higher values of r to allow them to quickly respond to episodic periods of high browse availability, but they are kept in check via predators. Thus, when nutrient supply is at average levels, predators cause high mortality on older and nutrition-ally weaker animals but in good years the population "irrupts" and over-runs predators to take advantage of sudden nutrient supply increases. Thus, the intrinsic growth parameters of these species may fall between the exploiters and the K-selected species but the effective growth rate after predation keeps them at equilibrium – or at least in regular cycles.

3.3. Dynamic behavior of populations

What are the implications of these differences in basic characteristics [which we have summarized in the single parameter $r(N)$] for population growth patterns over time? This question can be partially answered by considering the above model reduced to a single parameter model in r. Let $P_t = N(t)/K$ and measure time in units of the generation length (i.e. $\tau = 1$) so that (32) becomes:

$$P_{t+1} = P_t \exp\left[r(1 - P_t)\right] \equiv F(P_t; r). \tag{34}$$

By plotting the graph of F as in Figure 2.10, we can trace the course of the population ever successive generations as shown. As can be seen, the intersections of F with the 45° line yields the systems fixed points (equilibria values). More importantly, the *slope* of F at P^* determines the nature of the dynamical behavior, i.e. whether or not and how fast the system converges to P^*. As can be seen, the system is locally stable near P^* if the slope's absolute value is less than 1. For values equal to one, the equilibrium N is neutrally stable and P will oscillate in regular cycles around P whereas if the slope is greater than one in absolute value, the system diverges.

Such different behavior depending upon the slope raises questions about its relationship to r and hence implications for r- and K-selected populations. The first question is easily answered, since for this particular model the slope at P^* equals $1 - r$. As we discussed previously, evolution has created r-selected organisms in such a way that r is relatively large (greater than one, say) whereas K-selected organisms have relatively small values of r. If r is on the order of $0.05 - 0.015$ as it is for whales, for example, then the slope will be positive and perturbations away from K will be followed by an asymptotic approach as the diagram shows. Even if $r(N)$ increases in response to lower densities as it

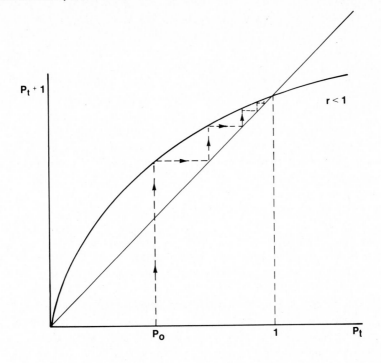

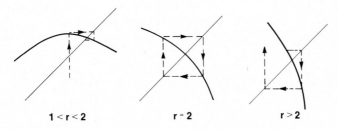

Figure 2.10. Stability and the intrinsic growth rate *r*.

typically does in K-selected organisms, the response will be a globally smooth asymptotic approach as long as $r(N)$ is less than one (making the slope still positive). As *r* becomes larger, corresponding to r-selected species, the slope becomes negative (as $r > 1$) and the return after a perturbation becomes cyclic with an overshoot followed by an undershoot, etc. As long as the slope is not too steep, (i.e. $1 - r < -1$ or $r < 2$), the oscillations converge.

To understand the intuitive meaning behind this behavior, return to our definition

$$r = \frac{\ln R}{\tau} \quad \text{or} \quad r\tau = \tau/t_c = \ln R. \tag{35}$$

In the above system we have defined time units to be generation lengths so that $\tau = 1$. Note that as we move from K-selected organisms, the lifetime replacement ratio R moves from values close to one to larger values. In the lower range, $1 < R < e$, $\ln R$ will lie between zero and one and (since $\tau = 1$) r will be less than one, resulting in no overshoot behavior. As $e < R < e^2$, $\ln R$ lies between one and two and there will be an overshoot, but it will be convergent. Interestingly, the bifurcation point between asymptotic and oscillating behavior ($r = 1$) has an interpretation relating to the ratio of generation time τ to recovery time t_c. Since $\tau = 1$ and $r = 1/t_c$, the break point $r = 1$ is actually where the ratio of generation time to recovery time is one. As $r > 1$, the system is one for which the generation time exceeds the recovery time and oscillations begin. But the generation time is really a lag time in this system in that effects in one period are felt by the next generation τ periods later. It is well known in engineering control systems that stable control results as long as the response time is close to the lag time of the signal. In these models, the signal is transmitted with a one generation (τ-period) lag and as response time begins to get smaller (i.e. response is faster) relative to this, the system tends to overshoot the signal. For very fast response time, some interesting and counterintuitive behavior begins to occur in fact.

As just discussed, for the above model, the slope at P^* equals $1 - r$ and, hence, the system is locally stable as long as $0 < r < 2$. As r increases past 2, however, the original equilibrium point becomes a repelling point and some suprising behavior begins to emerge [May and Oster (1976), May (1974a, 1976, 1977)]. Specifically, as r increases through 2, the possible equilibrium values of P^* move past a single value to two locally stable values which spread symmetrically away from $P^* = 1$ as r increases up to another bifurcation point. This implies that for each value of r greater than 2 and less than the next bifurcation value, the system is characterized by a two-period cycle whereby the population returns to each of the two equilibrium points every two periods. As r reaches its next bifurcation point (the exact value determined by the specific model), the two previous stable equilibria became unstable (as did the first as $r \to 2$, the first bifurcation point) and bifurcate into four fixed points implying four-period cycles, and so on. In general, as r increases, a hierarchy of cycling models arises, with periods $1, 2, 4, 8, 16, \ldots$, etc. As r continues to increase, the window within which each set of $2n$ equilibrium points remains stable decreases, however, so that r approaches some limiting value $\bar{r}$ [Li and York (1975)]. The branching diagram in Figure 2.11 shows the hierarchy of fixed points associated with increasing values of r. For example, if $r = r_0$ as shown, the system will be characterized by fluctuations where

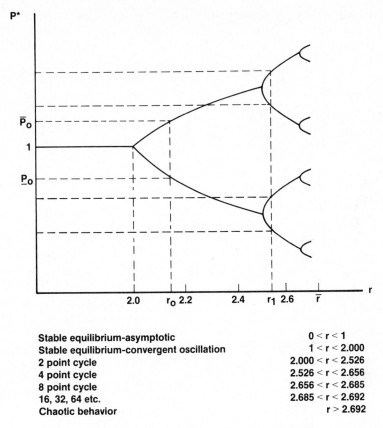

Stable equilibrium-asymptotic	$0 < r < 1$
Stable equilibrium-convergent oscillation	$1 < r < 2.000$
2 point cycle	$2.000 < r < 2.526$
4 point cycle	$2.526 < r < 2.656$
8 point cycle	$2.656 < r < 2.685$
16, 32, 64 etc.	$2.685 < r < 2.692$
Chaotic behavior	$r > 2.692$

Figure 2.11. Equilibria characteristics in a simple model.

$P = \overline{P}_0$ every other period, and $P = \underline{P}_0$ in intervening periods. If $r = r_1$ the system will return to each of four fixed points every four periods.

As r is increased beyond $\bar{r}$, the behavior becomes even more surprising as it enters into the so-called "chaotic" region. For the model in (34), for example, if $r > 2.6924$ there are an infinite number of cycles possible for each r, each one different from the other and dependent upon initial conditions. Moreover, there are an uncountable number of initial conditions for which resulting trajectories, though bounded, exhibit aperiodic behavior, i.e. the pattern never repeats itself no matter how long the time period simulated. Hence, surprisingly, even for a relatively simple model, dynamic behavior can range over an incredible richness of possibilities from asymptotic approaches to a single equilibrium, to cyclical with regular periodicity, to chaotic behavior which, although produced from a predictable mechanical deterministic model, may appear to be completely random and unpredictable.

The practical importance of such chaotic behavior is probably less than the intellectual interest it provides. This is because even if there are species whose *r*-values are high enough to imply chaotic oscillations, such behavior is not as relevant as that at other nonequilibrium population ranges. Since these organisms are opportunists, they are not really inhabiting an area with fixed carrying capacity for long and hence do not typically run up against strongly overcompensating density effects close to equilibrium. Instead, r-selected organisms operate at lower densities and expand rapidly and then move on to new patches. Thus, even though such odd behavior is predicted near the equilibrium value, it is a consequence of the high *r* in a model which is most relevant in population ranges

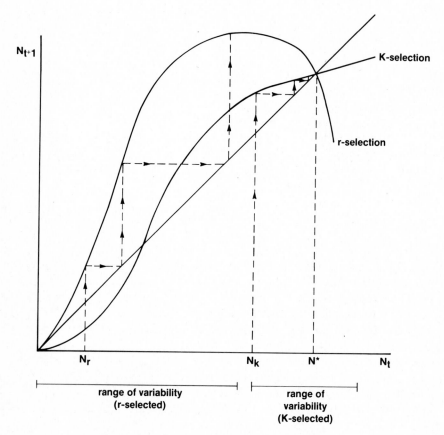

Figure 2.12. r- and K-selected growth characteristics.

which are removed from K. Figure 2.12 depicts differences between the two strategies for relevant population ranges.

In summary, this section expands on the simple logistic model description of populations by focusing on the two critical parameters, the intrinsic growth rate r and the carrying capacity K. We have attempted to maintain a "big picture" framework for discussion of individual organism characteristics by using a system perspective which depicts a spectrum of organisms evolving in response to habitat conditions. Thus, the r–K selection paradigm is the backdrop for explaining the variety of fecundity, mortality, generation time, and behavioral patterns we observe in nature. These individual organism characteristics are then used to develop some simple population process models and discuss their dynamical properties. It is shown that the intrinsic growth rate r is itself a parameter which summarizes natality/mortality factors and, in conjunction with generation time, a critical determinant of population stability.

4. Bioeconomics models of natural populations

4.1. Values derived from natural resources

In this section we tie together the introductory material in Sections 2 and 3 in a review of models of optimal natural resource use. As might be imagined, when one confronts the incredible variety of population processes in nature with the range of values which man derives from them, the possible permutations of optimal use models are large indeed.

The *potential* service flows from natural systems may be related to any of a number of characteristics of a population from pure numbers of organisms, to weight or biomass, to other age/size specific features. These service flows may also be stock related, flow related, or population-distribution related. For example, for a population which provides values to photographers or bird or animal watchers, the number of sightings may be important and hence generally related to the stock level. Hence, other things equal, the optimal policies would be aimed towards maintaining a large and viable population size by, for example, habitat investments or access controls which minimize adverse impact of these nonconsumptive users (who might indirectly be consumptive users if their activities adversely impacted habitats, etc.). Even this case is not totally straightforward, however, because the value *per encounter* may increase more than proportionately as the population is smaller and the number of encounters is reduced.

In a similar manner, man may derive values from a system in its "natural" state and hence, again, optimal use would aim at trading off the capturing of these values (by viewing or encounters) against the costs of such activities in terms of perturbations away from "naturalness". Thus we often limit access to particular endangered species' (condor). Current controversies over whether it is best to protect some species in controlled environments or leave them in natural systems reflect some of these value conflicts.

It is also sometimes the case that services are derived from numbers of organisms with particular characteristics. Examples are hunting for the more highly colored males of a bird species or hunting for large-antlered trophy animals. In these cases, optimal policies are geared towards selective harvesting which alters the population distribution while (perhaps) maintaining some total population size. The interactions between the distribution of characteristics and the total population size may be complex as ongoing controversies over either-sex deer hunting suggest.

In other cases more commonly examined, the value derived from natural resources is related to consumptive use by harvesting. In these cases the critical issues have to do with *timing* the harvest, determining how *many* to take, and determining the *characteristics* of those taken. In real populations, a population's number and characteristics are interrelated in sometimes complex ways and hence it is generally not enough to simply try and determine (for example) the optimal stock level. Generally, as a population is reduced by exploitation, the characteristics and distribution of individual population members change. For example, harvesting of whales has led to a decrease in age to maturity and an overall increase in size of younger-aged animals. Similarly, harvesting some bird populations often causes more frequent breeding and larger clutch sizes. Thus, the age and size distribution, at minimum, are usually altered by harvesting. These factors will be discussed in the next subsection which discusses life histories of different organisms. At this point, however, it is enough to recall the previous section on r–K selection pressures which, in the end, determine generally how we should expect a population to respond to exploitation.

A final factor which is critical to the structure of the appropriate model is the mechanism or technology of harvesting. Harvesting technology not only determines the appropriate cost structure (e.g. whether adjustment costs are substantial or not), but it also dictates precisely how the underlying population processes will be affected. In some situations it is virtually impossible to selectively harvest so that the age, sex, and size characteristics of the harvest are proportional to their representations in the population as a whole. Examples include trawl fishing or some long-line fisheries, some seine fisheries such as herring or anchovy fisheries, etc. In other cases, it is possible to select into two groups as, for example, minimum sizes for crab and salmon, prohibition against taking "berried" lobsters (females with eggs), forked antler or better deer hunts, mesh size restrictions in net fisheries, etc. At the end of the spectrum are the (rare) cases where perfect selectivity is feasible, such as land based fur seal harvests, some culling harvests of mammals, etc. The cost and purely physical characteristics of technology are not simply exogenous, of course, since it is sometimes cheaper to nonselectively harvest than selectively harvest.

In summary, the use of natural populations confronts us with choice problems of considerable complexity. It is especially important to keep in mind that the biological and the economic (or valuation) systems are intricately interrelated. In the short run with an unexploited stock, the existing population limits the number and kinds (and hence value) of what can be taken. As the population is drawn down, however, it is not only numbers taken but also the timing and the characteristics of those removed that determining the future service flow from the resource. In the long run, evolution may even be producing new organisms that are better designed to fit into their new (exploited) environment.

4.2. Life histories of organisms

In most resource-using situations where harvesting is taking place, the focus of management is on biomass rather than numbers alone. Thus, while it is often intellectually convenient to focus on the population as a whole, it is important for management purposes to understand how characteristics of individuals respond to exploitation as well. The response of individuals depends on the genetic code built into the organism, of course, and thus our discussion of r–K selection and its manifestation in fecundity and mortality patterns is useful here.

As a broad generalization, large organisms such as vertebrates are K-selected and small ones such as insects and bacteria are r-selected. This generalization is a bit too broad to be discriminating, however, and within major taxa there are generally both r- and K-selected examples. In what follows, we discuss general characteristics which seem to fit many (but not all) organisms in the fish, mammals and birds taxa.

4.2.1. Fish populations

The major stages of development of individual fish include the periods in which the organism is spawn (eggs), larva, juvenile, or pre-reproductive, adult (reproduction), and old age. Generally speaking there are density dependent effects in each of these life stages as well as external factors (predators, environmental perturbations, etc.) which impact survivorship and growth of the individual organisms in the population. With respect to natality factors, it is usually the case that fecundity and condition of the eggs are related to food supply available to the parent population prior to spawning [Nikolskii (1960), Weatherly (1972)]. A considerable amount of weight gain is associated with gonad production and when environmental conditions are unfavorable and/or the parent population is large relative to food supply, the amount and quality of spawn will be reduced and hence overpopulation will be regulated against [Bagenel (1976)].

During spawn and larvae stage, a significant mortality occurs due to predation and sensitivity to environmental changes. This stage is extremely important in determining the size and age configuration of many fish populations since adverse and favorable environmental conditions can impact relative numbers of survivors so radically. It is not uncommon for adjacent year classes to vary from 10 to 90 fold, a circumstance obviously important to the problem of optimal harvesting later in the life cycle.

As larvae become pre-reproductive juveniles, the mortality rate decreases as their mobility and ability to evade predators increases [Beverton and Holt (1957)]. Throughout this period, length increases approximately linearly with age at a rate dependent on food supply. Length gain tapers off near sexual maturity and increases slowly after that.

The above characterization suggests that fish populations on the whole are r-selected, i.e they have high fecundity, relatively low generation times, and experience high pre-productive mortality. The above life stage characteristics of fish also reveal something about how the population will respond to harvesting, i.e. other things equal, as the stock is reduced by harvesting, the mechanisms that are built in to increase an already high r will begin to operate. Beyond this simple statement, however, there exists a wide variety of other things (that are "not equal") which affect choice of the appropriate model. Some species, salmon for example, have a precise and invariant generation time and they appear at absolutely regular intervals to spawn and repeat the cycle. Others spawn almost continuously and have populations of mixed and overlapping age classes. Some species are small and short-lived (clearly r-selected) whereas others have long generation times (e.g. sturgeon over 100 years) and are more clearly classified K-selected. Another large group is in the middle of the spectrum, locked in a sometimes delicately balanced web of predator-prey interactions. Thus, even though as a group fish have r-selection characteristics, there is enough variety among fish species to warrant a range of modeling efforts, some of which may be based on r-selection, K-selection, or predator-prey assumptions.

4.2.2. Mammal populations

Mammals exhibit a lifetime growth pattern similar to fish in that individual weight increases rapidly early and then tapers off near sexual maturity. Unlike fish, seasonal weight variation around a mean may be substantial as browse, etc. availability follows normal seasonal patterns. In addition, many mammals actually lose weight during old age. The availability of food supplies does not seem in general to have as significant an impact on growth, and hence sexual maturity occurs at a particular age rather than size. Fecundity in mammals is much lower than for fish, on the order of one to ten per year as opposed to thousands for fish. The relationship between food and fecundity varies across species, but improved nutritional status of females often results in an increase in the number of young per pregnancy, a decrease in time between pregnancies, or a decrease in age to sexual maturity [Caughley (1976)].

Mortality among mammals follows the so-called "J-curve" relationship with high mortality of young, low mortality of reproductive age adults, and high mortality among old animals [Taber and Dasman (1958)]. The entire curve may be affected by periodic changes in food supply due to environmental changes, decreases in predators, etc. [see Caughley (1966) and Hutchison (1978)] curves for mammals.

4.2.3. Bird populations

Birds are similar to mammals in fecundity schedules in that fecundity rises to some relatively fixed level at sexual maturity and remains approximately constant. The level may be dependent on food supplies for some birds, however [Lack (1966)]. Abundant food supplies result in higher egg quality, an increase in clutch size in some species, and sometimes a second brood in the same breeding season. The growth rate of birds is similar also to mammals in that it follows an S-shaped curve with some within-season variations as food supplies fluctuate seasonally. There is some disagreement over whether a typical mortality profile exists but it is generally believed that the mortality rate is high for chicks and fledglings and then decreases to some constant or increasing pattern [Hutchison (1978)]. Mortality rates differ among territorial birds, with successful territory holders having lower rates than those without territories [Watson (1979)]. In addition, mortality is significant for many species during winter months, and thus protective habitat availability and winter food supplies are critical determinants of some populations.

These life history characteristics are helpful in predicting how an exploited population will differ from an unexploited population. Generally when the stock level is reduced there will be r- and K-selection responses in the birth and mortality rates due to reduced density dependence. These will manifest themselves differently between broad taxa and also between species within a major taxa. Figure 2.13 compares the critical parameters for fish, mammals, and birds in rough fashion. These form the basis for discussions of various models of exploited populations which appear in the next section.

4.3. Nonoverlapping generations models

Some species of organisms occur in regular (e.g. Salmon, 7 and 14 year Cicadas) or irregular (coniferous forests after a fire) cycles of same-aged cohorts. If these do not mix with other cohorts (as subspecies of salmon often *do* at river mouths, or as trees in a mixed forest often do) so that harvesting can be directly only at the cohort in question, then a particularly simple form of nonoverlapping generation model (NOGM) is appropriate.

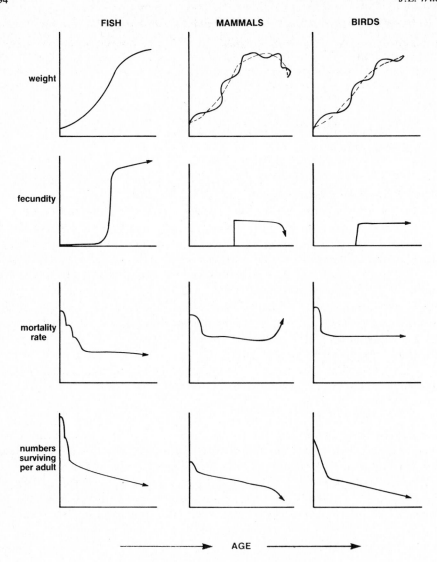

Figure 2.13. Fecundity and natality among fish, birds, and mammals.

There are basically two variants of NOGM depending upon how these populations are connected in time. At one extreme are situations where there is no intertemporal link so that the correct model is one that simply optimizes within each generation time in question. At the other extreme are cases where subsequent populations are affected by this period's "escapement" so that a multigenerational model is needed.

4.3.1. Cases of no intragenerational interdependences

On first thought it seems unlikely that we might find situations in nature where there is no connection between individuals in one generation and those in another. This is logically true given the nature of the reproductive process. There are still at least two classes of circumstances where ignoring intragenerational links is appropriate however. The first is where migration and mobility of the organisms are high. The second is where mortality in a particular pre-reproductive phase in the life process is a critical determinant of ultimate population size. Both of these characteristics are likely to arise in extreme r-selected species. The case of highly mobile species is easy to see if we think of an insect pest (e.g. cotton lygus) which invades a farmer's field [Southwood (1975)]. From the individual farmer's point of view, the decision of when to spray is not intragenerationally dynamic since migration basically determines the initial bug population in his field. There is an intergenerational dynamic problem, however, concerning optimal timing of sprays for the cohort in question.

The case where pre-reproductive mortality is limiting is more common and occurs for many small fish in particular. For these species, the reproductive (and harvestable) population size in one generation has virtually no impact on the subsequent generation's population size *within a substantial range*. To understand this mechanism, consider a case where the spawn of fish in one generation (S_k) turns into larvae (L_k) which survive into "recruits" (R_k). Recruits then are either harvested (H_k) or become parents (P_k) to the next generation so that we can write:

$$R_{k+1} = F(P_k). \tag{36}$$

This is a general expression for the Beverton–Holt (1957) stock-recruitment model which admits a variety of intragenerational mechanisms, the dynamics of which were discussed earlier. Of specific interest are cases where intragenerational impacts are negligible. To understand one of these cases, suppose that larval stage fish withstand some density-dependent mortality so that

$$\dot{L}/L = -m_1 - m_2 L_t. \tag{37}$$

If we let S be the spawn surviving into the larval stage and R the recruits leaving from the larval stage, we have $L(0) = S$ and $L(T) = R$. Then (37) can be solved over $[0, T]$ to yield:

$$R = \frac{aS}{1 + bS}, \quad \text{where } a, b > 0. \tag{38}$$

Note that $\lim_{S \to 0}(dR/dS) = a$ and $\lim_{S \to \infty} R = a/b$, where the constants a and b are related to m_1 and m_2. The above form for the solution also holds if m_1 and m_2 are arbitrary nonnegative functions of time, in which case a' and b' are new constants [related to $m_1(t)$ and $m_2(t)$] [Clark (1976)]. More interesting is the following [see Clark (1976)]: consider (37) with $m_2 = \overline{m} > 0$ for some interval $0 \leq t_L \leq t \leq t_u \leq T$ and zero elsewhere, i.e. where there is at least some density dependent mortality for $t_u - t_L$ units of time in the larvae life stage interval $[0, T]$. Then it can be shown that $R = L(T)$ has an upper bound,

$$R = L(T) \leq \frac{1}{m(t_u - t_L)}, \tag{39}$$

which is independent of $S = L(0)$. Thus, any arbitrary critical period in which density dependent survival of organisms occurs may fix the ultimate upper limit of recruitment. For species operating in a fluctuating environment, the conditions in this critical period may be virtually the sole determinant of the corresponding recruitment levels as discussed in the previous section. Thus, for species like salmon which undergo high and variable juvenile mortality while in streams, a policy such as encouraging aquaculture (nurturing during and releasing after the critical period) may be the only significant way of increasing potential catch.

The importance of the above result is that it shows that a critical phase in the pre-recruit stage of an organism's life history may be a far more important determinant of the ultimate harvestable population than the basic intragenerational relationship between parent stock P_{k-1} and spawn S_k. Thus, for some species, it is really not worth saving a large part of recruitment to become parent stock because the ultimate size of the next generation's recruitment will be almost wholly determined by random environmental factors anyway. In these cases, it is appropriate to optimize over each cycle separately.

The Beverton–Holt model also suggests another interesting special case where it is appropriate to ignore intragenerational links and formulate the problem as a one-generation optimization problem. This is the case where the fecundity of the species is very high. Consider an initially unexploited population characterized by the spawn/recruitment relationship in (38) and suppose that spawn depends upon the previous generation's parent stock so that $S = \alpha P$. Then, in equilibrium, $R_{k+1} = R_k = \overline{R} = P_{k+1} = P_k$ so that

$$R_{k+1} = P_{k+1} = \frac{aS_k}{1 + bS_k} = \frac{a\alpha P_k}{1 + b\alpha P_k}. \tag{40}$$

Note that the equilibrium value in terms of parameters is $\overline{R} = (\alpha a - 1)/(\alpha b)$. Now suppose that the recruitment is reduced (for example by harvesting) to some level so that the parent stock $P = \varepsilon\overline{R}$, where $0 < \varepsilon < 1$. Then the corresponding recruitment in the next generation will be:

$$R_{k+1}|_{P_k = \varepsilon\overline{R}} = \frac{\alpha a - 1}{\alpha b} \left[\frac{a\alpha\varepsilon}{1 + \varepsilon(\alpha a - 1)} \right] = \overline{R} \left[\frac{a\alpha\varepsilon}{1 + \varepsilon(\alpha a - 1)} \right]$$

$$= P_k \left[\frac{a\alpha}{1 + \varepsilon(\alpha a - 1)} \right]. \tag{41}$$

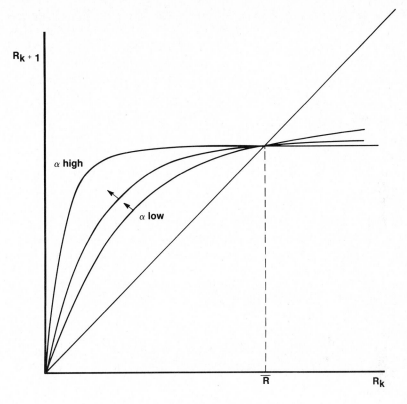

Figure 2.14. Recruitment and fecundity.

It will always be the case that harvesting some of last year's equilibrium recruitment will result in this year's recruitment being lower since the bracketed term is less than one for any ε, and as ε gets very small (i.e. harvest is large) there will be much less recruitment. Notice, however, that α can virtually swamp any values of ε if it is high enough, and, in fact, as $\alpha \to \infty$, the term in brackets approaches one. In words, this suggests that species with very high fecundity will allow a wide range of harvesting without substantially affecting next year's recruitment. The larger α is, the smaller ε can be (i.e. the larger harvest can be and still maintain next year's recruitment close to this year's). Figure 2.14 shows some of these relationships.

For many species of fish and insects, and perhaps some birds and mammals, either or both of the above mechanisms does seem to be operative and hence we can *assume* for all intents and purposes that there is no intertemporal link between generations within the relevent range of harvesting. Thus, the problem of

determining how *many* to harvest is unimportant and more important questions
have to do with *when* to harvest. With insect populations, for example, there may
be critical periods in their life-stages where controls are most effective. In fact, as
shown in (41) above, spraying or otherwise enhancing density dependence in this
critical window may be the best way to impact the ultimate population size and
hence minimize potential damage, other things equal.

4.3.2. Beverton–Holt single-cohort model

For fish or mammals, the issue of when to harvest is often where biomass has
reached some critical level. The optimal timing thus depends upon interrelationships between age, length, and weight. With fish and, in fact, most species, it has
been noted empirically that length, weight, and age of individual organisms tend
to follow a relatively predictable pattern. For length, for example, a widely used
model is the von Bertalanffy equation where length $l(t)$ grows at a rate depending
upon the difference between some maximum length $l\infty$ and the current length, i.e.

$$\dot{l}(t) = K\left[l\infty - l(t)\right] \tag{42}$$

This differential equation has the solution

$$l(t) = l\infty\left(1 - e^{-K(t-t_0)}\right). \tag{43}$$

Weight over the lifetime is generally related to structural characteristics of the
organisms and may follow the single allometric relationship:

$$W_t = al_t^b. \tag{44}$$

Weight has been found empirically to be correlated with the cube of length in a
wide variety of organisms so that (44) with $b = 3$ and (43) are often combined to
yield a von Bertalanffy weight equation:

$$W(t) = W\infty\left(1 - e^{-k(t-t_0)}\right)^3. \tag{45}$$

In this relationship the inflection point is approximately at the weight level which
is one-third of $W\infty$.

The von Bertalanffy weight equation may be combined with a Beverton–Holt
stock recruitment model to yield a single-cohort model of fishery biomass.
Consider, for example, a case where a relationship like (36) with $m_2 = 0$ describes
numbers during the harvestable recruit stage. This suggests that fish in the recruit
stage simply die at a constant density independent rate M. Note that we still may
assume a density dependent mortality process in the larvae or spawning prerecruit
stages so that intragenerational effects can be ignored. Assume that fishing at
different intensity levels adds another form of mortality F, so that:

$$\dot{N} = -N(M + F(t)), \qquad N(0) = N_0. \tag{46}$$

The economic problem is one of determining how to maximize the present value of the yield (biomass) from this cohort over its generation length assuming that the population mortality follows (45) and individual weight gain follows (45). The structure of this problem is general enough to admit several different harvesting possibilities. For example, if the fishery is a hook-and-line fishery, then one must decide a season opening date and level of fishing effort which maximize the present value of the biomass yield. If the fishery is a net fishery, the optimal season opening date has a direct counterpart in the optimal minimum mesh size, since fish girth will correspond in a particular way via the weight equation to age (season date) of the fish.

The general economic problem of maximizing the present value of harvest from this cohort may be written

$$\max_{F(t),\tilde{t}} \int_{\tilde{t}}^{\infty} [pF(t)N(t)W(t) - C(F(t))]e^{-\delta t} dt$$

s.t
$$\dot{N} = -N(M + F(t)),$$

(47)

where $\tilde{t}$ is the opening date (or corresponding age at which a particular mesh size $\tilde{m} = \tilde{m}(\tilde{t})$ captures fish). The solution to this problem depends critically on the nature of $C(\cdot)$ as would be expected from the discussion in Section 2.

The simplest case is where $C(F(t)) = 0$ and fishing mortality is unbounded so that impulse controls $F = \infty$ may be applied to harvest all of the biomass instantly at some particular age. This problem is basically a pure timing problem like the general asset aging model discussed earlier and the solution involves finding the optimal date $\tilde{t}^*$ at which to harvest all of the biomass. Not surprisingly, the optimal date can be characterized as a point $\tilde{t}^*$, where allowing the biomass one more time unit of growth results in an increase in value just equal to the opportunity cost of waiting that unit of time. In this case with zero harvesting costs, the integrand in (47) becomes

$$V(t) = pF(t)N(t)W(t) = pF(t)B(t).$$

To determine $B(t)$, we note that eq. (46) with $F = 0$ determines the number of recruits entering the fishery and (45) gives the weight per fish so that we have

$$B(t)|_{F=0} = N(t)W(t) = N_0 e^{-Mt} W_\infty (1 - e^{-Kt})^3.$$

(48)

Without fishing, biomass reaches a maximum at a point where $(\dot{B}/B) = (\dot{N}/N) + (\dot{W}/W) = 0$. By (46), $(\dot{N}/N) = -M$ without fishing so that biomass reaches a maximum where $(\dot{W}/W) - M = 0$. Once fishing is applied, beginning at some point $t = \tilde{t}$, the biomass is reduced by fishing mortality as well as natural mortality. For a constant level of fishing mortality F, the total value of the harvest would be

$$V(\tilde{t}, F) = N_0 p \int_{\tilde{t}}^{\infty} Fe^{-Mt} e^{-F(t-\tilde{t})} W(t) e^{-\delta t} dt.$$

(49)

With an impulse control of $F = \infty$ at $t = \tilde{t}$, (49) approaches a finite limit; namely the value of the biomass level of date $\tilde{t}$. The date at which to harvest is easily seen as that for which

$$\frac{\mathrm{d}V(\tilde{t}^*)}{\mathrm{d}\tilde{t}} = \delta V(\tilde{t}^*) \tag{50}$$

as in the basic timing problem introduced in Section 2. In this fisheries problem, if price is constant, the optimal impulse-harvest date is where

$$\frac{\mathrm{d}B}{\mathrm{d}\tilde{t}}\bigg|_{F=0} = \delta B(\tilde{t}), \tag{51}$$

which occurs where $[\dot{W}(\tilde{t})/W(\tilde{t})] = M + \delta$. As in the basic example discussed in Section 2, in this case the higher the discount rate the sooner the harvest. Also similarly, with zero costs and constant prices, the optimal harvest date is independent of the price level and depends only on selecting the date which balances the "own biological interest rate" ($p\dot{B}/pB$) with the discount rate.

More general models with positive harvesting costs may also be analyzed but with more analytical complexity and perhaps somewhat less intuitive results. For example, costs may be considered linear so that $C(F(t)) = C \cdot F(t)$ [Clark (1976)]. In this case, the solution involves a bang-bang control where no effort is applied until biomass grows beyond the level indicated in (51). Then a positive level of effort is applied for an interval of time $[t_L, t_0]$ which reduces the biomass to the level where $pB(t_0) = C$ (see Figure 2.15). As $C \to 0$, $t_L \to \tilde{t}$ and the optimal biomass path approaches the vertical asymptote at $\tilde{t}$. Thus the previous impulse-harvest problem is the limiting case of the linear cost problem.

With harvesting costs exhibiting adjustment costs, i.e. with $C(F(t))$ where $C' > 0$ and $C'' \neq 0$, the optimal solution involves a similar harvesting pattern where the biomass is allowed tồ grow until some critical time and then harvesting decreases the biomass. In this case, the optimal harvest rate adjusts so that an equality similar to that in the asset aging problem is maintained continuously throughout the harvest period. Let $\Pi = pBF_t - C(F_t)$. Then the optimal harvest rate is such that[11]

$$\frac{\mathrm{d}}{\mathrm{d}t}\left(\frac{\partial\Pi}{\partial F}\right) = \delta\left(\frac{\partial\Pi}{\partial F}\right) - pBF. \tag{52}$$

Since the growth constraint $\dot{N}/N = -(M + F)$ defines a relationship between N

---

[11] This is derived as follows. The current valued Hamiltonian is
  (a) $H = pBF - C(F) + \lambda\dot{B}$, where $\dot{B} = B[-(M + F) + (\dot{W}/W)]$.
The optimal level of fishing mortality satisfies:
  (b) $\Pi_F \equiv pB - C'(F) = \lambda B$.
The shadow price must evolve according to:
  (c) $\dot{\lambda} - \delta\lambda = -H_B = -pF - \lambda[-(M + F) + (\dot{W}/W)]$.
If we multiply this equation by B and rearrange, we get
  (d) $\lambda\dot{B} + \dot{B}\lambda - \delta B\lambda = -pBF$.
But by (b) above, $\lambda B + \dot{B}\lambda = \dot{\Pi}_F$, so that the optimal path calls for: $\dot{\Pi}_F(t) - \delta\Pi_F(t) = -pBF$.

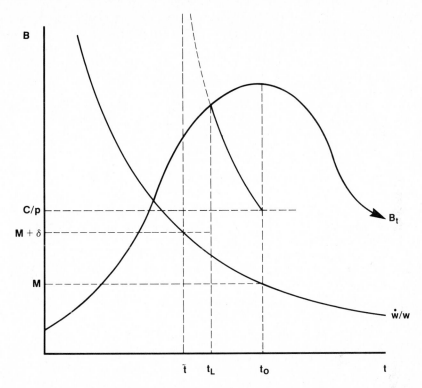

Figure 2.15. Optimal harvesting of a Beverton–Holt population – without costs of adjustment.

and F, and since $B_t = N_t W_t$, (52) can be solved for either the optimal path of F_t^* or for B_t^*, or N_t^* as a function of W_t and the other parameters. Although the solution is not readily obvious, its properties are qualitatively like the "turnpike" results discussed in Section 2. For example, if we consider the case where $C(F_t) = C \cdot (F^2/2)$ the optimal biomass and fishing effort levels must satisfy

$$B\left[\frac{\dot{W}}{W} - (M + \delta)\right] = \frac{C}{P} \cdot [\dot{F} - \delta F] \tag{53}$$

whenever F is positive. For this problem there is an initial phase where harvesting is not optimal; namely during periods ("close" to $t = 0$) when $\dot{W}/W$ is large. When $\dot{W}/W$ is large and positive, the own biological rate of interest $(\dot{W}/W - M)$ exceeds the discount rate and hence it pays to leave fish in the "biological bank". As time progresses $\dot{W}/W$ decreases until at $t = \tilde{t}$, the own biological interest rate equals the discount rate. At this point harvesting begins and biomass is reduced to zero asymptotically. Figure 2.16 compares this more general nonlinear case

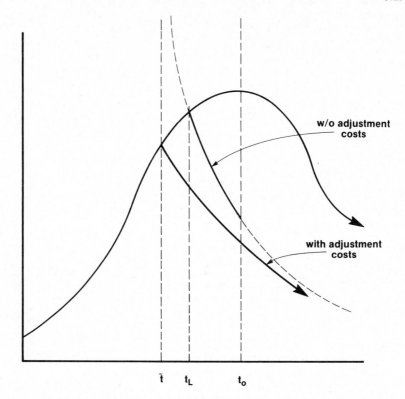

Figure 2.16. Optimal harvesting with adjustment costs – the Beverton–Holt model.

with the linear case. For this problem (with adjustment costs), the optimal path involves harvesting sooner because of the high costs which would otherwise be incurred if the harvest path more closely followed the linear-case singular path. Note, however, that the optimal path stays relatively close to its linear counterpart in the manner of the turnpike property discussed in Section 2.

4.3.3. Intragenerational interdependencies due to timing

The above model is applicable in situations where, as discussed before, there are virtually no density-dependent intergenerational links and generation time is fixed. A second situation which requires a slight modification is where there are intergenerational *timing* links occuring through the generation time. For example, in a mature forest, the canopy cover will be such that the next generation will be completely and continuously out competed by mature trees. As soon as mature trees are cut, however, the next generation seedlings begin to grow and hence the earlier (in age) one cuts the forest, the sooner new stocks can start and so on. This problem is a version of the point-input point-output problem already discussed except that the use of a critical fixed factor (space) must be optimized. The problem is the same one faces, for example, if one has fixed storage space and is deciding how to store bottles of wine that are increasing in value. The sooner one is removed, the sooner a new one can be started aging, etc.

To understand the nature of this problem, assume that we have a forest, or wine cellar, or herd of domestic animals, etc. on fixed space and the value of each cohort grows as a function of age. If there are also some fixed costs of amount C, incurred per harvest or sale we have:

$$PV = e^{-\delta t_1}[V(t_1) - C] + e^{-\delta t_2}[V(t_2) - C] + \cdots . \tag{54}$$

To make the problem tractable, assume that soil conditions, etc. do not deteriorate between rotations and that real prices and costs are constant. Then the problem looks the same from any time period we consider it (assuming infinite horizon) and $t_k = k \cdot t$. This reduces the series in (54) to

$$PV = e^{-\delta t}[V(t) - C)] + e^{-\delta 2t}[V(t) - C) + \cdots$$
$$= \sum_{i=1}^{\infty} e^{-rti}[V(t) - C] = [V(t) - C]\left(\frac{1}{e^{\delta t} - 1}\right). \tag{55}$$

Differentiating (55) with respect to t yields, after rearranging:

$$\dot{\Pi}(t^*) = \delta \Pi(t^*)\left(\frac{1}{1 - e^{-\delta t^*}}\right), \tag{56}$$

where $\Pi(t) = V(t) - C$. Note that this form is similar to both (20) and (52) in that the optimal time to harvest is one that almost equates the gain from waiting an extra unit of time (i.e. leaving one's capital in the forest bank) with the financial opportunity cost over the same period [i.e. $\delta \Pi(t)$]. The "almost" part is a modification in the basic rule which results in a harvesting date slightly sooner than the date where $\dot{\Pi}(t) = \delta \Pi(t)$. The intuition behind this is precisely that the intergenerational link makes it costly to wait too long with the existing crop since the whole sequence of future crops is thereby postponed. Thus, the optimal timing involves balancing off the gains from waiting one more time unit with the existing crop ($\dot{\Pi}$) against the costs – consisting of opportunity costs on the existing standing crop [$\delta \Pi(t)$] and the opportunity costs associated with *not* harvesting and beginning future rotations sooner. The latter opportunity costs can be seen from the above by noting that the RHS term in (56) can be rearranged to get

$$\delta \Pi(t)\left(\frac{1}{1 - e^{-\delta t}}\right) = \delta \Pi(t) + \delta \Pi(t)\left(\frac{1}{e^{\delta t} - 1}\right). \tag{57}$$

But the second term on the RHS of (57) is simply $\delta PV(t)$ from (55) above, i.e. it is the annualized value of the present value of the whole set of harvest rotations. This term is often referred to as the *site rent* $R_S(t)$ and it is basically the amount that the owner of the land should impute as a value to the piece of space involved. Since the owner always has the option of immediately harvesting the existing crop and (for example) selling the land at a price equal to (55) (presuming the best use is in the current crop and that the land market is competitive), he should be continuously "charging" himself an implicit rental rate equal to the annualized value of the land sale value ($R_S = \delta \cdot PV$) when he chooses *not* to sell and continue another year with the existing crop.

It almost goes without saying that structuring the above foresting problem in this particular way makes it a *timing* problem rather than an investment/disinvestment problem. By assuming simply fixed per rotation costs, we have disallowed any costs of adjustment which would make impulse controls (i.e. taking all of the standing crop at the instant $t = t^*$) suboptimal. A more general model with adjustment costs in harvesting would mix features of the Beverton–Holt single cohort model discussed earlier with the timing model just discussed [see Clark (1976)]. One would expect similarly mixed results, i.e. a continual harvest phase which allows standing crop value to peak and then decline as the harvest rate within each rotation increased. There are some problems with this more general structure, however, since one has to assume for tractability either (i) no trees grow where others have already been harvested until the last tree in the stand is taken; or (ii) the forest is already in an optimal uneven-age equilibrium configuration so that the yield over the span of any single rotation is equal to the yield of a given single-aged forest. The first assumption is unrealistic and the second assumption begs the difficult question of deciding how to get the forest in an optimal equilibrium forest in the first place [see Heaps and Neher (1979)].

4.3.4. Density-dependent intragenerational interdependencies

The final important class of models among nonoverlapping generations consists of those having to do with density-dependent intragenerational effects, i.e. where the numbers of organisms escaping capture in the previous generation affects the current generation's size. This is, it should be noted, a problem of determining *numbers* to be harvested (or actually, allowed to "escape" to become reproducers) as opposed to biomass as in previous models. Optimal escapement models are applicable in situations where harvesting must take place before recruits enter into the reproductive phase, for example, with ocean or river mouth fishing for salmon.

Let us refer to the recruits of generation k (R_k) as those organisms surviving early mortality phases to the point where they may either be harvested in amount H_k or become parent stock P_k or escapement which determine the size of the next generations recruit stock, i.e.

$$R_{k+1} = F(P_k) = F(R_k - H_k).\tag{58}$$

Examples of this form were discussed earlier in the case of the Ricker model, where stability in discrete generation models were discussed. We will assume that $F' > 0$ throughout so that the overcompensation cases giving rise to population oscillations are ruled out. (See discussion in Section 3.3.)

Let $\Pi(H_k, R_k) = pH_k - C(H_k, R_k)$ be the profits from harvesting recruits for a given generation and let i equal the discrete discount rate applicable to the length of the generation time. Then the economic problem is to determine a feasible sequence of harvests $\{H_1, H_2, \ldots\}$ which maximizes

$$PV = \sum_{k=0}^{\infty} \Pi(R_k, H_k)\left(\frac{1}{1+i}\right)^k \qquad (59)$$

subject to (58). This can be formulated in a manner completely analogous to the continuous problem discussed in Section 2, and the solution is likewise similar; namely, there exists some steady state escapement level $P^* = R^* - H^*$ which just balances off current marginal profit losses (gains) associated with allowing (harvesting) one more unit escapement with the higher (lower) subsequent profits for the new sustained escapement level. For a general profit function $\Pi(R, H)$ this condition can be written as [see Clark (1976)]

$$(1 + i)F'(P^*)\left(\frac{\partial \Pi}{\partial R} + \frac{\partial \Pi}{\partial H}\right) = \frac{\partial \Pi}{\partial H}. \qquad (60)$$

The approach path in this discrete case also depends upon Π and particularly on the nature of adjustment costs. If costs are linear in H, the adjustment path is a most rapid approach path to P^*, and if costs increase at an increasing rate in H, the adjustment is asymptotic.

4.4. Overlapping generations models

There are, in fact, very few situations in nature where organisms are segregated by cohorts in such a way that nonoverlapping generations models are accurate depictions of reality. As will be seen, the tractability of even these simple models rapidly disappears as more real-world complexities are introduced. As we move closer to more precise depictions of real populations, where different age and size classes are mixed, the analytical difficulties increase many fold. In this section, some examples of mixed-cohort models are discussed, some with corresponding optimal harvest solutions and some without. It is this "gray area" between simple single-cohort models and equally simple lumped parameter models (which aggregate and ignore age-specific complications) that is closest to reality but, as a consequence, also closest to being analytically intractable.

The difficulties involved in modeling overlapping generations stem from two factors – the degree of interdependence between organisms and the general inability in most real-world cases to selectively harvest due to the mixed structure of the population. Interdependencies between organisms in the same population may take many forms, including density-interdependence within cohorts of a single age class (e.g. when juveniles segregate and feed on a particular nutrient source), interdependence between cohorts depending upon total food supply and total population size, interdependence depending upon age distribution of the population (e.g. when there is cannibalism of juveniles by certain age classes), etc. In addition, there may be complex interdependencies between organisms in a given population and those in subsequent generations depending upon similar factors as just discussed. With respect to harvesting selectivity, cases range from circumstances where age/size can be perfectly selected and targeted, to the more common case of being able to select between two aggregate groups (e.g. when minimum mesh size is specified, or when forked-horn antler or full curl horn requirements are imposed in hunting), to no selectivity such as is the case in a trawl or hook-and-line fishing where each cohort's catch is roughly proportional to numbers present in the total population. In general, we would expect that the more complex are the interdependencies and the less selective the gear, the more difficult it is to characterize the optimal solution to the harvesting problem.

The easiest case to analyze is where organisms overlap but there are no intragenerational interdependencies and no intergenerational interdependencies between cohorts of the same population. In this case, we have basically a layered Beverton-Holt model in which the population consists of many age classes, each growing in total biomass until some age a_0 and then declining. Assume that recruitment to each age class is constant and independent of population size and age structure and that the generation time or time that organisms spend in the recruit phase is T. Then as we successively add and overlap new generations of cohorts over the interval $(0, T)$, we will obtain biomass curves which look like those in Figure 2.17. Note that as more generations are added, the population biomass approaches a constant equilibrium level with a particular equilibrium size/age distribution implied.

The first case to consider is where harvesting gear is completely nonselective. Let $N(t, a)$ be the remaining numbers of organisms at year t who entered the fishery as recruits in year a. Let $w(t, a)$ be the weight of a fish from cohort a at time t. Then the total biomass of age class a will be (without fishing)

$$B(t, a) = N(t, a)w(t, a), \qquad t \geq a. \tag{61}$$

The total fishable biomass at any point in time t will thus be the sum of all biomass from each age class a at time t, or

$$B(t) = \sum_{a=t-T}^{a=t} N(t, a)w(t, a), \tag{62}$$

and the general economic problem is to maximize

$$PV = \int_0^\infty e^{-rt}[F(t)B(t) - C(F(t))]\,dt$$
$$\text{s.t.}$$
$$\frac{dN(t, a)}{dt} = -[M + F(t)]N(t, a). \tag{63}$$

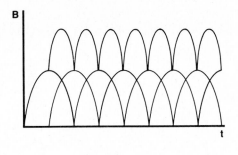

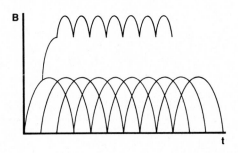

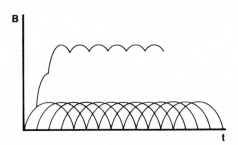

Figure 2.17. Biomass with overlapping generation.

Note that the formulation implies that harvesting will be taking from all age classes in proportion to their abundance in the total population – a feature of many bottom fish fisheries and other circumstances (perhaps bird and mammal hunting) where no selectivity is practiced.

The general problem in (64) has not been solved, although solutions to special cases have been attempted [see Clark (1971)]. The simplest case is one where $C[F(t)] = 0$ and price per unit biomass is constant. In this case, if we start with low fishable biomass, the growth in biovalue will be as shown in Figure 2.18. At

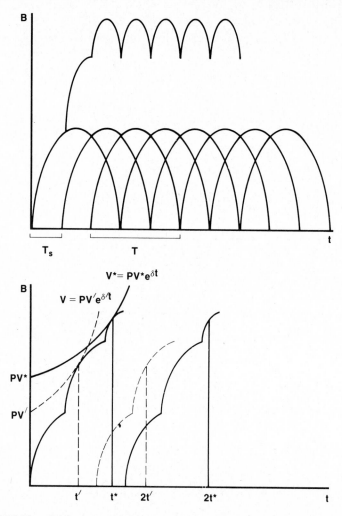

Figure 2.18. Nonselective harvesting in an overlapping generating population with zero costs.

first glance this looks like a rotation-type problem and, in fact, it has been cast as such in an attempt to solve it. This approach appears to be incorrect, however, since if successive cohorts are staged to enter the fishery as recruits in *fixed* intervals (usually one year in nature), then harvesting does *not* allow immediate re-initializing of the population as is assumed with forests. As we showed in the forestry case, waiting to harvest the current crop involves two costs; one on the current standing crop and the other on subsequent crops which could have been started immediately. This is a problem involving intragenerational interdependencies due to timing but, in an overlapping cohort fishery, there are no such interdependencies if the staging time between cohorts is exogenously fixed. Given that this is the case, the problem reduces to one of maximizing the present value of each set of cohorts overlapping in any given interval $[t - kT_s, t]$, where k is the (integer) number of cohorts which stage T_s periods apart over a total recruit interval T.

The solution to the above problem is basically similar to the one-shot timing problem introduced in Section 2. In the lower diagram of Figure 2.18, if the discount rate is δ, pulse harvesting at t^* maximizes the present value of the mixed cohort fishery. One can effectively optimize harvests over a given group of mixed cohorts since the timing of subsequent recruits is not affected. Note that as δ increases to δ', the harvest interval is reduced. In the example shown where $k = 3$ and $T_s = 1/3 \ T$, harvesting takes place during recruitment of the third, sixth, ninth and so on cohorts with a discount rate of δ and the second, fourth, sixth and so on with a discount rate of δ'. Thus, with nonselectivity and zero costs, the optimal overlapping generations problem collapses to a relatively simple sequence of single-shot timing problems.

With selectivity in harvesting, through mesh or hook size or minimum size regulations, for example, the optimal policy follows readily from the above as long as costs can be ignored. In situations where age of first capture may be chosen and smaller fish excluded from harvest, it is obvious that present value will improve over the no-selectivity case just discussed. In particular, we know from our earlier discussion that for single cohort harvesting with zero costs, the optimal mesh size is one associated with the size where the own biological rate of interest is just equal to the discount rate, or

$$\frac{\dot{W}(\tilde{\iota})}{W(\tilde{\iota})} - M = \delta. \tag{64}$$

Thus, the global optimum for the zero cost mixed-cohort case is one achieved by using a mesh size corresponding to (64). By pulse-fishing the fishery with the optimal mesh size, it is possible to optimize returns from each cohort separately and hence from all cohorts together. With cohorts entering the fishery in identical intervals and with identical numbers in the initial recruitment, the fishable biomass and yield will be approaching uniformity over time as Figure 2.19 shows. In the limit, with continuously infinite ("chattering") effort being applied, the continuous yield will approach the biomass of a given cohort at age $\tilde{\iota}$. With cohorts entering in nonuniform and/or at different initial levels, the optimal policy will still be the same, but of course the fishery will not be characterizable in any equilibrium fashion.

The introduction of costs of harvesting complicates the picture considerably and, in fact, the problem has not been solved analytically although some

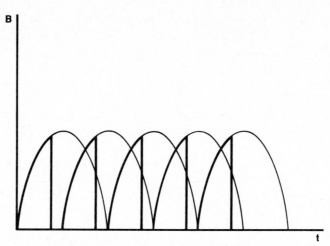

Figure 2.19. Perfect selectivity in an overlapping generating population with zero costs.

numerical studies have been done [Hannesson (1975)]. One situation where the problem is not different from a sequence of single-cohort selectivity problems is where recruits enter into a fishery in a staggered fashion with a staging time T_s between years classes which is longer than the time needed to optimally harvest a single cohort. Consider Figure 2.20, for example, where biomass of a given cohort without fishing has some finite life T after which the last fish dies. As we showed in the previous section, the optimal biomass path for a single cohort when costs are proportional to fishing effort follows the darkened line so that total harvesting time $T_h = t_0 - t_L$. An additional Δt_c units of time pass before the first cohort completely disappears after being fished down to $pB(t_0) = C$ (note that T_h is smaller as C gets larger). If it happens that the staging time between cohorts T_s is greater than $T_h + \Delta t_c$, then there is no problem of "cohort overlap" and one can simply choose mesh size corresponding to age t_L, harvest the first cohort for T_h periods, pause, and then harvest the next cohort as was done initially with the first. Obviously one cannot improve on the case which effectively optimizes each cohort separately.

As the staging time decreases relative to the harvest period T_h (which depends upon δ and C/P), cohorts overlap so that the originally optimal attempt to optimally harvest the first cohort will (for the mesh size corresponding to t_L) begin to pick up the second cohort's members as well. This is illustrated with the dotted lines; notice that during the early period of the second cohort's harvest, there are still first cohort members in the total biomass subject to capture. Thus the general problem is: when there are harvesting costs, what is overall optimal policy regarding effort levels, harvest intervals and mesh size with potentially

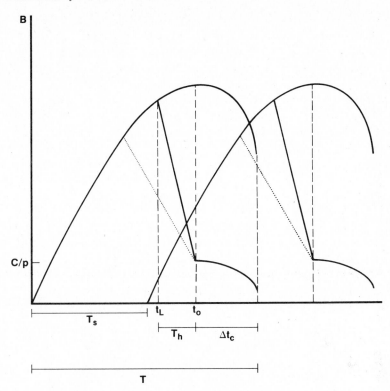

Figure 2.20. Optimal selective harvesting in overlapping populations – with costs.

overlapping cohorts? Notice that there is a link between staging time T_s and some critical mesh size size $m(T_s)$ or equivalently, critical starting harvest date t_L. If we can postpone harvesting past the date which causes overlapping and then harvest with a larger mesh and at a higher rate until $pB(t_0) = C$ is reached, the delay (as long as T_s is not shorter than Δt_c) will just allow us to harvest each stock separately. This is possible (see Figure 2.20) because delaying harvest shortens T_h and hence makes it less likely for given T_s that there will be overlap. Thus the problem could be solved if we could show that either it always pays to adjust mesh size to selectively harvest, or it never pays, etc. Unfortunately it is not clear whether either of these is generally true. It appears from empirical work that the answer may depend on the problem's parameters, and hence, in general, it may be optimal either to separately harvest cohorts in succession or harvest them together in overlapping populations. In the latter case, the earlier discussed mixed-cohort timing solution is apparently relevant but the path of harvesting and the mesh size in this case with positive harvesting costs have not been determined analytically. One can conjecture, however, that the solution would look like the single-cohort analogue, with a period allowing the mixed stock to build up, followed by sustained effort to drive it to the breakeven point, followed by a new sequence, etc. The optimal mesh size probably has to be one which allows harvesting to effectively separate the mixed-stock harvesting regimes somehow.

Beyond these attempts, little has been achieved in tackling more general models analytically. The critical simplifying assumption which needs relaxing to fit real-world circumstances is the assumption of no intragenerational links. A more complete model needs to account not only for the age/size specifics of the individual cohorts but also for density-dependent relationships between numbers in one cohort and those in the next. Thus, a hybrid of the Beverton–Holt and stock recruitment models is needed. From all current indications, however, it appears that such a model with realistic cost assumptions is analytically untractable and perhaps better approached with simulation techniques or by aggregating and thereby ignoring some of the explicit age/size relationships. Beyond this, there is need in some populations to consider between-cohort density dependencies. The simplest possibility is to make individual-cohort mortality rates a function of the total population but this too may miss important relationships which depend on the age distribution of the population – e.g. where older cohorts cannibalize younger cohorts.

4.5. Lumped parameter models

As discussed earlier, when making the modeling steps from individual to cohort to population we are confronted with different problems of aggregation at each level. Basically we must decide which features are critical and deserving of special focus and which may be safely ignored or parameterized in some way. Apparent from the preceding section is the fact that age/size specific models with realistic features become unwieldy rapidly, and in particular, when one wishes to include intragenerational interdependencies, the age/size specific details probably have to be sacrificed unless simulation studies are undertaken.

Another way to account for stock-recruitment relationships in an overlapping generations model is to use a "lumped parameter" model in which the object is a single variable like "numbers" or "biomass" of the organisms. Consider, for example, a fishery in which recruits live several years and spawning takes place every year. Clearly at any point in time, the fishable biomass will contain several cohorts and thus the population will change from year to year in some manner depending upon their numbers and on their age distribution. For example, an exceptionally large year class will have impacts which ripple over many successive generations and the impacts can be complex depending upon density dependent mechanisms operating between cohorts at each point in time and between generations. By making the simplifying assumption that we measure in some units such as biomass undifferentiated by age/size characteristics, we can model some of the possible intragenerational complexities at a cost of losing some of the specific details. These types of models may be appropriate when there is no harvesting selectivity possible, for example.

Sections 2 and 3 introduced two of the simplest lumped parameter models; namely, the logistic differential equation model and the discrete Ricker stock-recruitment model. Both of these imply relatively simple intragenerational density-dependent mechanisms which operate instantly (logistic case) or between adjacent time periods. The stock-recruitment model, in fact, implies that either organisms are recruited to the reproductive population in the first year and subsequently have no impact on this stock, or that generations are nonoverlapping and adults die after recruitment. For many species, however, reproductive maturity is reached only after some considerable time delay and organisms survive over longer periods. Let N_{k+1} be the reproductive population in year $k + 1$ and assume that the mortality rate between years of adults is m. If there is a delay in recruitment such that this year's new adult recruits are a function of adults β years ago, we have a delay-difference equation describing the population; namely,

$$N_{k+1} = (1 - m)N_k + F(N_{K-\beta}).$$ (65)

Clark (1976) has derived a solution to the fixed proportional costs optimal harvesting problem for this delay difference equation and the solution appears similar qualitatively to the simple one period delay already discussed. In particular, there is an optimal steady-state stock N^* defined by

$$(1 + i)\left[(1 - m) + (1 + i)^{-\beta}F'(N^*)\right]\left(\frac{\partial \Pi}{\partial H} + \frac{\partial \Pi}{\partial X}\right) = \frac{\partial \Pi}{\partial X},$$ (66)

where Π is as defined before. Note that this collapses to the solution derived earlier when $m = 1$ and $\beta = 0$, the one period stock recruitment case. The optimal approach to N^* in this more general case is no longer a most rapid approach path, but numerical methods applied to parameters for the Baleen Whale by Clark show that a MRAP is close to optimal.

For many species and harvesting situations, a discrete model is most appropriate. In fact, it is frequently the case that species give birth every year so that cohorts overlap by roughly one calendar year – particularly in temperate climates. In other cases, however, species may mate several times per year and even continuously in tropical climates. In these cases, we have overlapping generations but with very short staging times. In the limiting case where generations overlap continuously, we have a differential equation model of population growth.

The simplest way to arrive at a continuous overlapping generation model is to begin with a Ricker-type model where population members reproduce in generations which live τ years each. Then, if we add in other members uniformly in the interval $[0, \tau]$, the limit of such a process can be described with the delay-differential equation

$$\dot{N}(t) = N(t)[G(N(t-\tau))].$$ (67)

In this simplest case (uniform distribution is important), the functional form of G can be related to the corresponding difference equation form F so that with the appropriate choice of discrete model, we might have something like

$$\dot{N}(t) = rN(t)\left[1 - \frac{N(t-\tau)}{K}\right]$$ (68)

describing a logistic-type model of population growth. The dynamic behavior of this particular form depends critically, as did the discrete model, on $r\tau$, the product of the intrinsic growth rate and the generation time. The breakpoint between stabilizing and oscillating behavior is where $r\tau = (\Pi/2)$ [May (1973)]. For values less than $(\Pi/2) = 1.5707$, the system converges to a single stable equilibrium point $N^* = K$, and for values greater, the system oscillates in a limit cycle whose amplitude is increasingly severe as $r\tau$ gets larger [Jones (1962)].

A more general form which exhibits the wide variety of behavior earlier discussed for difference equations is [May (1980)]

$$\dot{N} = -\mu N + R[N(t-\tau)].$$ (69)

This is essentially the form utilized by the International Whaling Commission to model whale populations with

$$R[N(t-\tau)] \equiv N(t-\tau)\left[p + q\left\{1 - \left[\frac{N(t-\tau)}{K}\right]^Z\right\}\right].$$ (70)

In this model as τ lengthens and the density affects become increasingly severe (as Z increases), the model exhibits a stable equilibrium point, regular limit cycles, a hierarchy of cycles with doubling periodicity, and finally aperiodic or chaotic behavior with no recognizable structure. Interestingly, beyond the chaotic region lies another region where the system collapses back to simple limit cycle behavior.

Note that the above models (68) and (69) are essentially derived by uniformly overlapping a sequence of nonoverlapping populations whose individual generation times are τ. There are no explicit between-cohort density effects, and the resulting aggregated model reflects individual cohort-density effects and the general impact of the parent population exactly τ periods ago on today's (period t) population. More realistically, without a uniform initial distribution and with density effects that may occur at nondiscrete intervals of the life cycle, we would expect population changes today to be related in some more generally weighted fashion to past populations, rather than just the population τ years ago. Thus a generalized [May (1973)] version of the delay-differential model is

$$\dot{N}(t) = rN(t)\left[1 - \int_{-\infty}^{t} N(s)w(t-s)\,ds\right],$$ (71)

where $w(t-s)$ is a weighting function. The weighting function has some average time delay τ_0 associated with it and it turns out that the stability properties of this model are similar to (68) above; namely that for critical values of $r\tau_0 \approx 1.5$, the system exhibits either stabilizing or oscillating behavior, depending upon whether $r\tau_0$ is less than or greater than the critical value, respectively. In fact, our constant generation time model (68) is really a special case of this general model where the weighting function collapses to a Dirac Delta function (spike) at $\tau_0 = \tau$.

Not much work has been done on delay differential equation harvesting models although if the results from the discrete case are any indication, the qualitative properties of solutions to simple cases are similar to the instantaneous case. In particular, as long as the system is stable (which, recall, calls for $r\tau$ to be on the order of 1.5), it is most likely the case that a long-run steady state stock level N^* exists and is desirable to approach or achieve directly. Consider, as an example, the system in (68) with R a quadratic function. Figure 2.21 shows the steady-state yield curve which could be harvested continually if the system were in long-run equilibrium. Suppose that we wish to get to N^* and stay there forever after inheriting a stock which has been in long-run equilibrium at $\overline{N}$. If harvesting is unconstrained we could instantly reduce the stock level to $N_0 = N^* e^{-\mu\tau}$. Then the stock would grow according to

$$\dot{N}(t) = -\mu N_t + R[N(t-\tau)].$$ (72)

But for the first τ periods $R[N(t-\tau)] = R(\overline{N})$ and N will simply decline at a rate $-\mu$. If further harvesting is avoided over the first τ periods, N will simply decline to N^*. At that point, harvesting can proceed by taking just enough to hold the stock at N^*, or

$$h^*_{t+\tau} = -\mu N^*_{t+\tau} + R[N(t)], \qquad t \geq \tau.$$ (73)

Note that for the next interval $[\tau \leq t \leq 2\tau]$, $R[N(t)]$ will be changing as it reflects the decline from N_0 to N^* which took place in $[0, \tau]$. Thus, the harvest rate will increase until $t = 2\tau$, at which point it locks into the steady state.

It is reasonable to conjecture similar patterns when there are some constant unit harvesting costs which (for example) vary with the stock level lower than the above. With respect to the adjustment phase, again it is reasonable to expect a near most rapid approach path, with an initial period of zero harvest which allows delay effects to catch up. The higher the discount rate, of course, the more costly is this waiting period and hence the value of the liquidation benefits will weigh heavily in the selection of the ultimate steady state stock. Thus, *ceteris paribus*, it is probably the case that optimal steady-state stock levels in delay-systems are

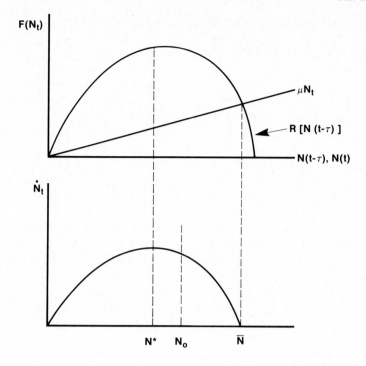

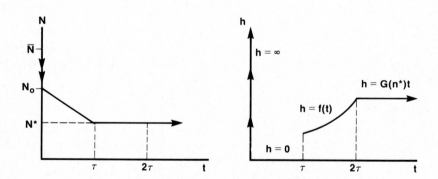

Figure 2.21. Delay-differential logistic model.

lower than in nondelay systems. Note, in addition, that stability of the system is important here since one cannot even achieve a steady-state stock level if the system is oscillatory. For these cases, the optimal solution is obviously much more complicated.

5. Summary and conclusions

This chapter has examined a range of models of optimal use of renewable natural resources. We began by using the simple logistic model to introduce problems of natural resource use and to illustrate the qualitative characteristics of timing and investment/disinvestment problems. Next, a fairly extensive examination of population processes was undertaken, framed in the concepts of r- and K-selection. This was done more as a pedagogical device to group organisms we observe in nature according to characteristics and their roles in the system. In reality, a whole spectrum exists with mixed and overlapping characteristics, but, as a rough guide, it is useful to think of extreme r-selected species as having high fecundity and mortality, small size, low generation times, and spatially mobile opportunistic behavior, whereas K-selected organisms are generally larger, longer-lived, slower growing, and more sedentary.

Given all of this natural variety in characteristics, it is risky, at best, to try to generalize and draw some broad conclusions. Nevertheless, there are a few synthesizing remarks which seem worth making if for no other reason but to stimulate thoughts. Perhaps not surprisingly, these thoughts fall out of an intellectual view which places man in the system as just another predator. With that perspective, the interesting questions have to do with how to "best" fit (as an exploiter) into a system which has evolved over numerous generations (often not exploited by men).

One obvious starting point is that man derives many values from his "use" of natural populations – from aesthetic-based, nonconsumptive, and nonparticipative values which are essentially "existence" values for natural systems to participative but nonconsumptive use values related to the stock size (e.g. bird watching) to the more familiar consumptive uses derived from harvesting.

The extent to which man succeeds in being an "efficient" component of the system has to do with how well his actions taken to use the system translate into values that he desires and how much and what kind of "feedback" the exploited natural system produces. At one end of the possibilities are situations where the values relate to an undisturbed system and the actions taken to produce those values are "benign". At the other end are circumstances where even minimal direct use of the system to obtain certain values completely overwhelms the "resilience bounds" of the system and collapse results. In between these cases, we

Table 2.2

Biological parameter			Economic parameter
Intrinsic growth rate	r	δ	discount rate
Generation time	τ		planning period
Breeding interval	T_s		harvesting selectivity
Biomass	B	V	net value

have a myriad of choice problems which involve precisely how to be an efficient "predator" and maximize values derived.

The section on population models and optimal use is a broad overview of the range of models which have been developed and the qualitative characteristics of some optimal use problems. The characteristics of optimal use patterns depend upon the interplay between biological and economic factors, of course, and there are some generalizations which can be made relating to an organism's position on the r–K spectrum. Table 2.2 lists some key biological parameters and some paired economic factors which characterize harvesting problems in particular.

For extreme r-selected species, r is high, τ is low (less than one year), and T_s is also low – usually coincident with τ. In temperate and more extreme climates, r-selected species are often locked into a one-year cycle where each generation is born, grows, reproduces, and dies in a year. In tropical climates, τ and T_s may be still low, but the species breeds continuously. Generally speaking, r-selected species are small and hence have a relatively low gross value per unit mass. Thus, with a few exceptions, costs of harvesting largely determine whether a species is feasible to exploit or not. Harvesting costs, moreover, are determined largely by the patchiness of the species. Small organisms spread out over large areas are too costly, whereas those which agglomerate or are otherwise densely found may be worth harvesting.

The principal economic problems (or efficiency problems) for r-selected species have to do mostly with *timing* rather than investment or disinvestment. Since r-selected species are mobile and small, they often become feasible economically only during a very short window in their lifetime – usually near their reproductive period. In the herring roe fishery, for example, harvest takes place only when the herring are schooled up during spawning. The timing that takes place in this fishery is often determined on-line and down to the minute in order to maximize roe biomass.

The more towards the r-selection end of the spectrum a species is, the smaller it will be, the shorter its generation time, and generally the more expensive it will be to harvest selectively. In temperate climates with one reproductive cycle per economic planning period (year), it will usually not be necessary to selectively harvest anyway since generations will not overlap. If escapement must be guaranteed for these species, it is most easily met with escapement targets rather than mesh size. In temperate climates, however, since cohorts will overlap and since harvesting may take place continuously, it may be necessary to use mesh size restrictions or other means to optimize both harvest and escapement.

In summary, for extreme r-selected species, the technology which has evolved (e.g. purse seines) and the biological mechanisms inherent in the species both lead to planning problems which are more likely to be short-horizon *timing* problems which imply *impulse*-type controls as the most efficient way to harvest. As we showed in Section 4, the characteristics of these solutions involve waiting until biomass reaches a certain critical age and then harvesting quickly. Usually, the discount rate δ is unimportant since it is swamped by r. The smaller the ratio (δ/r), the closer the critical date of first harvesting to maximum age. Similarly, the lower the costs of harvesting, the more complete will be the harvest (neglecting escapement concerns) and the shorter the harvest period. Thus, generally for these species, the goal of maximum *physical* yield is close to maximum *economic* yield.

In contrast, as we move towards K-selected species, r is low relative to δ and τ is long relative to the planning period. A low r means that the stock responds sluggishly to harvesting moratoria (investment) and in addition, since K-selected organisms are spread out over space, they become more costly to reduce (disinvest) as stock size gets smaller. Hence, K-selected species are characterized by *adjustment costs* and therefore present *investment/disinvestment* problems rather than (or in addition to) timing problems.

In addition, since τ is long and generally greater than T_s (i.e. the species breeds several times over a lifetime), the population will almost always overlap and consist of mixed sizes and ages. Fortunately, the larger the organism, the more feasible it becomes to use technologies and practices that are selective. Thus, the critical economic and efficiency problems have to do with determining the optimal biomass size, how to achieve it, and, perhaps most important, the composition of the harvest which will maximize the present value of resource flows over time.

As we saw in Section 4, the problems of determining optimal harvesting in mixed age/size populations is analytically difficult and generally unsolved. For simple circumstances, we can say some things, however. First, the discount rate is important in these problems, and, generally speaking, the higher the discount rate, the sooner one harvests a given cohort. Second, the qualitative nature of the solution depends dramatically on the types of costs incurred in harvesting. If costs are zero and perfect selectivity can be practiced, it is possible to optimize each cohort in a mixed age/size population separately. With positive but linear costs, it is no longer possible to generally characterize the optimal solution. Even if perfect selectivity is possible, it may be optimal to pulse harvest the population (use no selectivity) every few time periods, or alternatively it may be optimal to selectively harvest single cohorts more frequently. The answer appears to depend upon the costs and benefits of using more selective measures which, in turn, depend in a complex way on the generation time τ and the breeding interval T_s. The lower the ratio (T_s/τ), the more generations overlap and the more likely it is that one cannot answer the optimal harvesting pattern question readily.

Finally, a key aspect of K-selected organisms is their ability to adapt to altered densities by maturing earlier, changing mating behavior, etc. Thus, there is a complicated relationship between population dynamics, species density, and the

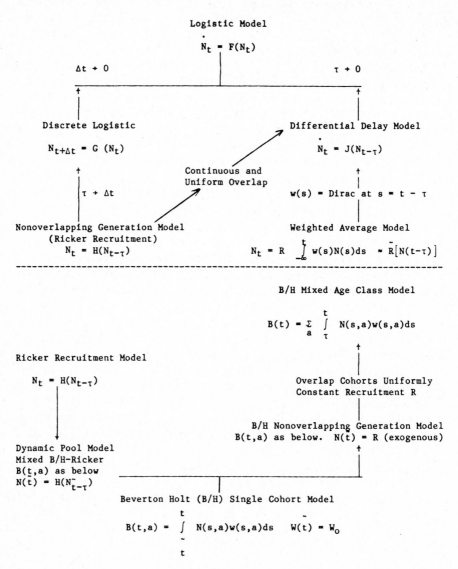

Figure 2.22. Logistic model.

age/size/sex distribution of the population. If selectivity is possible, both numbers *and characteristics* of those harvested must be chosen to optimize values derived. Thus, for example, if it is desired to adjust a deer population in a natural or overharvested equilibrium to a new one with a large number of large-antlered trophy males, it is obvious that the internal dynamics and age/sex structure consideration make the problem nontrivial. Similarly, if imperfect or zero selectivity hold, then each harvest rate and profile will have different impacts on the distribution of characteristics in the population. Finally, the longer is τ, the more likely it is that the population will oscillate in its approach to any equilibrium. This likelihood increases if harvesting also causes r to go up as density thins.

The above suggest that the logistic model is an oversimplification at best and perhaps better reserved for pedagogical uses with the caveat that it has little relevance to many (if any) real-world situations. It is not relevant to r-selection harvesting situations and is less relevant to K-selection cases because harvest patterns change the functional form as they impact the population distribution. One can relax the restrictive assumptions implicit in the logistic model and move towards simple and then complicated differential delay systems (see Figure 2.22), but to be accurate one still must know how harvesting different numbers with different age/size/sex characteristics affects the delays, weighting functions, etc. Hence, in the end, if we are interested in real-world management problems, we are inevitably forced to disaggregate to pick up the more complicated features of mixed age populations. Unfortunately, these appear to be the most intractable analytically for reasons discussed in Section 4. However, they have not really been given much attention until recently, and perhaps continued analytical and simulation work will shed further insight into the nature of solutions.

References

Allen, R.L. and P. Basasibwaki (1974) "Properties of Age-Structured Models for Fish Populations", *Journal of the Fisheries Research Board of Canada* 31, 1119–1125.

Anderson, L. (1977) *The Economics of Fisheries Management* (Johns Hopkins University Press, Baltimore) p. 214.

Arrow, K.J. (1964) "Optimal Capital Policy, the Cost of Capital, and Myopic Decision Rules", *Annals of the Institute of Statistical Mathematics* 16, 21–20.

Arrow, K.J. (1968) "Optimal Capital Policy With Irreversible Investment", in: J.N. Wolfe (ed.), *Value, Capital and Growth, Papers in Honour of Sir John Hicks* (Edinburgh University Press) pp. 1–20.

Bagenel, T.B. (1976) "A Short Review of Fish Fecundity", in: S.B. Gerking (ed.), *The Biological Basis of Freshwater Fish Production* (John Wiley and Sons, New York).

Beddington, J.R. and D.B. Taylor (1973) "Optimum Age Specific Harvesting of a Population", *Biometrics* 29, 801–809.

Beverton, R.J.H. and S.J. Holt (1957) *On the Dynamics of Exploited Fish Populations* (Ministry Agric. Fish and Food, London) Fish. Invest. Ser 2, no. 19.

Botsford, L.W. (1978) *Modeling, Stability, and Optimization of Aquatic Productive Systems*, Ph.D. thesis (University of California, Davis).

Botsford, L.W. (1981) "Optimal Fishery Policy for Size-Specific, Density-Dependent Population Models", *Journal of Mathematical Biology* 12, 265–293.

Botsford, L.W. and D.E. Wickham (1978) "Behavior of Age-Specific, Density-Dependent Models and the Northern California Dungeness Crab Fishery", *Journal of Fishery Resources Board Canada* 35, 833–843.

Brauer, F. (1977) "Stability of Some Population Models with Delay", *Mathematical Bioscience* 33, 345–358.

Brauer, F. and D.A. Sanchez (1975) "Constant Rate Population Harvesting: Equilibrium and Stability", *Theoretical Population Biology* 8, 12–30.

Brown, G., Jr. (1974) "An Optimal Program for Managing Common Property Resources With Congestion Externalities", *Journal of Political Economy* 82, 163–174.

Caughley, G. (1966) "Mortality Patterns in Mammals", *Ecology* 47, no. 6 pp. 906–918.

Clark, C.W. (1971) "Economically Optimal Policies for the Utilization of Biologically Renewable Resources", *Mathematical Bioscience* 12, 245–260.

Clark, C.W. (1976) "A Delayed-Recruitment Model of Population Dynamics, With An Application to Baleen Whale Population", *Journal of Mathematical Biology* 3, 381–391.

Clark, C.W. (1973a) "The Economics of Overexploitation", *Science* 181, 630–634.

Clark, C.W. (1973b) "Profit Maximization and the Extinction of Animal Species", *Journal of Political Economy* 81, 950–961.

Clark, C.W. (1976) *Mathematical Bioeconomics: The Optimal Management of Renewable Resources* (John Wiley and Sons, Inc., New York) p. 352.

Clark, C.W. and G.R. Munro (1975) "The Economics of Fishing and Modern Capital Theory: A Simplified Approach", *Journal of Environmental Economics and Management* 2, 92–106.

Clark, C.W. and M. Mangel (1979) "Aggregation and Fishery Dynamics: A Theoretical Study of Schooling and the Purse Seine Tuna Fisheries", *U.S. Fisheries Bulletin* 77, no. 2.

Clark, C.W., F.H. Clarke and G.R. Munro (1979) "The Optimal Exploitation of Renewable Resource Stocks: Problems of Irreversible Investment", *Econometrica* 47, no. 1.

Clark, C., G. Edwards and M. Friedlander (1973) "Beverton-Holt Model of A Commercial Fishery: Optimal Dynamics", *Journal Fish. Res. Board Can.* 30, 1629–1640.

Crutchfield, J.A. (1975) "An Economic View of Maximum Sustainable Yield", in: P.M. Roedel (ed.), *Optimum Sustainable Yield as a Concept in Fisheries Management*, American Fisheries Society Special Publication No. 9 (Washington, D.C.).

Crutchfield, J.A. and A. Zellner (1962) "Economic Aspects of the Pacific Halibut Fishery", *Fishery Industrial Research*, vol. 1, no. 1 (U.S. Department of the Interior, Washington, D.C.).

Faustmann, M. (1849) "Berechnung des Werthes, Welchen Waldboden Sowie Nach Nicht Haubare Holzbestande fur die Weldwirtschaft Besitzen", *Allgemeine Forst und Jagd Zeitung* 25, 441.

Gaffney, M.M. (1960) *Concepts of Financial Maturity of Timber and Other Assets* (Department of Agricultural Economics, North Carolina State College, Raleigh).

Hannesson, R. (1975) "Fishery Dynamics: A North Atlantic Cod Fishery", *Canadian Journal of Economics* 8, 151–173.

Heaps, T. and P. Neher (1979) "The Economics of Forestry When the Rate of Harvest is Constrained", *Journal of Environmental Economics and Management* 6, 297–319.

Holling, C.S. (1973) "Resilience and Stability of Ecological Systems", *Annual Review of Ecology and Systematics* 4, 1–24.

Hutchison, G.E. (1978) *An Introduction to Population Ecology* (Yale University Press, New Haven).

Jaquette, D.L. (1972) "A Discrete-Time Population Control Model", *Mathematical Bioscience* 15, 231–252.

Jones, G.S. (1962) "The Existence of Periodic Solutions of $f'(x) = -\alpha f(x - 1)[1 + f(x)]$", *Journal of Mathematical Analysis and Applications* 5, 435–450.

Keyfitz, N. (1968) *Introduction to the Mathematics of Population* (Addison-Wesley, Reading, Mass.).

Lack, D. (1966) *Population Studies of Birds* (Clarendon Press, Oxford).

Leslie, P.H., "On the Use of Matrices in Certain Population Mathematics", *Biometrika* 33, 183–212.

Li, T.Y. and J.A. Yorke (1975) "Period Three Implies Chaos", *American Mathematical Monthly* 82, 985–992.

Lotka, A.J. (1925) *Elements of Physical Biology* (Williams and Wilkins, Baltimore).

MacArthur, R.H. and E.R. Pianka (1966) "Optimal Use of a Patchy Environment", *American Naturalist* 100, 603–609.

MacArthur, R.H. and R. Levins (1967) "The Limiting Similarity, Convergence and Divergence of Coexisting Species", *American Naturalist* 101, 377–385.

MacArthur, R.H. and E.O. Wilson (1967) *The Theory of Island Biogeography* (Princeton University Press, Princeton).

May, R.M. (1973a) "Time-Delay Versus Stability in Population Models With Two and Three Trophic Levels", *Ecology* 54, 315–325.

May, R.M. (1973) "Stability in Randomly Fluctuating Versus Deterministic Environments", *American Naturalist* 107, 621–650.

May, R.M. (1973) *Stability and Complexity in Model Ecosystems* (Princeton University Press, Princeton).

May, R.M. (1974) "Biological Populations with Nonoverlapping Generations: Stable Points, Stable Cycles and Chaos", *Science* 186, 645–647.

May, R.M. (1975) "Biological Populations Obeying Difference Equations: Stable Points, Stable Cycles and Chaos", *Journal of Theoretical Biology* 49, 511–524.

May, R.M. (1976) "Mathematical Aspects of the Dynamics of Animal Populations", in: S.A. Levin (ed.), *Studies in Mathematical Biology* (American Mathematical Society, Providence, R.I.).

May, R.M. (1977) "Simple Mathematical Models with Very Complicated Dynamics", *Nature* 269, 459–467.

May, R.M. (1977) "Thresholds and Breakpoints in Ecosystems With a Multiplicity of Stable States", *Nature* 269, 471–477.

May, R.M. (1979) "The Structure and Dynamics of Ecological Communities", in: R.M. Anderson, B.D. Turner and L.R. Taylor (eds.), *Symposium of British Ecological Society* 20, *Population Dynamics* (Blackwell Scientific Publications, Oxford) pp. 385–407.

May, R.M. (1980) "Mathematical Models in Whaling and Fisheries Management", in: G.F. Oster (ed.), *Some Mathematical Questions in Biology*, vol. 13 (The American Mathematical Society, Providence, R.I.) pp. 1–64.

May, R.M. (1981) *Theoretical Ecology: Principles and Applications* (Sinauer Associates, Sunderland, Mass.).

May, R.M., G.R. Conway, M.P. Hassell and T.R.E. Southwood (1974) "Time Delays, Density Dependence, and Single Species Oscillations", *Journal of Animal Ecology* 43, 747–770.

May, R.M. and G.F. Oster (1976) "Bifurcations and Dynamic Complexity in Simple Ecological Models", *American Naturalist* 110, 573–599.

May, R.M., J.R. Beddington, C.W. Clark, S.J. Holt and R.M. Laws (1979) "Management of Multispecies Fisheries", *Science* 205, 267–277.

Maynard Smith, J. (1976) "Evolution and the Theory of Games", *American Scientist* 64, 41–45.

Maynard Smith, J. (1971) *Mathematical Ideas in Biology* (Cambridge University Press, Cambridge, England).

Nikolskii, G.V. (1969) *Theory of Fish Population Dynamics* (Oliver and Boyd, Edinburgh).

Oster, G. (1975) "Stochastic Behavior of Deterministic Models", in S.A. Levin (ed.), *Ecosystem Analysis and Prediction* (SIAM-SIMS Conference Proceedings, Alta, Utah) pp. 24–37.

Pearl, R. (1930) *The Biology of Population Growth* (Knopf, New York).

Pearse, P. (1967) "The Optimal Forest Rotation", *Forestry Chronicle* 43, 178–195.

Pianka, E.R. (1970) "On *r*- and *K*-selection", *American Naturalist* 104, 592–597.

Plourde, C.G. (1970) "A Simple Model of Replenishable Resource Exploitation", *American Economic Review* 60, 518–522.

Plourde, C.G. (1971) "Exploitation of Common-Property Replenishable Resources", *Western Economic Journal* 9, 256–266.

Quirk, J.P. and V.L. Smith (1970) "Dynamic Economic Models of Fishing", in: A.D. Scott (ed.), *Economics of Fisheries Management—A Symposium* (University of British Columbia, Institute of Animal Resource Ecology, Vancouver) pp. 3–32.

Reed, W.J. (1980) "Optimum Age-Specific Harvesting in a Non-linear Population Model", *Biometrics* 26, 579–593.

Ricker, W.E. (1954) "Stock and Recruitment", *Journal of Fisheries Resource Board Canada* 11, 559–623.

Rorres, C. (1976) "Optimal Sustainable Yields of a Renewable Resource", *Biometrics* 32, 945–948.

Rorres, C. and W. Fair (1975) "Optimal Harvesting Policy for an Age-Specific Population", *Mathematical Bioscience* 24, 31–47.

Rothschild, B.J. (1977) "Fishing Effort", in: J. Gulland (ed.), *Fish Population Dynamics* (John Wiley & Sons, New York) p. 372.

Schaefer, M.B. (1954) "Some Aspects of the Dynamics of Populations Important to the Management of the Commercial Marine Fisheries", *Bull. Inter-Amer. Trop. Tuna Comm.* 1, 26–56.

Schaefer, M.B. (1957) "A Study of the Dynamics of the Fishery for Yellowfin Tuna in the Eastern Tropical Pacific Ocean", *Bull. Inter-Amer. Trop. Tuna Comm.* 2, 247–285.

Schaefer, M.B. (1967) "Fishery Dynamics and the Present Status of the Yellowfin Tuna Population of the Eastern Pacific Ocean", *Bull. Inter-Amer. Trop. Tuna Comm.* 12, 89–137.

Silliman, R.P. (1969) "Analog Computer Simulation and Catch Forecasting in Commercially Fished Populations", *Trans. Amer. Fish. Soc.* 98, pp. 560–569.

Sinko, J.W. and W. Streifer (1967) "A New Model for Age Size Structure of a Population", *Ecology* 48, 910–918.

Smith, V.L. (1968) "Economics of Production From Natural Resources", *American Economic Review* 58, 409–431.

Smith, V.L. (1969) "On Models of Commercial Fishing", *Journal of Political Economy* 77, 181–198.

Solow, R. (1974) "The Economics of Resources or the Resources of Economics", *American Economic Review* 64, 1–14.

Southwood, T.R.E. (1975) "The Dynamics of Insect Populations", in: D. Pimentel (ed.), *Insects, Science and Society* (Academic Press, New York) pp. 151–199.

Southwood, T.R.E. (1977) "The Relevance of Population Dynamics Theory to Pest Status", in: J.M. Cherett and G.R. Sagar (eds.), *Origin of Pest, Parasite, Disease and Weed Problems* (Blackwell Scientific Publications, Oxford) pp. 35–54.

Southwood, T.R.E. (1981) "Bionomic Strategies and Population Parameters", in: R.M. May, *Theoretical Ecology* (Blackwell Scientific Publications, Oxford) pp. 30–52.

Southwood, T.R.E., R.M. May, M.P. Hassell and G.R. Conway (1974) "Ecological Strategies and Population Parameters", *American Naturalist* 108, 791–804.

Southwood, T.R.E. and H.N. Comins (1976) "A Synoptic Population Model", *Journal of Animal Ecology* 45, 949–965.

Spence, M. (1973) *Blue Whales and Applied Control Theory*, Technical Report No. 108, (Stanford University, Institute for Mathematical Studies in the Social Sciences).

Spence, M. and D. Starrett (1975) "Most Rapid Approach Paths in Accumulation Problems", *International Economics Review* 16, 388–403.

Taber, R.D. and R.F. Dasmann (1957) "The Dynamics of Three Natural Populations of the Deer Odocoileus Homeosus Columbiamus", *Ecology* 38, 233–248.

Thom, R. (1976) *Morphogenesis and Structural Stability* (Addison-Wesley, Reading, Mass.).

Verhulst, P.F. (1838) "Notice sur la Loi Que la Population Suit dans son Accroissement", *Correspondance Mathematique et Physique* 10, 113–121.

Volterra, V. (1931) *Lecons sur la Theorie Mathematique de la Lutte pour la Vie* (Gauthier-Villars, Paris).

Walters, C.J. (1969) "A Generalized Computer Simulation Model for Fish Population Studies", *Trans. Amer. Fish. Soc.* 98, 505–512.

Watson, A. (1977) "Population Limitation and the Adaptive Value of Territorial Behavior in Scottish Red Grouse", in: B. Stonehouse and C.M. Perrins (eds.), *Evolutionary Ecology* (University Park Press).

Chapter 3

SPATIAL ASPECTS OF ENVIRONMENTAL ECONOMICS

HORST SIEBERT*

Universitaet Konstanz

1. The spatial dimension of environmental systems

Environmental and renewable resource systems are defined over space; consequently, environmental problems have a spatial dimension. Examples are river
systems, groundwater systems, and atmospheric systems. The need to include
spatial relationships explicitly in many economic models concerning the natural
environment is another aspect that makes the field complex and inherently
interdisciplinary. Like the previous two chapters, this one is intended as a survey
and introduction to pertinent concepts and models, many of which are used in
subsequent chapters.

1.1. Space as a grid system

According to the concept of space as discussed by von Thuenen (1826), Loesch
(1944), and Isard (1956), it may be envisioned as a set of points or as a grid
system. At each point in space, one or more activities are defined to occur. The
grid system thus will tend to have a pattern or cluster of activities, and activities
in different grids may be interlinked with each other. Interdependence between
points in space may relate to environmental phenomena (transfer functions), to
economic and demographic variables (trade, migration), or to political processes
(bargaining). The problem of spatial environmental economics then consists in
analyzing the economic, environmental, and political interactions occurring in
space; in determining spatial patterns of environmental use; in specifying the
impact of economic activities on environmental allocation in space; and in
considering the influence of alternative institutional settings on the spatial dimension of the environment.

* This chapter is the result of my work in the Sonderforschungsbereich 5 "Allocation Policy in a
Market Economy" at the University of Mannheim and at the Center for Energy Policy Research at
M.I.T. I appreciate comments from Helga Gebauer, Dan Golomb, Ferdinand Dudenhoeffer, Allen V.
Kneese, Andreas Kotzorek and Ruediger Pethig.

Handbook of Natural Resource and Energy Economics, vol. I, edited by A.V. Kneese and J.L. Sweeney
© *Elsevier Science Publishers B.V., 1985*

1.2. *Delineation of environmental regions*

Conceiving space as a grid system has the advantage of explicitly presenting a map of spatial activities to any desired level of detail. This micro approach will be excessively detailed for some problems, and a less specific map can be created by aggregating points of space into regions. For instance, instead of analyzing each of the grids 1–36 in Figure 3.1 individually, we may consider the system of grids 1–36 as one aggregate spatial unit.

A region can be defined as a set of spatial points that are either homogeneous with respect to some characterization (criterion of homogeneity) or are more intensively interrelated among each other than with other spatial points (criterion of functional interdependence). Thus, environmental regions may be defined by environmental characteristics such as the level of pollution (polluted area). Alternatively, interaction among spatial points through environmental media such as the groundwater system, a river system, or a meteorological system may define an environmental region. Similarly, economic regions may be constructed according to socio-cultural or historical criteria or by using such economic variables as industrial structure, rates of unemployment, and per capita income. Or, economic regions may be delineated according to the intensity of economic exchange via commodity exchange and factor mobility. Administrative or political regions may be delineated according to the above mentioned criteria or according to historical or political phenomena.

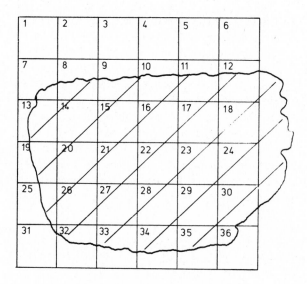

Figure 3.1. Example of a grid system.

As a rule, environmental regions corresponding to different media will not be identical. In Figure 3.1, sections 1 through 36 may denote air regions, and the shaded area may indicate a river system. Regions for different environmental media may overlap. Moreover, environmental regions and economic areas are generally not identical. An economic area delineated according to industrial structure (e.g. a coal district) or, according to the state of development (e.g. depressed area), may cut across an environmental region defined according to the spatial extent of an environmental system. For instance, in Figure 3.1, areas 1 through 36 may be interpreted as economic of planning regions, and the shaded area may be considered to be an environmental system.

1.3. Spatial extent of environmental systems

Depending on the spatial extent of the environmental media, we can distinguish among the following types of environmental systems:

(1) *Microlevel environmental systems* such as small ponds or even smaller units.

(2) *Regional environmental systems* within one country such as metropolitan air regions or river systems.

(3) *National environmental systems* where environmental boundaries coincide with political frontiers.

(4) *Transfrontier environmental systems* which transport pollutants from one nation to another by one- or multi-directional mechanisms (e.g. the potassium salt carried by the Rhine River to Holland and the acid rains originating in Western Europe and falling on Sweden).

(5) *International environmental systems* represent a public good common to at least two nations; they are spatial subsystems of the world, such as the Mediterranean and the Baltic Sea.

(6) *Global environmental systems* which are used as a public consumer good and as a receptacle of wastes for the earth as a whole (such as the earth's atmosphere or the ozone layer).

The existence of different spatial environmental systems implies that we have different types of environmental problems and also that different solutions may be necessary for the various cases.

2. The role of transfer functions

The transport of pollutants from one point in the grid system to another through environmental media gives rise to problems of environmental allocation in space. Therefore, the ability to model diffusion of materials in space is a prerequisite of regional environmental economics.

2.1. Media and forms of spatial diffusion

Transfer functions describe the spatial movement of pollutants including physical and chemical transformations; they relate a set of emissions at one or more points in space to an ambient level of concentration at one or more other points. The first type of point is usually called a "source" and the second a "receptor". Transfer functions thus provide information on how environmental quality in one spot is affected by alternative levels of emissions at other locations.

Pollutants are dispersed over space by different environmental media such as air, water systems (rivers, groundwater systems, oceans), and the biosphere. Diffusion may take different forms. It may be considered as a transportation problem with pollutants being physically transported from one point of the grid system to other points. Alternatively, diffusion may be considered as a chemical as well as a transport process with a pollutant material changing its chemical properties (as well as location) over time. Finally, diffusion may occur in the biosphere in food chains and through the mobility of animals and plants [Okubo (1980)].

2.2. Approaches to diffusion studies

Conservation of mass is the starting point for models for physical diffusion. There are two fundamental methods of describing the motion of fluid media (air and water): tracer and flow models.

2.2.1. Tracer models

The Lagrangian approach to diffusion describes the history of the properties of a specific particle (pollutant) or a set of particles in a flow medium. The Lagrangian approach thus traces the history of a pollutant in time. Consequently, the position of a pollutant can be modelled for different points in time (moving cell). Wind vectors and turbulence in the flow medium affect the trajectory of each pollutant.

An application of the Lagrangian approach is the Gaussian plume model used for short-range air dispersion modelling. Assuming no chemical reactions and a given wind direction, the ambient concentration of a pollutant, emitted from a source, will follow a Gaussian distribution vertical and horizontal to the axis of the plume. The plume model then specifies the downwind ambient level of pollution. This Gaussian plume model is widely used for benefit–cost analysis and environmental impact studies of power stations [Friedrich and Tsimopoulos (1983)]. The plume model is also used for meso-scale air quality impact analysis; for instance, for visibility studies [Golomb and Gruhl (1981)]. (For additional discussion, see Chapter 7 of this Handbook.)

2.2.2. Flow models

In contrast to tracer models, the Eulerian flow models analyze the flow properties of a fluid medium in a given point of space (grid) without recognition of the history of the properties associated with the myriad of fluid-borne particles which traverse the point in question [Dobbins (1979)].

An application of the Eulerian approach are box (cell or grid) models for atmospheric dispersion. In a very simple form, a region may be considered as a box, and the box may be analyzed by an input–output approach, i.e. the concentration of pollutants is calculated by emissions plus interregional imports minus interregional exports and deposition (wet and dry deposition). Splitting up the box into a set of boxes and introducing more than one pollutant (and allowing chemical interaction), the box model can be made more realistic. Then, the box (e.g. airshed) is divided into a set of communicating cells, which represent a well-stirred reactor for the purposes of calculating the chemical interaction or the depletion of pollutants. Such a model can include a large amount of detail on the regional meteorological features, a chemical reaction sequence, and a source inventory [Dobbins (1979)].

Figure 3.2 summarizes the main elements of diffusion models [Turner (1979), Wetstone and Rosencranz (1982)]. Though Figure 3.2 relates to atmospheric dispersion, the elements are common to all diffusion studies. The sources of emissions (stationary, mobile, type of pollutants, spatial distribution) are an important prerequisite of diffusion modeling as well as the properties of the flow medium (meteorology, wind or water velocity, temperature of air or water).

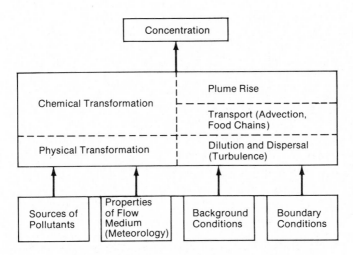

Figure 3.2. The main elements of diffusion models.

Background conditions refer to physical properties of the earth such as geological properties influencing the flow properties of groundwater (or the impact of urban structures and high stacks on meteorology). Boundary conditions relate to concentrations of the environmental system under consideration at the boundary, such as concentrations upwind of the region and the flux at the upper vertical boundary (or the pollution load of a river at the boundary of the region being considered).

Besides these "inputs" to diffusion studies, the other important aspect is to model the spatial, physical and chemical interaction of pollutants. For instance, for air dispersion models, photochemical reactions have to be included as well as dilution by the wind and dispersal due to turbulence and advection (wet and dry deposition). The output of the model is the ambient level of concentration of pollutants at receptor locations within the region.

2.3. Air

Atmospheric dispersion [Turner (1979)] requires short-range (0–100 km), meso-scale (100–300 km), long-range (300–2000 km) and global-scale modeling [Golomb and Gruhl (1981), Stern (1976)]. Short-range models may rely on the Gaussian plume rise whereas long-range transport models (acid rain, visibility impairing haze) start from the observation that some types of substances (sulfur oxides SO_x, nitrogen oxides NO_x) require long reaction periods in the atmosphere for the final pollutant (e.g. sulfuric or nitric acid) to develop. The "atmospheric" residence time of a pollutant [Golomb and Gruhl (1981)] is a basic starting point for long-range air diffusion modeling. For instance, the average atmospheric residence time for SO_x varies from one to six days [Rodhe (1979)]. Or, the halflife of SO_2 in the atmosphere is estimated to be in the 24-hour range [Golomb et al. (1983)]. At a wind velocity of 16 km/hour, the pollutant will be transported 256 km in 16 hours and about one half of the SO_2 will "disappear", i.e. it will be deposited or transformed into sulfate [Golomb and Gruhl (1981)]. Other substances have even longer average residence times. For instance, the average residence time for carbon monoxide is estimated at one year [Georgii (1981)], for carbon dioxide at two to five years [Georgii (1981); two to four years according to Robinson and Robbins (1969)] and for nitrogen oxides residence time is about four years [Robinson and Robbins (1969)]. For hydrocarbons, the residence time is indicated at 16 years [Robinson and Robbins (1969)].

2.4. Water

Diffusion studies of pollutants in water have to model the flow properties of water systems (river systems, groundwater systems, oceans) and the interaction of pollutants in the water system. A classical example is the Streeter–Phelps oxygen "sag" equation (1925) relating the dissolved oxygen deficit (DOD) at a point along the river and the biochemical oxygen demand (BOD) discharged at some upstream point, where BOD serves as an indicator how much oxygen is required to dissolve organic waste [Russell and Spofford (1972)]. Defining DOD in mg/t, letting t be the travel time from the point of discharge in days and denoting the ultimate first-stage BOD concentration (i.e. carbonaceous demand) at the point of discharge (mg/t), letting K_1 denote the BOD rate constant (days^{-1}) and K_2 the rate constant of reaeration of the body of water (days^{-1}), the Streeter–Phelps equation is

$$\text{DOD} = \frac{K_1 L}{K_2 - K_1}(e^{-K_1 t} - e^{-K_2 t}).$$

This equation does not consider several phenomena such as nitrogeneous oxidation, production of oxygen through photosynthetic activity (algae) and the effects of runoff and sedimentation. Moreover, the equation only relates to organic wastes. For a more detailed modeling of diffusion in river systems compare Kittrell (1969); with respect to groundwater see Matthess and Harvey (1982). (Also additional discussion is found in Chapter 7 of this Handbook.)

Diffusion processes may cut across media. Dry deposition and rainout of pollutants from the air have an impact on the pollution of the ground. Some substances in the ground (nitrates from fertilizer) eventually end up in rivers and lakes; evaporation recycles some pollutants from river systems into the air.

2.5. Integration of transfer functions into applied economic models

Different approaches attempt to incorporate diffusion into economic models.

2.5.1. Material balance models

The law of the conservation of matter [Georgescu-Roegen (1971)] is a basic premise of the material balance models developed at Resources for the Future [Kneese, Ayres and d'Arge (1970), Ayres (1972)]. Mass cannot be lost and material withdrawn from nature must eventually return to it (in physical terms). The material balance models allow one to follow the "flow" of material through the economic system.

2.5.2. Input–output models

Input–output analysis explicitly accounts for the interdependence of economic and ecological activities. By introducing emissions as an input to environmental systems and by treating natural resources as inputs provided by the environment, input–output models attempt to model the linkage between the economy and the environment and explicitly or implicitly contain diffusion processes [Leontief (1970), Isard (1972)].

2.5.3. Residual management models

Material-process models and input–output analysis are two components of residual management frameworks which represent optimization models including aspects of environmental diffusion and relating to a specific sector of the economy or to a specific region, e.g. the Delaware Estuary [Russell and Spofford (1972)]. These models are treated in some detail in Chapter 8 of this Handbook.

2.6. The relevance of transfer functions for environmental allocation

Transfer functions are relevant for environmental allocation because they mimic the natural systems through which economic externalities work. In a scenario of zero price for environmental use, transfer functions explain intervening variables between different economic activities. In the context of environmental policy, transfer functions are a link between ambient quality targets and environmental policy instruments for each source of pollution. Since the basic problem of environmental policy is to find institutional mechanisms for transforming quality targets into residuals control behavior at the individual source, information on transfer functions is crucial for implementing optimal environmental allocation.

When the grid aspect of space is aggregated into a regional analysis, two types of diffusion problems have to be explicitly taken into account in economic analysis: interregional diffusion and interregional public goods. In the case of interregional diffusion, environmental quality U^j in region j depends on emissions E^i in region i:

$$U^j = \phi\left(E^j, T(E^i)\right), \tag{1}$$

where T characterizes diffusion. The spillover may be uni-directional or multi-directional. In the case of an interregional public good, emissions from (economic) regions i and j affect the quality of the common environmental system k:

$$U^k = \Psi\left(E^i, E^j\right). \tag{2}$$

Further discussion of diffusion models can be found in Chapter 7 of this Handbook. The treatment there is in the context of embedding transfer junctions into economic regional models of environmental management. This has, as discussed there, frequently been done in applied environmental economics.

3. Environmental allocation in space: The basic issues

In order to analyze the regional allocation of the environment, one has to study how regions interact, which implications the principle of the optimal division of labor in space suggests, and which institutional approaches are feasible for implementation.

3.1. Interactions among regions

Environmental regions are interrelated. Environmental disruption in one area will cause repercussions in other areas. We may distinguish among the following mechanisms of interaction.

(1) Pollution in one area will affect the environmental quality of another region by the interregional diffusion of pollutants to the other area.

(2) Economic regions are interrelated through the mobility of commodities. A strict environmental policy in one economic region leads to an increased specialization of less pollution-intensive commodities while another area specializes in more pollution-intensive commodities. The exchange of goods will affect regional environmental quality.

(3) Factors of production migrate among regions, tending to leave those areas where factor prices have been reduced as a result of environmental policy.

(4) Residents migrate among regions owing to differences in environmental quality. Note that residents are not necessarily identical to workers and that environmental quality and wages both determine the mobility of labor. If residents have an influence in the political process, their mobility will affect the target values established by governments for environmental quality.

(5) Environmental quality in one area may be an argument variable in the welfare function (of the inhabitants) of another region, either because the other region assigns a value per se to these public goods or because the region uses them during holidays for recreational purposes (temporal mobility of residents). Also, demonstration effects may occur among regions, with environmental quality in one area influencing the aspiration levels in other regions.

(6) Administrative regions may be interrelated by institutional arrangements such as a grants-in-aid system among regions. Also, the assignment of different types of taxes and expenditures to regions may create an interdependency among regions.

3.2. The division of labor in space

The concept of the optimal division of labor with respect to space implies location of pollution-intensive activities in such areas that have a comparative price advantage in terms of environmental endowment. "It is quite...important to the happiness of mankind that our enjoyments should be increased by the better distribution of labor, by each country producing those commodities for which its situation, its climate, and its other natural or artificial advantages is adapted, and by exchanging them for the commodities of other countries..." [Ricardo (1817, p. 80)]. According to the Heckscher–Ohlin[1] theorem, a region has a comparative price advantage with respect to pollution-intensive products:

   (a) if the region has a larger assimilative capacity,

   (b) if the region can abate pollutants with lower costs,

   (c) if the region has a smaller demand for assimilative services due to industrial structure,

   (d) if the residents of the region put a lower value on environmental quality, and

   (e) if the region is less densely populated assuming that a given quantity of pollutants causes a lower social damage for a smaller population.

3.3. Short-run versus long-run allocation problems

The spatial implications of an optimal environmental allocation depend on the time span that is allowed for adjustment processes. In the short run, only a limited set of adjustment processes may occur. For instance, the location of labor and firms may be fixed in the short run, and abatement technology may be given. In the long run, however, labor may migrate to another region, firms may change their location and the technology may change.

3.4. National versus regional authorities

Environmental allocation in space depends on the institutional setting. An important issue is what role markets play and how markets are corrected by public policy. Another important feature of the allocation mechanism is the regionalization of environmental policy. The following problems must be distinguished.

   (1) Should the desired level of environmental quality be regionally differentiated or should it be nationally uniform?

   (2) Should nationally uniform or regionally differentiated environmental policy instruments be used?

   (3) Should environmental policy be pursued by national or regional agencies?

---

[1] Compare Heckscher (1919) and Ohlin (1929).

The first question relates to the regionalization of the target, the second to the regionalization of policy instruments (even in the case of identical regional targets) and the third problem refers to the organizational structure.

4. National approaches to environmental allocation

Assume that the definition of property rights for environmental use is vested with a national authority and that the national government maximizes social welfare for a system of regions ["politique pour la nation", Boudeville (1966)]. Then, an optimal allocation dictates that interregional spillovers are accounted for in the shadow prices of the economy. The polluter pays principle requires that a region bears the environmental costs that it causes in another area. Shadow prices should also reflect differences in environmental scarcity between regions. In the short-run, we can expect that environmental scarcity prices will be differentiated regionally. In the long run, when all adjustments have taken place, there is, under certain conditions, a tendency towards the equalization of environmental shadow prices. Finally, we can also expect that the target values of environmental quality may differ among regions.

4.1. A national allocation model

4.1.1. Assumptions

For simplifying purposes, a two-region case is considered. Every region can produce output Q_i in sector i with the resource input R_i ($Q_i = F_i(R_i)$). Production generates pollutants S_i^p according to a convex function ($S_i^p = H_i(Q_i)$), but pollutants can be abated (S_i^r) by using resources R_i^r ($S_i^r = F_i^r(R_i^r)$). The production and abatement functions are well behaved. Net emissions are defined as $E = \sum S_i^p - \sum S_i^r$; they generate pollutants ambient in the environment S which in turn affect environmental quality U ($U = G(S)$). For a given level of interregional diffusion, the transformation space of a region with respect to environmental quality and two commodities 1 and 2 can be illustrated as in Figure 3 of Siebert (1981). Furthermore, we assume that well-behaved welfare functions are separately formulated for each region; that is, the regional welfare W^j is affected only by the regionally consumed commodity C_i^j and the regional environmental quality U^j. Subscripts denote sectors; superscripts indicate regions.

$$W = \sum_j W^j(C_1^j, C_2^j, U^j), \qquad j = 1, 2. \tag{3}$$

In order to explicitly consider the interregional diffusion of pollutants, it is assumed that pollutants are diffused from region 2 to region 1 through environmental systems. Let S^{21} denote the quantities of pollutants being diffused from region 2 to region 1. Then the ambient pollutants in the environment of region j, S^j are defined as

$$S^1 = \sum \left(S_i^{p1} - S_i^{r1} \right) + S^{21}$$

and

$$S^2 = \sum \left(S_i^{p2} - S_i^{r2} \right) - S^{21}.$$

It is assumed that the quantity of "exported" pollutants represents a given part of net emissions:

$$S^{21} = \alpha^{21} \left[\sum \left(S^{p2} - S^{r2} \right) \right], \quad \text{with } 0 < \alpha^{21} < 1. \tag{4}$$

Commodities are mobile between the two regions:

$$C_i^1 + C_i^2 = Q_i^1 + Q_i^2. \tag{5}$$

The resource is mobile between the sectors of a region and between the two regions:

$$\overline{R} = \sum_j \sum_i R_i^j + \sum_j \sum_i R_i^{rj}. \tag{6}$$

The national authority maximizes the welfare of the two-region system.

4.1.2. Shadow prices

For the shadow price of pollutants ambient in the environment of region 1 we have, from the appendix:

$$\lambda_S^1 = \lambda_S^2 = \lambda^{21}. \tag{7}$$

The shadow price of the pollutants exported by region 2 is given by

$$\lambda^{21} = \lambda_S^1 - \lambda_S^2 = -W_U^{1'}G^{1'} + W_U^{2'}G^{2'}. \tag{8}$$

The shadow price of emissions in region 1 is

$$\lambda_{S_i^p}^1 = \lambda_S^1 = \lambda_{S_i^r}^1 = -W_U^{1'}G^{1'} = \frac{\lambda_R}{F_i^{r1'}}. \tag{9}$$

For the shadow price of emissions in region 2 we have

$$\lambda_{S_i^p}^2 = \lambda_S^2 + \alpha^{21}\lambda^{21} + \lambda_{S_i^r}^2 = -W_U^{2'}G^{2'} + \alpha^{21}\lambda^{21} = \frac{\lambda_R}{F_i^{r2'}} \tag{10}$$

or

$$\lambda_{S_i^p}^2 = \alpha^{21}\lambda_S^1 + \left(1 - \alpha^{21} \right) \lambda_S^2. \tag{11}$$

4.2. Interregional diffusion and the polluter pays principle

In region 1 the shadow price of emissions corresponds to the shadow price of pollutants and the shadow price of abated emissions [eq. (9)]. Similar to the model for a closed economy, we have as a condition for the optimum that the shadow price must be equivalent to the prevented marginal damage and the marginal costs of abatement [eq. (9)].

The shadow price of emissions in region 2, however, is no longer identical with the evaluation of the pollutants in region 2 [eq. (10)]. The shadow price is influenced by the interregional diffusion of pollutants. Assume that $\alpha^{21} > 0$ and let $\lambda^{21} > 0$, i.e. a unit of pollution in region 1 has a greater marginal damage than in region 2. If environmental policy is initiated, the polluters of region 2 will have to bear the environmental costs which they cause in region 1 (differential damage). On the one hand, region 2 is "relieved" by the diffusion of pollutants, and therefore its marginal damage decreases. On the other hand, the quantity of pollutants increases in region 1, and the marginal damage rises there. The polluters of region 2 have to bear the social costs of pollution which occur in region 2 as well as in region 1. Eq. (11) specifies that the shadow price for emissions in region 2 is determined by the weighted sum of damage occurring in region 1 and in region 2. Note that α^{21} represents that fraction of a unit of emission that reaches region 1; $1 - \alpha^{21}$ denotes the fraction remaining in region 2.

Compare this optimal result with the case when regional authorities do not take into account spillovers. With region 2 exporting pollutants free of charge, the implicit price of pollutants in region 2 is reduced. In region 2, the shadow price and the quantity of abated pollution fall. In region 1, however, pollutants ambient in the environment rise and pollution increases. If the interregional diffusion is not accounted for, region 2 will have an unwarranted locational advantage through this interregional diffusion factor. Not accounting for interregional diffusion from region 2 to region 1 would have the same effect as an extension of the assimilative capacity of region 2; region 1 would bear social costs which it has not caused.

The following cases have to be delineated.

(1) *Higher marginal damage.* If a unit of pollution causes a higher damage in region 1 than in region 2 ($\lambda^{21} > 0$), then the shadow price of emissions in the optimum is determined not only by the marginal damage caused in region 2 but also by the differential damage caused in region 1. The higher damage in region 1 may be due to a more vulnerable ecological system, a lower assimilative capacity, and stronger environmental preferences for environmental quality by a higher per capita income (in case of an income elasticity of environmental services greater than one).

(2) *Higher demand for assimilative services.* Region 1 may have a higher demand for assimilative services than region 2. The demand for assimilative

services depends on such factors as the level of regional development, the industrial mix, and the population density. The higher demand for assimilative services of region 1 can also be attributed to the fact that region 1 uses a more pollution-intensive production technology and emits a greater quantity of pollutants for identical output vectors.

(3) *Higher costs of abatement.* Region 1 may have higher marginal costs of abatement. This presupposes that the abatement technology varies regionally and that technical knowledge of abatement processes cannot be transferred interregionally, either because information concerning inventions in abatement technology confronts spatial obstacles or because innovations in both regions are not proportionately possible. This latter situation could arise if in one area older, less efficient abatement technologies exist. The disadvantageous marginal costs of abatement can also be based on a higher factor price in the case where partial immobility of factors exists.

(4) *Smaller damage in region 1.* If a unit of pollution causes a smaller damage in region 1 than in region 2 ($\lambda^{21} < 0$), then the shadow price for emissions can be set lower in region 1. In this case, region 1 is still sufficiently endowed with assimilative capacity. Since this assimilative capacity is not used by region 1, it can be utilized by region 2 through interregional diffusion.

(5) *Identical marginal damage.* If a unit of pollution causes the same marginal damage in regions 1 and 2 ($\lambda^{21} = 0$), then it does not matter in terms of the evaluation of pollutants in which region a unit of pollution is released into the environment. A differential damage does not arise. The shadow prices in the two regions are identical.

(6) *No diffusion.* If no interregional diffusion of pollutants takes place, that is, $\alpha^{21} = 0$, the shadow price of emissions in region 2 is, in the optimum, equivalent to the marginal costs of abatement and the prevented marginal damage of region 2.

4.3. Interregional spillover and location advantage

Shadow prices for pollutants affect the shadow prices of commodities and therefore the price advantage or location advantage of a region. The location advantage is indicated not by the consumer's price λ_i but by the producer's price (net price) λ_{Q_i}. As implications for the shadow price of commodities (producer's price) we have

$$\lambda^1_{Q_i} = W^{1'}_{C_i} + H^{1'}_i G^{1'} W^{1'}_U = W^{1'}_{C_i} - H^{1'}_i \frac{\lambda_R}{F_i^{r1'}}. \tag{12}$$

$$\lambda^2_{Q_i} = W^{2'}_{C_i} + H^{2'}_i \left(G^{2'} W^{2'}_U - \alpha_{21} \lambda^{21} \right) = W^{2'}_{C_i} - H^{2'}_i \frac{\lambda_R}{F_i^{r2'}}. \tag{13}$$

The (producer's) price of a commodity is determined by its regional evaluation and by the environmental costs which arise in its production. The environmental costs have to be subtracted from the social evaluation. For region 2 the environmental costs contain not only the environmental damages of region 2 but also the differential damage which arises because of the interregional diffusion of pollutants. In the context of a national optimization model, region 2 cannot obtain an unjustified location advantage by interregional diffusion because region 2 must bear the environmental costs caused by it.

Note that the location advantage of region 2 is also influenced by the assimilative capacity of region 1. Assume that the assimilative capacity of region 1 is reduced. Then λ^{21} must rise, and the production incentive in region 2 will be smaller. On the other hand, if the assimilative capacity in region 1 is increased, λ^{21} will be smaller and the production incentive in region 2 will rise.

4.4. Identical environmental shadow prices

An interesting question is under which conditions we can have identical shadow prices for emissions in both regions in the case of interregional diffusion ($\alpha^{21} > 0$).

4.4.1. Forces working towards an equalization of shadow prices

The mobility of resources and the interregional exchange of commodities represent mechanisms which reduce differences in the shadow prices for pollutants.

Assume that commodities are not exchanged between regions. Compare the cases when the resource is interregionally mobile and immobile. Consider a given initial situation in which the resource is (firms are) concentrated in region 2. Then pollution in region 2 will be high; pollution in region 1 will be low. (Alternatively, a large amount of resources has to be used in the abatement activities of region 2.) With the resource being mobile between regions, efficiency can be increased by reallocating the resource from region 2 to region 1. Pollution in region 2 will decrease; pollution in region 1 will increase. If the resource is immobile between regions, this change in pollution cannot be brought about. Consequently, the two cases imply different implicit shadow prices for pollution. The mobility of the resource means that the implicit value of pollution will adjust to some extent between regions.

Assume that the resource is immobile between the two regions. Compare now the case in which the commodities are exchanged interregionally with the case when the commodities are immobile interregionally. The mobility of the commodities has a similar effect as the mobility of the resource. By specializing away from the pollution-intensive product the polluted region can reduce pollution and thus reduce the implicit value placed on pollution (relative to a case when commodities are not exchanged between regions; compare Section 6).

The mobility of resources and commodities represents forces working towards a reduction of differences in the shadow prices of pollution. Identical shadow prices, however, can only be established under specific conditions.

4.4.2. Identical and linear damage and welfare functions

If the damage functions are identical in the two regions and if they are linear and if the welfare functions are identical and linear with respect to environmental quality, the shadow prices for pollutants will be identical. From appendix equations (A.3.1j) and (A.3.1k) we have:

$$\lambda^1_S = \lambda^2_S = W^{1'}_U G^{1'} = W^{2'}_U G^{2'}. \tag{14}$$

This result holds irrespective of the mobility of factors or of commodities.

4.4.3. Identical and linear production and emission functions

From eqs. (A.3.1b), (A.3.1d, e, f, g, h, i) and (A.3.1k) we have for the relationship between λ^1_S and λ^2_S:

$$\lambda^1_S \left[H^{1'}_i - \alpha^{21} H^{2'}_i \right] = \lambda^2_S H^{2'}_i (1 - \alpha^{21}) + \lambda_R \left(\frac{1}{F^{2'}_i} - \frac{1}{F^{1'}_i} \right) \tag{15}$$

Assuming identical production and emission functions for sector i in both regions is not sufficient to generate identical shadow prices for pollutants in both regions. Only if these identical functions are linear, we have $\lambda^1_S = \lambda^2_S$. Note that the linearity of the production function alone (or the emission function alone) is not sufficient.

4.4.4. Identical and linear abatement functions

Substituting eq. (11) into (A.3.1e) we have:

$$\lambda^1_S = \frac{F^{r2'}_i (1 - \alpha^{21})}{F^{r1'}_i - \alpha^{21} F^{r2'}_i} \lambda^2_S. \tag{16}$$

Thus, a linear and identical abatement function for sector i implies that differences in environmental endowment can be compensated by the mobility of the resource.

4.4.5. Other conditions

Some of the above-mentioned conditions are unnecessarily restrictive. For instance, eq. (14) can also be satisfied for $\lambda_S^1 = \lambda_S^2$ if

$$\lambda_S \left(H_i^{1'} - H_i^{2'} \right) = \lambda_R \left(\frac{1}{F_i^{2'}} - \frac{1}{F_i^{1'}} \right),$$

so that a higher pollution intensity of sector i in region 1 ($H_i^{1'} > H_i^{2'}$) is compensated by a favorable production technology ($F_i^{1'} > F_i^{2'}$).

4.4.6. Identical and linear-homogeneous overall production technology

Identical shadow prices for pollutants come about by specific combinations of the linearity of the production, emission and abatement functions. An alternative approach consists in combining the overall production technology into an overall production function. If the production, emission and abatement technology is compressed into a single production function [Pethig (1979)]:

$$Q_i = T_i \left(\tilde{R}_i, S_i \right), \tag{17}$$

with $\tilde{R}_i = R_i + R_i^{\mathrm{r}}$ and $S_i = S_i^{\mathrm{p}} - S_i^{\mathrm{r}}$, identical prices for pollutants in a two-region-system (for $\alpha^{21} \geq 0$) can be established if the production function is linear-homogeneous and identical for each sector in both regions [Dudenhoeffer (1983)].

The equalization takes place irrespective of preferences; it is due to the mobility of factors or the mobility of commodities (when factors are immobile). Due to the concept of the production function in eq. (17), emissions are interpreted as a traditional factor of production. Thus, we have a two-region (country) model with one mobile factor of production (the resource) and one immobile factor of production (tolerable level of emissions in each region). The quantity of the immobile factor of production (emissions) is fixed in the optimum [or by a standard-price approach in practical environmental policy; Baumol and Oates (1971)]. With the resource being mobile, the marginal value product of the resource must be identical in both regions. Defining $r_i = \tilde{R}_i / S_i$ and writing the per unit production function as $Q_i / S_i = v(r_i)$, the linear-homogeneity of equation 17 implies $v_i'(r_i^1) = v_i'(r_i^2)$. This guarantees that the marginal value product of emissions, i.e. the shadow price for pollutants is identical in the two regions.

With identical and linear-homogeneous overall production technologies, identical shadow prices for pollutants also will hold in the optimum if the resource is immobile and if commodities are exchanged interregionally. The result is due to the fact that the relative shadow price λ_r / λ_{Sj} for pollutants and the resource is identical between two regions due to the linear-homogeneity of the overall production function. From the identical relative shadow price λ_R / λ_{Sj} we can establish that the factor intensity r_i^j is identical in both regions which implies that the marginal value product of emissions must be identical. With identical shadow prices[2] for the commodity i the shadow price for pollutants is identical. This result generalizes the factor price equalization theorem [Samuelson (1953)] to the case of interregional spillover. Strictly concave (and identical) production functions [eq. (17)] are not sufficient to imply identical prices for pollutants in both regions.

4.4.7. Differences in environmental quality

Identical shadow prices for pollutants do not imply identical environmental qualities in both regions. Assuming $\lambda_S^1 = \lambda_S^2$, we have from eqs. (A.3.1c) and (A.3.1j) in the appendix:

$$\frac{W_U^{1\prime}[G^1(S^1)]}{W_U^{2\prime}[G^2(S^2)]} = \frac{G^{2\prime}(S^2)}{G^{1\prime}(S^1)}. \tag{18}$$

Only if both the (concave) utility function and the (concave) damage function are identical in both regions, will $\lambda_S^1 = \lambda_S^2$ imply that environmental qualities are identical in both areas. If, however, the utility and damage functions differ, $\lambda_S^1 = \lambda_S^2$ does not necessarily imply identical environmental quality in the optimum.

4.5. Trade and resource mobility

The optimal allocation model presented in the appendix also yields results on the specialization of production in space when the interregional diffusion is ignored ($\alpha^{21} = 0$). The problem then is to analyze the role of trade and of resource mobility for environmental allocation. This issue will be taken up in Section 6.

4.6. Regional impact of uniform national policy instruments

A potential outcome of a national approach to environmental allocation may be that nationally uniform policy instruments are applied throughout a nation. This may be necessary in the real world, for example, where it may prove to be too complicated to implement regionally differentiable emission taxes, for example. It is a fallacy, however, to believe that nationally uniform policy instruments have identical regional impacts. Charging the same emission tax throughout a nation does not imply that each region is affected in the same way by environmental policy. This is immediately apparent, if regions are differently endowed with environmental quality.

---

[2] In a model with a linear-homogeneous production function there is no difference between a consumer's and producer's price.

Nationally uniform policy instruments are defined differently by different disciplines. For an economist, a nationally uniform policy instrument is the price for emissions. For the lawyer, a nationally uniform policy instrument may exist if a specific technological requirement such as the "state of the art" is applied nationwide. It can be shown that nationally uniform legal requirements as used in a permit system (emission permits) do have different impacts under different conditions. For instance, the "permit" approach implies that nonattainment areas exclude the location of new activities, that barriers to market entry in nonattainment areas are erected and that the labor market of the area is closed to newcomers [Siebert (1982a)].

4.7. Regional restraints for environmental policy

Maximizing national welfare may result in a differentiation of regional welfare. In the interest of "pour la nation" a specific region may have to accept a loss in welfare. Interregional specialization can also mean that regions will achieve differing amounts of environmental quality. This result can be in conflict with a spatially interpreted equity goal. Therefore, one possible strategy is to introduce restrictions on the interregional differences in welfare [Siebert (1975)]. In practical economic policy, one can expect that the restrictions are not defined with respect to the regional welfare level, but rather in relation to the determining factors of regional welfare. Thus, articles 72 and 106 in the Constitution of the Federal Republic of Germany require that living conditions be similar for all regions. This requirement may be interpreted to mean a similarity in environmental quality. Therefore, we could introduce additional constraints into our allocation model, such as $U^1 = U^2$, which would require identical environmental quality among regions. Alternatively, we could require that a minimum quality $U^j \geq \overline{U^j}$ be reached in each region.

If the equity constraint is not formulated in terms of regional welfare, but rather is broken down into different constraints on welfare determinants, then the constraint becomes more restrictive through partitioning [Siebert (1982b)]. Typical welfare determinants are social overhead capital, environmental quality, and income per capita. Identical welfare could be achieved in these regions by a judicious combination of these determinants. Interregional constraints on each welfare determinant, however, reduce the solution set considerably. In practice, constraints are not implemented rigorously and thus are used more as guidelines. Since these equity considerations may be thought of as a spatial implication of the welfare approach, a state of this type can be classified as a welfare state with a federal structure [Frey (1979)].

An alternative approach to equity restrictions on environmental quality is a specialization among regions, such as a "black-spot policy" where pollution-intensive activities are concentrated in certain areas. This spatial-separation approach attempts to bring about a specialization of national territory and relies heavily on land-use planning as an instrument of environmental-quality management. This approach allows for better protection of less polluted areas; at the same time, it concentrates the "public bad" in designated areas.

4.8. Siting issues and the national interest

The location of private and public large-scale ventures (airports, power plants) has become a major political issue, especially in densely populated economies. No allocation problem arises when all layers of society experience a net benefit, i.e. the region (local community) and the nation both have a net advantage. A problem arises when the benefits of a large-scale project and its costs relate to different regions and when at least one layer of society (a region) experiences a net loss that cannot be compensated. Then, from a national perspective, a region has to experience a net loss if the system as a whole can gain. From the regional perspective some protection is warranted. We have a problem of a constitutional dimension. The basic question is whether the constitution of a country should protect a minority of citizens experiencing the opportunity costs (for instance in a region) or whether a group of society can be expected to tolerate the opportunity costs in order to allow overall net benefits. The ethical-economic aspects of such situations are examined in Chapter 5 of this Handbook.

5. Regional autonomy and environmental allocation

The alternative to a national environmental policy is to vest environmental allocation into regional authorities. Then regional authorities will maximize regional welfare ["politique pour la region", Boudeville (1966)]. The typical example is the classical federal state such as Switzerland and the United States [Frey (1979)]. The motivation for assigning environmental allocation to regional authorities is founded on the argument that regional authorities may be suited best to discover regional preferences and to implement regional targets. Regional authorities also may have an information advantage compared to national authorities with respect to the implementation of environmental policy instruments.

5.1. The spillover problem

When environmental policy is vested into autonomous regional authorities, the regional authorities maximize regional welfare separately instead of national welfare. They have an incentive not to take into account the interregional diffusion of pollutants. The pollution-exporting region regards the export of pollutants as a welcome extension of its assimilative capacity. Compared with a national maximization problem, the price of environmental use is set too low in the pollution-exporting region; this region has a location advantage at the expense of other regions. In the region importing pollutants, the shadow prices are set too high; they reduce the production of pollution and goods more than is economically desirable.

In such a setting, allocation efficiency is violated because environmental scarcity is not signaled correctly in the shadow prices for pollutants. Besides this general distortion, the misallocation may take specific forms. A region may follow a high-stack policy in order to reduce its abatement costs. Or pollution-intensive producing activities may be concentrated in downwind (downstream) areas close to the neighbor. Thus, Sweden has concentrated some industry close to Norway [Potier (1979)]; France charges lower effluent charges in the "agence de bassin" close to its border.

In order to solve the interregional spillover problem in the case of regional authorities, three approaches are discussed. The regional authorities may engage in a bargaining process in order to reduce allocation inefficiency (Section 5.2). Spillovers may be internalized by institutional arrangements, especially by defining new property rights (Section 5.3). Finally, national restraints may be imposed for regional authorities (Section 5.4).

5.2. The bargaining problem

In the bargaining process between autonomous regions, we meet all the problems of environmental policy "in nuce". Environmental quality is a public good; and the environmental media are common property resources; consequently the downwind region has no property title to force abatement in the polluting area; it is not possible to exclude the polluting area from using the environment as a receptacle of waste. The polluting area can behave as a free rider. Without clearly defined rights, both regions have to determine the tolerable level of pollution in a bargaining process. Their willingness to pay may differ, and more specifically their bargaining position is different due to the asymmetry of the spillover. The following cases have to be distinguished.

5.2.1. One-directional spillover

In a scenario in which the upwind region uses the environment as a free good, bargaining implies that both regions can only benefit if the pollutee compensates the polluter to reduce pollution in the upwind region (victim-pays-principle). Unilateral action of the downwind region cannot improve efficiency. In this simple scenario, the bargaining position of the downwind country is given by its marginal benefit curve; the bargaining position of the upwind country is determined by its marginal cost curve of abatement. When bargaining costs are neglected, a solution of the game is found in which marginal damage prevented (in the downwind country) equals marginal costs of abatement (in the upwind country). This bargaining result represents a Coase solution (1960) and a Nash solution (1950) in a cooperative game.

5.2.2. Multi-directional spillover

When spillovers are multi-directional [eq. (1)], each region has a threat potential irrespective of compensation. A cooperative and a noncooperative solution may exist. In the case of noncooperative behavior, reaction functions $S^i = \Psi^i(E^j)$ are determined and an equilibrium point or a Nash equilibrium of the game is sought. For a Nash equilibrium, four postulates are required: joint efficiency, symmetry, linear invariance and independence of irrelevant alternatives [Pethig (1982, p. 80)]. Joint efficiency requires that the solution cannot be improved to the advantage of both regions. Joint efficiency implies individual rationality, i.e. the solution must be at least as favorable as the initial situation for each participant.

5.2.3. Common environmental systems

The bargaining solutions differ when environmental quality relates to an environmental system common to more than one region (country) such as the Ozone layer. The transfer function then is given by eq. (2) and the reaction function has to take into account that each polluter hurts himself. Consequently, unilateral action may now improve the welfare of one player [Pethig (1982)].

5.2.4. Intertemporal aspects

Interregional spillovers may be of an intertemporal nature. Pollutants transported into a region may accumulate there over time (e.g. sulfuric acid from acid rain accumulates in the lakes). With the damage showing up in future periods, the bargaining behavior of the pollutee now has to take into account the variation over time of a stock variable. The problem then has to be analyzed as a cooperative or noncooperative differential game [Leitmann (1974)] which shows the properties of a steady-state in a two-region system and the time paths of pollution in both regions towards the steady state [Gebauer (1982)].

5.2.5. *Property rights*

The Coase theorem [Coase (1960)] applies to the bargaining solution. With clearly defined regional property titles and no transaction costs and with regions maximizing their utility (being nonaltruistic), a bargaining solution will result in a Pareto-optimal allocation of the environment. The resulting environmental quality is independent of the initial distribution of property rights. Thus the bargaining equilibrium is not affected in the case of one-directional spillovers when the property right is given to the downwind region instead of the upwind region. A different allocation of property rights only influences distribution but it does not affect efficiency.

5.2.6. *Reciprocal-compensation procedure*

In the face of transfrontier pollution, the reciprocal-compensation principles has been proposed [OECD (1973)]. This principle is based on the assumption that in the bargaining process, the polluter will exaggerate the costs of pollution abatement in order to reduce the demands of the other region. Similarly, it is expected that the victim will exaggerate the extent of the incurred damages, in order to maximize the assessment of corrective measures needed. In order to avoid this deliberate falsification of information about the damages and costs of abatement, it has been suggested that an interregional fund be established to which the polluting region would pay according to its assessment of the damages and the polluted region would pay according to its assessment of the costs of abatement. This approach is designed to guarantee that the factors determining the emission tax are set as realistically as possible. The funds collected from the two parties would then be redistributed to them for the implementation of the environmental-protection measures. It is essential that the regions do not know the rate by which the tax receipts will be redistributed because this information would distort their estimates of the costs and damages.

5.2.7. *Cost sharing*

A related concept is the idea of cost sharing which requires that the costs of pollution abatement should be shared by the regions involved. The costs of attaining and maintaining an acceptable level of quality in the transfrontier environmental medium would be added and distributed among the regions according to a set rate. Since costs are determined by the desired level of environmental quality, the approach can only be used if the environmental quality target is determined. Moreover, the criteria by which abatement costs can be attributed to different regions must be specified.

5.3. Internalizing spillovers through institutional arrangements

Can institutional settings be found that allow internalizing spatial spillovers into regional organizational structures? If this can be accomplished, the areas experiencing the benefits of environmental policy and carrying its costs coincide.

5.3.1. Federalism

In the classical federal state such as Switzerland and the United States [Frey, 1979)], regional preferences are assumed to differ among regions; goal conflicts are solved by regional authorities according to the preferences of the regional population. A pure federalism presupposes that no serious interregional spillovers exist. The role of the federal government is limited to a "skeleton law" (Frey) on environmental protection to guarantee that spillovers are internalized.

5.3.2. Fiscal equivalence

Olson's concept of fiscal equivalence (1969, 1979) describes an institutional arrangement in which the group of people benefiting from environmental policy (experiencing environmental damage) are more or less identical with those financing environmental improvement. The task of an institutional arrangement then consists in finding such a delineation of environmental regions that guarantees the spatial overlapping of benefits and costs. One can conceive the space of an economy as being superimposed by a net of jurisdictions of different extensions and relating to different types of environmental problems.

5.3.3. Tiebout theorem

Applying the Tiebout theorem (1956) to environmental allocation, an optimal solution can be found for local environmental qualities under a set of given conditions. The most important prerequisite [Stiglitz (1977)] is that interregional spillovers are not serious and that consumers are mobile and vote with their feet. Each voter will migrate to the region in which he can maximize his utility. An equilibrium is reached when no consumer is induced to change his location. The willingness-to-pay for the regional environmental qualities is expressed correctly. Thus, voting with one's feet will guarantee a Pareto-optimal environmental allocation.

The Tiebout theorem is oriented towards allocation efficiency and does not consider equity problems. As an extreme solution, the exclusion or property right may not be vested into a government agency but into an individual [Wegehenkel (1980)]. Those not willing to pay must leave the area. Apparently, such a solution is not acceptable in a culture which has experienced the *cujos regio, ejus religio principle.*[3] Moreover, such an exclusion right would impede the citizens' freedom of movement. Thus, basic values of a society limit the range of institutional settings for environmental allocation.

5.3.4. Liability rules

Other institutional arrangements are liability rules or compensation schemes. The advantage of this approach is to attribute environmental costs to the individual polluter and to internalize them at the lowest level; with an appropriate specification of spillover costs, institutional arrangements for the regional level will be unnecessary. Interpreting environmental allocation as a principal–agent problem, the agent "region" becomes redundant. The problem of these approaches, however, consists in transaction costs due to legal procedures.

The four institutional approaches discussed above all presuppose that environmental property rights can be defined such that interregional spillovers are internalized. Such an approach is promising in the case of local public goods. However, when spillovers are dominant, other solutions may have to be found.

5.4. Centrally imposed restraints on regional autonomy

A suboptimal environmental allocation in the case of autonomous regional authorities may be prevented by imposing national restraints. One approach is to define interregional diffusion norms. These norms specify the ambient level of pollution tolerated at the regional border. This approach can be easily implemented in the case of water quality management; such an approach, however, is much more difficult in the case of air quality management.

5.4.1. Regional water associations

Regional water associations [Kneese and Bower (1968), Klevorick and Kramer (1973)] represent an institutional setting which allows a regionalization of environmental policy. The delineation of the environmental system (river system) can be easily achieved. Moreover, the spillover problem can be solved if water quality at the mouth of a river or of a tributary is specified by interregional bargaining or by national laws. Interregional diffusion norms then are identical to ambient standards at a given spot of a river and they can be considered as the target variable of environmental quality.

---

[3] This principle was used at the end of the Thirty Year's War in 1648 when the sovereign determined the religion of subjects.

5.4.2. Regional markets for transferable discharge permits

If environmental policy uses permits as a strategic variable and if these permits are made transferable (markets for emission licenses, bubbles), a regulatory device exists which takes into account the national interest and also permits regional autonomy within the given restraints. In this approach, regions have to be defined in which licenses are transferable. Moreover, interregional spillovers have to be taken into account explicitly when the tolerable level of emissions is specified. Otherwise inefficiencies result with respect to environmental quality or with respect to allocation efficiency. If the environmental region is defined too large, "hot spots" in the region will develop [Tietenberg (1980)]. If the environmental region is defined too small, serious spillovers will arise. These matters are discussed further in Chapter 10 of this Handbook.

5.5. Restraints on regional and national authorities

We come to the conclusion that autonomous regional authorities need nationally imposed restraints in order to guarantee a solution to the interregional diffusion problem. For instance, interregional diffusion norms have to limit the interregional spillover problem. National authorities, however, require restraints protecting regional interests (Section 4). The two conclusions do not necessarily contradict each other. They point out the restraints of a more nationally or a more regionally oriented approach to environmental allocation.

6. Environmental endowment as a determinant of trade

Environmental abundance or environmental scarcity influence interregional or international trade. In order to simplify the analysis, we only consider international trade although all results also relate to interregional trade. We neglect the diffusion aspect between countries ($\alpha^{21} = 0$). Let us assume that we have identical production, pollution, and abatement functions for commodity i in both countries. Then the country which is richly endowed with assimilative capacity will specialize in the production of the pollution-intensive commodity. This is due to the fact that the country has a comparative price advantage for the pollution-intensive commodity. We analyse how environmental policy will affect comparative price advantage, and how trade flows and factor mobility will influence environmental quality in both countries and under what conditions the price for pollutants will tend to equalize between the countries. In order to incorporate the results into traditional trade theory, we do not argue in the context of an optimization model but with an explication model. This means that allocation now is the result of decentralized decisions of utility-maximizing households and profit-maximizing firms.

6.1. Environmental endowment and comparative price advantage

6.1.1. Conditions for a reduction of comparative advantage

A country richly endowed with environmental services has a comparative price advantage relative to other areas; a country with environmental scarcity has a price disadvantage. Consider two commodities, let $p = p_1/p_2$ denote the relative price of the home country in the autarky situation, and let p^* be the relative price of the foreign country. Then the condition for establishing trade is $p \lessgtr p^*$. If $p < p^*$, then the home country has a comparative price advantage for commodity 1, and thus it will export commodity 1. Assume that the home country pursues an environmental policy, that an emission tax z is levied and that commodity 1 is the pollution-intensively produced commodity. Then the relative price of the pollution-intensive commodity 1 increases because the environmental costs of production are attributed to its price. This means that the comparative price advantage of the home country is reduced. The competitive position of the country is negatively affected, and exports will be reduced.

In an explication model using the same restraints as in the appendix and introducing a demand equation $C_i = C_i(p, Y)$ and a definition for national income $Y = p(Q_1 + Q_2)$, relevant conditions for an increase in the relative price of commodity 1 are its pollution intensity and its lower income elasticity. The lower income elasticity of the pollution-intensively produced commodity guarantees that the reduced demand due to falling income does not compensate the cost effect: the relative price rises and comparative advantage is reduced [Siebert et al. (1980, p. 73)].

If the production, emission and abatement technology is expressed by the linear-homogeneous equation (17) and if the input $\tilde{R}_i$ is split up into labor and capital, the emission intensity of commodity 1 has to be defined with respect to capital and labor. Thus, if commodity 1 is only emission intensive per unit of capital and not emission intensive per unit of labor, the deterioration of comparative advantage is not definite [Gronych (1980), Siebert et al. (1980)].

6.1.2. Graphical illustration

Figure 3.3 explains the argument. *AGBCH* represents the transformation space of the home country as described in the restraints of the Lagrangian function in the appendix. In order to keep the diagram simple, we do not show the transformation space of the foreign country. Rather, we indicate its production block *XYZ*

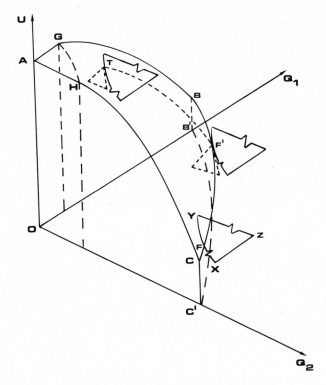

Figure 3.3. Trade and comparative advantage.

where environmental quality is not explicitly considered for the foreign country. Furthermore, the production block is drawn scaled down for simplicity. Note that the production block of the foreign country XYZ lies horizontally in the UQ_1Q_2 space.

If environmental policy is undertaken by the home country in an autarky situation (point F), p must rise since the environmental costs of production are attributed to the pollution-intensive commodity 1. The home country will move along the transformation curve from point F towards F'; its comparative price advantage will be reduced.

6.1.3. Protection versus environmental scarcity prices

Consider now a case in which the initial situation F with $p < p^*$ no environmental policy is undertaken and let the home country commence trade. In order to interpret the diagram, we assume that the home country is a small country so that the foreign country dictates the relative price p^*. Assume that the trade equilibrium is given at point F', where the production block of the foreign country is tangential to the transformation space of the home country. The home country specializes in the production of commodity 1. This happens to be the pollution-intensive commodity. As a consequence of international trade, the home country will produce more of the pollution-intensive commodity, and environmental quality will decline. This case can be interpreted as not expressing environmental scarcity correctly. The zero price of environmental use has the same effect as a protection of the pollution-intensive sector.

It can be expected that in the political debate environmental policy may not be understood as an allocation problem. Especially it is realistic to assume that specific groups of society will be negatively affected by environmental policy, such as the export- and import-substitute sector and workers (or trade unions) in these sectors. These political forces will ask for compensations or countervailing measures to make up for the loss of their relative autarky position. If these political groups are successful, environmental policy may give rise to new trade distortions.

Against these political demands for "restoring" a given competitive position the economist has to point out that without environmental policy comparative advantage is distorted and the pollution-intensively producing sector receives a hidden subsidy. The allocation of resources is biased in its favor. Environmental policy is an attempt to express the correct social costs. Similarly, since it would be absurd to compensate international disadvantage in endowments with respect to labor, skills, capital, and land by policy measures, we have to let environmental advantages rule in the long run.

6.2. Environmental endowment and location advantage

The change in comparative price advantage also indicates a variation in location advantage. If environmental policy is pursued in countries poorly endowed with assimilative services, then the production conditions of the pollution-intensive sector will be negatively affected. Its production costs will rise. At the same time the relative location advantage of an environmentally rich country improves. If capital is internationally mobile, one can expect that, *ceteris paribus*, capital of the environmentally poor country will be transferred to the environmentally rich country. The impact of environmental policy on the location advantage will also depend on the type of policy instrument used. An emission tax or transferable emission licences will serve to correct relative prices and will change comparative advantage; a permit system will be likely to make location space temporarily unavailable, and thus it may have much stronger effects on location.

6.3. Effects of environmental policy on trade and specialization

A reduction in the home country's comparative price advantage only indicates that potential exports of the pollution-intensive commodity will fall. In order to determine the change in actual exports arising from environmental policy, we must start from an initial trade equilibrium point F' in Figure 3.3 without environmental policy and ask how the trade volume will be affected by environmental policy. Let the trade flows in the initial situation be shown by the trade triangle at point F'. Assume that the home country undertakes environmental policy. Also assume that the home country is small and that the relative price p of situation F' will be dictated by the foreign country. In this case, we can define an isoprice line for constant $\bar{p}$ and alternative emission tax rates for the home country. This isoprice line $F'T$ indicates the adjustment process which will occur in the home country. The export quantity is reduced for a given relative price. The imports also have to decrease. The trade triangle depicted by the triangle drawn at point T becomes smaller.

If we assume that the home country is not small, environmental policy of the home country will lead to an increase of p in the world market. Thus, the new trade position, which takes into account the home country's environmental policy, lies to the left of the isoprice line $F'T$. Because of this influence by the home country on relative price p, its comparative advantage is reduced even more. A formal analysis of this problem for a two-country model confirms the conditions of pollution-intensity with respect to capital and labor as well as the low income elasticity of the pollution-intensive commodity 1 [Siebert (1979), Siebert et al. (1980)].

6.4. The equalization of prices for emissions

The mobility of resources and of commodities represent mechanisms which work towards an equalization of prices for emissions. In contrast to the optimal allocation problem of Section 4, interregional spillover is now neglected ($\alpha^{21} = 0$). Moreover, the movement of resources and the exchange of commodities is the result of decentralized decisions. Finally, environmental abundance is regulated by environmental policy in each country, for instance by a standard-price approach.

In the context of such an explication model, an equalization of emission taxes can be easily established along the lines of the factor price equalization theorem [Samuelson, (1953)], if the production, emission and abatement technologies can be compressed into eq. (17), if eq. (17) is assumed as linear-homogeneous and if each sector in both countries is characterized by identical production functions. Then emission taxes (factor prices) are equalized by trade irrespective of resource endowments, resource immobility and demand conditions [assuming the relative factor endowment falls into the cone of diversification; Pethig (1976)]. Environmental scarcity can be interpreted as an additional factor of production in the Heckscher–Ohlin context. Note that identical shadow prices for pollutants in both countries do not imply identical environmental qualities in both countries.

6.5. Factor mobility and migration of residents

Factor mobility between two areas (nations, regions) also works towards the equalization of environmental shadow prices. Assume that commodities are immobile and that traditional resources (labor, capital) are totally mobile between two areas and infinitely divisible while the environment is an immobile factor of production. Then the emission tax will adjust itself in the long run between the areas. The mobility of labor and capital will be sufficient to equalize the price of the immobile factor "environmental abundance" assuming identical and linear-homogeneous production functions for each sector in the two regions.

This tendency of equalization of the factor price of the immobile factor of production through the mobility of other factors of production or the exchange of commodities, however, does not work, when the mobility of labor also depends on regional environmental quality and when the evaluation of environmental quality is determined by individual preferences (majority voting). Individuals will migrate to the area with a better environmental quality and increase the demand for environmental goods there, raising the emission tax. In the vacated area, however, the demand for environmental quality will decrease and the emission tax has to fall there. Due to the fact that labor mobility depends on the wage rate and on regional environmental quality, the labor market may be segmented. The polluted area may have a higher wage rate and a lower emission tax; the emission tax may not be identical between regions. Apparently, this argument is more relevant in an interregional context, for instance in a Tiebout scenario. We cannot exclude the case that a spatial specialization of environmental use and a polarization of land-use will result [Myrdal (1957)].

6.6. Pollute thy neighbor via trade

Environmental policy in one country can affect environmental quality in another country even if the home country's pollution is confined to national environmental media. This comes about by specialization and trade. Assume that the home country introduces an emission tax and thereby impairs its comparative price advantage for the pollution-intensive commodity. Its exports will fall, and the production of the pollution-intensive commodity will be reduced. A reallocation of resources takes place. However, resource use is increased in the abatement process while resources are withdrawn from the pollution-intensive sector. Production in the environmentally favorable sector is expanded. In sum, the environmental quality of the home country has to increase.

Since the comparative price advantage of the home country deteriorates for the pollution-intensive commodity, the comparative price advantage of the foreign country rises. It is profitable for the foreign country to increase the production of this commodity. In the foreign country, a reallocation of its resources occurs in favor of the pollution-intensive commodity so that emissions increase and environmental quality abroad worsens. In short, the environmental policy of the home country negatively affects the environmental quality in the foreign country through specialization and by trade.

The "pollute thy neighbor via trade" thesis does not mean that the home country can impose detrimental environmental conditions on the foreign country. First, environmental policy involves costs for the concerned nations, namely, in terms of the resources used as well as in terms of the target losses in other policy areas. A country is only willing to tolerate these costs of a better environmental quality to a certain extent. Second, the costs of a better environment (costs of pollution abatement) increase progressively, thereby placing severe limitations on environmental policy. Third, the environmentally rich country can protect itself by introducing environmental policy measures. By imposing such measures as emission charges on polluting products, the environmentally rich country will reduce the attractiveness of these goods for international trade and thereby avoid specialization in the production of environmental-intensive products.

6.7. Trade, welfare and environmental quality

The primary motivation for engaging in foreign trade is the prospect of gains, that is, that countries expand their consumption opportunities through trade. If a country exports the pollution-intensive commodity, it reduces its environmental quality. So, in this case, the traditionally defined gains from trade have to be compared with the deterioration of environmental quality. Trade pays for an economy only when net welfare increases, that is, when the traditional gains from trade overcompensate the deterioration of environmental quality. From this consideration it also follows that in an open economy, the reduction of the gains from trade can be considered as target losses of environmental policy.

6.8. Environmental regulation and trade barriers

Trade distortions arise if product norms are used as a policy instrument. For example, there are product norms with regard to the tolerable content of chemicals (DDT) or emission norms for technical processes (capital goods). In this case, the export opportunities of a nation are impaired. This barrier to trade through product standards is aggravated if one discriminates between product standards for domestic and foreign goods. GATT regulations do not permit a discrimination and product standards should be applied on import goods as well as on import substitutes. In reality, however, product standards can be formulated in such a way as to permit national industries to meet the standards more easily than foreign competitors.

7. Global environmental systems

7.1. Characteristics of the problem

The problem of international and transfrontier pollution is similar to that of interregional spillover (Section 5.2) with the additional complication that no international authority exists empowered to implement environmental protection measures and that national sovereignty is involved. Problems must be solved by international bargaining processes which embrace the divergent interests of two or more states. Moreover, global environmental systems tend to be characterized to a larger extent by a common good aspect [eq. (2)] than by one- or multi-directional diffusion [eq. (1)].

7.2. Policy instruments

7.2.1. Bargaining

The bargaining process for pollution rights will not only be influenced by the different positions with respect to down- or upwind location; other phenomena such as the relative political strength, public opinion, per capita income of the countries involved and type of economic system will affect the outcome of the bargaining solution.

7.2.2. Nationalization

The creation of national property rights such as nationalizing a 200-mile zone of the ocean along coastlines presupposes – as the regional case – that spillover problems are not too serious.

7.2.3. Unilateral action

Unilateral action is individually rational for each nation if it can control an important aspect of the environmental quality. For instance, a nation may be able to improve the environmental quality at its seashore or it may be able to improve national air quality even if it looses comparative advantage.

7.2.4. Imposing international constraints

International constraints would represent rules under which national environmental policies could operate. Such constraints imply an agreement on the level of interregional diffusion (water quality of rivers; air quality) or on the environmental quality of a common environmental system. Since international constraints restrict national sovereignty, it will be extremely difficult to institutionalize such constraints. For instance, the idea of international cost sharing presupposes some agreement on the environmental quality target and on the criteria for cost sharing. Or, some nations have to agree on environmental quality of a common environmental system.

7.2.5. International agency

It is conceivable that nations could surrender a part of their sovereign rights concerning the environment to an international environmental agency which could tax emissions and thereby control transfrontier environmental quality.

If countries could agree on an appropriate institutional setting or on an international tax rate, national environmental agencies could set a supplementary tax on emissions within its own borders. This proposal represents an international application of the "polluter pays" principle. However, it is politically unrealistic since nations are not willing to relinquish their sovereignty over this area. Moreover, international organizations tend to be rather inefficient.

8. Summary comments

Environmental problems have a spatial dimension since environmental media are defined over space. Environmental quality at one point in space is influenced by the spatial transfer of pollutants as well as the interdependence of spatial points via economic mechanisms. The problem of environmental allocation in space consists in analyzing environmental interactions occurring in space; in determining spatial patterns of environmental use; in specifying the impact of economic activities on environmental allocation in space; and in discussing the influence of alternative institutional settings on the spatial dimensions of the environment.

From a national point of view, optimal allocation requires that interregional spillovers are accounted for in the prices of the economy. A region has to bear the environmental costs that it causes in another area through interregional spillovers. Not internalizing the impact of interregional diffusion implies a distortion in spatial allocation and an unwarranted location advantage for the polluting area relative to the region being polluted. Moreover, prices have to reflect differences in environmental endowment. The region richly endowed with environmental goods (assimilative capacity) will have a lower price for emissions. In the long run, both the interregional mobility of resources and commodities will work towards an equalization of prices for emissions. The equalization of prices for emissions, however, can only be established under specific conditions such as the linear-homogeneity of overall sectorial production functions in which the production and abatement activities are captured.

In a national allocation context a division of labor in space will tend to imply a difference in regional environmental qualities even if the emission price is identical between regions. Therefore, constraints protecting regional interests may be called for.

If environmental policy is vested into autonomous regional authorities, the regional authorities have an incentive not to take into account the interregional diffusion of pollutants. The price of environmental use is set too low in the pollution-exporting region; and the polluting region has a location advantage at the expense of other regions. Bargaining between autonomous regions may result in a Pareto-optimal allocation in a theoretical framework; but in practice, bargaining between autonomous regions (countries) does not seem to bring about solutions. Spillover problems may be minimized by appropriately delineating environmental regions and defining regionalized property rights for environmental use (federalism, fiscal equivalence, Tiebout approach, liability rules). These approaches, however, work best when spillovers are not dominant. Alternatively, national restraints have to be imposed in a context of autonomous regions (interregional diffusion norms). Thus, autonomous regional authorities require nationally imposed restraints whereas national authorities may have to be restricted in order to protect regional interests. The solution to these allocation problems thus depends on the institutional consensus (central versus federal state).

When the problem of spatial environmental allocation is extended to sovereign countries, the solution to the spillover issue becomes even more complex. Besides international diffusion, the international division of labor gives rise to specific questions: Environmental policy of one country will negatively affect its comparative advantage, its exports and the terms of trade representing additional categories of opportunity costs of environmental policy. These costs have to be weighted against the benefits from an improved environmental quality. Environmental abundance is one additional factor explaining international specialization;

comparative environmental advantage has to rule in the long run similarly as advantages with respect to labor, capital and land.

Appendix

The maximization problem consists of maximizing the sum of regional welfare subjects to a set of constraints:

$$
L = \sum_j W^j\left(C_1^j, C_2^j, U^j\right) - \sum_i \lambda_i\left[C_i^1 + C_i^2 - Q_i^1 - Q_i^2\right]
$$

$$
- \sum_j \sum_i \lambda_{S_i^p}^j\left[H_i^j(Q)_i^j\right) - S_i^p\right] - \sum_j \sum_i \lambda_{Q_i}^j\left[Q_i^j - F_i^j(R_i^j)\right]
$$

$$
- \sum_j \sum_i \lambda_{S_i^j}\left[S_i^j - F_i^j(R_i^j)\right] - \lambda_S^1\left(\sum_i S_i^{p1} - \sum_i S_i^{r1} + S^{21} - S^1\right)
$$

$$
- \lambda_S^2\left(\sum_i S_i^{p2} - \sum_i S_i^{r2} - S^{21} - S^2\right) - \sum_j U^j\left[U^j - G^j(S^j)\right]
$$

$$
- \lambda_R\left(\sum_j \sum_i R_i^j + \sum_j \sum_i R^{rj} - \overline{R}\right) - \lambda^{21}\left[\alpha^{21}\left(\sum_i S_i^{p2} - \sum_i S_i^{r2}\right) - S^{21}\right].
$$

$$(A.3.1)$$

The Kuhn–Tucker conditions are:

$$
\frac{\partial L}{\partial C_i^j} = W_{C_i}^{j\prime} - \lambda_i \le 0, \qquad\qquad C_i^j \frac{\partial L}{\partial C_i^j} = 0, \qquad\qquad (A.3.1a)
$$

$$
\frac{\partial L}{\partial Q_i^j} = \lambda_i - \lambda_{S_i^p}^j H_i^{j\prime} - \lambda_{Q_i}^j \le 0, \qquad\qquad Q_i^j \frac{\partial L}{\partial Q_i^j} = 0, \qquad\qquad (A.3.1b)
$$

$$
\frac{\partial L}{\partial U^j} = W_U^{j\prime} - \lambda_U^j \le 0, \qquad\qquad U^j \frac{\partial L}{\partial U^j} = 0, \qquad\qquad (A.3.1c)
$$

$$
\frac{\partial L}{\partial R_i^j} = \lambda_{Q_i}^j F_i^{j\prime} - \lambda_R R \le 0, \qquad\qquad R_i^j \frac{\partial L}{\partial R_i^j} = 0, \qquad\qquad (A.3.1d)
$$

$$
\frac{\partial L}{\partial R_i^{rj}} = \lambda_{S_i^r}^j F_i^{rj\prime} - \lambda_R \le 0, \qquad\qquad R_i^{rj} \frac{\partial L}{\partial R_i^{rj}} = 0, \qquad\qquad (A.3.1e)
$$

$$
\frac{\partial L}{\partial S_i^{p1}} = \lambda_{S_i^p}^1 - \lambda_S^1 \le 0, \qquad\qquad S_i^{p1} \frac{\partial L}{\partial S_i^{p1}} = 0, \qquad\qquad (A.3.1f)
$$

$$\frac{\partial L}{\partial S_i^{p2}} = \lambda_{S_i^p}^2 - \lambda_S^2 - \alpha^{21}\lambda^{21} \leq 0, \qquad S_i^{p2}\frac{\partial L}{\partial S_i^{p2}} = 0, \qquad \text{(A.3.1g)}$$

$$\frac{\partial L}{\partial S_i^{r1}} = -\lambda_{S_i'}^1 + \lambda_S^1 \leq 0, \qquad S_i^{r1}\frac{\partial L}{\partial S_i^{r1}} = 0, \qquad \text{(A.3.1h)}$$

$$\frac{\partial L}{\partial S_i^{r2}} = -\lambda_{S_i'}^2 + S^2 + \alpha^{21}\lambda^{21} \leq 0, \qquad S_i^{r2}\frac{\partial L}{\partial S_i^{r2}} = 0, \qquad \text{(A.3.1i)}$$

$$\frac{\partial L}{\partial S^j} = \lambda_S^j + \lambda_U^j G^j \leq 0, \qquad S^j\frac{\partial L}{\partial S^j} = 0, \qquad \text{(A.3.1j)}$$

$$\frac{\partial L}{\partial S^{21}} = -\lambda_S^1 + \lambda_S^2 + \lambda^{21} \leq 0, \qquad S^{21}\frac{\partial L}{\partial S^{21}} = 0, \qquad \text{(A.3.1k)}$$

$$\frac{\partial L}{\partial \lambda} \geq 0, \qquad \lambda\frac{\partial L}{\partial \lambda} = 0. \qquad \text{(A.3.1l)}$$

An interior solution to the problem is assumed so that the relevant variables are positive.

References

Ayres, Robert U. (1972) "A Materials-Process-Product Model," in: Allen V. Kneese and Blair T. Bower (eds.), *Environmental Quality Analysis* (Johns Hopkins University Press, Baltimore, Md.) pp. 35–68.

Bath, C. Richard (1978) "Alternative Cooperative Arrangements for Managing Transboundary Air Resources Along the Borders", *Natural Resources Journal* 18, 181–198.

Baumol, William J. and Wallace E. Oates (1971) "The Use of Standards and Prices for the Protection of the Environment", *Swedish Journal of Economics* 73, 42–54.

Boeventer, Edwin von (1962) *Theorie des raeumlichen Gleichgewichts* (J.C.B. Mohr (Paul Siebeck), Tuebingen).

Boudeville, Jacques Raoul (1966) *Problems of Regional Economic Planning* (Edinburgh University Press).

Brookshire, David S. (1978) "A Macroeconomic Analysis of Regional Environmental Modeling and Planning", *Journal of Environmental Economics and Management* 5, 268–282.

Coase, Ronald H. (1960) "The Problem of Social Cost", *Journal of Law and Economics*, 3, 1–44.

Cumberland, John H. and Robert J. Korbach (1973) "A Regional Interindustry Environmental Model", Papers of the Regional Science Association, 30, 61–75.

Dobbins, Richard A. (1979) *Atmospheric Motion and Air Pollution* (John Wiley & Sons, New York).

Dudenhoeffer, Ferdinand (1983) *Mehrheitswahl-Entscheidungen uber Umweltnutzungen. Eine Untersuchung von Gleichgewichtszustaenden in einem mikroaekonomischen Markt- und Abstimmungsmodell* (Peter Lang, Frankfurt, Main und Bern).

Dudenhoeffer, Ferdinand und Helga Gebauer (1982) "Die Allokation oeffentlicher Gueter bei Konsumentenmobilitat. Eine Anmerkung zum Tiebout-Theorem", in: Horst Siebert (ed.), *Umweltallokation im Raum* (Peter Lang, Frankfurt/Main und Bern) pp. 93–144.

Forsund, Finn R. (1972) "Allocation in Space and Environmental Pollution", *Swedish Journal of Economics*, 74, 19–34.

Frey, Rene L. (1979) "Interregional Welfare Comparisons and Environmental Policy", in: Horst Siebert, Ingo Walter and Klaus Zimmermann (eds.), *Regional Environmental Policy: The Economic Issues* (New York University Press) pp. 97–108.

Friedrich, Peter and Dimitrios Tsimopoulos (1983) Volkswirtschaftliche Vor- und Nachteile der Fernwaermeauskopplung aus dem Grobkraftwerk Franken II, Teil 1: Die Umwelteffekte, Diskussionspapier Nr. 7, Universitaet Bamberg.

Gebauer, Helga (1982) Zur Intertemporalen regionalen Umweltallokation, in: Horst Siebert (ed.), *Umweltallokation im Raum* (Peter Lang, Frankfurt/Main and Bern) pp. 191–228.

Georgescu-Roegen, Nicholas (1971) *The Entropy Law and the Economic Process* (Harvard University Press, Cambridge).

Georgii, Hans W. (1981) "Globale Aspekte der Luftverunreinigung", in: Gerhard von Olschowy (ed.), *Oekologische Grundlagen des Natur- und Umweltschutzes* (Parey, Hamburg and Berlin) pp. 216–224.

Golomb, Dan and James Gruhl (1981) *Long Range Transport of Air Pollutants from Energy Development: Assessment of the Modeling Studies*, Energy Laboratory Working Paper No. MIT-EL81-063WP.

Golomb, Dan and James Gruhl (1983) *Atmospheric Environment*, 17, 645.

Gronych, Ralf (1980) *Allokationseffekte und Aussenhandelswirkungen der Umweltpolitik* (J.C.B. Mohr (Paul Siebeck), Tuebingen).

Heckscher, Eli (1919) "The Effect of Foreign Trade on the Distribution of Income", *Ekonomisk Tidskrift*, 21, 1–32.

Isard, Walter (1956) *Location and Space-Economy* (MIT Press, Cambridge).

Isard, Walter (1972) *Ecological-Economic Analysis for Regional Development* (The Free Press, New York).

Kittrell, F.W. (1969) *A Practical Guide to Water Quality Studies of Streams*, (U.S. Department of the Interior, Federal Water Pollution Control Administration, Washington, D.C.).

Klevorick, Alvin K. and Gerald H. Kramer (1973) "Social Choice on Pollution Management: The Genossenschaften", *Journal of Public Economics*, 2, 101–146.

Kneese, Allen V. (1964) *The Economics of Regional Water Quality Management* (Johns Hopkins University Press, Baltimore).

Kneese, Allen V. and Blair T. Bower (1968) *Managing Water Quality: Economics, Technology and Institutions* (Johns Hopkins University Press, Baltimore).

Kneese, Allen V., Robert U. Ayres and Ralph C. d'Arge (1970) *Economics and the Environment: A Materials Balance Approach* (Johns Hopkins University Press, Baltimore).

Leitmann, George (1974) *Cooperative and Non-Cooperative Many Players Differential Games* (Springer, Wien, New York).

Leontief, Wassily (1970) "Environmental Repercussions and the Economic Structure: An Input-Output Approach", *The Review of Economics and Statistics*, 52, 262–271.

Losch, August (1944) Die Raeumliche Ordnung der Wirtschaft, 2. Aufl. (Gustav Fischer, Jena). English Edition: (1954) *The Economics of Location* (Yale University Press, New Haven).

Matthess, Georg and John C. Harvey (1982) *The Properties of Groundwater* (John Wiley & Sons, New York).

Myrdal, Gunnar (1957) *Rich Lands and Poor* (Harper and Row, New York).

Nash, John F. (1950) "The Bargaining Problem", *Econometrica*, 18, 155–162.

Nijkamp, Peter (1978) "Competition Among Regions and Environmental Quality", in: Walter Buhr und Peter Friedrich (eds.), *Konkurrenz zwischen kleinen Regionen* (Nomos Verlagsgesellschaft, Baden-Baden) pp. 153–171.

OECD (1973) *The Mutual Compensation Principle: An Economic Instrument for Solving Certain Transfrontier Pollution Problems*, (OECD-Document, Paris).

Ohlin, Bertil (1929) *Interregional and International Trade* (Harvard University Press, Cambridge).

Okubo, Akira (1980) *Diffusion and Ecological Problems: Mathematical Models* (Springer, Berlin, Heidelberg, New York).

Olson, Jr., Mancur (1969) "The Principle of 'Fiscal Equivalence': The Division of Responsibilities Among Different Levels of Government", *American Economic Review*, Papers and Proceedings, 59, 479–487.

Olson, Jr., Mancur (1979) "On Regional Pollution and Fiscal Equivalence", in: Horst Siebert, Ingo Walter and Klaus Zimmermann (eds.), *Regional Environmental Policy: The Economic Issues* (New York University Press), pp. 181–186.

Peltzmann, Sam and T. Nicolaus Tideman (1972) "Local Versus National Pollution Control: Note", *American Economic Review*, 62, 959–963.

Pethig, Ruediger (1975) "Umweltverschmutzung, Wohlfahrt und Umweltpolitik in einem Zwei-Sektoren-Gleichgewichtsmodell", *Zeitschrift fur Nationaloekonomie* 35, 99–124.

Pethig, Ruediger (1976) "Pollution, Welfare and Environmental Policy in the Theory of Comparative Advantage", *Journal of Environmental Economics and Management*, 2, 160–169.

Pethig, Ruediger (1982) "Reciprocal Transfrontier Pollution", in: Horst Siebert (ed.), *Global Environmental Resources* (Peter Lang, Frankfurt/Main and Bern), pp. 57–92.

Potier, Michel (1979) "Environmental Aspects of Industrial Policy in a Regional Setting", in: Horst Siebert, Ingo Walter and Klaus Zimmermann (eds.), *Regional Environmental Policy: The Economic Issues* (New York University Press) pp. 221–240.

Ricardo, David (1817) *On the Principles of Political Economy and Taxation* (Olms, Hildesheim, New York (1977); reproduction of the issue, London, 1817).

Robinson, E. and R.C. Robbins (1968) *Sources, Abundance, and Fate of Gaseous Atmospheric Pollutants*. (Final Report, Standard Research Institute, SPI-Project PR6755, Menlo Park).

Rodhe, H. (1978) "Budgets and Turnover Times of Atmospheric Sulfur Compounds", *Atmosphere Environment*, 12, 671–680.

Rothenberg, Jerome (1969) "The Economics of Congestion and Pollution: An Integrated View", *American Economic Review*, 60, 114–121.

Russell, Clifford S. and Walter O. Spofford, Jr. (1972) "A Quantitative Framework for Residuals Management Decisions", in: Allen V. Kneese and Blair T. Bower (eds.), *Environmental Quality Analysis: Theory and Method in the Social Sciences* (Johns Hopkins University Press, Baltimore).

Samuelson, Paul A. (1953) "Prices of Factors and Goods in General Equilibrium", *Review of Economic Studies*, 21, 1–20.

Siebert, Horst (1974a) "Comparative Advantage and Environmental Policy: A Note", *Zeitschrift fur Nationolokonomie*, 34, 397–402.

Siebert, Horst (1974b) "Environmental Protection and International Specialization", *Weltwirtschaftliches Archiv*, 110, 494–508.

Siebert, Horst (1975) "Regional Aspects of Environmental Allocationk", *Zeitschrift fuer die Gesamte Staatswissenschaft*, 131, 496–513.

Siebert, Horst (1977) "Environmental Quality and the Gains From Trade", *Kyklos*, 30, 657–673.

Siebert, Horst (1978) "Environmental Policy, Allocation of Resources, Sector Structure and Comparative Price Advantage", *Zeischrift fuer Wirtschafts und Sozialwissenschaften*, 17, 281–293.

Siebert, Horst (1979) "Environmental Policy in the Two-Country-Case", *Zeitschrift fuer Nationaloekonomie*, 39, 259–274.

Siebert, Horst (1981) *Economics of the Environment* (D.C. Health Company, Lexington).

Siebert, Horst (1982a) Emissionslizenzen, Monopson und die raeumliche Abschottung von Arbeitsmaerkten. Eine Anmerkung, Zeitschrift fuer Wirtschafts und Sozialwissenschaften, 102, 279–287.

Siebert, Horst (1982b) "The Partitioning of Constraints", *Zeitschrift fuer die Gesamte Staatswissenschaft*, 138, 109–117.

Siebert, Horst (ed.) (1982) Umweltallokation im Raum, Schriftenreihe "Staatliche Allokationspolitik im marktwirtschaftlichen System", Bd. 1 (Peter Lang, Frankfurt/Main and Bern).

Siebert, Horst, Juergen Eichberger, Ralf Gronych and Ruediger Pethig (1980) *Trade and Environment – A Theoretical Enquiry* (Elsevier, Amsterdam).

Siebert, Horst, Ingo Walter and Klaus Zimmermann (eds.) (1979) *Regional Environmental Policy: The Economic Issues* (New York University Press).

Soderlund, R. and B. Svenson (1976) "The Global Nitrogen Cycle", Ecological Bulletin 22 (Swedish National Research Council, Stockholm).

Stein, Jerome L. (1971) "The 1971 Report of the President's Council of Economic Advisors: Micro-Economic Aspects of Public Policy", *American Economic Review*, 61, 531–537.

Stern, A.C. (1976) Air Pollution, Vol. 1, *Air Pollutants, Their Transformation and Transport* (Academic Press, New York and London).

Stiglitz, Joseph E. (1977) "The Theory of Local Public Goods", in: Martin S. Feldstein and Robert P. Inman (eds.), *The Economics of Public Services* (The MacMillan Press Ltd., London) pp. 274–333.

Streeter, H.W. and E.B. Phelps (1925) "A Study of the Pollution and Natural Purification of the Ohio River", Public Health Bulletin No. 146 (U.S. Public Health Service, Washington, D.C.).

Thuenen, Johann Heinrich von (1826) Der isolirte Staat in Beziehung auf Landwirtschaft und Nationaloekonomie, 1. Theil, Hamburg, (1826); 2. Theil, 1. Abteilung: Rostock (1850), 2. Theil, 2. Abteilung und 3. Theil: Rostock (1863).

Tiebout, Charles Mills (1956) "A Pure Theory of Local Public Goods", *Journal of Political Economy*, 64, 416–424.

Tietenberg, Thomas H. (1978) "Spatially Differentiated Air Pollutant Emission Charges: An Economic and Legal Analysis", *Land Economics* 54, 265–277.

Tietenberg, Thomas H. (1979) "On the Efficient Spatila Allocation of Air Pollution Control Responsibility", in: Horst Siebert, Ingo Walter and Klaus Zimmermann (eds.), *Regional Environmental Policy: The Economic Issues* (New York University Press) pp. 79–93.

Tietenberg, Thomas H. (1980) "Transferable Discharge Permits and the Control of Air Pollution: A Survey and Synthesis", *Zeitschrift fuer Umweltpolitik*, 3, 477–508.

Turner, D. Bruce (1979) "Atmospheric Dispersion Modeling. A Critical Review", *Journal of the Air Pollution Control Association*, 29, 502–519.

Van Zele, Roger L. (1978) "An International (Interjurisdictional) Analytical Framework for Environmental Management", (Regional Science Dissertation & Monograph Series No. 7, New York).

Walter, Ingo (1975) *International Economics of Pollution* (MacMillan, London).

Wegehenkel, Lothar (1980) *Coarse-Theorem und Marketsystem* (J.C.B. Mohr (Paul Siebeck), Tuebingen).

Wetstone, Gregory and Armin Rosencranz (1982) Final Report: Acid Rain in Europe and North America: National Responses to an International Problem. A Study for the German Marshall Fund of the United States (Environmental Law Institute, Washington, D.C.).

Chapter 4

ECONOMICS OF NATURE PRESERVATION

ANTHONY C. FISHER

University of California, Berkeley

and

JOHN V. KRUTILLA

Resources for the Future, Washington

1. Introduction

Another broad area of concern in environmental and natural resource economics is the preservation of nature. This issue was raised in Chapter 2 of this Handbook as being one end of the spectrum of interactions between man and the rest of the living world. In this chapter we develop some of the economic theory relevant to decisions about nature preservation. The theory is motivated by a discussion of current issues: the disposition of wilderness lands and the protection of endangered species. One may question the importance of wilderness and endangered species as "economic resources". We indicate how and why they are important.

Two key concepts emerge from the discussion: uncertainty and irreversibility. Uncertainty is pervasive economic life, of course. But more than the usual degree of uncertainty surrounds the potential future benefits from conserving ecosystems. Most endangered species, for example, remain as yet undiscovered in tropical moist forests that are at the same time undergoing rapid and (from the point of view of the indigenous species) destructive development. In these circumstances it is hard to predict what values – a cure for (some form of) cancer, a liquid hydrocarbon, a perennial corn, to name just three of the more interesting among current possibilities – will ultimately emerge if the species that may produce them are not lost.

Irreversibility is clearly central to thinking about endangered species or ecosystems because extinction or loss of wildlands is indeed irreversible. Again, other things are irreversible. But we shall argue that distinctions can be made among decisions and actions on the basis of whether their *consequences* are difficult or impossible to ameliorate. We shall further argue that wholesale loss of species or

Handbook of Natural Resource and Energy Economics, vol. I, edited by A.V. Kneese and J.L. Sweeney
© *Elsevier Science Publishers B.V., 1985*

wilderness ecosystems fall in the category of consequences that are impossible to reverse and difficult to ameliorate.

In this setting we develop a model of decision-making under uncertainty and irreversibility. The model is used to prove (given some further assumptions detailed in the text) that the optimal use of a natural environment is more likely to be continued preservation where the passage of time brings information about potential future benefits of preservation (and alternative uses) than where it does not. A related result is that the fraction of the area optimally preserved (where partitioning is possible) is larger.

The concept of "option value" which has played a large role in the literature on wilderness preservation – and elsewhere, for that matter – is clarified by our model. Here we define option value as the gain from being able to learn about future benefits that would be precluded by development (of an area) if one does not develop in the current period; in other words, the gain from retaining the option to preserve or develop in the future. Under the assumptions of our model, option value is nonnegative. A related concept, the value of information, is shown to differ in general from option value – contrary to recent claims in the literature. Option value is, in our analysis, a *conditional* value of information and is (not strictly) greater than the unconditional value of information.

The plan of the chapter is as follows. In Section 2 current conservation issues – species protection and wilderness use – are reviewed. Section 3 is a discussion of the nature and significance of irreversibility in economic processes. Section 4 is the development of our formal model of decision-making under uncertainty and irreversibility. Section 5 uses the model to clarify the discussion of option value and the value of information. Section 6 offers some thoughts on other applications of the concepts and models presented here. Although developed for terrestrial ecosystems, they may have relevance to hydrospheric and atmospheric environments as well. In Section 7 we briefly review our findings.

2. Contemporary conservation issues

2.1. Wilderness and other unmodified natural areas

Some parts of the world, principally in temperate zones, have long been settled by societies that have become intensively industrialized and have populations that are large in relation to their land areas. In consequence of this, little land remains in a condition unmodified by man. In the New World, Australia, perhaps elsewhere in the subarctic and arctic regions, and in parts of the tropics, however, there still remains a significant amount of largely uninhabited or sparsely inhabited land that retains virtually all of the attributes that characterized it in pre-Columbian times. Some of this land is of remarkable scenic quality, other is notable less for scenic grandeur than for having preserved a complex ecosystem that retains a complete set of naturally evolved species of flora and fauna; and still other tracts represent repositories of remnant populations of flora or fauna that have been extirpated where their natural habitats have been destroyed to accomodate the requirements of industrial societies.

A considerable amount of the North American continent has remained in a largely undeveloped state. This has occurred in some cases because of the inaccessibility of high-elevation mountainous terrain, in others because of the excessive heat and aridity characterizing deserts which contain some of the most remarkable canyon lands, and in still others because of the general inhospitability or arctic and subarctic regions. These areas have provided in relatively recent times the wherewithal to establish the systems of national parks, national forests, national wildlife refuges and ranges, and public domain lands used for grazing domestic livestock as well as ungulate wildlife populations. These public lands, in turn, provide for functional systems established by law that ensure the preservation of wild and scenic rivers in an unmodified state as well as the national wilderness system and natural scientific research areas. The administration of wild lands in Canada is somewhat different at least partly because jurisdiction over resources resides with the provincial governments rather than the federal government of Canada.

In many countries which have established national wildlife sanctuaries and designated wilderness areas, the protection afforded these public lands varies considerably. In the United States, which appears to have pioneered the concept of national parks and protected wilderness areas, national parks are off limits to all extractive industries.[1] But in other countries, for example Australia and Canada, this protection often does not extend to exclusive use for recreation and scientific purposes. Extraction of minerals is commonly permitted, and building of hydroelectric facilities is a very common objective that contests the exclusive use of the area for activities that do not disturb the unmodified environment. Murchison's Falls, in Uganda, at the outlet to Lake Nyanza (Victoria) and the Lower Gordon in the Southwest Tasmanian Wilderness are cases in point.

In the United States, the wild rivers and wilderness systems intend to afford the most secure protection against man-made modifications. Here, generally speaking, not even the construction of roads or other facilities is permitted. Enjoyment of the natural environment, if it involves travel, must be by foot, horseback, or motorless craft (canoe, raft, etc.). This is at least the intent of the legislation

---

[1] In a small number of national parks where extractive activities may have occurred prior to the establishment of the park, such activities may be permitted under a grandfather clause, but typically they are prohibited.

providing for the establishment of such wilderness and wild rivers in the United States.

Although the unroaded and unoccupied areas of the United States (including Alaska) are very large in absolute terms, the amount of this land that has been set aside under the wilderness legislation amounts to approximately 33 million hectares as of the beginning of 1982 or about 3.5 percent of the total area of the United States. Of this amount, over 70 percent (23 million hectares) is the result of the Alaska National Interest Lands Conservation Act of 1979. This action completes, for all intents and purposes, national park and wilderness set-asides in Alaska. In the coterminous United States, not all of the roadless areas which were to be reviewed for possible inclusion in the wilderness system have been reviewed and acted upon. Some 10 million hectares of unroaded public domain lands under the administration of the Bureau of Land Management remain to be considered, and not all of the 25 million hectares of unroaded national forestlands that are recommended for inclusion into the wilderness system, or deferred pending further study, have received legislative attention. Accordingly, a large part of the unroaded and uninhabited public lands are not included in the current statutory wilderness system. In this respect, the wild lands remaining outside the system are in much the same status as the Australian or Canadian and other wild lands around the world; they have remained undeveloped for reasons of inaccessibility or inhospitability but are subject to conversion similar to that experienced by all present developed land.

The issue of development or preservation of wild lands is a lively one even in connection with the statutory National Wilderness System in the United States. This arises, in spite of the intent to protect these areas from development, because of a compromise that was needed to accomodate interests inimical to the wilderness legislation in order to secure its passage. To that end, the Wilderness Act of 1964 left open the possibility of mineral exploration for two decades following passage of the Act. Because this exemption will expire at the end of 1983, very intense interest has developed on the part of the extractive industries to enter the existing statutory wilderness areas for exploration. Removal of the time limit for exploration in wilderness areas has also been advanced vigorously. Serious attention has been given additionally to defeat the legislation required to establish each of the wilderness areas recommended by the relevant agencies from the roadless areas reviewed for this purpose. In this action, the extractive industries have been joined by the timber industry since wilderness areas, as well as national parks, are off limits to the resource commodity industries.

Although the bulk of the statutory wilderness areas, as well as the undeveloped wild land recommended for wilderness designation, do not occupy significant areas of commercial timberland or promising locations for fuel and nonfuel minerals, there are two regions where the opportunity returns that would be forgone by establishing protected wilderness areas could be non-negligible. In the Pacific Northwest, also referred to as the Douglas Fir Region, the value of standing old-growth timber is significant. The old-growth stands, however, host old-growth-habitat-dependent species which are already endangered and thus the allocation of such land to timber production must take into account not only the recreational benefits forgone but also the potential value of the several endangered species. We shall return to the endangered species question presently.

A second area in which significant economic trade-offs are likely to arise is in the Overthrust Belt of the Rocky Mountains where, because of advances in drilling technology, it is now possible to tap promising geological formations in its "underthrust" portion, that is, the earth's mantle overlain by the overlapping formation. Here it is possible that not only some gas but also even petroleum in appreciable quantities will be discovered. It needs to be noted, however, that the portion of the existing wilderness system and recommended additions that overlap the Overthrust Belt represent only about 5 percent of the latter. The remainder, along with other prospective oil-bearing public lands, could occupy a prudent level of exploration for a very long time.

Because of the 20-year exemption from the provisions of the Wilderness Act that exclude entry into statutory wilderness[2] for extractive purposes and the ongoing process of fleshing out the statutory wilderness system, the issue of wilderness set-asides has been receiving a great deal of attention. This has occurred not only in public debate but also in legislative strategems that intend to trade off some (limited) additions to the National Wilderness System for legislation releasing other lands from the prospect of protected status. While the wilderness preservation issue has taken front stage, a similar controversy has developed over the prospect of landscape degradation that would spill over into the national parks. Indeed, under the policies of the Secretary of the Interior in the Reagan Administration, proposals are being considered to exchange national parklands with mineral potential for lands owned by the State of Alaska to permit the state to exploit these deposits.[3] But quite apart from the degradation from extractive activities on or within the boundaries of national parks, the establishment of mining and milling operations in proximity to park attractions such as Yosemite Valley or Jackson Hole in the Tetons can cast a pall, literally, over some of the most scenic and serene areas on the North American continent. In this respect, then, the potential erosion of national park protection could in time change the protected status of national parks to a status of lesser protection not unlike that encountered in some other nations.

---

[2] We need to distinguish between the statutory wilderness and other unroaded, uninhabited *de facto* wilderness areas. Only the statutory wilderness is protected from entry along with lands within the national park system.

[3] *Wall Street Journal* (1 September 1982), p. 36.

2.2. Endangered species

We have noted that one of the valuable features of wild lands is the variety of natural populations they host. The conventional view of the threat to natural populations – endangered species – is that it is due to overexploitation. In some cases, this is undoubtedly correct. But the major threat to biological resources is habitat modification. This can take several forms: direct conversion, as in drainage of wetlands or development of drylands for agriculture, housing, and transportation; chemical pollution, as from acid rain; and "biological pollution", the introduction of exotic species. Of these, the most important currently appears to be direct conversion for agricultural and other development. Thus, the issue of endangered species protection is intimately related to that of wilderness preservation.

How serious is the threatened loss of species? There is a good deal of uncertainty here, but let us see what kinds of numbers serious students of the problem are using. In the United States, over 500 species are known to have become extinct since 1600 or between one and two per year. By contrast, over a 3000-year span during the Pleistocene period, a period of glaciation when many individual organisms died, less than 100 species were lost in North America [Opler (1971)]. About two-thirds of the recent losses have been in Hawaii due to the clearing of forests for cropland and the introduction of exotic species. This is significant because, despite the considerable interest in the problem in the United States, by far the greater number of species and endangered species are found in the tropical moist forests of the world. Wholesale extinctions are threatened by the clearing of forests for cropland and fuel wood. Some biologists believe that 1000 species are disappearing worldwide each year and that this rate may reach 10 000 annually by the end of the decade [Myers (1981)]. By one estimate, as many as a million of the current 5 to 10 million species could be gone by the year 2000 [Myers (1983)]. Again, these numbers are highly conjectural but extinction on anything like this scale would clearly be catastrophic for reasons we might now briefly consider.[4]

Why should anyone care if unprecedented levels of extinctions over the next few decades send uncounted species the way of the dodo and the dinosaur? Would human welfare really be much affected? The question here is, how does preservation of plant and animal populations *not now harvested* contribute to human welfare? There are at least two distinct ways in which they do this, more if we count "nonmaterial" welfare. Recently, a wild grass related to corn was discovered in a remote, mountainous area in Mexico slated for development. The wild grass is a perennial whereas domesticated corn must be planted annually [Vietmeyer (1979)]. A successful hybrid could result in substantial savings due to elimination of the need to prepare the ground and reseed each year. Seed and

---

[4] For a critical look at Myers' and other estimates, see Lugo and Brown (1982).

preparation costs for corn run about $150 per hectare in the United States which has about 28 million hectares planted to corn. Annual savings could thus be on the order of $4 billion.[5] This number is highly conjectural, but the point is clear. Just one apparently trivial botanical discovery can result in dollar savings that even an economist would agree are not trivial. More generally, this example – and there are many others – illustrates one way a currently unharvested species contributes to human welfare: by conserving genetic information that may in the future be useful in some form of economic activity.

A second major way in which species are useful is as components of living ecosystems that provide the basic physical and biological supports for human life. These include maintenance of the quality of the atmosphere, control and amelioration of climate, regulation of freshwater supplies, generation and mainte- nance of soils, disposal of wastes, and cycling of nutrients.[6] Removal of any one species can cause a system to break down because each has evolved a set of characteristics that make it a unique functional part of the system. To some extent, it may be possible to substitute for ecosystem services. For example, nitrogenous fertilizers can substitute for nitrogen-fixing organisms. But even here there are environmental problems associated with heavy use. Agriculture in the United States, already a heavy user, still derives considerably more nitrogen from natural systems [Delwiche (1970)]. In general, it seems fair to say that some services of ecosystems are not substitutable at all; and for those that are, the direct and indirect (or external) costs of substitution are likely to be high.

Loss of natural populations can also adversely affect human welfare in less tangible ways. People derive pleasure from the contemplation of strikingly varied life forms such as the perhaps 15 000 different species of butterflies. Surely this pleasure would be much reduced if, for example, all butterflies looked alike. And we ought to at least note, though we can do little more here, that some of the concern for endangered species is of a religious or ethical nature which does not easily fit into our utilitarian framework. Ethical aspects of environmental econom- ics are addressed in the following chapter.

Protection of endangered species, and of the wild lands that are their native habitat, is being given increased emphasis by researchers and policy-makers. In the United States, where as we have observed the potential losses are less severe than elsewhere in the world, a variety of statutes dealing with wildlife protection have been passed culminating in the Endangered Species Act of 1973. This Act contains several rather strong provisions, most importantly one that authorizes the Secretary of the Interior to designate areas of "critical habitat", and that

[5] The cost and acreage estimates are from Andrew Schmitz (personal communication). The savings estimate could be too high since yields of a perennial might not reach those of the leading hybrid strains, and a perennial might also require increased use of chemical herbicides and pesticides. On the other hand, elimination of the annual plowing would probably reduce soil erosion.

[6] For a detailed discussion of the role of ecosystems and individual species in these processes, see Ehrlich and Ehrlich (1981).

requires all federal agencies to ensure that actions authorized, funded, or carried out by them do not jeopardize the existence of endangered species or modify their critical habitat. In addition to these key restrictions, the Act directly prohibits the taking or possession of any member of an endangered species and establishes a list of such species down to the level of subspecies and distinct populations of listed species. The restrictions on activities that affect habitat have become quite controversial as they have seemed to some a blank check for regulation. Somewhat suprisingly, in view of the controversy, the Act was reauthorized for three years with a large majority and with only minor changes by the U.S. Congress in 1982. An explanation for this anticlimactic action may be that, as suggested in a recent study, the alleged potential impacts of the Act on economic activity have been largely unrealized [Harrington and Fisher (1982)].

Much more serious are the impacts on economic activity that could result from a thoroughgoing attempt to prevent extinctions in the tropical moist forests that are home to most species and most endangered species. These forests are currently being converted – cleared for farming and fuel wood – at a rate that has been estimated as between 100 000 and 200 000 km², or between 1 and 2 percent of the total annually.[7] Any attempt to prevent this largely subsistence-level activity would clearly be very costly unless alternative sources of food or fuel were found for those affected. On the other hand, a continuation threatens enormous losses.

The challenge is twofold. First, ways must be found to discriminate among areas slated for conversion so that those richest in species can be afforded some measure of protection. Such an approach would recognize that some conversion will take place. The object would be to minimize the related losses.[8] Second, ways must be found to finance the desired protection. The 1975 Convention on International Trade in Endangered Species, which prohibits trade in specimens of endangered species, does not address the more serious and more difficult problem of preserving large areas of habitat for the thousands and maybe millions of plant and animal species that have yet to be listed as endangered because they have yet to be discovered and separately identified. The protection of even limited areas of habitat could be very costly, as we have noted; and the poor countries where they largely occur are not likely to want to bear these costs by themselves, especially when most of the potential benefits go to agriculture, industry, and medicine in the rich countries. Perhaps development aid could be tied to a measure of environmental protection. The World Bank is already beginning to do this, and the practice might be extended to cover habitat preservation. Aid has often been tied in the past, but it has been tied to purchase of the donor country's goods. Recipients might prefer a tie to protection of their own potentially valuable biological resources.

---

[7] The high estimate is due to Myers, the low one to Lugo and Brown. For further details, see Harrington and Fisher (1982).

[8] For a discussion of some promising ways to discriminate, see Harrington and Fisher (1982).

3. The nature and significance of irreversibility in economic processes[9]

We have discussed in an informal way what appear to us to be the major contemporary issues in nature preservation. Why should there be more concern about disturbing scenic natural areas and endangered species' habitats than about issues involving the allocation of other resources of comparable value? The reason is at least partly because wild lands and natural populations are the results of geomorphologic and biologic processes that represent a time frame measured in eons and, thus, cannot be produced by man. If these are destroyed, or otherwise adversely affected, they cannot be replaced or restored. There is thus a basic irreversibility that attends the modification of unique scenic or biological environments. These have been referred to as the "gifts of nature" since they cannot be reproduced in all of their essential features by the efforts of man.

A question will often arise as to whether this irreversibility is different from other examples of which we can conceive. It is sometimes suggested that all decisions, since they are time related, once taken cannot be "untaken" because this implies the ability to return to some prior moment in time. Although the theory of relativity suggests that moving backward through time is a theoretical possibility, it remains of little relevance to the solution of practical economic problems. Apart from this, there are differences among decisions because their effects can be ameliorated in some cases but not in others. There are several aspects to this observation.

The distinction between reversible and irreversible decisions in economic processes has sometimes been illustrated by the differences we can observe between production and investment decisions. A producer with a given plant and equipment, inventory of raw materials, and stock of finished goods faces the expected demand which he intends to meet. His decision on level of output in each product line may not be entirely consistent with the actual demand, and these discrepancies will be observed by changes in finished stock inventories. If errors as to the level of production required to meet the demand are encountered, stocks in inventory will rise (fall) to the extent of the over- (under-)estimate, and he can thus adjust output level by product line to conform to the actual demand. While his original decision may not be rescindable for any given production batch, he can alter the consequences by adjusting production on subsequent production runs. In this sense, we can consider decisions reversible; that is, if the consequences of a decision can be readily altered with negligible losses, it may be likened to a decision that is reversible.

If the decision, however, relates to the capacity of his plant so that he will be required to make decisions on the amount to be invested for its construction, the consequences of a poor decision will have longer duration. Investment in plant and equipment, unlike investment in raw materials inventory, cannot be liqui-

---

[9] This section draws heavily on Krutilla and Fisher (1975, ch. 3).

dated in any short period of time. Indeed, if the capacity originally estimated to be required exceeded the market potential for his output, he would have made an irreversible commitment because capital is neither fungible nor readily liquidated. This, then, characterizes one aspect of irreversibility in economic processes – the inability to recoup investment in excess capacity.

While the overinvestment in plant and capacity represents an irreversibility and a matter of some significance to the individual investor, in most cases it will be a marginal decision considering the economy as a whole and can be dismissed as negligible. This is probably true of the bulk of investment decisions regardless of their significance to the individuals involved.

There are, however, consequences arising out of individual actions that do have consequences of long duration, the effects of which may be anything but trivial for society as a whole. Consider, for example, the allocation of resources that are a result of the accident of geological processes – the geysers in Yellowstone National Park. This remarkable phenomenon has at least two incompatible uses. It can serve as a geothermal source of energy for the production of electricity, or it can be reserved as a unique natural phenomenon providing opportunity for viewing and related recreational activities and as part of the national heritage. A decision to reserve the area for nature appreciation, related recreation, and scientific purposes is a decision that has been made but, of course, is not immutable. It is true that Yellowstone National Park represents a serious legislative commitment to preserve the natural features, but should the existence of society depend on its being rededicated to another use, no *technical* constraint would prevent a reversal of the original decision regarding its use.

If the geothermal resources of Yellowstone National Park were to be allocated to energy production, there would be a set of consequences stemming from this decision that would have more permanent implications. Construction of steam electric power plants, switchyards, transmission towers, etc. would result in a permanent adverse modification of the visual environment in the park. Mining of the superheated water would, in sufficient time, reduce subsurface pressures to eliminate the periodic geyser action and in time remove the reason for which the area was established as a national park. A decision to "restore" the area following depletion of the geothermal resources would not be technically capable of implementation. The adverse consequences of the decision to use the geothermal resources for energy production would be experienced in perpetuity. In the one case, we have the opportunity returns forgone from energy production that are limited by the availability of substitute prime movers for generating electrical energy, but retain the option to reverse the original decision, since legislation can be repealed if necessary. In the alternative case, the decision will involve precluded opportunity returns in perpetuity. There are no technical means of restoring the original character of a natural environment including the periodic eruption of Old Faithful.

Any investment in specialized plant and equipment will, in a sense, represent an irreversible commitment of capital to an undertaking and, from the standpoint of the individual investor, is not a decision to be taken lightly. But in a wider social setting, the irreversibility here it not unlike that which attends the death of any single member of a natural population. There does not appear to be overwhelming concern, except by the individual directly involved, for the demise of a member of a species provided that reproductive capability is retained within the population. The risk of the loss of the last viable mating pair, hence the genetic information essential to survival of the species, is, however, a matter of much greater moment. The investment analogy here might be the loss of all the information necessary to reproduce capital goods for the services of which there may be a future demand. This accounts also for the concern which society exhibits for the losses associated with dying arts and crafts. The extinction of these reduces cultural diversity in the same way as the loss of a species reduces biological diversity. Both represent reductions in the options available to a society and, thus, violate a central postulate of welfare economics: expansion of choice represents a welfare gain, reduction of options a welfare loss.

Not all environmental modifications need to be technically irreversible to provide a basis for more than usually deliberate societal decisions. As Weisbrod (1964) has noted, if restoration to an original state is excessively costly – whether in terms of the resources that must be allocated or the time required – a case exists for explicitly recognizing the option value associated with preservation of the original state.

The problems associated with restoration should receive explicit consideration. There are two important considerations that require attention. One involves the duration over which the adverse consequences of a decision must be suffered. The other involves the absence of authenticity in a reproduction or "restoration".

Consider the conversion of a wilderness ecosystem to meet the demands for the output of extractive industries. If the environmental modification results in the elimination of essential habitat for a given species – for example, the passenger pigeon or the grizzly bear – restoration is impossible or at least incomplete without the fauna dependent on the original plant associations. But, even if the survival of a species is not at issue, restoration is not a simple remedy for redressing the impact of an inappropriate decision that disturbed the original ecological environment. The clear-cutting of a climax species is equivalent to the removal of the results of ecological succession that represents, in many cases, centuries of ecological processes rather than a simple production cycle in the world of more typical choices.[10] The removed climax species would be succeeded

---

[10] This, of course, assumes that the clear-cutting does not involve critical modifications to the abiotic base, such as soil erosion, siltation of spawning beds for salmon and trout fisheries, and other similar processes, that would permanently foreclose the restoration of original ecological relationships.

by various seral species in a procession of changing plant and animal communities, culminating in the original ecological relationships only after a lapse of much time. In tropical climates, this restoration might be accomplished over a period of several generations sufficiently to bear at least a superficial resemblance to the original conditions for the less discriminating observer. But it is unlikely that even here the original faunal communities will be reestablished in their original associations. For example, the woods bison, the eastern race of elk, and the caribou, along with the predator populations that made up in part the eastern United States wilderness ecosystems, are doubtless features of the original wilderness that are permanently lost to society in modern times. In the arid and semiarid West – and in the higher elevations in alpine settings in western mountains of the United States and in much of the Canadian and Alaskan subarctic and arctic life zones – perturbations to the ecological environment would take centuries to restore, if indeed it is even possible.

Environmental modifications that affect the abiotic base are even more difficult to contend with. If the basic geological and soils conditions are adversely affected, replacement by perhaps more primitive, pioneer biotic communities might occur eventually; but restoration of the original biological environment will not be possible in anything like the time span that is meaningful for human societies. Vast open-pit mining operations, transportation facilities in ecologically fragile environments, such as in high mountain elevations or in the arctic, and some water resource developments are among the activities that have a potential for affecting the abiotic base in a manner that is irreversible by ecological processes for all practical purposes within the frame of human time spans.

Consider some of the complications that attend the development of a water storage reservoir in an ecologically fragile area. A faulty decision to construct a dam as revealed by hindsight involves more in its "restoration" than the dismantling of the structure when its existence is realized to incur environmental costs exceeding the returns from development. Supersaturation of the reservoir banks at full pool elevations may result in sloughing and landslides into the reservoir on drawdowns. An example of this condition is reflected in the experience of the Brownlee Reservoir in the upper reaches of the Hells Canyon in western United States. Moreover, to add to the reservoir-filling process, the retention of water in reservoirs impounding streams of high turbidity permits accumulation of sediment loads. To allow operation of the storage facility for its projected life requires allocation of storage space for the impoundment of sediment that settles out as the stream velocity is reduced in the slack-water pools. Dismantling of the structure at some future time will leave the impoundment area with an entirely different abiotic base from that which existed under original conditions. As a consequence, an entirely different ecological environment will be in prospect even if the dam is removed and natural restorative processes are permitted.

In arctic regions, removal of the primitive vegetal cover to expose mineral earth has long-run disruptive effects. The absorption of more solar heat may affect the very unstable soils relationships in areas of permafrost, with thawing, erosion, and gullying that leaves a condition of serious landscape disfigurement permanently and of growing severity with the passage of time.

A question can be raised, however, whether it is not possible to mobilize the knowledge that also accumulates with time, to short-circuit the time element in restoration. This is doubtlessly a possibility in many cases involving rather ordinary landscapes, particularly in the more rapid restoration areas of subhumid and humid climatic zones. But when we consider the extraordinary natural environments that are prized for their scientific research materials or their unusual scenic or natural features as part of the nation's ecological heritage, the problem takes on a different dimension. If the objective is simply to restore some type of outdoor recreational facility in place of the original, it is doubtlessly possible to replicate in some particulars the original features that would satisfy a part of the demands of those seeking outdoor recreation. On the other hand, of the 77 million hectares of national forestlands in the United States, for example, only some 25 million remain in a relatively undisturbed natural state and are suitable for reservation for the national wilderness system. The remaining 52 million hectares that have been modified in some particular, perhaps by roading, are available for the types of recreation that is serviced by facilities which restoration can provide.

But, there is a legitimate question whether undisturbed natural environments should be allocated to extractive industrial activities on the supposition that they can be restored eventually to provide replicas of the original that would satisfy the recreational interests of only the less discriminating clientele. The matter turns on the importance of authenticity as an attribute of the recreational experience, quite apart from the matter of preserving relevant research materials for advancing knowledge in the life and earth sciences. The demand for authenticity in undisturbed natural areas may be likened to the demand for authenticity in the visual arts. For the bulk of the art museum clientele, the difference between an original work of art by one of the masters and a copy by one of his proteges, or a contemporary artist, is perhaps undetectable. But to a connoisseur of the arts, the mere suspicion of a forgery, even one so expert that art critics will differ in their opinions as to its authenticity, will result in a drastic reduction in the market value of the *objet d'art* – as many museum curators have been embarrassed to discover. The question then turns on what is the clientele, or market, that a particular amenity resource is to satisfy.

The outdoor recreation market is, in fact, a vast and complicated structure of submarkets. A developed campground in an attractive roadside location may be all that the "typical" family-car camper would desire. A more developed campground with electrical outlets for portable televisions and other appliances, however, seems to be in great favor also by many, and a primitive undeveloped site that can be reached only by a day of strenuous backpacking is likely to hold no attraction for this clientele. But for these submarkets, there are state, regional, and National Park and Forest Service areas in the United States totaling upwards of 60 million hectares for their accommodation. Still other individuals, whose numbers appear to be growing, seek solitude and primeval settings. This group represents a distinct submarket among outdoor recreation enthusiasts. But, even within the ranks of the wilderness seeker, there appears to be a bimodal distribution among "purists" and "nonpurists". In the important work of Stankey (1972), an analysis was made of the values reflected in the Wilderness Act (United States) and its legislative history and the degree to which wilderness users subscribed to the values for which the Wilderness System was established in law as a basis for distinguishing among users – the attribute preferences that should be taken into account in the administration of the system. A bimodal distribution along a purist–nonpurist scale was apparent with the preference for authenticity markedly exhibited by the group with values corresponding to those reflected in the Wilderness Act.[11] To members of this puristic submarket – no less so than to the life and earth scientist – restoration, no matter how "exact", is as unsatisfying a remedy for the disturbed natural environment as is the art forgery to a connoisseur, no matter how difficult to detect it may be to the bulk of the art museum clientele.

The reason for the unsatisfying nature of exact forgeries for the purist is not, of course, a matter of scientific knowledge. There may be an aura about the works of creative genius that the work of the most gifted imitator cannot provide. There may even be a cult comprised of those who revere the works of nature in a sense similar to that in which the Buddhists revere them, which may not be dissimilar from the reverence that primitive societies confer on nature in their religious observances. To those who number among the purists, preservation of the constituents of the biosphere in precisely the way it has evolved without disturbances from industrial man is a matter of great significance in a profound personal sense. Such feelings, in fact, have been captured in the works of Wordsworth and Emerson in very moving fashion. Whatever the reasons may be, whether mystical or religious, they are felt with great intensity. For analytical purposes, this translates into a highly inelastic demand for the "originals". This clientele represents, currently, a significant market that appears to be recruiting members rapidly as the income and educational and urban composition of American society changes. Moreover, this is a market for which refinements in restorative technology will do little by way of recreating "undisturbed" natural environments. Accordingly, the argument for irreversibility is a powerful one

---

[11] Purism, as measured by Stankey (1972), was positively related to educational attainment and interestingly to urban, rather than rural origin among wilderness users.

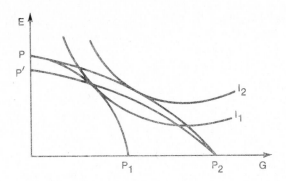

Figure 4.1. Production possibilities and preferences for produced goods and environmental amenities.

where the clientele group places a high value on the attribute of authenticity in the amenity services yielded by given natural environmental resources.

4. Modeling irreversibility

4.1. An informal, diagrammatic approach

To economists, the important question about irreversibility is this: What are the implications for resource allocation? If the *in situ* resources of an environment are declining in value relative to the extractive resources, then, clearly, irreversibility poses no special problem. An optimal investment program will call for conversion at a rate dictated by the changing relative values. Unfortunately, just the reverse is likely to be true, at least in the industrialized countries. Unique natural environments are in many cases likely to appreciate in value relative to goods and services they might yield if developed. Then the restriction on reversibility matters because value would be increased by going back to an earlier, less developed state.

The situation is represented in a broad aggregative fashion in Figure 4.1.[12] A production-possibilities curve having the usual concavity properties describes the trade-off between services of the *in situ* resources of natural environments, E, and produced goods, G, in an economy. The curve PP_1 gives this relationship for period 1, and the curve PP_2 gives it for period 2. PP_2 is flatter reflecting the increased output of G (but not E) made possible by technical progress. Curve $P'P_2$ is still flatter reflecting the economy's inability to yield the period 1 level of

---

[12] The discussion here draws on the early contribution of Krutilla (1967). Like the original, it is rather informal. For a more rigorous exposition that also deals with the richer and more realistic three-good case, see the work of Smith (1974).

E because of irreversible conversion of some part of the natural environment in the process of producing period 1's G.

In order to say something about the relative values of the two goods, let us indicate I_1 and I_2 as community indifference curves for periods 1 and 2, respectively. Note that, even if tastes do not change from one period to the next, so that I_2 is roughly parallel to I_1, the slope at the new tangency point is flatter. If tastes do shift in favor of the environment, as some evidence suggests, the slope is still flatter; in other words, the relative price ratio P_G/P_E is still lower. The point is not that consumption of E is increased relative to G(in fact, just the reverse occurs) but that the relative value of E is increased.

The argument about technical change, relative values, and irreversibility then goes something like this. Technical change is asymmetric. It results in expanded capacity to produce ordinary goods and services, but not natural environments. As long as consumer preferences do not shift sufficiently in favor of the ordinary goods (and we have evidence that they are likely to shift in the opposite direction), the supply shift implies an increase in the relative value of the *in situ* resources. This is pertinent to the assessment of any proposed conversion of the resources (the construction of a large dam, say, or an open-pit mine). Because the value of the *in situ* resources may be increasing relative to that of the water, power, or minerals produced by the development project, and development is irreversible, we might reasonably expect project investment criteria to be somewhat conservative. A rigorous theoretical exercise will establish this more precisely.

4.2. The investment decision under uncertainty

We have thus far not dealt formally with uncertainty about the value of *in situ* resources though it is at least implicit in all of our examples. There is a *chance* that conserving ecosystems and their component populations will lead to the discovery of a cure for cancer, a substitute for petroleum, or a perennial corn; but, obviously, this will not be known at the time a decision about a particular natural environment is taken. Less dramatically, it is quite possible, as we have suggested, that the value of *in situ* resources will rise relative to that of extractive resources; but even if this were generally true, it need not be for a particular tract of wild land. In this section we present a model of the development decision that takes account of both the irreversibility of development and uncertainty about the values development would preclude.

Our model is based on the original formulations of Arrow and Fisher (1974) and Henry (1974), but we adopt the more transparent notation and approach of Hanemann (1982). The two-period setting of Section 4.1 is retained. The decision problem is: How much of a tract of wild land should be developed in each of the two periods? We choose units of measurement such that the maximum level of development (or preservation) is just unity. Then, there are three substantive assumptions. First, development in any period is irreversible. Second, the benefits of development in the first period are known, those of development in the second period are not. These assumptions capture the essential features of our problem. A third, made more for ease in obtaining unambiguous results, is that benefits are a linear function of the level of development. Later on we consider what happens when this assumption is relaxed.

Let us interpret the assumed structure a bit to indicate both its rationale and its limits. The benefits associated with a given level of development are the benefits of development *and* the benefits of preservation. Let the former be given, for the first period, as

$$B_{1d}(d_1) = \alpha d_1, \tag{1}$$

where d indicates development; d_1, the level of development in period 1; and α, a positive constant. Notice that $0 \le d_1 \le 1$.

Let the benefits of preservation be

$$B_{1p}(d_1) = \beta - \gamma d_1, \tag{2}$$

where p indicates preservation and β and γ are positive constants. Then, benefits in period 1 are

$$B_1(d_1) = B_{1d}(d_1) + B_{1p}(d_1)$$
$$= \beta + (\alpha - \gamma)d_1. \tag{3}$$

The (linear) relationship between B_1 and d_1 is graphed in Figure 4.2 for the two possible cases of $\alpha > \gamma$ and $\alpha < \gamma$. Clearly, first-period benefits will be maximized by choosing either $d_1 = 0$ (if $\alpha < \gamma$) or $d_1 = 1$ (if $\alpha > \gamma$). Thus, the problem is restricted to a choice of corner solutions. The argument would be more complicated were we to consider uncertain second-period benefits as well, but this key restriction carries over.

Second-period benefits are $B_2(d_1 + d_2, \theta)$, where d_2 is the amount of land developed in period 2 and θ is a random variable.[13] Thus, second-period benefits depend on development in periods 1 and 2 and are uncertain. Notice that $d_2 \ge 0$ and $d_1 + d_2 \le 1$. We shall assume that the problem is to maximize *expected* benefits over both periods. This is one particular way of dealing with the uncertainty. It is not, however, as restrictive as it may seem since we have not specified that benefits are measured in money units. If, for example, benefits are measured in utility units, then our formulation is equivalent to the quite general expected utility maximization.

---

[13] Second-period benefits can be viewed as present values. We suppress the discount factor here because including it would not affect our results.

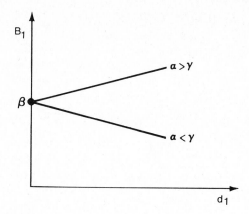

Figure 4.2. The linear relationship between benefits and development.

The remaining structural element of the problem involves the behavior of uncertainty over time. More specifically, we consider two possible cases. In the first, nothing further is learned about the value of θ by period 2 so that d_1 and d_2 are chosen in period 1. In the second, the value of θ is learned by period 2 so that it makes sense to defer a decision on d_2 to period 2. Now comes a very important assumption. It is that the learning, in case 2, does not depend on first-period development, d_1. *For the kind of uncertainty we are trying to capture*, this seems appropriate. Uncertainty is largely about the future (period 2) benefits of pre-servation – the value that may be discovered in some indigenous species, for example. This will be determined *not* by developing its habitat but by undertak-ing research into its medicinal or other properties. The research is not endogenous to our problem, but we do assume that the answer it yields, concerning the value of θ, does not depend on the development of the tract in question. Not suprisingly, this assumption importantly affects the results we shall obtain. At that point, we shall have more to say about the alternative assumption and its consequences.

Now let us write down expressions for the value to be maximized under each information structure. Where no new information is forthcoming by the second period, define $V^*(d_1)$ by

$$V^*(d_1) = B_1(d_1) + \max_{\substack{d_2 \\ 0 \le d_1 + d_2 \le 1 \\ 0 \le d_2}} \left\{ E\left[B_2(d_1 + d_2, \theta) \right] \right\}. \tag{4}$$

Then, the maximum value is $V^* = V^*(d_1^*)$, where d_1^* maximizes $V^*(d_1)$ subject to $0 \le d_1 \le 1$.

Where new information is forthcoming, define $\hat{V}(d_1)$ by

$$\hat{V}(d_1) = B_1(d_1) + E\left[\max_{\substack{d_2 \\ 0 \le d_1 + d_2 \le 1 \\ 0 \le d_2}} \{B_2(d_1 + d_2, \theta)\}\right]. \tag{5}$$

The maximum value in this case is $\hat{V} = \hat{V}(\hat{d}_1)$, where $\hat{d}_1$ maximizes $\hat{V}(d_1)$ subject to $0 \le d_1 \le 1$.

What can we say about value-maximizing, or optimal, development in the first period in each case? Clearly, since $V^*(d_1)$ and $\hat{V}(d_1)$ are different, d_1^* and $\hat{d}_1$ will be different. A natural hypothesis is that $\hat{d}_1 \le d_1^*$ since it would seem to make sense to put off development, which is irreversible, if there is a prospect of better information about the benefits it will preclude. Put differently, if the decision-maker ignores the prospect of better information, first-period development will be too great. We can prove this result, not in general, but where the choice is between no development ($d_t = 0$) and full development ($d_t = 1$). Recall that this is precisely the choice implied by our linearity assumption.

We wish, then, to compare the alternatives of developing and preserving in each information setting. Where no information is forthcoming, we have

$$V^*(0) = B_1(0) + \max\{E[B_2(0,\theta)], E[B_2(1,\theta)]\} \tag{6}$$

and

$$V^*(1) = B_1(1) + E[B_2(1,\theta)]. \tag{7}$$

Then,

$$d_1^* = \begin{cases} 0, & \text{if } V^*(0) - V^*(1) \ge 0, \\ 1, & \text{if } V^*(0) - V^*(1) < 0. \end{cases} \tag{8}$$

Where new information is forthcoming, we have

$$\hat{V}(0) = B_1(0) + E[\max\{B_2(0,\theta), B_2(1,\theta)\}] \tag{9}$$

and

$$\hat{V}(1) = B_1(1) + E[B_2(1,\theta)]. \tag{10}$$

Then

$$\hat{d}_1 = \begin{cases} 0, & \text{if } \hat{V}(0) - \hat{V}(1) \ge 0, \\ 1, & \text{if } \hat{V}(0) - \hat{V}(1) < 0. \end{cases} \tag{11}$$

Notice that $V^*(1) = \hat{V}(1)$. With full development in the first period, total value over both periods must be the same since the development is locked in for the second period regardless of what is learned about the random variable θ in the first.

We have still not shown the relationship of d_1^* to $\hat{d}_1$. For this, just one more step is needed. From the convexity of the maximum operator, and Jensen's Inequality, it follows that

$$\hat{V}(0) - V^*(0) = E\left[\max\{B_2(0,\theta), B_2(1,\theta)\}\right]$$
$$- \max\{E[B_2(0,\theta)], E[B_2(1,\theta)]\} \geq 0. \tag{12}$$

Since $\hat{V}(0) \geq V^*(0)$ and $\hat{V}(1) = V^*(1)$, $\hat{d}_1 \leq d_1^*$. In practice, what this means is that optimal first-period use of the area is less likely to be full development ($d_1 = 1$) where it is possible to learn about the benefits precluded than where it is not.

To produce this result, we made a couple of assumptions that deserve further comment. First, about the linearity of the benefit function which allowed us to compare just the two alternatives of development and preservation in each information setting. Hanemann (1982) has shown that the result ($\hat{d}_1 \leq d_1^*$) does not follow in the general case where d_1 can take any value in the interval $[0,1]$. On the other hand, it may be produced in a variety of special cases.

For example, suppose we partition the area into a number of separate subareas with its own (linear) benefit function. Then, each can be ranked by suitability for development; the one for which benefits are greatest is no. 1 and so on. Suppose further that the subarea benefit functions are independent; that is, benefits of developing subarea no. 1 do not depend on whether no. 2 is developed and so on. Now proceed exactly as before for each subarea starting with no. 1. If it pays to develop in a given information setting, move to no. 2 and ask the same question. Continue until the subarea is reached for which optimal development is zero. Since $\hat{d}_{1i} \leq d_{1i}^*$, where i indexes the subarea, the number of subareas optimally developed will be less in the new-information case than in the no-information case. In other words, the fraction of the original area developed will be less.

Of course, additional assumptions were needed to get this result. In our judgment, partitioning of an area, particularly if it is large or diverse, is plausible as is piecewise linearity. Independence of subarea benefit functions is less so. Other less restrictive assumptions about benefit functions might be devised that will yet be consistent with $\hat{d}_1 \leq d_1^*$. The judgment about all such assumptions is ultimately an empirical one.

The second key assumption we made was that resolution of the uncertainty is independent of development in the first period. We have argued that this is plausible; but, again, the judgment is an empirical one. It is fairly obvious that, if resolution depends on development, and, in particular, on a positive level of development, then (some) development may be optimal *for the purpose of providing information* even where this involves an irreversible commitment of resources that turns out be a mistake. Such a result is obtained in a recent study by Miller and Lad (1984). Similarly, development for the purpose of providing information about whether the development is, in fact, irreversible may be optimal as has been shown by Viscusi and Zeckhauser (1976). The reader is free to choose among these alternative assumptions about the structure of information, but we continue to feel that ours is most plausible *for our problem*, i.e. relevant information about the properties of indigenous species will come not from developing their habitat but rather from research that, if anything, depends on preserving habitat.

5. Option value and the value of information

In the literature on nature preservation, the concept of "option value" has played a prominent role. Beginning with the article by Weisbrod (1964), there has been a notion – advanced by some, including Weisbrod, disputed by others – that preservation carries with it a value (option value) above and beyond conventional consumer's surplus. A number of articles following Weisbrod established that option value could be identified with a risk premium: the difference between what a risk-averse consumer is willing to pay for the option of consuming (wilderness recreation, say), at a predetermined nondiscriminatory price, and his expected consumer's surplus.[14] These and other studies also exposed a difficulty; namely, that preservation, as well as development, can bring risks, e.g. floods or power failures.[15] The net option value of preserving a wilderness environment could then be negative. And, in any case, option value in this interpretation depends on risk aversion.

A different interpretation has been put forward by Arrow and Fisher (1974) and Henry (1974) and, more recently, by Conrad (1980), Hanemann (1982), and perhaps others. Unlike the first, it does not depend on risk aversion. Also, unlike the first, it is explicitly dynamic. In fact, it falls out quite naturally from the model presented in the preceding section. Option value, in this interpretation, is the gain from being able to learn about future benefits that would be precluded by development if one does not develop initially – the gain from retaining the option to preserve or develop in the future. In our terminology, this is

$$OV = \hat{V}(0) - V^*(0). \tag{13}$$

From eq. (12), option value, OV, is non-negative.

We can obtain this result in a somewhat different fashion following Arrow and Fisher's (1974) original presentation. Suppose the decision-maker ignores the prospect of new information. Then he will compare $V^*(0)$ and $V^*(1)$. A correct decision – one that takes account of this prospect – can be induced, in principle, by a subsidy to preservation. The optimal subsidy will clearly be one which leads

---

[14] See, for example, Zeckhauser (1969) and Cicchetti and Freeman (1971).
[15] For an argument along these lines, see Schmalensee (1972) and Henry (1974).

the decision-maker to compare $\hat{V}(0)$ and $\hat{V}(1)$. To solve for the subsidy, S, write

$$[V^*(0) + S] - V^*(1) = \hat{V}(0) - \hat{V}(1), \tag{14}$$

so that

$$S = [\hat{V}(0) - \hat{V}(1)] - [V^*(0) - V^*(1)]. \tag{15}$$

Since, from eqs. (7) and (10), $V^*(1) = \hat{V}(1)$, eq. (15) reduces to eq. (13). The subsidy, S, is just what we mean by option value – the extra value attaching to the preservation option that would be overlooked in a conventional decision, a decision that did not take account of the prospective gains from information.

It is tempting to identify this concept of option value with another one familiar in decision theory: the value of information, or more precisely, the expected value of perfect information. However, the identification is not quite correct. Option value in this interpretation is, as Hanemann (1982) shows, a *conditional* value of information, conditional on $d_1 = 0$.

The *unconditional* value of information is $\hat{V}(\hat{d}_1) - V^*(d_1^*)$ or, in other words, the gain from being able to learn about future benefits provided d_1 is optimally chosen in each case. This may mean $\hat{d}_1 = d_1^* = 0$ or it may not. In fact, two other outcomes are possible: $\hat{d}_1 = d_1^* = 1$ and $\hat{d}_1 = 0$, $d_1^* = 1$. (Note that $\hat{d}_1 = 1$, $d_1^* = 0$ is ruled out by the result that $\hat{d}_1 \le d_1^*$.) If $\hat{d}_1 = d_1^* = 1$, the value of information is $\hat{V}(1) - V^*(1) = 0$, whereas option value is still $\hat{V}(0) - V^*(0) \ge 0$. If $\hat{d}_1 = 0$ and $d_1^* = 1$, the value of information is $\hat{V}(0) - V^*(1)$. Notice that option value is once again greater than the value of information since $\hat{V}(0) \ge \hat{V}(1) = V^*(1) \ge V^*(0)$.

To summarize, then, option value is not identical to the value of information in the development decision problem. Option value is instead a conditional value of information, conditional on a particular choice of first-period development ($d_1 = 0$) and, moreover, is equal to or greater than the (unconditional) value of information.

6. A digression on extended applications

Our arguments and illustrations have been developed within the context of terrestrial ecosystems. But nature preservation need not be confined to this limited domain; it can be perceived to include hydrospheric and atmospheric environments as well. Viewed in this light the problem may take on additional dimensions, and the arguments addressing irreversibility and option value may require some further elaboration. But the approach taken in this chapter appears to be generally applicable to the natural environment conceived in its broadest terms.

In our treatment of the terrestrial ecosystem, we considered whether or not the "real estate" in question could be partitioned into smaller parcels and whether the consequences of development, or experimentation, on a given parcel as a way to acquire information were separable and noncumulative for the remainder of the given ecosystem. In the case of the problem associated with atmospheric carbon dioxide concentrations, partitioning the atmosphere in order to carry out isolated experiments is, of course, impossible despite the liklihood that information could be gained on the relation between fossil fuel combustion and atmospheric carbon dioxide. It is not clear, however, that information of the sort sought would necessarily depend on continuing "experimentation". If suitable information can be obtained deductively from basic principles of atmospheric physics, an argument for continued combustion of fossil fuels *as a way to acquire information concerning its atmospheric consequences* is weakened despite whatever independent reasons can be given for their continued use.

There are likely to be cases where the adverse effects may be compounded by lags in detection and in responses to exposures (where health effects are involved) so that significant adverse irreversibilities may be set in motion by continued experimentation that are not subject to control except long after their undesirability is recognized. In the case of chlorofluorocarbons used in refrigeration, for example, the emissions do not occur significantly while the equipment is in use but only upon the escape of the gases from deteriorating containers some time after the equipment is scrapped. This delay in emissions and, hence, in observing the consequences on the ozone shield, along with the lagged response of skin cancer to reduced protection against solar radiation does not provide a proper context for a meaningful information acquisition strategy.

The introduction of lagged responses to lagged consequences of taking liberties with indivisible natural environments alters the context of the choice problem but not the general thrust of the value of retaining options where irreversibilities are encountered.

If the example of refrigerants and the ozone shield seems a bit strained, one can develop a suitable example to illustrate the point using persistent pesticides (chlorinated hydrocarbons, not detectable until after spread throughout the globe by vaporization, and concentrated through bioamplification, etc.). Other examples involve dioxin or heavy metals, again amplified by filter feeders and similar lags in detection. And where carcinoma rather than somatic illness is involved, there will be a lagged *detectable* response to exposure. This exacerbated condition, it seems, strengthens the argument for option value where the irreversible conditions may continue to grow even after detection because of past actions having lagged effects.

7. Concluding remarks

The major finding of this chapter is a purely theoretical one: where economic decisions have an impact on the natural environment that is both uncertain and irreversible, there is a value to retaining an option to avoid the impact. Put differently, a development project that passes a conventional benefit–cost test might not pass a more sophisticated one that takes account of the uncertain and irreversible impact of the project on the environment. We designate the difference as option value: the gain from being able to learn about future benefits, especially those that would be *precluded* by the project, if one does not undertake it right away.

Option value, in this analysis, has something of the flavor of the value of information and indeed has been identified with this concept from decision theory. We show that option value is in fact a *conditional* value of information, conditional on a particular choice of first-period development, namely none. We further show that option value is greater than or equal to the (unconditional) value of information.

Examples of situations to which the analysis would apply are preservation of wilderness ecosystems, protection of endangered species, and maintenance of the integrity of nonterrestrial (atmospheric and hydrospheric) environments.

References

Arrow, K.J. and A.C. Fisher (1974) "Environmental Preservation, Uncertainty, and Irreversibility", *Quarterly Journal of Economics* 88.

Cicchetti, C.J. and A.M. Freeman (1971) "Option Demand and Consumer Surplus: Further Comment", *Quarterly Journal of Economics* 85.

Conrad, J.M. (1980) "Quasi-Option Value and the Expected Value of Information", *Quarterly Journal Of Economics* 94.

Delwiche, C.C. (1970) "The Nitrogen Cycle", *Scientific American* 223, no. 3.

Ehrlich, P. and A. Ehrlich (1981) *Extinction: The Causes and Consequences of the Disappearance of Species* (Random House, New York).

Hanemann, W.M. (1982) "Information and the Concept of Option Value", Department of Agricultural and Resource Economics Working Paper No. 228 (University of California).

Harrington, W. and A.C. Fisher (1982) "Endangered Species", in: P.R. Portney (ed.), *Current Issues in Natural Resource Policy* (Resources for the Future, Washington).

Henry, C. (1974) "Investment Decisions Under Uncertainty: The Irreversibility Effect", *American Economic Review* 64.

Krutilla, J.V. (1967) "Conservation Reconsidered", *American Economic Review* 57

Krutilla, J.V. and A.C. Fisher (1975) *The Economics of Natural Environments*: Studies in the Valuation of Commodity and Amenity Resources (Johns Hopkins University Press, Baltimore).

Lugo, A. and S. Brown (1982) "Conversion of Tropical Moist Forests: A Critique." *Interciencia* 2, no. 2.

Miller, J. and Lad (1984) "Flexibility, Learning, and Irreversibility in Environmental Decisions: A Bayesian Approach", *Journal of Environmental Economics and Management* 11.

Myers, N. (1981) "The Exhausted Earth", *Foreign Policy* no. 42, Spring.

Myers, N. (1983) *A Wealth of Wild Species* (Westview Press, Boulder).

Opler, P.A. (1971) "The Parade of Passing Species: A Survey of Extinction in the U.S. ", *The Science Teacher* 44.

Schmalensee, R. (1972) "Option Demand and Consumer's Surplus: Valuing Price Changes Under Uncertainty", *American Economic Review* 62.

Smith, V.K. (1974) *Technical Change, Relative Prices, and Environmental Resource Evaluation* (Johns Hopkins University Press, Baltimore).

Stankey, G.H. (1972) "A Strategy for the Definition and Management of Wilderness Quality", in: J.V. Krutilla (ed), *National Environments*: *Studies in Theoretical and Applied Analysis* (Johns Hopkins University Press, Baltimore).

Vietmeyer, N.D. (1979) "A Wild Relative May Give Corn Perennial Genes", *Smithsonian* 10, no. 9.

Viscusi, W.K. and R.J. Zeckhauser (1976) "Environmental Policy Choice Under Uncertainty", *Journal of Environmental Economics and Management* 3.

Weisbrod, B. (1964) "Collective-Consumption Services of Individual-Consumption Goods", *Quarterly Journal of Economics* 78.

Zeckhauser, R.J. (1969) "Resource Allocation with Probabilistic Individual Preferences", *American Economic Review*. 59.

Chapter 5

ETHICS AND ENVIRONMENTAL ECONOMICS

ALLEN V. KNEESE

Resources for the Future, Washington

and

WILLIAM D. SCHULZE

University of Colorado, Boulder

> The moral problem is a conflict that can never be settled. Social life will always present mankind with a choice of evils. No metaphysical solution that can ever be formulated will seem satisfactory for long. The solutions offered by economists were not less illusory than those of the theologians that they displaced.
>
> All the same, we must not abandon the hope that economics can make an advance toward science, or the faith that enlightenment is not useless. It is necessary to clear the decaying remnants of obsolete metaphysics out of the way before we can go forward   [Robinson (1963, p. 146)].

1. Introduction

Welfare economics, one of the foundations of conventional environmental economics, can be thought of as being an enormous elaboration of the utilitarian moral philosophy developed by Bentham, Mill, and others in the eighteenth and nineteenth centuries. There are, however, rival ethical systems that also put forward rules for individual and social moral behavior that are different from those of utilitarianism.

But why be concerned with moral philosophy in a book on environmental economics? There are two main reasons, one having its origins in economics and the other in philosophy. The first stems from the increasingly strained applications of benefit–cost analysis to large environmental issues and the concerns this raises about the adequacy, in these applications, of its conceptual, as well as empirical, basis. From the side of moral philosophy, there has been a great upsurge of interest by philosophers in the ethical implication of man's impacts on the environment. One result has been a spate of writings endeavoring to develop a nontheological, nonhumanistic, environmental ethic. The ideas of these philosophers, if accepted, would have large implications for environmental economics

Handbook of Natural Resource and Energy Economics, vol. I, edited by A.V. Kneese and J.L. Sweeney
© *Elsevier Science Publishers B.V., 1985*

which, because of its basis in welfare economics, is intensely humanistic in its orientation.[1]

In the next two sections, we elaborate first on the concerns emanating from the economic side and then from the standpoint of the new naturalistic philosophers.

Following that, we discuss several efforts by economists and others to develop criteria of "sustainability" with respect to both particular resources and the whole economic system. These are meant to provide ethical guidance concerning appropriate behavior where resource depletion or environmental degradation threaten to reduce the welfare of future generations. Particularly, we discuss the ideas of the economist Page and their relationship to the writings of the philosopher Rawls.

Then we consider a critique of all the major humanistic ethical ideas in Western philosophy after Aristotle. This critique is contained in an important recent book by the philosopher MacIntyre. This assessment sets the stage for a statement about our own stance concerning the alternative humanistic ethical systems we analyze further on in terms of their implications for environmental economics.

To permit this latter analysis to proceed with some rigor, it is necessary to state the alternative ethical ideas in their simplest possible terms. Therefore, they can in that form be linked only in a loose sense to the writings of any particular philosopher.

Having accomplished this epitomization, we apply several examples of the alternative humanistic ethics we have formalized to some particularly vexing problems in environmental economics. These are the analysis of environmental risks and the problems associated with discounting of environmental benefits and costs over long periods of time. We combine these problems in an illustrative analysis of the problem of storing radioactive nuclear wastes. Because of limitation of information, many questionable assumptions have to be made and the analysis should be taken as being nothing more than an effort to add a certain amount of concreteness to an otherwise very abstract discussion.

We close with a section that, in a sense, takes us back to the opening parts of the chapter. Here we consider a policy issue, the use of economic incentives in environmental policy, that has divided economists who emphasize economic efficiency from many environmentalists who take a different ethical view of environmental policy. This discussion focuses on an important recent book about environmental economics and ethics by political scientist Kelman. It also provides us with a vehicle for a closing statement of perspective on ethics and environmental economics.

---

[1] It is worth noting, however, in passing, that Bentham's utilitarianism was not anthropocentric. He wrote, "the French have already discovered that the blackness of the skin is no reason why a human being should be abandoned without redress to the caprice of a tormentor. It may come one day to be recognized, that the number of legs... or the termination of the os sacrum are reasons equally insufficient for abandoning a sensitive being to the same fate" [Bentham (1789), quoted in Passmore (1974 p. 14)].

In closing the present section of this chapter, we want to remark that we set out on the tasks just outlined with humility. Neither one of us is a trained philosopher, and we feel sure that professional philosophers reading this chapter would find many of the things we say, at least, simplistic. Still, we think the issues are potentially so important for the future of environmental economics that we feel the attempt must be made.

2. Ethical concerns of benefit–cost analysis

Benefit–cost analysis is discussed in other parts of this Handbook. Our intent here is not to instruct about its application, but rather to provide a brief historical perspective on why some of its newer applications are raising increasingly large ethical concerns among some economists.

Benefit–cost analysis was developed initially to evaluate water resources investment made by the federal water agencies in the United States, principally the United States Bureau of Reclamation and the United States Corps of Engineers. The general objective of benefit–cost analysis in this application was to provide a useful picture of the costs and gains from making investments in water development. The intellectual "father" of the technique is often said to be Jules Dupuit, who in 1844 wrote a frequently cited study "On the Measure of the Utility of Public Works". In this remarkable article, he recognized the concept of consumer's surplus and saw that consequently the benefits of public works are not necessarily the same thing as the direct revenues that the public works projects will generate.

Early contributions to development of benefit–cost analysis generally did not come from the academic or research communities but rather from government agencies. The agencies responsible for water development in this country have for a long time been aware of the need for economic evaluation of projects and the benefit–cost procedure is now embodied in agency policy and in government legislation. In 1808, Albert Gallatin, Jefferson's Secretary of the Treasury, produced a report on transportation programs for the new nation. He stressed the need for comparing the benefits with the costs of proposed waterway improvements. The Federal Reclamation Act of 1902 which created the Bureau of Reclamation, and was aimed at opening western lands to irrigation, required economic analysis of projects. The Flood Control Act of 1936 proposed a feasibility test based on utilitarian welfare economics which requires that the benefits to whomsoever they accrue must exceed costs. This directive told the agencies to ignore the distribution of benefits and costs and give attention only to their total amounts.

In 1946, the Federal Interagency River Basin Committee appointed a subcommittee on benefits and costs to reconcile the practices of federal agencies in making benefit–cost analyses. In 1950, the subcommittee issued a landmark report entitled "Proposed Practices for Economic Analysis of River Basin Projects". While never fully accepted either by the parent committee or the federal agencies, this report was remarkably sophisticated in its use of economic analysis and laid the intellectual foundation for research and debate which set it apart from other major reports in the realm of public expenditures. This document also provided general guidance for the routine development of benefit–cost analysis of water projects which persists to the present day.

Following this report came some outstanding publications from the research and academic communities. Several books appearing over the past quarter century have gone much further than ever before in clarifying the welfare economics concepts applicable to our water resources development and use and in exploring the fundamental rationale for government activity in the area. Otto Eckstein's (1958) book is particularly outstanding for its careful review and critique of federal agency practice with respect to benefit–cost analysis. While naturally a bit dated, this book is still well worth reading.

A clear exposition of principles together with applications to several important cases was prepared by Jack Hirschleifer and collaborators in 1960. Other reports appeared during the early 1960s. One, which was especially notable for its deep probing into applications of systems analysis and computer technology within the framework of benefit–cost analysis, was published in 1962 by a group of economists, engineers, and hydrologists at Harvard [Maass et al. (1962)]. The intervening years have seen considerable further work on the technique and a gradual expansion of it to areas outside the water resources field.

The most striking development in benefit–cost analysis in recent years has been an increasing application of the technique to the environmental consequences of new technologies and scientific programs. For example, the U.S. Atomic Energy Commission (1972) (before ERDA and the DOE were created) used the technique to evaluate the fast breeder reactor research and development program. It has also been applied to other potential sources of environmental pollution and hazard. Two studies which come to quite contrary conclusions have been made of the Automotive Emissions Control Program. The first was prepared by a Committee of the National Academy of Sciences (1974). The other study is by the research arm of a major automotive producer [Jackson et al. (1976)]. Still other studies have been or are being conducted in the area of water quality analysis, emissions from stationary sources, and toxic substances including nuclear waste disposal.

Even while the benefit–cost technique was limited largely to the relatively straightforward problem of evaluating water resources investments, there was much debate among economists about the proper way of handling both empirical and conceptual difficulties with it. Some of the discussion surrounded primarily technical issues, e.g. ways of computing consumer surplus and how best to estimate demand functions for various outputs. Others were more clearly value and equity issues, e.g. whether the distribution of benefits and costs among individuals needed to be accounted for or whether it was adequate to consider, as the Flood Control Act directed, only aggregates, and what is the appropriate rate of time discount to use on water projects.

Application of the technique to issues such as nuclear energy development programs, the storage of atomic waste, man-induced climate change, and the regulation of toxic substances aggravate both the empirical and value issues which existed in water resource application. There are several reasons for this.

First, while water resource applications often involve the evaluation of public goods (in the technical economic sense of goods exhibiting jointness in supply) the bulk of outputs pertain to such things as irrigation, navigation, flood control, and municipal and industrial water supplies which usually could be reasonably evaluated on the basis of some type of market information. In the newer applications, we are dealing almost entirely with public goods where market surrogates are much more difficult to establish.

Secondly, such matters as nuclear radiation and toxic materials relate to exposure of the whole population or large subpopulations to very subtle influences of which they may entirely unaware. It is difficult to know what normative value individual preferences have under these circumstances.

Thirdly, the distributional issues involved in these applications entail not only monetary benefits and costs, but the distribution of actual physical hazard. While it is not out of the question that monetary equivalents to these risks could be developed, the ethical issues appear to be deeper than just the economic returns which are involved. This is especially so if compensation is not actually paid to losers, as it is in practice unlikely to be.

Fourthly, we are in some cases dealing with long-lived effects which could extend to hundreds of thousands of years and many, many human generations. This raises the question of how the rights and preferences of future generations can be represented in this decision process. Realistically, the preferences of the existing generation must govern. The question is whether simple desires of existing persons are to rule or whether it is necessary to persuade the present generation to adopt some ethical rule or rules of a constitutional nature in considering questions of future generations.

The new applications of benefit–cost analysis bristle with ethical and value issues. These are the concerns raised from the side of economics.

3. The new naturalistic ethics

Some philosophers have recently chosen to address the difficult issues of ethics and policy presented by environmental concerns by abandoning humanistic philosophy altogether. These have been referred to as the "new naturalistic philosophers" [Marietta (1982)]. This group is rapidly producing a large new literature.

Actually, in many cases the discussion starts with the question of what is the nature and extent of man's obligation to nonhuman creatures – there is by now a large "animal rights" literature. From there, by some, extensions are made to nonliving entities, and by yet others, ideas having originated in humanistic philosophy are abandoned entirely and a purely naturalistic view of the ethical aspects of man in nature is advocated.

In a few instances the writing is rather hysterical and reminiscent of the more extreme kind of environmentalist prose of the later 1960s and early 1970s. For example, the main themes of a book, *Why the Green Nigger? Re-mything Genesis* [Gray (1979)] is stated by a reviewer [Shute (1980)] as follows:

> In *Why the Green Nigger?* Elizabeth Dodson Gray attempts to show that it has been the use of a male-constructed, hierarchical picture of the world (with men at the top) that has been responsible for making nature a "green nigger." Possessing no rights, feminine and inferior nature is mastered, manipulated and oppressed by superior men. This male-constructed hierarchical picture of reality, Gray says, is posing a threat to the survival of life on the planet Earth. But Gray sees hope for changing the status and treatment of nature if we understand that reality is not hierarchical, but is a "complex and dynamic web of energy" (p. 67) which men are not only dependent upon, but in which they are inextricably enmeshed as beings with value no greater than that of anything else.

Most of the writing, however, has been a sober and well-intentioned attempt by the pertinent group of moral philosophers to tussle with some hard issues. There is no hope in the scope of a chapter to comprehensively survey all the contributions to this literature, but the interested reader can find a concentrated supply of articles from it in the journal *Environmental Ethics*. We choose a few of what we take to be among the best efforts of this genre and try to state the main ideas succinctly. We start with one that is a "slight" extension of some typical humanistic type arguments, then go through one that tries to extend man's obligations to all living things, a possible rationale for Albert Schweitzer's famous "respect for life", to a further one that extends ethical standing even to nonliving things, and finally to a set of writing that abandons the humanistic anchors altogether.

The first piece is by philosopher Richard A. Watson (1979). The idea of reciprocity is frequently invoked in the philosophical discussion of morality, and Watson uses a reciprocity framework to try to explain and justify the attribution of moral rights and duties.

We pause to note that the reciprocity is used in two separate senses in the literature under consideration. In the first it refers to the possibility of *actual* reciprocal action between or among agents. In the second it is used more in the "golden rule" sense of doing to others of what you would have them do unto you.

A related idea is Kant's categorical imperative that views ethical behavior as being that which the acting party believes should be universalized into a rule so that it would apply to everyone else, including their actions toward him. The second version does not necessarily imply that real reciprocal action is possible and therefore, as can be seen in the paper following Watson's, may apply to a broader range of phenomena.

Another pause is merited to explain a further distinction. In the pertinent literature, "right" (as in "animal rights") is taken to have at least two meanings. There can be "legal rights", and there can be moral rights or "inherent rights". That nonhuman entities can have legal rights is, of course, manifest. Corporations have rights in the legal sense as do wilderness areas and laboratory animals, although in the last case, enforcement is virtually nil. The real issue is whether nonhuman entities can have intrinsic rights inherent in the thing itself (das Ding an sich).

Now to return to Watson. He claims that to say that an entity has rights makes sense only if that entity can fulfill reciprocal duties, i.e. can act as a moral agent. To be such, again he claims, an entity must be (1) self-conscious, (2) understand general principles, (3) have free will, (4) understand the given principles, (5) be physically capable of acting, and (6) intend to act according to or against the given principles. So far, this line of argument would not be surprising to a conventional ethical philosopher even though he might not necessarily agree with it. It could be taken to define a human milieu which is moral as contrasted with a nonhuman one which is not.[2]

But Watson goes on to argue that a few animals besides humans, especially chimpanzees, gorillas, dolphins, and dogs, "...which, in accordance with good behavioral evidence, are moral entities, and sometimes moral agents. On the grounds of reciprocity, they merit, at a minimum, intrinsic or primary rights to life and to relief from unnecessary suffering" [Watson (1979, p. 99)].

Again, an interpretive note. Having heard an argument of this nature, it seems that many, if not most, economists would be puzzled as to why the philosopher making it should expect anyone else to believe him. By what authority can you, the philosopher, tell me what is morally right or morally wrong? A theological explanation, which is not invoked in humanistic philosophy, might not be believed, but it would probably be regarded as an understandable argument. But this attitude misunderstands the point of view of at least some, perhaps most, ethical philosophers. They do not appeal to higher authority, but believe that if they are clever enough and think hard enough about a moral problem, they should be able to come up with principles or rules that will persuade anyone else,

---

[2] It should be noted, however, that those who argue from *real* reciprocity seem to have a lot of trouble with the rights of very young children, the insane, hopeless idiots, and the helpless old.

or at least those who have an informed and sensitive moral intuition, of their validity.

With this background, and a set of arguments that gives "moral standing" to a few chimps and such, let us turn to a set of arguments that opens a much wider field of beings to moral claims. In a widely respected, which is not necessarily the same as to say widely agreed with, article, philosopher Kenneth E. Goodpaster (1978) approaches the question of man's responsibility to nature in a different way. Instead of addressing questions raised by the inherent rights concept, he asks the question, what makes a being morally "considerable"? The issue is one raised in an earlier book by philosopher G.J. Warnock (1971). Warnock asks what is the condition of having a claim to be "considered" by rational agents to whom moral principles apply. Goodpaster rephrases Warnock's question, "...for the terminology of R.M. Hare (or even Kant) the same questions might be put thus: In universalizing our putative moral maxims, what is the scope of the variable over which universalization is to range?", and a little further on, "For all A, X deserves moral considerations from A where A ranges over rational moral agents and moral 'consideration' is construed broadly to include the most basic forms of practical respect (and so is not restricted to 'possession of rights by X')" [Goodpaster (1978, pp. 308–309)].

Still further on, he states the conclusion to which his thoughts about this question have led him. "Neither rationality not the capacity to experience pleasure and pain seem to me necessary (even though they may be sufficient) conditions of moral considerability. And only our hedonistic and concentric forms of ethical reflection keep us from acknowledging this fact. Nothing short of the condition of being alive seems to me to be a plausible and nonarbitrary criterion" [Goodpaster (1978, p. 310)].

Having as he said, "put his cards on the table", and having further introduced distinctions and terminology we do not have space to explain (thus our characterization will necessarily do offense to the richness of his arguments and ideas), he begins with a critique of how Warnock answered his own question. As a matter of deserving moral consideration, Warnock rejects the reciprocity argument used by Watson, as explained above, at least partly based on the "infants and imbeciles" argument suggested in Watson (1979, p. 99). Instead, Warnock proposes that the criterion of moral considerability arises from the capacity to suffer.

Or stated in the more formal manner introduced earlier: for all A, X deserves moral considerations from A if and only if X is capable of suffering pain (or experiencing enjoyment).

Note that this may sound utilitarian, but unlike utilitarianism, it does not provide a criterion for action, but merely for consideration, by moral agents. While according to Goodpaster, Warnock in some places writes as though he is only including humans, but by the end of the book, he has broadened his scope to include nonhumans. Still, the operative idea is sentience.

Goodpaster is not convinced. He writes, "Biologically, it appears that sentience is an adaptive characteristic of living organisms that provides them with a better capacity to anticipate, and so to avoid threats to life. This at least suggests, though of course it does not prove, that the capacities to suffer and to enjoy are ancillary to something more important rather than tickets to considerability in their own right" [Goodpaster (1978, p. 316)]. He continues, "Nor is it absurd to imagine that evolution might have resulted (indeed might still result?) in beings whose capacities to maintain, protect and advance their lives did not depend upon mechanisms of pain and pleasure at all" [Goodpaster (1978, p. 317)].

Following this line of thinking, he proposes, but does not claim to have proved, that the quality of being alive is a better claim to moral considerability than sentience.

He then considers some possible objections, especially on the part of those who have claimed that sentience is the key and therefore moral considerability should be limited to humans and a few of the higher animals. In particular, he discusses a paper by Feinberg (1974) which he takes to be the best representative of that point of view. The main point argued by Feinberg is that a being cannot intelligibly be said to deserve moral considerability unless it satisfies the "interest principle". Feinberg notes,

> The sorts of beings who can have rights are precisely those who have (or can have) interests. I have come to this tentative conclusion for two reasons: (1) because a rightholder must be capable of being represented and it is impossible to represent a being that has no interests, and (2) because a rightholder must be capable of being a beneficiary in his own person, and a being without interests is a being that is incapable of being harmed or benefited, having no good or "sake" of its own [Feinberg (1974, p. 51)].

Goodpaster objects to the claim that "interests" logically presupposes desires or wants or aims, the equipment for which is not available to plants. He states that there is no absurdity or unintelligibility in imagining the representation of the needs of a tree for sun and water in the face of a proposal to cut it down or pave its surrounding space for a parking lot. Because of plants' clear tendencies to maintain and heal themselves, he finds it very difficult to reject the idea of interests on their part in staying alive. This he contrasts with "mere things" that are not alive and therefore have no interests.

But in commenting on Goodpaster's article, philosopher W. Murray Hunt (1980) claims that even the condition of living is too narrow a criterion for moral considerability, and that "being in existence" is *at least* as plausible and nonarbitrary a criterion as is life. Hunt's argument rests on two main bases. The first is the "continuity" between living and nonliving things. The second is a counterexample to the proposition that the consideration of "being alive" is sufficient for moral considerability. His example is the problem of fulfilling the wishes of a person who has died. The being alive criterion would imply that such wishes have no moral standing, an implication that Hunt says would not be acceptable to most ethicists. He argues that if the response is that this is because he once was alive, then the criterion would have to be amended to "being alive or once having been alive". In this case, moral consideration would have to be given to "mere things", like coal, since the material composing it was once alive. Essentially, Hunt argues that having started on the "slippery slope" of abandoning strict adherence to humanism, there is no stopping point short of according moral considerability to everything in existence.

Finally, we turn to a very brief discussion of the work of some philosophers who do not even start with humanistic traditions. These are the true "new naturalistic philosophers". Aldo Leopold (1949) is the father of naturalistic ethics, and his famous statement from *A Sand County Almanac*, "A thing is right when it tends to preserve the integrity, stability, and beauty of the biotic community. It is wrong when it tends otherwise", is frequently quoted in this literature. The Summer 1982 (vol. 4, no. 2) of *Environmental Ethics* is a symposium issue, "Environmental Ethics and Contemporary Ethical Theory". In it are contained several papers of this genre. We quote the succinct description of them given in the introduction to the volume by the journal editor:

> In the first paper, Peter Miller argues that psychologically based environmental ethics are ill suited to characterize natural intrinsic value. To solve this problem Miller proposes the acceptance of a metaphysical or metaethical category of richness. In the next paper, Donald Scherer argues that natural value need not depend on psychologically based judgments of human beings. Scherer imagines a series of planets with ever more highly organized levels of life, each of which yield new forms of value. These values are, Scherer argues, neither anthropocentric nor holistic. Holmes Rolston, III develops a position similar to Scherer's, but he finds value in nature beyond life: in geological, tectonic and entropic nature as well. Rolston is concerned with establishing the objective existence of nonpsychological values although he allows that there is a subjective (psychological) component as well, and finds a place for it in his view.

In closing this section, we must reiterate that we have been able to give the reader no more than a glimpse at the new literature in environmental ethics. But we trust it will give the economist reader a feel for the types of arguments made. Whether one is inclined to accept them or not, it is clear that these ideas are much too abstract, or insufficiently formed, to mesh tightly with actual public policy issues or with economic concepts. For the remainder of this chapter, with the exception of the last section, we return to the humanistic fold, and explore some of the implications for environmental economics of ideas stemming from that tradition. But first we develop a perspective on Western humanistic moral philosophy to which we hold for the remainder of this chapter.

4. A plague on all your houses, and a perspective

As our discussion so far should indicate, unanimity of view is not one of the stronger characteristics of environmental ethicists. One might think that might be true primarily of those whom their more orthodox brethren would take to be on the fringe of the discipline, such as the new naturalistic philosophers. But this is not the case. Disagreement abounds among those who espouse utilitarian views on the one hand and libertarian views on the other. The one looks to actions that maximize the good of the whole, and the other to individual rights. Others still are Kantians or Rawlsians, both emphasizing universibility, but in different contexts. Other views exist in addition. In an important recent book, philosopher Alasdair MacIntyre (1981) has performed a critical evaluation of all of the major ethical views in Western philosophy over the last few centuries and found them all wanting. To him they are a combination of fragments of the "older" (aristotelean) tradition and certain modern "novelties". He writes,

> It follows that our society cannot hope to achieve moral consensus. For quite non-Marxist reasons Marx was in the right when he argued against the English trade unionists of the 1860s that appeals to justice were pointless, since there are rival conceptions of justice formed by and informing the life of rival groups. Marx was of course mistaken in supposing that such disagreements over justice are merely secondary phenomena, that they merely reflect the interests of rival economic classes. Conceptions of justice and allegiance to such conceptions are partly constitutive of the lives of social groups, and economic interests are often partially defined in terms of such conceptions and not vice versa. None the less Marx was fundamentally right in seeing conflict and not consensus at the heart of modern social structure. It is not just that we live too much by a variety and multiplicity of fragmented concepts; it is that these are used at one and the same time to express rival and incompatible social ideals and policies *and* to furnish us with a pluralist political rhetoric whose function is to conceal the depth of our conflicts [MacIntyre (1981, p. 235)].

We share MacIntyre's skepticism about man's efforts to find principles of morality through the exercise of his powers of reason and, in his detailed analyses, he makes a convincing case that expressions of ethical views are intertwined with other less minded interests. At the same time, we find his own prescriptions, which would require re-establishment of something like an Athenian city state, equally unconvincing.

If this is the case, one may well ask, why bother with this ethical exercise at all? There are reasons. First, it is indisputably true that most people have moral beliefs and concerns. Perhaps that is what distinguishes them most from even the other higher animals. We think it is very much worthwhile to examine what implementation of those beliefs would imply for environmental economics and decisions on environmental problems – a task to which we turn in succeeding sections. Second, we have a different view of pluralistic society and the function of political processes than expressed in the quotation from MacIntyre. We believe that the pluralism of modern society is simply a fact and that the development of political processes to peacefully and reasonably fairly resolve value conflicts is a high achievement. We also believe that economic-ethical analysis can make an important contribution to informing those processes about implications of viewing things from different moral perspectives. Finally, the philosophical foundation of modern neoclassical economic thought is the ethical doctrine of utilitarianism, albeit in considerably amended form from classical utilitarianism (as we will explain subsequently). We feel that it is worthwhile to try to understand what implications other competing ethical ideas might have for the economic analysis of environmental problems. On this we also hope to make some progress in succeeding sections. Before proceeding, however, to the comparative analysis of several competing ethical systems in the context of some large questions in environmental economics, we turn briefly to the ideas of a few economists who have stepped partly out of the utilitarian framework to consider one such large question. That is our obligation to future generations in the face of resource depletion and potential environmental degeneration.

5. Sustainability

The idea of managing resources in such a way as to maintain a sustainable yield has had appeal to many conservationists. The concepts they have put forward have often drawn the criticism of economists as is explained in Chapters 2, 12 and 14 of this Handbook. However, some economists have been drawn to close relatives of the sustainable yield concept in considering questions about our obligations to the "further future", as some philosophers put it. An early instance was S.V. Ciriacy-Wantrup. In a classical book [Ciriacy-Wantrup (1952)] he advocated the idea of requiring a "safe minimum standard of conservation" as a matter of resources and environmental policy. He wrote "a safe minimum standard of conservation is achieved by avoiding the critical zone – that is those physical conditions, brought about by human action, which would make it uneconomical to halt and reverse depletion" [Ciriacy-Wantrup (1952, p. 253)].

In recent writings, economist Talbot Page (1977, 1982) has elaborated a related idea. He argues that preserving *opportunities* for future generations is a common sense minimal notion of intergenerational justice. He writes,

It seems sensible to focus on the limit our responsibility to what we can foresee and control. As future opportunity is more in our control than future utility, it would seem that opportunity is a more sensible object of intergenerational justice. With some effort we can control the form of the heritage to be passed on to the next generation. It is beyond the control of the present generation to ensure that the next one will be happy or hardworking. It is beyond our control to increase their welfare; we can only assure them of certain opportunities for happiness that we foresee will be essential. But we *can* preserve certain essentials, such as the valuable parts of the cultural and natural resource base. If we cannot ensure that these will in fact be passed on to future generations, we can at least keep from ensuring that they will not be passed on.

From his writings, it is clear that Page includes environmental resources in his concept of the "resource base".

While appealing to common sense, Page, however, also makes appeal to the ideas of two moral philosophers John Locke and John Rawls. Locke's ideas, especially that of "just acquisition" are also incorporated into modern libertarian thought. Page writes:

The most absolute claim of just acquisition is an individual's claim to work wholly created by himself. Thus, Byron had a right to burn his books, but his wife did not, without his permission. (The classical utilitarian would not see the point of this distinction and might deny Byron the right to burn his own books.) The next strongest claim of just acquisition is by an individual who "produces" an object by mixing his labor with a resource of which there is "enough and as good" left for others. The last claim, in fact no claim at all, of just acquisition [for it] concerns the resource base passed into the hands of the present generation by the mere passage of time.

By this argument, the present generation does not have a right to deplete the opportunities afforded by the resource base since it does not "own" it. This is not to say that the resource base, including environmental resources, must be held physically intact, but that when there is depletion, is must be compensated for by technological development or capital investment.

The other ethical philosopher to whose ideas Page appeals is John Rawls (1971). Rawls' book, *A Theory of Justice*, has been exceptionally widely noted and commented upon.

Rawls' just society is based on principles contracted with the mutual consent of all society in an "original position", behind what he calls a "veil of ignorance". Behind the veil, everyone has the general knowledge for determining what principles of justice will regulate society, but lacks knowledge about his own individual case. Rawls writes:

No one know his place in society, his class position or social status; nor does he know his fortune in the distribution of natural assets and abilities, his intelligence and strength, and the like. Nor, again, does anyone know his conception of the good, the particulars of his rational plan of life, or even the special features of his psychology such as his aversion to risk or liability to optimism or pessimism. More than this, I assume that the parties do not know the particular circumstances of their own society. That is, they do not know its economic or political situation, or the level of civilization and culture it has been able to achieve. The persons of the original position have no information as to which generation they belong [Rawls (1971, p. 139)].

Rawls goes on to formulate principles of justice that he thinks would be chosen by society behind the veil of ignorance so that: (1) "each person is to have an equal right to the most extensive basic liberty compatible to similar liberty for others"; (2) "social and economic inequalities are to be arranged so that they are both: (a) reasonably expected to be to everyone's advantage, and (b) attached to offices and positions open to all" [Rawls (1971, p. 68)].

These are principles for intragenerational justice. To the extent that he treats the intergenerational question at all, and his treatment is very limited, he views it primarily in terms of the present generation's duty to save. Page finds this argument unsatisfactory. To him, one of the important ideas of the original position is that it links all generations together with a common perspective [Page (1977, p. 203)]. In the original position, there is no shift in time perspective from one generation to another. It seems plausible that if those in the original position did not know which generation they were going to be part of, they would emphasize intergenerational equity for the same reasons that Rawls supposed that they would do in developing principles of intragenerational justice.

We now proceed to the task of taking five humanistic criteria, utilitarian, benefit–cost analysis (which is an application of a special case of neo-utilitarianism), egalitarian, libertarian, and elitist, and simplifying and defining them in such a way that they can be used in a reasonably rigorous manner for analyzing large problems in environmental economics. This is not an exhaustive list of possible criteria, but they do reasonably span the range of the essence of ideas advocated by humanistic philosophers in the last few centuries. Later we will show how three of these (utilitarian and libertarian as compared to benefit–cost analysis) can be applied to the problem of storing radioactive wastes.

6. Comparative analysis of ethical systems

6.1. Introduction

As we have already said, developing these criteria for analysis involves some radical simplification of the complex frameworks developed by actual moral philosophers. We turn first to utilitarianism. We discuss it somewhat more fully than our other systems. There are two reasons for this: (1) a highly evolved (neo-classical) utility theory is the basis for modern welfare economics and, to an extent, its applied arm, benefit–cost analysis, and (2) the other ethical systems we present are in our version much less complex.

6.2. Utilitarian

In *classical* utilitarianism, individual or collective actions were to be taken in such a manner as to maximize the good of the whole society. Thus, it is quite possible that a person would be called upon to take an action injurious to himself for the good of the whole. *Neoclassical* utilitarianism requires that the individual maximize only his own utility. Neoclassical welfare economics demonstrates that, *under certain very restrictive conditions*, this results in a welfare maximum for the whole economic system, *for a given distribution of claims to assets*. Therefore, neo-classical utilitarianism must take the distribution of income as fixed in proving its welfare theorem and admit that there is also a similar welfare maximum that corresponds to every conceivable income distribution and, as such, it cannot choose among them. Choice of income distribution must be based on concepts other than utility, e.g. justice. Page comments on these matters in an illuminating way:

> To state the matter a little more soberly, many economists rejected classical utilitarianism in favor of its neoclassical version when they decided that utility was entirely nonobservable. At the same time it became clear that most of the structure in economics could be preserved by thinking in terms of preference orderings instead of quantitative utilities. Preference orderings have the advantage of being, at least in principle, observable by choices actually made. This rejection of classical, quantitative utility has two repercussions noteworthy for our purposes.
>
> First, if interpersonal comparisons of utility are impossible, then we are no longer able to maximize the sum of utilities across people. So the neoclassical utilitarian defends a weaker kind of maximization process in which each one maximizes his own utility. The classical utilitarian's moral principle, which says to maximize the sum of utilities, is strong in the sense that it sometimes directs people to act against their own selfish interests. The corresponding, weaker neoclassical utilitarian's moral principle says that we should move toward Pareto optimality. This principle is weaker in not requiring individuals to act against their own selfish interests. It is also weaker because in many situations it does not tell us what to do (it is a partial ordering).
>
> Second, the rejection of observable utilities leads toward a behaviorist or black-box theory of the mind. The only evidence allowed for inferences about happiness or satisfaction is observable behavior: for example, actual purchases

in markets. Evidence from introspection is looked upon with suspicion, as are surveys of stated preferences. The situation is a little like trying to infer the structure of a car's motor by observing the car's operation. With this black-box approach it is not surprising that we might be limited to simple concepts of the motor [Page (1982)].

Thus, the most modern versions of economic welfare theory are said to be *ordinal* utility theories while the classical utility theories assume measurable or cardinal theory. It is now possible to see where benefit–cost analysis sits in all this. Actually, it is an amalgam of classical and neo-classical ideas. It is neo-classical in that it assumes the maximization of individual utilities rather than the utility of the whole, but it is classical in that in actual quantitative application it must, contrary to the neo-classical tradition, assume both measurable and comparable utility. However, it cannot *actually* measure utility, and to get around this fact, to exclude considerations of income distribution, and to maintain its logical integrity, it must make some very strong assumptions; for example, that the marginal utility of income is constant and equal for everyone.[3] Under this assumption, in terms of maximizing net total utility, it does not matter who gets a dollar's worth of benefit or who bears a dollar's worth of costs.

But before turning to our next ethical system, which emphasizes the *justice* of income distribution rather than the maximization of utility (although the principle can, as we shall see, be interpreted in utility terms), it will be a useful lead in to discuss the income distribution question a little more formally. Here we assume, as does benefit–cost analysis, that utility is cardinal and maximized by individuals. However, we assume, consistent with the classical utilitarian view, that marginal utility diminishes with increased income for each individual and may differ between individuals.

First, we will examine the case, consistent, for example, with the view of Pigou (1920), where all individuals have (about) the same relationship between utility and income. Thus, for example, if two individuals, A and B, have utility U_A and U_B, respectively, derived from incomes Y_A and Y_B, respectively, and if Mr. B is initially wealthier than Mr. A., $Y_B^0 > Y_A^0$, then B has a higher total utility level than A. But given the traditional utilitarian assumption of diminishing marginal utility, that the utility curves in Figure 5.1 flatten out as income increases, it is easy to show that society's total utility could be enlarged by giving A and B the same income, $\overline{Y}$. This follows because, by raising A's income from Y_A^0 to $\overline{Y}$, we get a gain in utility of ΔU_A compared to the loss in utility ΔU_B to B, resulting from lowering B's incomes from Y_B^0 to $\overline{Y}$. Note that $Y_B^0 - \overline{Y} = \overline{Y} - Y_A^0$, so we take income away from B to give to A to get a gain in total utility, $U_A + U_B$, since $|\Delta U_A| > |\Delta U_B|$, or A's gain exceeds B's loss.

---

[3] Although it must be pointed out that benefit–cost analysis may be defensible in logically looser ways.

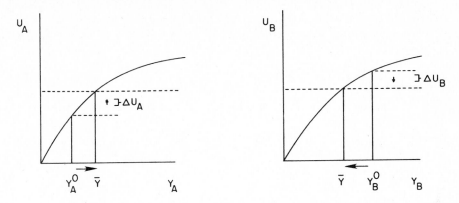

Figure 5.1. Utility as a function of income for two hypothetical individuals.

The same solution results from solving the following problem:

$$\max U_A(Y_A) + U_B(Y_B)$$
s.t.
$$Y_A + Y_B = Y_A^0 + Y_B^0,$$

which implies at the optimum that $\Delta U_A/\Delta Y_A = \Delta U_A/\Delta Y_B$, or that the rate of increase of utility with income (marginal utility) must be equal for the two individuals. Since the two individuals in our example have similar utility functions, marginal utilities are equated where incomes are the same, $Y_A = Y_B = \overline{Y}$.

But, on the other hand, we can assume different individuals have different utility functions. For example, Edgeworth (1967), in *Mathematical Psychics* (first published in 1881) argues that the rich have more sensitivity and can better enjoy money income than the poor. We then end up with a situation like that shown in Figure 5.2. Y_A^* and Y_B^* are utility maximizing incomes for A and B because the marginal utilities of income are equated. Mr. A gets more income then Mr. B because he obtains more utility from income than B does. In Edgeworth's view, Mr. A by his sensitivity should have more money to be used in appreciating fine wine than Mr. B who is satisfied with common ale. In the extreme case, Mr. A might be a "utility monster", i.e. his marginal utility of money income might everywhere exceed Mr. B's marginal utility of income, in which case all of society's income should go to Mr. A.

Clearly, then, in the utilitarian framework, depending on beliefs about the particular nature of utility functions, any distribution of income can be justified, ranging from an egalitarian viewpoint (Pigou) to an elitist viewpoint (Edgeworth).

There do exist ethical systems which are totally egalitarian on the one hand, and totally elitist on the other. These diametrically opposed ethical systems are described next. We realize that probably very few people, if pushed to the wall,

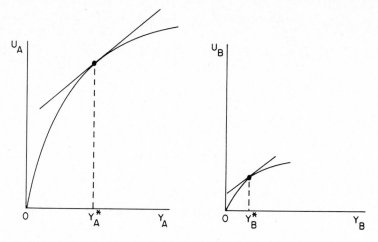

Figure 5.2. Society maximizes total utility by giving more income to A than to B.

would actually support the implementation of either of these extreme systems in its pure form. But is is useful to analyze them as representing the ends of the spectrum.

6.3. Egalitarian

The egalitarian view holds that the well-being of a society is measured by the well-being of the worst off person in that society. This criterion would, if fully adopted, lead to a totally equal distribution of utility.[4]

The egalitarian criterion can be expressed mathematically in economic terms as follows: for two individuals A and B, where utility is denoted U, if $U_A < U_B$, we maximize U_A subject to $U_A \leq U_B$; if $U_B < U_A$, then we maximize U_A subject to $U_B \leq U_A$. If we reach a state where ($U_A = U_B$, then we maximize U_A subject to $U_A = U_B$. The implication of this for redistribution of income is that we begin by adding income to the worst off individual (taking income away from wealthier individuals) until he catches up with the next worst-off individual. We then add income to both individuals until their utility levels (well-being) have caught up to the third worst off, etc. Eventually, this process must lead to a state where $U_A = U_B = U_C = U_D \ldots$ for all individuals in a society, where all utilities are identical, or to a state where further redistributions will make everyone worse off, e.g. through negative impacts on incentives. This criterion can be written more

---

[4] Contemporary egalitarianism is often associated with the writing of John Rawls but it should be clear from even our brief earlier discussion of his ideas that his theory of just distribution is much more complex than the simple egalitarian criterion we analyze here.

compactly for a two-person society as $\max \min \{U_A, U_B\}$, so we are always trying to maximize the utility of the individual with the minimum utility. Implicit also in the argument is the assumption that the individuals' utility functions with respect to income are about the same. Thus, this ethical criterion would work toward a relatively equal distribution of income among individuals in a single generation or, in an intergenerational situation, across generations.

6.4. Elitist

An elitist criterion can be derived as the precise opposite of the egalitarian criterion. The well-being of society is measured by the well-being of the best off individual. Every act is "right" if it improves the welfare of the best off and "wrong" if it decreases the welfare of the best off.[5]

We discuss this criterion primarily to display the polar opposite of the egalitarian case. But it should be mentioned elitist arguments are sometimes made and action taken on them even in our society. The gasoline shortage of the summer of 1979 moved Senator Hiyakawa of California to comment: "The important thing is that a lot of the poor don't need gas because they're not working." Economic productivity can in this sense rationalize a defined "elite". Thus, concepts of merit can be elitist in nature, e.g. those who produce the most "should" have the largest merit increases in salary (even though they may already have the highest salaries).

The income distribution implied by this criterion is not simply to give all of society's wealth to the best off. This is true because, if between two individuals A and B we are attempting to

$$\max \max \{U_A, U_B\},$$

or to maximize the utility of the individual who can attain the greatest utility, we must first find the solution for $\max U_A$, and then separately for $\max U_B$, and then pick whichever solution gives the greatest individual utility. Obviously, it will usually be better to keep B alive to serve A, i.e. to contribute to his well-being than to give B nothing if A is to be best off. Thus, subsistence (which in a broader context might include minimal education, health care, etc.) is typically required for B. Similarly, if we have two succeeding generations, it may well be "best" for the first generation to save as much as possible to make the next generation better off. This attitude has been manifest among many immigrants to the United States with respect to their children. Thus, an elitist viewpoint may support altruistic behavior.

[5] The elitist view is often associated with the writing of Fredrich Nietzsche, *Beyond Good and Evil* (1886). But, as noted in connection with Rawls, Nietzsche's ideas are much more complex than the simple criterion adopted here.

The ethical systems we have considered so far have been in one way or another concerned with the welfare or the "goodness" of the whole society. There is another class of ethical systems that concerns itself not with society at large, but with protecting individual rights. In regard to public policy issues, as we will see, the two are usually in conflict.

6.5. Pareto criterion

The fourth ethical system is an amalgam of a number of ethical principles embodied in part in a Christian ethic (the Golden Rule) as well as in the U.S. Constitutional viewpoint that individual freedoms prevail except where others may be harmed. These views which emphasize individual rights have been formalized by Nozick (1974) in a strict libertarian framework. We are not here concerned with changing the initial position of individuals in society to some ideal state, as were all the ethical systems discussed earlier, but rather in benefiting all or at least preventing harm to others, even if those others are already better off. This ethic has been embodied often by economists in the form of a criterion requiring "Pareto superiority", that is, an unambiguous improvement in welfare requires that all persons be made better off by a change in resource use or at least as well off as before. Any act is then immoral or wrong if anyone is worse off because of it. Any act which improves an individual's or several individuals' well-being and harms no one is then moral or "right".

If, for example, Mr. A and Mr. B initially have incomes Y_A^0 and Y_B^0, then we require for any new distribution of wealth (Y_A, Y_B) – for example, if more wealth becomes available and must be distributed – that

$$U_A(Y_A) \geq U_A(Y_A^0)$$

and

$$U_B(Y_B) \geq U_B(Y_B^0),$$

or each individual must be at least as well off as he initially was. Any redistribution, e.g. from wealthy to poor or vice versa, is specifically proscribed by this criterion. Thus, this criterion, while seemingly weak – i.e. it does not call for redistribution – can block many possible actions if they do as a side effect redistribute income to make *anyone* worse off, however slight the effect may be. Often, then, to satisfy a libertarian or Pareto criterion requires that gainers from a particular social decision must *actually* compensate losers. In practice, in public policy decisions, this rarely occurs, at least fully, and there are some important situations where it is technically impossible.

7. An application to the problem of nuclear waste storage

This section is an attempt to look beyond traditional benefit–cost analysis to consider long-term nuclear waste storage from both an ethical and an economic perspective. The problem of nuclear waste storage exemplifies the type of problem where benefit–cost analysis has most often been criticized. We conjecture that the dual problem of valuing risk to life of future generations motivates these criticisms. To address these issues, we develop formal economic models of alternative decision criteria for nuclear waste storage which are based, at least loosely, on alternative ethical positions. In particular, two of the alternative ethical positions outlined above are contrasted with each other and then with standard benefit–cost analysis.

First, the utilitarian ethic is used to explore the notion that the proper goal for society is to pursue the good of the whole both across individuals and more importantly across time. Second, we focus on the Pareto or libertarian criterion where the protection of individual rights both across individuals and across generations is more important than the good of the whole. It should be noted that these criteria share two characteristics. First, in each, man is the measure of all things. Thus, in contrast to the naturalistic ethic the only value of the natural environment is the value human beings place on it, and so nonhuman objects have no intrinsic value. Second, these criteria are consistent with the neo-classical notion of economic efficiency and are consequentialist in nature – focusing on outcomes of the decision process. It should be noted that philosophers view any consequentialist analysis to be at least utilitarian in spirit as opposed to other humanistic ethics which focus on procedures or due process.

Given the formalization of the Utilitarian and Pareto ethics presented in the previous section, we can model the choice to store nuclear wastes using an expected utility framework as follows: we assume that there are only two generations. Generation one, the current generation, has to decide whether or not to develop nuclear facilities. Utility of generation one, $U_1(Y_1)$ depends on generation one's income, Y_1, which initially is $\overline{Y}_1$. For this illustrative example we assume that generation of one's income can be augmented by utilizing nuclear power which adds B dollars in net to income (net benefits to generation one of nuclear power) but in turn depends on generating nuclear wastes of w tons. Thus, B is an increasing function of w, $B(w)$. Income to generation one is then $\overline{Y}_1 + B(w)$. However, generation one may decide to compensate the future generation, generation two, for the hazards of nuclear waste storage imposed on them. Thus, generation one might reduce their income by C dollars to be invested for the benefit of generation two, leaving a net income of $Y_1 = \overline{Y}_1 + B(w) - C$. Generation two, with an initial income of $\overline{Y}_2$, may then receive an income of $Y_2 = \overline{Y}_2 + (1 + r)C$ if generation one invests C dollars at a rate of return r for the period of time between the two generations. If, however, the two generations are separated by 10 000 years, it is highly doubtful that compensation is possible, i.e. the odds are zero that a financial institution will survive over such a period to accumulate compound interest at rate r. Of course, we still may properly assume that risk of death to individuals in generation two, $\Pi_2(w)$, is a function of the quantity of nuclear wastes created by generation one, since nuclear wastes will still be radioactive even after 10 000 years have passed. We assume, to focus just on the intergenerational risk issue, that risks to generation one are fixed at Π_1^0. Utilizing the two ethical criteria, we will now explore under what decision rule nuclear power should be pursued by generation one, thus transferring nuclear waste to generation two.

We can summarize the notation outlined above as follows:

Π_i = probability of death in generation i,

U_i = utility in generation i where $U_i' > 0$; $U_i'' < 0$,

Y_i = income in generation i,

$B(w)$ = net benefits (additional income) of having nuclear power, an increasing function of the quantity of nuclear waste (w),

r = interest rate,

C = compensation from generation one to generation two: $C \geq 0$.

For generation one, expected utility (E_1) is equal to the probability of death times the utility obtained from initial income ($\overline{Y}_1$) plus the benefits associated with nuclear power, minus compensation paid (if any) to the future generation:

$$E_1 = \left(1 - \Pi_1^0\right)U_1\left(\overline{Y}_1 + B(w) - C\right). \tag{1}$$

The second generation's expected utility is dependent upon the probability of death as a function of the amount of nuclear waste times the utility from initial income ($\overline{Y}_2$) plus compensation paid (if any) compounded at the rate of interest, r:

$$E_2 = \left(1 - \Pi_2(w)\right)U_2\left(\overline{Y}_2 + (1 + r) \cdot C\right). \tag{2}$$

The Utilitarian criterion states that the sum of the total expected utilities of both generations, T, should be maximized;

$$\max_{w, C} T = E_1 + E_2, \tag{3}$$

where the choice variables are the levels of compensation (C) and generation of nuclear waste (w). We make the following assumptions of symmetry between generations: (1) $U_1(Y) \equiv U_2(Y)$ or both generations have the same utility functions; (2) $\overline{Y}_1 = \overline{Y}_2$ or both generations have the same initial income; and (3) $\Pi_1^0 = \Pi_2^0$ or both generations have the same initial risk. Thus, we explore an egalitarian formulation of the Utilitarian ethic similar to that associated with Pigou in the preceding section.

The first-order conditions are:

$$\partial T/\partial C = -(1 - \Pi^0)U_1' + (1 - \Pi_2)U_2'(1 - r) \leq 0 \tag{4}$$

and

$$\partial T/\partial w = (1 - \Pi^0)U_1'B' - \Pi_2'U_2 \leq 0. \tag{5}$$

The decision of whether or not to build nuclear power plants thus generating nuclear wastes can be analyzed in two contexts. The first situation is that where compensation between generations is impossible or undesirable $(C = 0)$ so (4) holds with inequality. The second case is where compensation is possible and desirable $(C > 0)$ so (4) holds with equality. We will evaluate whether or not nuclear facilities should be built, generating waste, by evaluating $\partial T/\partial w$ at the point where $w = 0$. Rearranging (5) yields:

$$B'(0) \gtrless \frac{\Pi_2'U_2}{(1 - \Pi_1^0)U_1'}, \quad \text{for} \quad \left.\frac{\partial T}{\partial w}\right|_{w=0} \gtrless 0. \tag{6}$$

Let us consider the case where compensation between generation one and two is impossible. Utilizing the assumptions of symmetry between generations, the assumption of no compensation and $w = 0$ implies that utility in each generation is the same, or $U_2(\bar{Y}_2) = U_1(\bar{Y}_1)$. This implies the marginal utility of generation one (U_1') is equal to marginal utility of generation two (U_2'). Additionally, evaluating the decision at $w = 0$ implies the same risk levels or $\Pi_1^0 = \Pi_2(0)$. Thus, (6) can be rewritten by substituting U_2' for U_1' and $\Pi_2^0(0)$ for Π_1^0 yielding:

$$B'(0) \gtrless \frac{\Pi_2'U_2}{(1 - \Pi_2(0))U_2'}, \quad \text{for} \quad \left.\frac{\partial T}{\partial w}\right|_{w=0} \gtrless 0. \tag{7}$$

(7) states that generation one can evaluate whether or not to build a nuclear facility by determining whether the marginal benefits of nuclear power are greater than, less than, or equal to the incremental risk (Π_2') times the marginal compensation for increased risk of death or value of safety $U_2/(1 - \Pi_2(0))U_2'$ for generation two which, given our assumptions, is the same as the marginal value of safety for generation one. Assuming that compensation is impossible results in no discounting of future damages (the cost of risk to generation two). Thus, in order to pursue nuclear power (so optimally $w > 0$) the marginal benefits to generation one must be greater than the associated incremental risk to generation two times the marginal value of safety of generation two both evaluated at $w = 0$. The discount rate where no compensation is possible under an egalitarian specification of the Utilitarian ethic is thus equal to zero.

Let us now consider the decision for generation one under the Utilitarian criterion where compensation is possible and desirable. In this scenario, condition

(4) holds with equality and the assumption of equal initial income does not hold: $U_1(\overline{Y}_1) \neq U_2(\overline{Y}_2)$. Rearranging condition (4) and solving for U_1' yields:

$$B'(0) \lessgtr \left[\frac{1}{1+r}\right][\Pi_2']\left[\frac{U_2}{(1-\Pi_2)U_2'}\right].\tag{8}$$

If the marginal benefits of nuclear power are greater than or equal to the discounted value, $[1/(1+r)]$, of the incremental risk (Π_2') to generation two, times the marginal value of safety $[U_2/(1-\Pi_2)U_2']$ for generation two, then a policy of nuclear power should be pursued under the Utilitarian criterion. Thus, if compensation is possible under an egalitarian specification of the Utilitarian ethic the discount rate should be equal to the rate of interest.

The Pareto or Libertarian criterion can be stated as follows. If generation one's well-being is improved by using nuclear power and production of nuclear waste, then generation two must be at least as well off as before. The expected utilities for generations one and two defined in (1) and (2) can be used to state the Libertarian criterion:

$$\max_{w,c}(1-\Pi_1^0)U_1(Y_1+B(w)-C)$$

s.t.　　　　　　　(a)

$$(1-\Pi_2^0(w))U_2(Y_2+(1+r)C) \geq (1-\Pi_2(0))U_2(\overline{Y}_2).$$

　　(b)　　　　　　　　　　　　　(c)

$$(9)$$

We maximize the expected utility of generation one [term (a)] subject to the condition that the expected utility of generation two [term (b)] is greater than or equal to the initial utility of generation two [term (c)] where no nuclear waste is produced. Thus, the rights of generation two are defended by the constraint. The first-order conditions are

$$\partial L/\partial C = -(1-\Pi_1^0)U_1'+\lambda(1-\Pi_2)U_2'(1+r)=0\tag{10}$$

and

$$\partial L/\partial w = (1-\Pi_1^0)U_1'B'-\lambda\Pi_2'U_2 \leq 0.\tag{11}$$

Again, assuming an egalitarian symmetry between generations, the condition for evaluating the decision to build a nuclear facility from the perspective that initially $w=0$, is obtained by rearrangement of (11) which yields:

$$B'(0) \gtrless \frac{\lambda\Pi_2'U_2}{(1-\Pi_1^0)U_1'}.\tag{12}$$

Only one situation relating to compensation is available for analysis in the Libertarian case due to the structure of the constraint. That is, if no compensation is possible then the amount of nuclear waste must be zero or the Pareto criterion is violated. This is, the term (b) in eq. (9) would be less than term (c) and generation two would not be at least as well off as before. Thus the only situation of interest for the decision to build a nuclear facility is where compensation for generation two due to the existence of nuclear waste is possible. Solving for λ in condition (10) assuming compensation is possible yields:

$$\lambda = \frac{\left(1 - \Pi_1^0\right)U_1'}{\left(1 - \Pi_2\right)U_2'(1 + r)}.$$ (13)

Substituting into (13) yields:

$$B'(0) \gtrless \frac{1}{1 + r} \frac{U_2}{\left(1 - \Pi_2\right)U_2'}.$$ (14)

A policy of nuclear power should be pursued under the Libertarian ethic only when compensation is possible and the marginal benefits to generation one are greater than the discounted marginal value of risk to generation two.

We can summarize our results as follows. The Utilitarian ethic, in the case where identical initial incomes and utility functions are assumed, would require discounting only if compensation can actually be paid. Otherwise a zero discount rate is appropriate. The Libertarian case would reject nuclear waste storage outright if compensation cannot be paid, but accepts the discounting procedure if compensation between generations is possible. Since it is unreasonable to assume that compensation can be paid to generations 10 000 years or more in the future for the storing of nuclear waste, this analysis leads under the assumption of an egalitarian specification of the Utilitarian ethic, to the use of a zero discount rate or, under the assumption of a Libertarian ethic, to the outright rejection of nuclear waste storage. Traditional benefit–cost analysis, on the other hand, would almost certainly lead to the conclusion that nuclear waste storage is unimportant in the nuclear power decision since future damages would, at any usual positive rate of interest, be discounted to near zero.

8. Conclusion: Ethics and a policy debate

In discussing environmental policy, economists have tended to favor approaches that emphasize economic incentives (e.g. effluent charges) in contrast to command and control regulation (e.g. effluent standards). Many environmentalists have also supported economic incentives as part of environmental policy. A large and influential group of environmentalists have, however, been adamantly opposed to the use of charges to help manage environmental quality. This group of environmentalists and economists who advocate charges have not found it possible (or perhaps desirable) to communicate with each others positions and therefore have been unable to understand each other properly. In an important recent book political scientist Kelman (1981) attempts to interpret each group to the other.

We close this chapter with a brief discussion of that book and a statement of our own perspective on ethics and environmental economics.

In the first chapter, Kelman presents the economists' rationale for charges in a highly simplified form. The argument is that charges will be more efficient than uniform emission standards in the sense that a given level of ambient environmental quality can be attained by their use at less cost than by the implementation of standards. Theory and several quantitative case studies support this view, but the issue is a lot more complex than one would gather from this chapter. This is no real complaint, however, because, for the sake of understanding the differences between economists who support effluent charges and those environmentalists who oppose them, the relative efficiency of charges can be taken as given, for the argument is not primarily about that.

The second chapter presents a discussion of ethical theory and the case for concern about charges. This is the chapter that is most salient to our present concerns, and we will dwell mostly upon it in this discussion. We note in passing that if one only read this chapter, one would get the impression that on ethical grounds, *all* environmentalists are opposed to charges. This, as we just noted, is not true. The interviews reported in the third chapter of Kelman's book show that the community of environmentalists is divided on the question. Indeed, for a time in the 1970s, there existed a group of environmental organizations called the "Coalition to Tax Pollution". In particular, they supported a charge on sulfur compounds emitted to the atmosphere. Once again though, for the sake of ethical discussion, this split among the environmentalists does not matter. A large number of environmentalists are opposed to charges. Also, the ethical positions described in Kelman's chapter two do probably fairly characterize the group of environmentalists, both inside and outside of government, who drafted and lobbied through Congress the basic national air and water pollution legislation in the early 1970s. This legislation rejected charges and established effluent standards based on concepts of "best available technology".

The remaining chapters of the book are not of particular pertinence to the present discussion. Let us therefore return to the presentation in Chapter 2 of the ethical ideas that in Kelman's view are held by those hostile to charges. This chapter proved to us, as economists, extremely revealing and insightful. As noted in earlier discussion, in the normal course of things, economists take people's preferences as given. They do not inquire into people's motives except, also as previously discussed, that they assume people are guided mostly by their self-interest, at least in economic matters. This assumption of self-interest is at the heart of the efficiency case for charges.[6] To capture the essence of the idea, if public policy specifies that emissions to the atmosphere be reduced by a certain amount, say in a metropolitan area, this could be accomplished in alternative ways. All discharges could be cut back by a certain fraction by enforcing

---

[6] Charges and standards are discussed in detail in Chapter 10 of this Handbook.

emissions standards. Alternatively, a charge could be levied on each unit of discharge and each emitter could be left to decide how much to control and how much to discharge. Acting in his own best interest, he would reduce discharge until the cost of another unit of discharge reduction is equal to the charge. This is because up to that point, his overall costs will be lower if he curbs the discharge than if he pays the emissions fee. If cost of reducing discharge are different for different dischargers, as in practice they are, much control will be induced at points where control costs are low and little control where costs are high. Thus, if the charge is set at the appropriate level, the combination of the economic incentive provided by it and the self-interest of the dischargers will produce a situation where the same amount of overall discharge reduction can be achieved as with emission standards, but at lower (possibly much lower) overall cost. This means that the real cost to society is lower with charges than with standards to achieve the same social objective.

But according to Kelman's analysis, the environmentalist hostile to charges would not find the results of applying the charges technique acceptable even if he agreed that the outcome just indicated would really happen. He would object that discharging substances to the environment that put others at risk or harm them economically is ethically wrong. As we saw in the discussion above, the Pareto or Libertarian ethical system could provide a foundation for this view of the matter.

The environmentalist in question then *does* care about motives, and he *does not* want to create a situation in which discharges to the environment appear to those doing them to be legitimate. This, apparently, is what is behind the cliche "license to pollute" that some environmentalists have so long used to inveigh against charges and which has so long baffled economists. The economist tends to see emissions standards that do not forbid discharges entirely (and for practical reasons, few do) as the real license to pollute. This is because once the standard is met, remaining discharges to the environmental commons can occur with no penalty at all to the polluter. In other words, they are free gifts to the polluter.

Again, here economists and environmentalists sail past each other in the night. According to Kelman, even though environmentalists are realistic enough to see that zero discharges is, in most cases, an impossible dream, they feel that polluting activity should be stigmatized by making it illegal and by persuading others to share their ethical view of the matter. If the emitter cannot realistically stop entirely, then he should want to "do his best" to do so. This appears to be the ethical foundation, at least in those particular environmentalists' minds, for using discharge permit systems that require "best available technology" somehow defined. If the discharger is within his permit requirements, he is by definition doing his best. Regulatory systems incorporating economic incentives are not acceptable because they do not ensure that everyone will be doing his best, even if they result in lower costs to society, of meeting the same environmental goals, or in meeting higher environmental goals at the same cost.

This environmental policy stance is only apparently oriented to results. In fact, it does not care about the overall efficiency of the system, it neglects opportunities for improving environmental quality other than by discharge reduction (for example, by reservoir operations in a river system), and in its extreme sense, it does not even care about environmental quality as long as everyone is doing his best.

It seems clear to us that the ethical attitude described by Kelman has left us with environmental policies that produce both higher costs and less environmental quality than an approach that would have paid attention to efficiency. That situation in itself presents an interesting ethical dilemma.

As discussed in Chapter 1 the first law of thermodynamics requires that the mass of materials extracted from nature and used in man's production and consumption activities must be returned in some manner to the natural environment because matter is not destroyed in these activities. All that can be altered is the form and location of these residuals discharges or the total throughput can be altered somewhat by recycling of used materials. It strikes us as distinctly odd to regard a socially necessary activity, residuals generation, dictated by natural law, as being *inherently* immoral in the same way that most people, including economists, regard rape or murder as immoral. Much more appropriate, in our opinion, is to regard it as an important societal problem that requires collective choices and public management as part of which a variety of policy instruments may be employed.

In closing, it may be interesting to discuss briefly how the ethical ideas put forth in the preceding parts of this chapter would view polluting activity. A utilitarian would presumably conclude that if the utility to the polluter outweighed the utility to the damaged parties, polluting would be all right. To an egalitarian, presumably whether the activity led to a more or less equal distribution of utilities or opportunities would be the dominant consideration.

In cases where damaged parties cannot be, or are not, compensated, i.e. almost always, two other ethical rules are unequivocal and, in result, agree with the environmental fundamentalism described by Kelman if the status quo point is taken to be a condition of no pollution. A libertarian presumably would reject any polluting activity because it infringes on the rights of others. Interestingly, a rule derived from economic theory, the Pareto principle discussed earlier, also leads to the environmentalists' result. This criterion, as the reader will recall, holds that an action can only be regarded as an unambiguous economic improvement if it makes at least one person better off and no one else worse off. In the absence of compensation, application of this criterion would foreclose any polluting activity. However, if the status quo is taken to be the actual state of pollution, the criterion would counsel us to do nothing or else compensate the polluters. Economists interested in public policy almost always reject the Pareto criterion because it enshrines the status quo and would prevent virtually any public action. This is the trouble with absolutist criteria of any kind. Their application would either hang up any possibility of action or otherwise muck up the functioning of the economic and social system in an unacceptable manner.

A more suitable way to think about ethical aspects of public policy might be to view it in terms of combinations of criteria. An appropriate ethical, as contrasted to political, goal or public policy might be a utilitarian one (since we do care about the good of the whole), but constrained by Libertarian considerations (limits on how much individual interests may be intruded upon) and egalitarian considerations (permit differences of income based primarily on productivity incentive objectives). Should one view the matter in this way, economic theory and method might make some interesting contributions to philosophical discourse, for the stuff of microeconomics is optimization under multiple constraints. Intriguing thought!

References

Bentham, Jeremy (1789) *Introduction to the Principles of Morals and Legislation* (London). Quoted in John Passmore (1974) *Man's Responsibility for Nature* (Charles Scribner's Sons, New York).

Ciriacy-Wantrup, S.V. (1952) *Resource Conservation: Economics and Policies* (University of California Press, Berkeley and Los Angeles).

Committee of the National Academy of Sciences (1974) "Air Quality and Automotive Emissions Control", vol. 4, *The Costs and Benefits of Automotive Emissions Control*, serial no. 19–24 (GPO, Washington, D.C.).

Eckstein, Otto (1958) *Water Resources Development: The Economics of Project Evaluation* (Harvard University Press, Cambridge).

Edgeworth, Francis (1967) *Mathematical Psychics: An Essay on the Application of Mathematics to the Moral Sciences* (A.M. Kelley, New York).

Feinberg, Joel (1974) "The Rights of Animals and Unborn Generations", in: William T. Blackstone (ed.), *Philosophy and the Environmental Crisis* (University of Georgia Press, Athens).

Gray, Elizabeth Dodson (1979) *Why the Green Nigger? Re-Mything Genesis* (Roundtable Press, Wellesley)

Goodpaster, Kenneth E. (1978) "On Being Morally Considerable", *The Journal of Philosophy* 75, 308.

Hirschleifer, Jack, James De Haven and Jerome Milliman (1960) *Water Supply: Economic Technology and Policy* (University of Chicago Press, Chicago).

Hunt, W. Murray (1980) "Are 'Mere Things' Morally Considerable", *Environmental Ethics* 2, no. 1, 59.

Jackson, Clement, et al. (1976) "Benefit-Cost Analysis of Automotive Emissions Reductions", General Motors Research Laboratory GMR 2265.

Kelman, Stephen (1981) *What Price Incentives–Economists and the Environment* (Auburn House Publishing Company, Boston).

Leopold, Aldo (1949) *A Sand County Almanac and Sketches Here and There* (Oxford University Press, New York).

Maass, Arthur, Maynard Hufschmidt, Robert Dorfman, Harold A. Thomas, Jr., Stephen Margin and Gordon Fair (1962) *Design of Water Resource Systems* (Harvard University Press, Cambridge).

MacIntyre, Alasdair (1981) *After Virtue* (University of Notre Dame Press, Notre Dame).

Marietta, Don E., Jr. (1982) "Knowledge and Obligation and Obligation in Environmental Ethics: A Phenomenological Analysis", *Environmental Ethics* 4 no. 2, 155.

Nozick, Robert (1974) *Anarchy, State and Utopia* (Johns Hopkins University Press, Baltimore).

Page, Talbot (1977) *Conservation and Economics Efficiency* (Johns Hopkins Press for Resources for the Future, Inc., Baltimore).

Page, Talbot (1982) "Intergenerational Justice As Opportunity", in: Douglas MacLean and Peter Brown, (eds.), *Energy and the Future* (Rowman and Littlefield, Totowa).

Pigou, A.C. (1920) *The Economics of Welfare* (Macmillan, London).

Rawls, John (1971) *A Theory of Justice* (Harvard University Press, Cambridge).

Robinson, Joan (1963) *Economic Philosophy* (Aldine Publishing, Chicago).

Shute, Sara (1980) *Environmental Ethics* 2 no. 2, 187.

U.S. Atomic Energy Commission, Division of Reactor Development and Technology (1972) *Updated 1970 Cost–Benefit Analysis of the U.S. Breeder Reactor Program* (Washington, D.C.).

Warnock, G.J. (1971) *The Object of Morality* (Methuen, New York).

Watson, Richard A. (1979) "Self-Consciousness and the Rights of Nonhuman Animals and Nature", *Environmental Ethics* 1 no. 2, 99.

PART 2

SELECTED METHODS AND APPLICATIONS OF ECONOMICS TO ENVIRONMENTAL PROBLEMS

Chapter 6

METHODS FOR ASSESSING THE BENEFITS OF ENVIRONMENTAL PROGRAMS

A. MYRICK FREEMAN, III*

Bowdoin College, Brunswick, Maine

1. Introduction

Environmental regulations that lead to the reduction in the emissions of air and water pollutants presumably are undertaken because of the welfare gains they generate for people. Most economists who have written about environmental policy have endorsed the notion that the beneficial effects of environmental quality improvement should be quantified and measured in monetary terms for comparison with the costs of environmental improvement; and this prescription was adopted during the Reagan Administration in the form of Executive Order 12291 issued in 1981. This Order calls for the measurement in monetary terms of all of the beneficial and adverse effects of proposed regulations and stipulates that, unless otherwise precluded by law, regulatory policies should be designed to maximize net economic benefits.

If it is granted that the public goods attributes of most dimensions of environmental quality preclude the development of well functioning markets for air and water quality, how are the monetary values of improvements in environmental quality to be measured? The past ten to fifteen years have seen the rapid development of the economic theory and techniques for measuring the demands for non-marketed goods. Many of these techniques rely on observations of market related behavior and changes in market prices and quantities that result from changes in environmental quality. For example, if an environmental improvement affects the productivity or production costs of firms, these effects may be reflected in higher output, lower prices to consumers, and changes in factor incomes and quasi-rents. Alternatively, changes in environmental quality may cause individuals to alter their purchases of goods and services which are complements or substitutes for environmental quality in their preferences orderings. One major approach to measuring public goods demands has been to develop models of production and costs, factor and product markets, and individual choice which make possible the calculation of welfare gains in money terms from observed market data.

The second major approach has been to ask people how they would respond to hypothetical changes in environmental quality. Several models and techniques have been developed to interpret individuals' responses to such questions and to allow the calculation of the money benefits of the hypothetical changes.

* I am grateful to V. Kerry Smith for helpful comments and suggestions on this paper.

Handbook of Natural Resource and Energy Economics, vol. I, edited by A.V. Kneese and J.L. Sweeney
© *Elsevier Science Publishers B.V., 1985*

In this chapter I will describe the principal economic techniques for estimating the benefits of environmental quality improvements with special emphasis on the underlying economic theory and models.[1] The early empirical literature contained many examples of efforts to estimate benefits which were based on invalid concepts of welfare gain or involved faulty models of economic behavior and relationships. The emphasis on economic theory and method in this paper should make it possible for readers to develop conceptually correct methods for estimating benefits in new circumstances and to evaluate the theoretical validity of empirical benefit studies.

The plan of the chapter is as follows. Section 2 lays out a simple model of the process through which an environmental regulation results in economic benefits. The purpose of this model is to show that economic measures of benefits require an understanding of the underlying physical, chemical, and biological processes which make up the environment (see also Chapters 2 and 3 of this Handbook). Section 3 considers some fundamental questions in the definition and measurement of welfare change. Sections 5–7 examine models based upon the revealed behavior of producers and consumers responding to price signals and changes in environment quality and models based upon how people say they will respond to specific hypothetical changes. A conclusion is given in Section 8.

2. The basic model

The ultimate objective of the analysis is a measure of welfare gains associated with an environmental regulation. The regulation affects the decisions and behavior of sources of pollution. As a consequence there are changes in the rates at which polluting substances are discharged to the environment. These changes in turn lead to changes in the concentrations of substances in the environment over some geographical area. Changes in measures of environmental quality affect the uses made of the environment by both producers and households. It is these changes in the uses of the environment that have welfare implications which can be measured in money terms. The behavioral and economic consequences of changes in environmental quality may extend over a much larger geographical area than that in which physical changes in the environment occur. The geographic scope of the benefits estimation model should be broad enough to capture all of the important physical, environmental, and economic relationships affected

---

[1] The reader who is interested primarily in the empirical results of benefit estimation studies should see Freeman (1982a) and references therein. This book presents a critical review and evaluation of studies estimating air and water pollution control benefits in the United States. Readers who wish to get some sense of the development of the state of the art over the past fifteen years should see my earlier survey article [Freeman (1975)] and more recent book [Freeman (1979a)].

by the regulation being analyzed. A review of many of the spatial aspects of environmental economics is found in Chapter 3 of this Handbook.

To formalize these considerations in the context of benefit estimation, consider the following model. Assume that there is only one polluting substance being discharged into the environment. Let D represent the quantity of this substance which is discharged per year. Suppose that environmental quality can be measured by a single parameter, Q. Let X represent the level of an activity which is adversely affected by pollution. Finally, let W represent the level of economic welfare associated with X, measured in money. It might be helpful to think of the following concrete example: D is biochemical oxygen demand (BOD); Q is dissolved oxygen (DO); X is recreation days per year. The model can be expressed as:

$$Q = Q(D), \quad (dQ/dD < 0), \tag{1}$$

$$X = X(Q), \quad (dX/dQ > 0), \tag{2}$$

$$W = W(X), \quad (dW/dX > 0). \tag{3}$$

By substitution we have:

$$W = f(D), \quad (dW/dD < 0).$$

The benefit of a pollution control regulation that reduces D from D_1 to D_2 $(= \Delta D)$ is:

$$B = \Delta W = f(D_2) - f(D_1)$$

$$= B(\Delta D),$$

where B is an aggregate of the compensating or equivalent variations of all people affected by the change in D.

Estimating the benefit of a proposed regulation entails first predicting the responses of affected dischargers, that is, ΔD, and then tracing the effects of ΔD through the links described by eqs. (1)–(3) to calculate the resulting welfare change in monetary terms. Predicting dischargers' responses to regulations is itself a challenging task that raises issues beyond the scope of this paper. Suffice it to say that both theory and observation show that the analyst should not assume perfect compliance with all terms of the regulation (regulation and alternative policy instruments are discussed in Chapter 10 of this Handbook).

Of course this simple representation of the problem obscures a number of details and complications that have to be reckoned with. First, as explained at length in Chapter 3 of this Handbook, most environmental problems have important spatial components. Discharges may come from several (or many) sources at different locations. Thus, D may be interpreted as a vector, D_i, where i indexes sources by location.

$Q = Q(D)$ represents the atmospheric or hydrological model of the physical chemical and biological processes by which pollutants alter environmental quality. The nature of these models was also explained in Chapter 3. Q may vary across space according to the spatial pattern of discharges, dispersion, and so forth. These spatial characteristics must be reflected in the benefits model. There may also be an important temporal dimension to discharges and measures of environmental quality. Some activities may be sensitive primarily to changes in long term averages of pollution levels while others are affected primarily by peaks of pollution causing acute effects. The environmental model must be available if the analyst is to provide estimates of the benefits of a regulation. Many benefit studies proceed by taking the vector of changes in Q as given. These may be interesting and useful exercises in economic technique. But without the link of eq. (1) they cannot be used effectively in policy analysis.

The relationship, $X = X(Q)$, reflects in part the physical and biological consequences of pollution. For example, it could reflect the impact of ozone on agricultural crop yields, of sulfur compounds on materials corrosion rates, or of total suspended particulates on human health. Understanding these impacts is primarily the province of the plant scientist, the materials engineer, and the health scientist. But this relationship must also incorporate producers' and individuals' behavioral responses to these physical and biological effects. Individuals and producers can engage in averting behavior and mitigating activities. Farmers can shift away from pollution sensitive crops and cultivars or change planting times and fertilization regimes. Producers can protect against corrosion by applying coatings or shifting to less sensitive materials. And pollution sensitive individuals can attempt to protect themselves by purchasing air filters for their homes or even by moving to less polluted areas. Changes in the uses of the environment and the welfare implications of these changes depend in part on the opportunities for and costs of mitigating and averting activities. Benefit estimation models must attempt to capture the major averting and mitigating activities available to people. Modeling these activities is definitely within the province of the economist.

The third stage in estimating benefits involves determining the monetary values that people place on such things as increased agricultural productivity, improved human health, and improved opportunities for water based recreation. Regarding the analysis of this stage there is a well developed theory of economic value. The theory provides a number of approaches for estimating these values under different circumstances. The estimation of these values is the responsibility of economists.

In the rest of the chapter, I focus on the economic dimension of the problem, that is, on eq. (2), the uses of the environment, and on eq. (3), economic values. In doing so, it will be assumed throughout that the remaining relationships in this system (1)–(3) are well understood. This is appropriate for expository purposes, even though in practice the lack of knowledge of many of these links is a major barrier to empirical estimation of pollution control benefits.

3. Defining a measure of welfare change

We seek a money measure of an individual's gain in utility brought about by an environmental improvement. In this section I modify the standard model of individual preference and demand to incorporate environmental quality as an argument in the utility function. Then I consider the alternative measures of welfare change associated with changes in the prices faced by an individual, the individual's income, and environmental quality.

Consider an individual whose utility is a function of private goods purchased and the level of environmental quality, Q. Assume that tastes and preferences are given and do not change. The individual faces a set of given prices for the private goods and an exogenously determined level of environmental quality. The individual chooses quantities of the private goods so as to maximize utility given constraints of prices, fixed money income M, and the given Q. In other words,

$$
\begin{aligned}
&\max U = U(X, Q) \\
&\text{s.t.} \\
&\sum_{i=1}^{n} PX \leq M,
\end{aligned}
\tag{4}
$$

where $X = x_1, \ldots, x_i, \ldots, x_n$ and $P = p_1, \ldots, p_i, \ldots, p_n$. The solution to this problem leads to a set of ordinary or Marshallian demand functions:

$$
x_i = x_i(P, Q, M).
\tag{5}
$$

Notice that in principle the demand function for every good can include all prices and the level of environmental quality as arguments. The indirect utility function can be found by substituting the demand functions (5) into (4). This gives

$$
U = V(P, Q, M).
\tag{6}
$$

This expression gives utility as a function of prices, income, and environmental quality. In general, an improvement in environmental quality could affect utility through any or all of these sets of variables. For example, an improvement in air quality over an agricultural region could lead to lower food prices and an improvement in utility. It could also lead to higher rents to farm land and increases in the utility of land owners through higher M. Then, finally improved air quality could lead to better health and improved visibility amenities, both of which lead to increases in utility independent of price and income changes. If money income changes, the welfare effect is measured by the change in income. But the problem is more complicated for changes in P or Q. What is required is a method for calculating a measure of the welfare effects of the changes in P and Q – a measure that is commensurate with the money measure of the welfare effects of income changes.

The expenditure function provides a useful means of analyzing and evaluating measures of welfare change.[2] Assume that the solution to the maximization problem of eq. (4) is U_m. The dual of the maximization problem is

$$\min \sum PX$$
s.t.
$$U(X, Q) \geq U_m.$$

The solution to this problem is the expenditure function which shows the minimum money expenditure necessary to achieve a specified utility level, given market prices. That is,

$$E = E(P, Q, U_m). \tag{7}$$

The expenditure function has a number of useful properties for applied welfare analysis. First, the derivative of the expenditure function with respect to any price gives the Hicks-compensated demand function for that good, that is,

$$\partial E / \partial p_i = x_i^* = x_i^*(P, Q, U_m), \tag{8}$$

where the asterisk signifies a Hicks-compensated demand function. Similarly the derivative of (7) with respect to Q gives the Hicks-compensated inverse demand function or marginal willingness to pay for changes in Q. In other words,

$$- \partial E / \partial Q = w^* = w^*(P, Q, U_m), \tag{9}$$

where the asterisk signifies a compensated inverse demand function.

We now have the apparatus to consider the three alternative measures of welfare change: ordinary consumer surplus (S), compensating variation (CV), and equivalent variation (EV). Taking first the case of a price change and then a change in environmental quality, I will define these three alternative measures, discuss the theoretical and likely empirical differences among them, and discuss in general terms how these measures can be computed from observed market behavior.

3.1. Price change

The measure which most closely corresponds to our desired objective, a money equivalent of utility change, is the equivalent variation. This measure asks what change in income (given the original prices) would lead to the same utility change as the change in the price of a good. Suppose that the price of x_1 falls from p_1' to p_1''. According to eq. (4) or (6), utility will increase from U' to U''. The expenditure function can be solved to determine the expenditure necessary to

---

[2] For a general discussion of the expenditure function, see Diamond and MacFadden (1974). Mäler (1974) develops the concept of the expenditure functions and relates it specifically to the welfare effect of changes in environmental quality.

sustain U'' given the original price set and environmental quality. The EV is the increase in income necessary to sustain this higher expenditure. In other words,

$$EV \equiv E(P', Q, U''_m) - E(P', Q, U'_m), \tag{10}$$

where P' is the initial price set. When prices change with income unchanged, the result is unchanged total expenditure but a change in utility to U'', that is:

$$E(P', Q, U'_m) = E(P'', Q, U''_m).$$

Substituting in (10) gives:

$$EV = E(P', Q, U''_m) - E(P'', Q, U''_m).$$

There is a Hicks-compensated demand curve for x_1 of the form of (8) associated with U''. The EV is measured by the area under this demand curve between the two prices, that is:

$$EV = \int_{p''_1}^{p'_1} x_i^*(P, Q, U''_m) \, \mathrm{d}p_1.$$

The compensating variation is that offsetting change in income which would make the individual indifferent between the original price set and the new price set. The CV is defined by

$$CV \equiv E(P'', Q, U''_m) - E(P''Q, U'_m).$$

The CV compares expenditures required to sustain two alternative utility levels given the new price set. Again by substitution, we can write

$$CV = E(P', Q, U'_m) - E(P'', Q, U'_m).$$

The CV can be calculated from the area between the two price lines bounded by the demand curve compensated to U', or

$$CV = \int_{p''_1}^{p'} x_1^*(P, Q, U'_m) \, \mathrm{d}p_1.$$

The third measure is offered without rigorous theoretical justification but as a useful approximation to either the CV or EV. It is the Marshallian surplus, S, the area between the two price lines bounded by the ordinary demand curve. In other words

$$S = \int_{p''_1}^{p'_1} x_1(P, Q, M) \, \mathrm{d}p_1.$$

As is well known, the three measures yield different values for the welfare change unless the income elasticity of demand for the good whose price changes is zero. With zero income elasticity, there is no income effect of the change in price; and the compensated demand curves and the ordinary demand curve coincide. The EV corresponds to the conceptually desired measure of welfare change. But when there are changes in the prices of more than one good, the calculation of the *EV* from the areas under the compensated demand curves is not independent of the path of integration except in the unusually restrictive case of homothetic preferences.[3] This problem does not arise with the *CV*. But when there are changes in the prices of more than one good and when there is more than one pair of price sets to be compared, the *CV* does not provide a consistent ordinal ranking of the alternatives, that is, the *CV* is not a monotonic transformation of the utilities of the alternatives.[4]

If the direct or indirect utility function is known, any of the three measures can be calculated in a straightforward manner. But there is no reason to calculate the *CV* or *S* measures, since the *EV* is the preferred measure. In principle, it is possible to determine the utility function from an estimate of a complete system of demand functions such as (5).

What is required is that the integrability conditions be satisfied.[5] However, as Mäler (1974, pp. 121–125) has shown, the calculated expenditure and indirect utility functions do not contain Q as arguments. So it is possible to compute the *CV* and *EV* of a price change other things equal. But the solution sheds no light on the direct effect of changes in Q on utility.

Suppose that the available demand information covers only those goods whose prices change. Either the *CV* or *EV* can be calculated directly if the demand data are in the form of the Hicks-compensated demand functions. But the Hicks-compensated demand functions are not generally derivable from observations on market behavior. The analyst would be fortunate to have reliable estimates of the ordinary demand functions for the goods in question. If this is all that is available, what is to be done? There are two possible answers to the question.

The first is that in many situations, the ordinary consumer surplus will be a reasonable close approximation to either the *CV* or *EV*. Willig (1976) has offered rigorous derivations of expressions relating *CV*, *S*, and *EV*. These expressions provide a way of calculating the magnitude of the differences among the three measures for given prices, quantities, and income. The differences among the three measures depend on the income elasticity of demand for the good in question and consumer surplus as a percentage of income or expenditure. The differences among the measures appear to be small and almost trivial for most realistic cases. The differences are probably smaller than the errors in the estimation of the parameters of demand functions by econometric methods.

Willig takes into account the possibility that for finite changes in price and quantity, the income elasticity of demand may vary over the range of the price change. He derives rules of thumb for estimating the maximum error in using *S* as an approximation for *EV* or *CV*. The analysis is carried out for the case of a

---

[3] See Mohring (1971) or Silberberg (1972) for a complete discussion of this point.
[4] This is shown in Freeman (1979a).
[5] See, for example, Hurwicz (1971).

single price change. But Willig has extended the analysis to the case of multiple price changes [Willig (1973a, 1973b, 1979)].

The rules of thumb are applicable if the following conditions are met:

$$\left| \frac{S}{M} \frac{\underline{E}_m}{2} \right| \leq 0.05,$$

$$\left| \frac{S}{M} \frac{\bar{E}_m}{2} \right| \leq 0.05, \tag{11}$$

and

$$\left| \frac{S}{M} \right| \leq 0.9, \tag{12}$$

where

$\underline{E}_m$ = smallest value of income elasticity of demand for the good in the region under consideration, and

$\bar{E}_m$ = largest value of income elasticity of demand for the good in the region under consideration.

Given these conditions, the rule of thumb for CV is

$$\frac{|S|}{M} \frac{\underline{E}_m}{2} \leq \frac{CV - S}{|S|} \leq \frac{|S|}{M} \frac{\bar{E}_m}{2}. \tag{13}$$

The rule of thumb for the EV is

$$\frac{|S|}{M} \frac{\underline{E}_m}{2} \leq \frac{S - EV}{|S|} \leq \frac{|S|}{M} \frac{\bar{E}_m}{2}. \tag{14}$$

The first thing to note is the conditions under which these rules of thumb are valid. Consider eq. (12) first. Consumer surplus (S) as a percentage of income depends on the size of the price change, the price elasticity of demand, and expenditure on this good as a percentage of total income. The smaller the price change and the smaller the proportion of income spent on the good, the smaller is S/M. It can readily be shown that for a price increase:[6]

$$\frac{|S|}{M} \leq \frac{|\Delta P|}{P} \frac{P \cdot X}{M}. \tag{15}$$

This shows that, for example, for a good absorbing 50 percent of total income and for a 100 percent price increase, S/M cannot exceed 0.5, while for a 10 percent price increase for a good absorbing 10 percent of income, S/M will be less than 0.1. Thus, condition (12) is likely to be satisfied except for very large price increases for goods with low price elasticities which also absorb a large proportion of the total budget. For price decreases, the direction of the inequality in (15) is

---

[6] From a given initial situation, S is largest when the demand curve is perfectly inelastic. Then $S = X\Delta P$. Condition (15) follows readily.

reversed. But sample calculations show that condition (15) is likely to hold except for combinations of very high price elasticities, large price decreases, and high expenditure shares.

As for condition (11), the smaller that consumer surplus is as a percentage of income, or the smaller that the income elasticity of demand is, the more likely (11) is to be satisfied. For example, if consumer surplus is 5 percent of income, the income elasticity of demand can be as high as 2.0 and still satisfy (11). If S/M just barely satisfies condition (12), the income elasticity cannot exceed 0.11 to satisfy (11).

Assuming that conditions (11) and (12) hold, let us turn to the rules of thumb. First, according to (11), the maximum error involved in using S as an approximation for either CV or EV is 5 percent. Second, the smaller the change in income elasticity over the range being considered, the more precise are (13) and (14) as statements of the error involved in using S rather than CV or EV. If the income elasticity of demand does not change with the range being considered ($\underline{E}_m = \overline{E}_m$), (13) and (14) become equalities and are exact statements of the error. Finally, as the income elasticity of demand for the good decreases, the differences among ordinary consumer surplus, CV, and EV decrease, disappearing as E_m goes to zero.

In summary, Willig's analysis provides a strong justification for using the empirically observable consumer surplus measure of welfare change as a valid approximation for either of the theoretically preferred measures EV or CV. Each of the latter has conceptual and theoretical problems in its interpretation in some circumstances, but these appear to be relatively minor at the practical level.

The second answer to the above question is that as Hausman (1981) has shown, it is possible to compute the indirect utility function from the ordinary demand function. Once the indirect utility function is known, it is a straightforward procedure to compute either the EV or CV. The solution for the indirect utility function is based on Roy's Identity:

$$x_i(P, M) = -\frac{\partial V/\partial p_i}{\partial V/\partial M}.$$

Since the left-hand side of this expression is known, the indirect utility function can be recovered by integration.

Notice that the demand function in this expression does not include Q as an argument. If Q is an argument in the ordinary demand function for the good, the integrability conditions are not satisfied [Mäler (1974, pp. 183–189)]. Thus, Hausman's procedure cannot be applied. This means that the procedure is valid for those goods for which some form of separability restriction can be invoked to eliminate Q from the demand function. But this may often be reasonable. For example, individual's demands for food products are probably independent of the level of air pollution. Thus, if air pollution control increases agricultural productivity and lowers the prices of food products, Hausman's procedure can be used to calculate an exact measure of the welfare change from the demand functions for these products.

3.2. Changes in environmental quality

As with the case of price changes, there are three alternative measures available. The CV and EV are exact measures, although measures of slightly different things. Differentiating the expenditure function with respect to Q gives the compensated inverse demand function or marginal willingness to pay function for Q:

$$- \partial E / \partial Q = w^* = w^*(P, Q, U_m).$$

The EV is the area under the compensated willingness to pay curve for Q associated with the new level of U and bounded by the two levels of Q. In mathematical notation:

$$EV = \int_{Q'}^{Q''} w^*(P, Q, U_m'') \, dQ.$$

The CV is similarly defined with reference to the initial utility level, U_m'. Finally, the consumer surplus measure is the area under the uncompensated inverse demand curve, or

$$S_Q = \int_{Q'}^{Q''} w(P, Q, M) \, dQ,$$

where $w(\cdot)$ is the ordinary inverse demand curve for Q.

The CV or EV could be computed if the expenditure function or indirect utility function were known. But as Mäler (1974, pp. 121–125, 183–189) has shown, even if a complete system of demand functions for market goods has been estimated, it is not in general possible to solve for the expenditure function by integration. The result of the integration will contain unknown terms which are themselves functions of Q and the constants of integration.[7]

As will be shown in Section 5, there are circumstances in which the ordinary inverse demand function for Q can be estimated. If $w(P, Q, M)$ is known, there are two alternatives paths to calculating benefit measures. The first is an adaption of Hausman's (1981) method of calculating exact welfare measures for price changes. By a procedure similar to the derivation of Roy's Identity, it is possible

---

[7] Mäler also identified additional restrictions which do make it possible to solve for the expenditure function. These are discussed in Section 5.

to obtain the following expression:[8]

$$w = \frac{\partial V / \partial Q}{\partial V / \partial M}.$$

If the left-hand side is known, this expression can be solved for the indirect utility function. Expressions for the CV and EV measures for changes in Q follow readily.

The second path follows Willig's (1976) analysis of the errors involved in using S as an approximation of the CV or EV. Randall and Stoll (1980) have established measures of these errors where quantity change rather than price is involved. They show that in many circumstances these errors are acceptably small.

They show that when

$$\left| \frac{E_Q S_Q}{2M} \right| \le 0.05,$$

the error bounds are

$$\frac{|S_Q|}{M} \frac{\underline{E}_Q}{2} \le \frac{CV - S_Q}{|S_Q|} \le \frac{|S_Q|}{M} \frac{\overline{E}_Q}{2}$$

and

$$\frac{|S_Q|}{M} \frac{\underline{E}_Q}{2} \le \frac{S_Q - EV}{|S_Q|} \le \frac{|S_Q|}{M} \frac{\overline{E}_Q}{2},$$

where E_Q is what they call the price flexibility of income. It is defined as

$$E_Q \equiv \frac{\partial w(P, Q, M)}{\partial M} \cdot \frac{M}{w}.$$

The lower and upper bars denote the smallest and largest values of E_Q when E_Q is not constant over the relevant range.

4. Methods for measurement: An overview

Methods for obtaining monetary values of changes in environmental quality can broadly be categorized as relying either on observed behavior and choices (revealed preferences) or on responses to hypothetical situations posed to individuals by interviewers. The first category includes all of those techniques relying on observed demand functions or cost functions, changes in prices of goods or factor inputs, or observed changes in some nonmarket activity such as recreation. Under

---

[8] The procedure involves substituting the expenditure function for M in the indirect utility function and differentiating with respect to Q.

certain circumstances the demand for improvement in Q can be estimated from market data about the demand for goods and services which have substitute or complementary relationships with Q or whose prices and quantities are affected by changes in Q. Examples of these approaches include: the use of property value differentials; household expenditures on cleaning, maintenance, and repair of materials damaged by pollutants; and travel costs incurred to participate in outdoor recreation.

Also in the first category are those methods which utilize data on voting to infer values. Suppose that a referendum is held on alternative levels of Q and the associated tax increases necessary to finance them. Under certain circumstances the outcome of the voting process will be consistent with, and therefore reveal information about, the underlying demand curve for improved Q. The outcome of a referendum in any one jurisdiction only reveals whether the proposed level of Q and the associated tax burden were preferable to the status quo for a majority of voters. However, if the outcomes of elections or referenda in a large number of jurisdictions are observed simultaneously, it can be assumed that they approximate the median preferences in each jurisdiction. Then each jurisdiction can be taken as a sample unit, and the data on the quantity of the good or service, price or tax share, and socioeconomic characteristics such as income, education, and occupation can be pooled and analyzed by multiple regression techniques to determine the relevant price and income elasticities of demand. Examples of this approach include Bergstrom and Goodman (1973) and Borcherding and Deacon (1972).

Where all costs are financed through taxes in the voting jurisdiction and all benefits accrue to residents, voting can yield unbiased information on demand and on the optimum provision of Q. But where some of the benefits accrue outside the region, voting behavior does not capture all of the relevant demand for Q. And where some of the costs are shifted out of the jurisdiction, voters are not responding to the true price; thus voting reveals information about only a limited (and not the most relevant) portion of the demand function. Voting models will not be discussed further in this chapter.

The second category includes asking people directly about values as in willingness to pay surveys, bidding games, and contingent valuation surveys. This category also includes those techniques in which people are asked how their behavior would change with a change in environmental quality (e.g. would you choose a different recreation site?) or to rank alternative scenarios involving different bundles of environmental quality and other attributes (contingent ranking studies). These techniques all have in common the fact that the choice or value questions involve hypothetical situations. Thus, the reliability of such methods is contingent upon a close correspondence between how people would actually choose in a particular situation and how they say they would choose when asked by the interviewer.

In the next two sections I discuss methods for estimation based on observed behavior. Section 5 deals with those cases where Q affects utility directly or has an effect on individual behavior. Section 6 covers cases where Q affects productivity and cost and yields benefits in the form of price and income changes. Section 7 presents a relatively brief discussion of contingent valuation and contingent ranking approaches.

5. Measuring an individual's demand for environmental quality

The welfare gains due to an improvement in environmental quality can be approximated by the appropriate area under an individual's inverse demand function for environmental quality. The main purpose of this section is to describe the available techniques for estimating individuals' marginal values and their inverse demand function from data on revealed behavior and choice. Our general strategy will be to use various *a priori* assumptions to impose certain restrictions on the form of the utility function and/or demand functions for market goods. These assumptions and restrictions include various forms of separability and substitute and complement relations between market goods and environmental quality.[9] Different types of restrictions have different implications for the measurability of the demand for environmental quality.

5.1. A hopeless case

Suppose that the utility function is strongly separable with Q as the single argument in one of the subsets. In other words:

$$U = V\left[u^a(X_a) + u^b(X_b) + u^c(Q)\right],$$

where X_a and X_b are subsets of market goods. Strong separability means that the marginal rates of substitution between any pair of goods in X are independent of Q. Changes in Q have no effect on the marginal rates of substitution of any of the marketable goods; Q can be excluded as an argument in all of the market demand functions. Although changes in Q affect utility, they leave no record of this impact in the data on market transactions. Thus, in principle it is not possible to estimate the demand for Q from observable market data on transactions in X when the utility function is strongly separable in Q.

Strong separability is a property of two of the most commonly used functional forms for utility functions – the Cobb–Douglas ($U = a\prod x_i^{\alpha_i} Q^{\beta}$) and CES [$U = a(\sum_i \alpha_i x_i^{-\rho} + \beta Q^{-\rho})^{-1/\rho}$]. This can be seen by writing them in their log transformations. Separability may be a characteristic of an important class of benefits.

[9] On separability see Goldman and Uzawa (1964) or Katzner (1970).

For example, those amenities of the urban environment which are not directly associated with private goods consumption and the preservation values of unique natural environments may be separable.

5.2. Substitutes, defensive expenditures, and averting behavior

The first class of restrictions which may allow estimation of the demand for Q is that where Q and some private good are substitutes in the utility function. Mäler (1974, pp. 116–118) has shown that the partial derivative of the expenditure function with respect to Q can be expressed in terms of the price of any private good and the marginal utilities of that good and Q. The expression is

$$w = -\frac{\partial E(P, Q, U_M)}{\partial Q}$$

$$= P_i \left(\frac{\partial U/\partial Q}{\partial U/\partial x_i} \right)$$

$$= P_i MRS_{Qx_i}.$$

This would be a useful practical result if it were possible to derive simple expressions for the marginal rates of substitution.

Suppose the utility function is weakly separable and is of the following form:

$$U = V\left\{ u^a(X_a), \left[cx_i^{-\rho} + (1-c)Q^{-\rho} \right]^{-1/\rho} \right\}$$

(x_i is not in X_a). Given the separability assumption, the marginal rate of substitution between x_i and Q is independent of the quantities in X_a. The *MRS* is

$$MRS_{Qx_i} = \frac{c}{1-c} \left(\frac{Q}{x_i} \right)^{\rho-1}$$

$$= \frac{c}{1-c} \left(\frac{Q}{x_i} \right)^{1/\sigma},$$

where σ is the elasticity of substitution, which is constant. Therefore, the marginal benefit of Q is

$$w^* = P_i \frac{c}{1-c} \left(\frac{Q}{x_i} \right)^{1/\sigma}.$$

This expression gives the compensated inverse demand function for Q.

In general, to use this formulation, we need to know both the elasticity of substitution, σ, and c. There is one special case where the expression reduces to a usable term. If x_i and Q are perfect substitutes in consumption, the elasticity of substitution between them is infinite, and the expression for the marginal demand price of Q reduces to $P_i r_i$, where r is the equivalence or substitution ratio between x_i and Q $[r = c/(1 - c)]$. If perfect substitutability can be assumed, r (or c) should be computable from known or observable technical consumption data.

The perfect substitutability assumption lies behind the "defensive expenditures" technique for estimating benefits of pollution control. Defensive expenditures are made to prevent or counteract the adverse effect of pollution. They are also referred to as averting expenditures or averting behavior [Zeckhauser and Fisher (1976)]. In effect, a defensive expenditure is spending on a good which is a substitute for higher Q. An increase in Q is assumed to lead to a decrease in spending on the substitute. Examples of studies which have used the decrease in spending as an estimate of benefits include Jackson et al. (1976), Liu and Yu (1976), and Ryan et al. (1981).

Is this approach logically correct? Can decreases in spending on a substitute good be taken as a measure of the benefits of an increase in Q? In general the answer is "No", even in the case when Q and the market good are perfect substitutes. The intuition behind this answer is straightforward. Assume that Q and x_i are perfect substitutes. The benefit of a change in Q is equal to the reduction in the spending on x_i which is required to keep the individual on the original indifference curve. This is measured by $P_i r$ as described above. But in general, the individual will not reduce his spending on x_i by this amount. There is an income effect as well as a substitution effect. The increase in Q means that the same level of utility can be maintained with a smaller expenditure on x_i. As a consequence, the individual will reallocate expenditure among all goods, including x_i, so as to maximize the increase in total utility. This will result in increases in the expenditures of all goods with positive income elasticities of demand. Hence, the observed decrease in spending on x_i will be less than $P_i r$. And the reduction in defensive spending will be an underestimate of the benefits of higher Q.

Even with less than perfect substitutes,

$$w = P_i MRS_{Qx_i}$$

$$= -P_i \frac{\partial X_i}{\partial Q}.$$

Spending on $x_i (D = P_i x_i)$ is reduced by

$$\frac{dD}{dQ} = P_i \frac{dx_i}{dQ} + x_i \frac{dP_i}{dQ}.$$

The second term is zero, and $|dx_i/dQ| < |\partial x_i/\partial Q|$ unless x_i has a zero income elasticity of demand.

Similar results have been established rigorously by Courant and Porter (1981). They impose additional structure on the problem by assuming that Q and some market good are substitutes in the household production of some valued attribute. For example, suppose that clean air and soap are substitutes in the production of cleanliness.[10] Specifically, let

$$U = U(C, X),$$

where C is cleanliness and X is a vector of market goods. C is produced by households by combining market good Y (soap) and air quality according to the production function:

$$C = C(Y, Q),$$

with positive partial derivatives for both arguments. If D is total spending on Y ($P_Y Y$), then the price or marginal cost of $C(P_c)$ is $\partial D / \partial C$. The indirect utility function is

$$U = V(P, P_c, M),$$

where P is the vector of prices of market goods X. The benefit of an increase in Q is that change in M that leaves $dV/dQ = 0$. Totally differentiating gives

$$-\frac{dM}{dQ} = \frac{\partial V/\partial P_c}{\partial V/\partial M} \cdot \frac{dP_c}{cQ}.$$

Using Roy's Identity,

$$C = -\frac{\partial V/\partial P_c}{\partial V/\partial M},$$

gives

$$\frac{dM}{dQ} = C\frac{dP_c}{dQ} < 0.$$

An increase in Q lowers the marginal cost of cleanliness.[11] The benefit is equal to the reduction in expenditure required to achieve the initial level of C. The actual change in expenditure on C is

$$\frac{dD}{dQ} = C\frac{dP_c}{dQ} + P_c\frac{dC}{dQ} < 0. \tag{16}$$

The first term is negative and is the benefit of the increase in Q. The second term reflects the increase in expenditure because more cleanliness is purchased. Since it

[10] The use of household production function models for estimating the benefits of Q will be given a more complete treatment below.

[11] Sufficient conditions for the marginal cost of cleanliness to decrease are that the marginal product of Y increase with increases in Q and that the marginal product of Q be nonincreasing. Courant and Porter (1981) considered the implications of alternative properties of the production function for C.

is positive, the observed decrease in defensive or averting expenditure is smaller than the benefit of higher Q.[12]

Courant and Porter also consider the case where Q enters the utility function directly in addition to through its contribution to C. Taking the total differential of the indirect utility function and solving for the compensating change in income gives

$$\frac{\mathrm{d}M}{\mathrm{d}Q} = C\frac{\mathrm{d}P_c}{\mathrm{d}Q} + \frac{\partial V/\partial Q}{\partial V/\partial M}.$$

Comparing this with eq. (16) shows that the reduction in defensive expenditure is an exact measure of benefits only if the second terms of the two expressions sum to zero. The change in defensive expenditure is an underestimate if

$$\frac{\partial V/\partial Q}{\partial V/\partial M} + P_c\frac{\mathrm{d}C}{\mathrm{d}Q} > 0,$$

which would be true if the second term were positive or negative but smaller in absolute value. $\mathrm{d}C$ has two components: a positive one reflecting the increase in C due to its lower price, and a component which could be positive or negative depending on whether C and Q were complements or substitutes in the utility function. From this it can be seen that whether changes in defensive spending are good approximations of benefits or seriously over or underestimate benefits depends on the specific properties of the utility function and the implied relationships between Q and market goods. This analysis illustrates the importance of developing explicit models of the role of Q in utility and how it affects choices of market goods before attempting to draw inferences about the magnitude of benefits from changes in market goods demands.

One such model is based on a special form of demand interdependence which has been termed weak substitutability by Feenberg and Mills (1980). Q and a market good, x_1 sold at $\overline{P}_1$, are weak substitutes if the following two conditions hold:

(a) $\partial x_1(\overline{P}_1, P, M, Q)/\partial Q < 0$, and

(b) $\partial E(\hat{P}_1, P, Q, U_m)/\partial Q = 0$, at $0 \leq \hat{P}_1 < \overline{P}_1$.

The first condition means that at $\overline{P}_1$, an increase in Q shifts the demand curve for the x_1 to the left. The second condition means that there is some lower price for x_1 at which the individual becomes indifferent to changes in Q. At this lower price $\hat{P}_1$, changes in Q have no effect on the quantity demanded of x_1.

The implications of weak substitutability for measuring the benefits of the change in Q can most easily be seen graphically. In Figure 6.1, the demand curve

---

[12] Courant and Porter (1981) go on to show a situation in which the change in averting expenditure is an overestimate rather than an underestimate of benefits. The case requires that Q be an inferior input in the production of cleanliness.

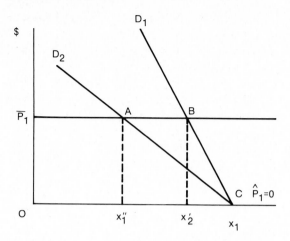

Figure 6.1. Benefits of an improvement in environmental quality under conditions of weak substitutability.

D_1 is the demand for x_1 given some initial level of Q. D_2 gives the demand for x_1 at some higher level of Q. If $\hat{P}_1$ of condition (b) is equal to zero, the two demand curves will intersect at c. The measurement of the benefits of the increase in Q, given $\overline{P}_1$ proceeds as follows:

(1) Given the initial level of Q and D_1, assume that P_1 falls to zero. The gain to the individual is equal to the area $O\overline{P}_1BC$.

(2) Given $P_1 = \hat{P}_1 = 0$, an increase in Q has no effect on the welfare of the individual. However, the demand curve above and to the left of point C shifts to the left to D_2.

(3) Now assume an increase in price back to $\overline{P}_1$. The welfare loss associated with this price increase is equal to the area $O\overline{P}_1AC$. The net gain in welfare for these three steps combined is equal to the triangle ABC.

In summary, given the conditions of weak substitutability, the benefits of an improvement in Q can be measured by the area between the initial and final demand curves for x_1 bounded above by $\overline{P}_1$ and below by $\hat{P}_1$. It is interesting to note that in the case shown in Figure 6.1 with linear demand curves and $\hat{P}_1 = 0$, the area measuring benefits is just one-half of the area measuring the decrease in expenditure on x_1. The decrease in expenditure over estimates benefits by a factor of 2. With straight line demand curves and $\hat{P}_1 > 0$, the reduction in expenditure overestimates benefits by more than a factor of 2.

This result apparently stems from the rather special nature of the substitution relationship imposed by condition (b) above. For example, suppose that the increase in Q resulted in a parallel leftward shift of the demand curve for x_1. The area between the demand curves would exactly equal the change in spending. But both areas would underestimate benefits, since in contrast to step (2) above they would not capture the benefit associated with the increase in Q when $P_1 = \hat{P}_1 = 0$.

As this analysis has shown, there are conditions under which the benefits of a change in Q can be estimated from information on the demand functions for market goods. What is necessary is that the specification of these market good demand functions reflect the interaction between Q and the market goods in the utility function. The estimation of such demand functions can be made easier if it is reasonable to invoke some form of separability assumption to limit the number of prices of other goods which must be included in the model specification.

5.3. Complements

It is possible that Q and some market good, say x_1, have some form of complementary relationship. If this is true, there are conditions under which the benefits of changes in Q can be estimated from knowledge of the demand function for the complementary market good.

Consider first the case of perfect complements. For a given quantity of Q the demand for x_1 is a decreasing function of P_1 up to some level, call it x_1^*, after which the marginal utility of x_1 becomes zero and the demand curve for x_1 becomes perfectly inelastic. The quantity of x_1 at which the demand becomes zero depends on the complementarity relationship between x_1 and Q. For P_1 greater than P_1^* the income constraint prevents the individual from purchasing enough x_1 to utilize fully the available Q. Hence, the marginal utility and demand price of additional Q are zero. For prices below P_1^*, the individual would purchase more x_1 if he could obtain more Q to go with it. Hence, the marginal utility and demand price of Q are greater than zero.

Mäler (1974, pp. 180–183) has shown that if the demand functions for x_1 and for other market goods are known, it is possible to compute the expenditure function and the demand price for Q when P_1 is less than P_1^*. The exact expression for the demand price for Q depends upon the specification of the true demand curves. There is no simple generalization of the technique.

A less restrictive form of complementary relationship has been identified and analyzed by Mäler (1974, pp. 183–189). He called this "weak complementarity".[13] Weak complementarity is defined by Mäler to occur if when the quantity demanded of a private good, x_1, is zero, the marginal utility or marginal demand price of Q is zero. The weak complementarity assumption would seem to apply to a number of useful situations. For example, the marginal value of water quality in a particular lake could be assumed to be zero for those people who did not use the

---

[13] For similar treatments of this topic see Bradford and Hildebrandt (1977) and Feenberg and Mills (1980, pp. 75–80).

lake for recreation. The marginal value of air quality over a particular residential site would be zero for those who did not live at that site.

Mathematically, weak complementarity involves two conditions:

(a) that there be a price, $\hat{P}_1$, for x_1, such that

$$x_1(\hat{P}_1, P, Q, M) = 0;$$

(b) that for the expenditure function

$$E = E(\hat{P}_1, P, Q, U_m),$$

$$\partial E / \partial Q = 0.$$

Conditions (a) and (b) together establish an initial position for the individual which is used to determine the constants of integration. These conditions describe a position for the individual which satisfies the first-order conditions of a utility maximization problem in which the individual can choose the quantities of all goods, including Q, at given prices including a zero price for Q.

Since direct application of the weak complementarity method as described by Mäler (1974, pp. 183–189) would require the econometric estimation of complete systems of demand equations, it would appear to be of relatively limited practical significance. Fortunately, the weak complementarity conditions also permit the estimation of the demand price for Q without solving for the underlying utility and expenditure functions. This latter method requires only information on the demand for x_1.

Assume that for a given level of Q, the demand curve for x_1 has been estimated econometrically. This demand curve is labeled D_1 in Figure 6.2. Assume that the

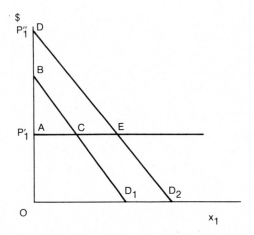

Figure 6.2. Benefits of a change in environmental quality under conditions of weak complementarity.

price of x_1 is given at P_1' and does not change throughout the analysis. The ordinary consumer surplus associated with the use of x_1 is the area ABC under the demand curve. Now assume that Q is increased. The increase in Q associated with the use of x_1 is assumed to increase the demand for x_1, thus shifting the demand curve outward to D_2. The calculation of the benefit associated with this change is straightforward, and can be divided into three steps.

(1) Given the old demand curve of D_1 postulate a hypothetical increase in price from P_1' to P_1''. In order to leave the individual no worse off, he must be compensated by the area ABC.

(2) Now postulate the improvement in quality and the shift in the demand curve to D_2. Given the weak complementarity assumption, utility is unaffected since the consumption of x_1 is zero. Therefore, there is no need for compensation, either positive or negative.

(3) Now postulate a return to the old price of P_1'. The individual is made better off by the area ADE. In order to restore the individual to his original welfare position, he must be taxed by this amount. The net effect of these changes is a gain to the individual (in the absence of the hypothetical compensating payments described) of the area $BCED$ ($= ADE - ABC$). This is the benefit of the change in Q.

If weak complementarity did not hold, there would be a positive benefit associated with the increase in Q even though the quantity demanded of x_1 were zero in step (2) above. In this case, the area $BCED$ would be an underestimate of the benefits of increasing Q.

5.4. The household production framework

The household production function model provides a framework for examining interactions between demands for market goods and availability of a public good such as environmental quality. The household production framework assumes that there is a set of technical relationships among goods used by households in the implicit production of utility yielding final services.[14] Examining the household production technology may be one approach to gaining knowledge of the relationship between market goods demands and the value of environmental quality change.

In the household production framework, utility is a function of the level of final service flows:

$$U = U(Z) = U(z_1, \ldots, z_j, \ldots, z_m). \tag{17}$$

[14] In the household production function literature, the utility yielding final services are often termed "commodities" while market goods are simply "goods". The terminology used in this chapter is more descriptive of the relationship between goods being bought in the market and what finally yields utility to individuals.

z is produced according to a technology common to all households and assumed to be known:

$$z_j = z_j(X, Q), \quad \text{for } j = 1, \ldots, m. \tag{18}$$

X represents a vector of market goods $(x_1, \ldots, x_i, \ldots, x_n)$, while Q represents a vector of environmental quality attributes.

Formally, the individual choice problem is to maximize (17) subject to the constraints provided by (18), the given level of Q, and the budget constraint $\sum_i^n P \cdot X \leq M$. This problem can be solved in a two step procedure in which the first step is to combine market goods and Q so as to minimize the costs of producing the z_j. This determines the implicit prices or marginal costs of final services, P_{z_j}. The second stage is to maximize (17) subject to the budget constraint, $C(Z, P_z) = C(x, P_x, Q) \leq M$. The observable manifestation of the solution is a set of derived market goods demands:

$$x_i = x_i(P_{x_i}, Q, M).$$

One approach to using this information to determine the benefits of changes in Q was outlined by Hori (1975). He showed that under fairly general conditions knowledge of the household production function, the market goods demands, and the level of Q is sufficient to determine the ratios of the marginal costs of production (i.e. the marginal rate of transformation), $MRT_{z_j z_j'}$ for any pair of final service flows. If the individual is in equilibrium, knowledge of the z_j values and the marginal costs gives the individual's marginal rates of substitution, since $MRS_{z_j z_j'} = MRT_{z_j z_j'}$. Hori argued that this establishes the marginal rate of substitution as a function of the arguments of the marginal rate of transformation, i.e. market goods (or their prices) and the vector of Q's. If this is so, integration to the utility function is straightforward.

In effect, Hori used the household production function to transform the conventional problem where the market reveals only the prices of market goods into a situation where the implicit prices of all utility-yielding goods are known from the conditions of household production. In effect, the Hori model transforms the conventional problem of public goods preference revelation into one of household production function revelation. The usefulness of this approach depends on the ability to determine the household production function. Hori's main objective was to show that under four different specifications of the production technology it is generally possible to compute z_j values (which are not directly observable) and their marginal costs. In all four cases one and only one environmental attribute enters into the production function for each final service.

Whether Hori's approach represents a practical advance in technique over models such as those discussed above may be open to question. As Smith (1979) has noted, Hori's model imposes more restrictive assumptions even in those cases where other models can be used. For example, let us consider the simplest case of nonjoint production where each market good enters the production of only one final service flow:

$$z_1 = z_1(x_1, \ldots, x_s, q_1),$$

$$z_2 = z_2(x_{s+1}, \ldots, x_t, q_2), \text{ etc.} \tag{19}$$

Hori shows that with knowledge of Q, the demand functions for X, and the household production function, it is possible to compute the z_j values and their marginal costs for any given set of market goods prices. This case can be presented in the conventional framework by a weakly separable utility function by substituting eq. (19) into eq. (17):

$$U = \left[z_1(x_1, \ldots, x_s, q_1); z_2(x_{s+1}, \ldots, x_t, q_2), \ldots \right].$$

Weak separability means that the *MRS* between any two goods in one partition, say, between x_1 and q_1, is independent of the quantities in any other element.

If x_i and q_1 are perfect substitutes in consumption (or what is the same thing, in household production), the *MRS* is a constant, r. As shown earlier, the marginal demand price for q_1 can be readily computed. If x_1 and q_1 are perfect complements, it is also possible but more cumbersome to compute the marginal demand price for the public good. For most cases between the polar extremes one must specify the form and parameters of the separable branch of the utility function – or of the production function for z_1. There is no essential difference between the nonjoint production framework and the separable utility framework. Any inference that can be drawn about technical production relationships between public and private goods can also be expressed in the conventional framework in terms of a specification of the MRS_{xq}. Knowledge of the whole household production technology is required to solve for the utility function following Hori's approach, while the analysis of the demand for one public good can proceed with a more limited set of data under the conventional approach.

There has been at least one attempt to implement a variation on Hori's model based on household production theory. In a recent study for the U.S. Environmental Protection Agency, Mathtech (1982) used household expenditure data to estimate a system of demand functions for market goods and the underlying demands for final service flows. They proceeded with the following steps.

(1) Using a linear expenditures system and assuming weak separability, a system of demand functions was estimated for goods grouped into seven categories: food, shelter, home operation, home furnishings and equipment, clothing, transportation, and health and personal care. Each category was assumed to correspond to one final service flow. For example, home operations was assumed to represent the final service flow, cleanliness. A measure of air pollution was included as an argument in the market good demand functions.

(2) The parameters of the estimated market good demand functions were used to calculate price or cost and quantity indices for the final service flows. The price or cost indices were increasing functions of air pollution.

(3) The price and quantity indices were used to estimate the demand functions for each of the seven final service flows.

(4) In those cases where air pollution was statistically significant in market goods demand functions, an improvement in air quality would lower the price of the corresponding final service flow. Calculation of the benefits of improved air quality is straightforward once the corresponding final goods demand functions are known.

5.5. Hedonic property values

The techniques described so far have been developed for the case where the level of environmental quality is fixed and the same for all individuals. There are some important cases where individuals have some freedom to choose their effective level of Q through their selection of a private market goods consumption bundle. Where these choices are possible, information on the demand for Q is embedded in the prices and consumption levels for market goods. For example, if air quality varies across space in an urban area, individuals may choose their exposure to air pollution through their residential location decision. Residential housing prices may include premiums and discounts for locations in clean or dirty areas. It may be possible to estimate demand for clean air from the price differentials revealed in the housing market. The hedonic price technique has been developed for this purpose.

The hedonic technique is a method for estimating the implicit prices of the characteristics which differentiate closely related products in a product class.[15] For example, houses constitute a product class differentiated by characteristics such as the number of rooms, size of lot, and location. In principle, if there are enough models with different combinations of rooms, etc. it is possible to estimate the implicit price relationship which gives the price of any model as a function of the quantities of its various characteristics. The implicit prices of characteristics are given by the partial derivatives of the hedonic price equation with respect to these characteristics.

More formally, assume that utility is a function of housing services consumed as well as the consumption bundle of other market goods, X, where housing services are defined by the quantities of the attributes of the housing bundle

---

[15] The hedonic price technique was developed by Griliches (1971) and others initially for the purpose of estimating the value of quality change in consumer goods. For further development of the theory and discussion of empirical issues in applying the concept to valuing environmental quality, see Freeman (1979a). For a discussion and evaluation of criticisms of the techniques on theoretical and empirical grounds, see Freeman (1979b), and references therein.

consumed. Let the attributes be represented by S, a vector of structural attributes such as size and number of bathrooms, by N, a vector of neighborhood attributes such as accessibility and quality of schools, and by Q, a measure of, for example, air quality at the house site. The price of any house will depend upon the quantities of the various attributes that it embodies. Let $P_H = P_H(S, N, Q)$ be the function that maps bundles of attributes to market prices of houses. This is the hedonic price function. The derivative of this function with respect to any attribute, say, Q, is the marginal implicit price of that attribute. In general, the marginal implicit price of an attribute can be a function of all of the attributes of housing.

Assuming that the individual consumes only one house, the individual's choice problem is to

$$\max U(X, S, N, Q)$$
s.t.
$$P \cdot X + P_H \leq M.$$

The first-order conditions include:

$$\frac{\partial P_H}{\partial Q} = P_{X_i} MRS_{Qx_i}.$$

As was shown above, the right-hand side of this condition is equal to w which represents the individual's marginal willingness to pay for Q. The left-hand side is the marginal implicit price of Q reflected in the market and as revealed by the hedonic price function. In other words, if the individual is in equilibrium, the marginal implicit price of Q for that individual can be taken as a measure of the individual's marginal willingness to pay or marginal benefit of an improvement in Q.

If the hedonic price function is known, the marginal implicit prices of Q can be computed for each individual in the housing market. The sum of these individual marginal implicit prices gives the aggregate marginal benefit for a change in Q affecting all houses in the market. But it is not possible to calculate benefits for non-marginal changes without knowledge of the inverse demand function for Q.[16] I turn now to the problem of estimating these inverse demand functions from hedonic price data.

If the hedonic price function is non-linear (and there is no reason to expect linearity in the case of housing), different individuals selecting different housing bundles will have different marginal implicit prices and values for Q and other attributes. There is one situation where the inverse demand function can be immediately identified. That is if all individuals have identical incomes and utility functions. Then the marginal implicit price function is itself the demand function.

---

[16] For a discussion of some approaches to approximating the benefits of nonmarginal changes, see Freeman (1979a, pp. 143–147).

Recall that the marginal implicit price curve is a locus of equilibrium points on individuals' inverse demand curves. With identical incomes and preferences, all individuals have the same inverse demand curve. Since all the equilibrium points fall on the same inverse demand curve, they fully identify it.

Where differences in incomes, preferences, or other variables lead to different inverse demand functions, Rosen (1974) and Freeman (1979a) argued that implicit price and quantity data from a single market could be used to estimate this inverse demand function provided that the standard identification problem of econometrics could be solved. It has now become apparent that our analysis was incorrect. It was argued that estimates of marginal implicit prices from a single market could be used to estimate $w(P, Q, N)$ for the individuals in that market if those individuals had identical utility functions and provided that the standard identification problem could be solved. Brown and Rosen (1982) have shown that these conditions are not sufficient.[17] The problem is that the data from a single market reveal only the outcome of a single market experiment. As Brown and Rosen put it:

Contrary to Rosen's original statement, we claim that marginal attribute prices constructed as above will not necessarily play the same role in estimation that direct observations on prices would play if they were available. Because such constructed prices are created only from observed sample quantities, any *new* information that they may provide (i.e. any information beyond that already provided directly by observed sample quantities) can only come from *a priori* restrictions placed on the functional form of the price function $P_{\mathrm{H}}(\cdot)$. In the absence of such additional restrictions, second-stage 'structural' estimation of the sort suggested by Rosen may only reproduce the information already provided by the first-stage estimation of the $P_{\mathrm{H}}(\cdot)$ function [Brown and Rosen (1982, p. 176); notation change by the author].

Although empirical estimates of the benefits of air pollution control based on the Freeman–Rosen technique are invalid, there are at least two ways in which estimates of inverse demand functions for Q can be obtained from hedonic analysis. The first is to increase the quantity of information obtained from marginal implicit prices by estimating hedonic price functions for several separate markets and then pooling the cross-sectional data on the assumption that the underlying structure of supply and demand is the same in all markets [Freeman (1974) and Brown and Rosen (1982)]. The second approach is to impose additional structure on the problem by invoking *a priori* assumptions about the form of the underlying utility function. Quigley (1982) has shown how estimates of marginal implicit prices can be used to estimate the parameters of the previously specified generalized constant elasticity of substitution utility function.

[17] See also Brown and Mendelsohn (1983) and Bartik (1982).

If the utility function correctly describes preferences, then once its parameters are known, estimating the benefits of changes in attributes is straightforward.

5.6. Environmental quality and recreation site demand

Perhaps as much as one-half of the total benefits for controlling water pollution in the United States can be attributed to improvements in water-based recreation opportunities [Freeman (1982a, pp. 169–171)]. An improvement in the quality of water in a given lake or stretch of river may be of no value to an individual unless the individual partakes of recreational activities at that site. If that is the case, then water quality, Q, and recreation activities measured by visits to the site are weak complements as defined above. This means that if a demand function for visits to the site incorporating Q as an argument can be estimated, then the benefits of an increase in Q can be calculated from the area between the demand curves before and after the improvement in Q, other things equal.

In this section I will briefly describe the by now familiar Hotelling–Clawson–Knetch (H–C–K) travel cost model for estimating recreation site demands.[18] I will then outline several approaches to introducing water quality as a variable in the analysis of site demands. The travel cost method has found many applications in the evaluation of outdoor recreation opportunities in general. Because of this it is discussed in much greater detail in Chapter 15 of this Handbook, which is devoted entirely to the econometrics of outdoor recreation.

The problem of estimating the demand for visits to a recreation site would be straightforward if the normal practice were to charge an entry fee and if the fee varied over time. But the typical practice for publicly provided recreation sites is to charge a zero price or only a nominal entry fee. The basic assumption of the H–C–K model is that it is possible to infer how a given group of people would respond to changes in the entry price of a site by examining data on how different people respond to differences in the cost of traveling to that site. For a simple exposition of the model, let us assume that there is only one recreation site available to individuals in a given region. It must be assumed that the primary purpose of the recreation trip is to visit the site. When trips involve purposes other than visiting the site, at least some portion of the travel cost is a joint cost which cannot be allocated meaningfully to the visit.

The first step in the analysis is to determine the influence of travel costs on the number of visits to the site per period of time for households living at different distances from the site. This entails the estimation of a visitation function of the

---

[18] The basic references are Clawson and Knetsch (1966) and Knetsch (1964). For a clear exposition with a numerical example of its application, see Mäler and Wyzga (1976). A number of conceptual and empirical issues concerning the travel cost model, for example, the role of travel time and on-site time, congestion, and the role of substitute sites, are discussed in Freeman (1979a, ch. 8).

following form:

$$V_i = V(M_i, S_i, C_i),$$

where

V_i = number of visits of the ith individual,
M_i = income
S_i = relevant socio-economic characteristics of the individual, and
C_i = a measure of the total cost of visiting the site.

The cost of visiting the site includes the entry fee, if any, the out-of-pocket and time cost of round-trip travel to the site, and the opportunity cost of time spent at the site.[19] The entry fee is the same for all individuals but the other components of cost vary across individuals according to their location, etc.

One point on the demand curve for the site is known. That is the total number of visits observed at the existing entry fee. To determine how the number of visits would vary with changes in the entry fee, it is necessary to calculate the following expression:

$$V^j = \sum_i V_i(M_i, S_i, C_i + j\Delta C), \quad \text{for } j = 1, \ldots, m,$$

where ΔC is the postulated increment in the entry fee. V^j as a function of $j\Delta C$ is the demand function for visits to the site.

In order to estimate the benefits of a change in Q, we need to know how this site demand function shifts with changes in Q. This may prove difficult to determine in practice. I first outline the general nature of the problem and describe several approaches to solving the problem that has been described in the literature.

Consider a region with a single recreation site. The site demand function can be written as

$$V = V(M, S, P_V, Q),$$

where P_V is the price or admission fee at the site, and M and S characterize the incomes and other relevant socio-economic characteristics of the population served by the site. If this site demand function were estimated from visitation data collected at a point in time, there would be no variation in Q across the sample. If the data were collected over a longer period of time during which Q changed, it may be very difficult to separate the effects of quality change from other factors which are also changing over time. If the site was originally so polluted that recreational activity was precluded, then the travel cost method cannot be used to estimate site demand and pollution control benefits *ex ante*. However, in this case, an *ex post* analysis of site demand after pollution control

---

[19] On this point, see Freeman (1979a, pp. 206–208), Scott (1966), Cesario and Knetsch (1970), McConnell (1975), and Wilman (1980).

would provide a measure of benefits. The entire site value would be attributable to pollution control which made the site usable for recreation.

Suppose alternatively that there are several sites within the region, each with a different level of water quality. The demand function for the ith site can be written as

$$V_i = V_i(M, S, P_{V_i}, P_{V_j}, Q_i, Q_j), \qquad j \neq i,$$

with $\partial V_i/\partial P_{V_j} \geq 0$ and $\partial V_i/\partial Q_j \leq 0$ to reflect possible substitution relationships among sites. Using the H–C–K travel cost model, the site demand function would be derived from visitation equations of the following form:

$$V_{ik} = V_i(M_k, S_k, C_{ik}, C_{jk}, Q_i, Q_j), \qquad j \neq k, \tag{20}$$

where i and j indicate sites and k indicates individuals or origin zones. If this expression is estimated for each site in a simple linear form, there will be no variation across individuals in the observed values of Q_i and Q_j. What is required is some form of interaction term between Q_j and distance C_{jk} to reflect the fact that changes in Q at more distant sites will have a smaller influence on the number of visits an individual makes to the ith site.[20] One trouble with this approach, however, is that theory provides little guidance as to the form that the interaction terms should take.

An alternative approach to introducing quality effects is to estimate demand functions for each site separately without quality variables, and then to attempt to explain differences in the coefficients on price terms by regressing them on the quality variables. To take a simple example, the demand function

$$V_j = a + b_j P_{V_j}$$

would be estimated by the H–C–K technique. This equation could include prices of substitute sites. The own-price coefficients would be regressed against the quality variables

$$b_j = c + \mathrm{d}Q_j.$$

By substitution, this is equivalent to including interaction terms. That is,

$$V_j = a + c P_{V_j} + \mathrm{d}Q_j P_{V_j}.$$

This equation could be specified to include only quality variables for site i, or it could include quality variables for other sites as well, to test for substitution effects.[21]

[20] Cesario and Knetsch (1976) estimated a system of site demand functions using distance weighted interaction terms for an index of the attractiveness of substitute sites.

[21] For further discussion of this approach and the econometric issues involved, see Saxonhouse (1977). An application of this approach can be found in Desvousges, Smith and McGivney (1983). This report includes an extensive discussion of the theoretical justification for this model specification.

It may often be the case that when faced with an array of alternative sites at various distances and with different Qs, individuals will choose to make the most of their visits to one or two sites and make no visits to most of the alternative sites in the region. If this is the case, estimation of a system of visitation equations as eq. (20) by ordinary least-squares regression would be appropriate because of the large number of zero values for the dependent variable. For example, such a specification implies that the effect of a change in Q at site j on visits by an individual to site i is the same regardless of whether site j is visited or not. In these circumstances, the logit model can be used to analyze individual site visitation data [Feenberg and Mills (1980)]. The logit model can be interpreted as estimating the probability that an individual will visit a given site as a function of characteristics of the individual and the available sites. A derivation of the logit model and an application to recreation site visit data for the Boston region is presented in Feenberg and Mills (1980).

The logit model provides a straightforward basis for calculating the benefit per visits of an improvement in Q at a site, at least if a measure of price or travel cost is included in the logit equation. Other things equal, an increase in Q leads to an increase in the probability of visiting that site and higher level of utility for the individual. Total differentiation of the logit equation makes it possible to calculate the increase in price or travel cost per visit which would leave the probability of visiting unchanged after an increase in Q. This compensating increase in price is the benefit per visit of the higher Q. Feenberg and Mills provide sample calculations for their Boston model (1980, p. 115). They also derive a measure of total benefits which takes account of the likelihood that the total number of visits will increase with improvements in Q.

The last approach to estimating the value of Q to be considered here involves a combination of aspects of the hedonic and travel cost models. It has been developed and applied to estimate the value of fishing success by Brown and Mendelsohn (1983), and has been termed by them the hedonic travel cost model.

In their model a recreation site is a differentiated good which can be described by a vector of its attributes or qualities. An individual at a given location faces an array of alternative sites with different characteristics and each available at a different price where price includes any entry fee and the cost of travel to the site. A hedonic price function can be estimated for these sites as a function of site attributes. The hedonic price function is specific to the individual's location, since a major cause of this variation in prices of sites is variation in the travel cost to those sites from the individual's location.

If there were a sufficient number of sites so that the availabilities of different attributes could be represented by continuous functions, then utility maximizing individuals would select sites so that their marginal willingness to pay for each attribute were equal to its marginal implicit price. With knowledge of the sites actually selected by individuals, it would be possible to calculate the marginal willingness to pay or marginal benefit of improvements in any of the site attributes. But as was pointed out above, in the absence of additional information or added restrictions, it is not possible to estimate demand functions for attributes from this data.

Brown and Mendelsohn solved this problem in the recreation setting by estimating separate hedonic price functions for groups of individuals residing in different localities within a region but making use of the range of recreation sites in that region. Their specific application involved fishermen in various residential localities and river fishing sites in western Washington. In effect, they treat each separate locality as a separate market for characteristics for purposes of hedonic analysis. After calculating hedonic price functions for each locality and determining the observed equilibrium marginal implicit prices of attributes, they estimated inverse demand functions for attributes by regressing observed marginal implicit prices for all fishermen against observed quantities of attributes and socio-economic variables.

5.7. The value of reduced mortality and morbidity

One of the most controversial issues in benefit estimation is how to value improvements in human health, and especially those which lead to reductions in mortality.[22] Broadly speaking there are two types of approaches to estimating values which have appeared in the empirical literature. The first is a resource cost or opportunity cost approach and is typified by measures of the medical cost of illness and wages lost during periods of illness or because of premature death. The second approach is to estimate either through observational or hypothetical means what people would be willing to pay to experience a reduction in illness or an increase in life expectancy. Willingness to pay measures are consistent with the economic theory of welfare change. Resource or opportunity cost measures have the virtue of being more easily measurable in some circumstances. But they should only be used if it can be reasonably argued that they are approximations of the conceptually correct willingness to pay measure.[23] In this section I first derive a willingness to pay measure for valuing reductions in mortality. I then derive similar measures for valuing reductions in morbidity and compare them to

---

[22] A separate question is whether air or water pollution causes ill health and increased mortality. While this might be considered primarily a biomedical question, economists have played an important role in efforts to test the hypothesis of a pollution-health effect and to quantify the exposure/effort relationship. For discussion of methodological and empirical issues in estimating pollution/exposure/effect relationship see Lave and Seskin (1977), Lave and Seskin (1979), and Freeman (1982b). For a review of recent efforts to estimate exposure/effect relationships for air pollution, see Freeman (1982a, ch. 4), and references therein.

[23] Both theory and available empirical evidence show that lost earnings is a very poor measure of the willingness to pay to reduce the risk of death or increase life expectancy. See Freeman (1979a, pp. 166–174), and Freeman (1982a, pp. 37–43).

measures of resource cost or cost of illness. These comparisons reveal that in general cost of illness measures are likely to be poor approximations of willingness to pay.

Let us first consider a very simple one-period model.[24] Assume that an individual derives utility from consumption of a composite good, X. The initial endowment of X and the probability of surviving to enjoy its consumption, p, are both given to the individual. Let X^0 and p^0 represent the initial endowment and probability. The element of choice arises if the individual has the opportunity to rearrange his consumption and survival position through exchange, for example, by giving up some X in order to improve his changes of surviving to enjoy the remainder. Let P_s represent the price at which consumption can be exchanged for enhanced survival probability, or vice versa. The choice problem, then, is to

$$\max_{\text{s.t.}} E[U] = pU(X)$$
$$P_x X + P_s p - P_x X^0 - P_s p^0 = 0,$$

on the assumption that the utility associated with nonsurvival is zero. The first-order conditions for a maximum of expected utility are

$$P_s = P_x \frac{U(X)}{p \, \partial U / \partial X}.$$

This expression requires that the individual equate his marginal willingness to pay for enhanced survival (the right-hand side of the expression) with a given price of enhanced survival.

The expenditure function can be written as

$$E = E(P_x, P_s, U_m).$$

The function

$$\frac{\partial E(P_x, P_s, U_m)}{\partial P_s}$$

gives the compensated demand curve for p.

Alternatively, suppose that the survival probability depends only on the level of some environmental quality measure:

$$p = p(Q), \qquad \partial p / \partial Q \geq 0$$

This is the mirror image of an expression relating the risk of death to some measure of pollution. Assume that Q only affects utility through its influence on

---

[24] Comprehensive models encompassing bequest motivation and insurance behavior can be developed. See, for example, Jones-Lee (1976), Conley (1976), Weinstein, Shepard and Pliskin (1976), and Thaler and Rosen (1976).

p. If Q is exogenous to the individual, the expenditure function is

$$E = E(P_x, p(Q), U_m),$$

and its derivative,

$$\frac{\partial E(P_x, P(Q), U_m)}{\partial Q} = -P_x \frac{U(X)}{p\, \partial U/\partial X} \frac{\partial p}{\partial Q} = -w,$$

gives the marginal benefit of improving Q. As shown above, the first term in the middle expression is the willingness to pay for a small increase in survival probability. Both this willingness to pay and the effect of Q on the probability of survival must be known in order to estimate the benefit of an improvement in Q.

The most frequently used approach to estimate the willingness to pay for increased survival probability has been the hedonic wage model where wage differentials are explained by differences in the rate of death by accident across occupations or industry. For reviews and analysis of empirical estimates based on this technique and others, see Bailey (1980) and Freeman (1982a, pp. 39–43).

An individual's willingness to pay for changes in survival probability can be translated into a more convenient figure for use in benefit–cost analysis, namely the value of *statistical life*. Suppose in a group of 1000 similar individuals, each individual has a willingness to pay $1000 for a policy that would reduce the probability of his or her death by 0.01. This policy is a form of collective good for the individuals involved. The benefit to the group is found by adding across all individuals. The aggregate willingness to pay is $1 million, and the expected number of deaths avoided is 10. Thus the group's aggregate willingness to pay to avoid one death is $100 000. This is the statistical value of life.

As mentioned above, the resource cost approach to valuing morbidity reductions takes the reduction in medical costs and lost wages as a measure of benefits. Models of individual choice that incorporate responses to illness and expenditures for the purposes of preventing illness can be used to show that the resource cost of illness will often be a poor measure of the benefits of reducing morbidity. In many cases resource costs can be shown to be underestimates of benefits. But this depends upon the particular features of the model being analyzed. The following analysis is based on Harrington and Portney (1983). Similar results were obtained by Cropper (1981). Her model incorporates the dynamic optimization of investment in preventing illness.

For the simplest model, let utility depend upon the consumption of a composite good, X, and the quantity of leisure time, L. Assume that improvements in Q result in fewer days of illness, S:

$$S = S(Q) \geq 0$$

and

$$\partial S/\partial Q \leq 0; \qquad \partial^2 S/\partial Q^2 \geq 0.$$

For simplicity assume that all days of illness are of equal severity. Finally, assume that illness requires treatment and that the medical cost, C, is given by the increasing function $C(S)$. As specified, an increase in Q affects utility only through its impact on the budget constraint:

$$P_x X + C[S(Q)] \leq M + rH(Q) = M + r[T - L - S(Q)],$$

where r is the daily wage rate, H is days worked, T is the total endowment of time, and M is non-labor income. The benefit of Q is the amount of money that could be taken from the individual leaving him or her indifferent to the change in Q. This is the offsetting change in M that leaves the budget constraint unchanged. By differentiating, this is

$$dM = (dC + r) \partial S / \partial Q,$$

or the sum of the reductions in medical costs and lost earnings. In this simple model the change in the cost of illness is an exact measure of the benefits of Q.

This conclusion does not hold if illness causes disutility or if the effect of pollution on health can be mitigated by defensive expenditures. Now let the utility function be $U(X, L, S)$ with $\partial U / \partial S < 0$. Also suppose that sickness can be reduced by defensive expenditures such as air conditioning or asthma medications, that is, $S = S(Q, D)$, with $\partial S / \partial D < 0$. The budget constraint is

$$M + r(T - L - S) - P_x X - C[S(Q, D)] + D \geq 0.$$

The relevant first-order conditions include:

$$\frac{\partial U}{\partial X} - \lambda P_x = 0,$$

$$\frac{\partial U}{\partial L} - \lambda r = 0,$$

$$\frac{\partial U}{\partial S} \frac{\partial S}{\partial D} - \lambda - \lambda \frac{\partial C}{\partial S} \frac{\partial S}{\partial D} - r\lambda \frac{\partial S}{\partial D} = 0;$$

or, by rearranging:

$$\frac{\partial U}{\partial S} - \lambda \frac{\partial C}{\partial S} - \lambda r = \frac{\lambda}{\partial S / \partial D}. \tag{21}$$

A measure of the benefits of an increase in Q can be derived by total differentiation of the indirect utility function $V(P_x, M, r, Q)$ to find the compensating change in income, that is,

$$\frac{dV}{dQ} = \frac{\partial V}{\partial M} \frac{dM}{dQ} + \frac{\partial V}{\partial Q} = 0$$

or

$$\frac{dM}{dQ} = -\frac{\partial V / \partial Q}{\partial V / \partial M}.$$

Differentiating the indirect utility function with respect to Q and recalling that $\lambda = \partial V / \partial M$ gives

$$\frac{\partial V}{\partial Q} = \left(\frac{\partial U}{\partial S} - \lambda \frac{\partial C}{\partial S} - \lambda r \right) \frac{\partial S}{\partial Q}.$$

Substituting from (21) gives

$$\frac{\partial V}{\partial Q} = \lambda \frac{\partial S / \partial Q}{\partial S / \partial D}.$$

Thus, the measure of benefits is

$$\frac{\mathrm{d}M}{\mathrm{d}Q} = - \frac{\partial S / \partial Q}{\partial S / \partial D},$$

or in effect the marginal rate of technical substitution between Q and D in reducing sickness. To use this measure of benefits as in the simple model, the role of pollution in inducing sickness must be quantified. In addition, in this model the relationship between defensive expenditures and sickness must be known.

It can now also be shown that the change in the cost of illness is an underestimate of the benefits of Q. The change in the cost of illness, R, is

$$\frac{\mathrm{d}R}{\mathrm{d}Q} = r \frac{\mathrm{d}S}{\mathrm{d}Q} + \frac{\partial C}{\partial S} \frac{\mathrm{d}S}{\mathrm{d}Q}$$

$$= \left(r + \frac{\partial C}{\partial S} \right) \frac{\mathrm{d}S}{\mathrm{d}Q}.$$

Rearranging the third first-order condition gives

$$r + \frac{\partial C}{\partial S} = \frac{1}{\lambda} \frac{\partial U}{\partial S} - \frac{1}{\partial S / \partial D}$$

The total change in sickness itself has two components:

$$\frac{\mathrm{d}S}{\mathrm{d}Q} = \frac{\partial S}{\partial D} \frac{\partial D}{\partial Q} + \frac{\partial S}{\partial Q}.$$

Substituting these two terms gives

$$\frac{\mathrm{d}R}{\mathrm{d}Q} = \frac{1}{\lambda} \frac{\partial U}{\partial S} \frac{\mathrm{d}S}{\mathrm{d}Q} - \frac{\partial D}{\partial Q} - \frac{\partial S / \partial Q}{\partial S \partial D}$$

or

$$- \frac{\partial S / \partial Q}{\partial S / \partial D} = \frac{\mathrm{d}R}{\mathrm{d}Q} - \frac{1}{\lambda} \frac{\partial U}{\partial S} \frac{\mathrm{d}S}{\mathrm{d}Q} + \frac{\partial D}{\partial Q}.$$

The left-hand side is the true measure of benefits. Since all of the terms in this expression are negative, $\mathrm{d}R / \mathrm{d}Q$ is smaller in magnitude than $\mathrm{d}M / \mathrm{d}Q$ by the second and third terms on the right-hand side. That is, the reduction in cost of illness is smaller than the compensating income change which properly measures benefits. This conclusion would still hold if either $\partial U/\partial S$ or $\partial D/\partial Q$ were zero. The change in the cost of illness is an exact measure of benefits only if *both* terms are zero. Finally, if sickness does not reduce utility, benefits can be measured by the sum of the reduction in the cost of illness and the reduction in defensive expenditures.

Harrington and Portney (1983) go on to establish similar conclusions for the case where Q is an argument in the utility function itself and individuals receive paid sick leave rather than losing earnings for sick days. They also examine the case where chronic illness reduces productivity resulting in a lower market wage rate. In that case, the reduction in the cost of illness could be either an underestimate or an overestimate of the benefits of improving Q.

5.8. Hedonic wages

From a worker's perspective a job can be viewed as a differentiated product, that is, a good with a bundle of characteristics such as working conditions, prestige, training and enhancement of skills, and degrees of risk of accidental injury for exposure to toxic substances. If workers are free to move from one urban area to another, then jobs are differentiated, in part, by the environmental and other characteristics of the urban area in which the job is located. If workers can be assumed to be free to choose from a menu of differentiated jobs, then the hedonic price technique can be applied to the data on wages, job characteristics, and worker characteristics in an effort to estimate the marginal implicit prices of these job characteristics. In this section I first take up the specification of a model for hedonic wage estimation. I then turn to some questions in the interpretation of hedonic wage data and the derivation of benefits measures from hedonic wage functions.

When the hedonic price technique is applied to the study of wage rates, the theory must be modified to take account of an important feature of labor markets. In the typical application of the hedonic theory to differentiated goods, producers are viewed as selling a good embodying a package of characteristics and as being indifferent to the characteristics of the purchaser of the good. In hedonic wage studies, the employer is viewed as selling a package of job characteristics (including environmental quality associated with the job location); but at the same time the employer is purchasing work effort and cannot be indifferent to the productive characteristics of employees. Thus, the hedonic wage equation must be interpreted as a reduced form equation reflecting not only the interaction of supply and demand for job characteristics but also the interaction of supply and demand of worker characteristics [Lucas (1977), Rosen (1979)]. This means that both worker and job characteristics must be included as arguments in the estimated hedonic wage equation.

When hedonic wage or price functions are estimated, it is necessary that the market be in equilibrium and that the market not be segmented into submarkets with incomplete mobility among segments [Freeman (1979a, pp. 142–143; 1979b)]. When hedonic wage equations are estimated using data from several urban areas, it is necessary to assume that these areas are part of a single market. In practice, labor markets can be segmented on the basis of geography with moving costs and lack of information on job alternatives imposing barriers between labor markets in different parts of the country. Markets also might be segmented on the basis of education and skill requirements and between blue collar and professional/ managerial workers. Geographic segmentation can lead to different marginal implicit price schedules in different regions. Segmentation on the basis of occupation or education level can lead to different marginal implicit price functions across occupational categories.

One approach to the problem of geographic segmentation is to estimate the hedonic wage function only for occupational groups which are believed on *a priori* grounds to be part of a national labor market. In general, the extent of market segmentation and its significance for empirical estimation of hedonic wage functions is not known.

As in the case of hedonic property values, the derivative of the hedonic wage function with respect to Q is the marginal implicit price of Q; and assuming that the labor market is in equilibrium, this can be taken as an estimate of the marginal willingness to pay or the marginal value of Q. Of course, this marginal value is in dollars per hour. To obtain an annual willingness to pay, it is necessary to multiply this figure by the number of hours worked per year. This gives the change in annual income necessary to just compensate for the change in Q. Since in general the hedonic wage function need not be linear, the marginal values may be different for different workers located in different urban areas. Also as in the case of the hedonic property values, aggregate marginal benefits for small changes in Q can be calculated by summing the marginal values of affected workers.

In order to estimate benefits of a nonmarginal change in Q, it is necessary to know the inverse demand function for Q. But as in the case of hedonic property values, the inverse demand function cannot be estimated from data from a single labor market unless additional restrictions are imposed. When hedonic wage functions have been used to estimate benefits, the typical approach has been to make some arbitrary assumption about the shape of the inverse demand function through a known point. See for example, National Academy of Sciences (1974, pp. 243–255) and Bayless (1982).

Finally, it should be noted in passing that the interpretation of wage differences as reflecting compensation for amenity differences is based on an essentially partial equilibrium view of the economy. There has been relatively little work done on the development of comprehensive general equilibrium models of the economic relationships among production, trade, and labor migration among cities or on the relationships among markets, goods markets, land markets, and the generation of pollution externalities. Rosen (1979, pp. 78–79, 84) alludes to some of the problems. Freeman (1979a), pp. 118–121) lays out some of the issues in an informal manner. And Roback (1982) does consider interactions between labor markets and the land markets in a general equilibrium interurban setting. But some of the conclusions reached do not appear to be consistent. As has been shown in this chapter, proper interpretation of the empirical evidence generated by market behavior requires careful modeling of the economic relationships that are affected by pollution and environmental quality.[25] Modeling of the relationship between environmental quality and wages is a very fruitful area for further research.

6. Environmental quality as a factor input

I will refer to Q as a factor input whenever Q enters positively in the production function of a good (or when pollution enters negatively). When Q is a factor of production, changes in Q lead to changes in production costs which in turn affect the price and quantity of output or the returns to other factor inputs or both. The benefits of changes in Q can be inferred from these changes in observable market data. There are several examples where Q can be interpreted as a factor input. The quality of river water diverted for irrigation affects the agricultural productivity of irrigated land. The quality of intake water may influence the costs of treating domestic water supplies or the costs of production in the industrial operations utilizing water for processing purposes. Agricultural productivity is impaired by some forms of air pollution. And to the extent that air pollution causes material damages, it can affect the cost of production for a wide variety of goods and services.[26]

Assume that good X is produced with a production function

$$X = X(K, L, Q),$$

where K and L are capital and labor, respectively, and where the marginal product of Q is positive. Since Q affects the production and supply of a marketable good, the benefits in changes in Q can be defined and measured in terms of changes in market variables related to the X industry. A change in Q can cause shifts in both cost curves and factor demand curves. The consequences of

[25] For example, the National Academy of Sciences (1974, pp. 243–255) found that higher wages were associated with higher levels of nitrogen oxide in the atmosphere. A major source of nitrogen oxides is the emissions from automobiles. If higher earnings and real incomes lead to greater use of automobiles, then the relationship between nitrogen oxides and wages is a simultaneous equation system. These relationships must be reflected in the econometric techniques used to estimate the hedonic wage function.

[26] See Freeman (1982a, pp. 86–97, 102–104, 168–169) and references therein.

shifts depend on conditions in factor and product markets. There are two channels through which changes in Q can produce benefits. The first is through changes in the price of X to consumers. The second is through changes in the incomes recieved by owners of factor inputs used in X production.

To illustrate the first channel, assume that X is produced in a competitive industry under conditions of constant cost, that is, factor supplies to this industry are infinitely elastic. Assume that the change in Q affects the cost curves of a significant proportion of producers in the market. As a result the supply curve shifts downward, causing a fall in the price and an increase in total quantity. The benefit of the price reduction accrues to consumers and can be measured by the methods described in Section 3.

The second channel is through changes in the incomes received by factors of production. Consider only one producer who is a price taker in all markets. If the change in Q affects only this producer, output price will not be changed. Since the change in Q affects the marginal costs of production, the firm's marginal cost and supply curves are shifted down. In this case the benefit is equal to the increase in quasi-rents to the firm. This benefit will accrue to the owner of a fixed factor, land for example, or to the residual income claimant as profit. In this case, benefits can be measured by changes in profits and fixed factor incomes. However, if the producers affected by changes in Q face less than perfectly elastic factor supply curves, at least some of the benefits will be passed on to factors through changes in factor prices and incomes. The factors' shares of benefits can be approximated by the areas to the left of factor supply curves [Freeman (1979, pp. 50–51), Mishan (1959)].

The effects of these two channels are combined in Figure 6.3. When the supply curve of the industry is shifted down to S_2, price decreases to P_2. Consumers benefit by the area P_1BCP_2. Part of this, P_1BFP_2, is at the expense of reduction in producer and factor surpluses; so the net gain from the lower price is BCF. The lower supply curve results in producer and factor surpluses equal to P_2CE. The net increase to producers is $AFCE$. So total benefits are equal to $ABCE$.

Implementation of these measures requires knowledge of the effects of changes in Q on the cost of production, the supply conditions for output, and the ordinary demand curve for good X. There are two special cases which make estimation of benefits relatively straightforward. First, in the case where Q is a perfect substitute for other inputs in the production of a good, an increase in Q leads to a reduction in factor input costs. If the substitution relationship is known, the decrease in per unit production costs is readily calculated. For example, if water quality improvement results in a decrease in chlorination requirements for drinking water supplies, the decrease in chlorination costs per unit of output can be readily calculated. Where the change in total cost does not affect marginal cost and output, the cost saving is a true measure of the benefits of Q. If the change in Q affects variable and marginal costs, the cost saving measure should include the

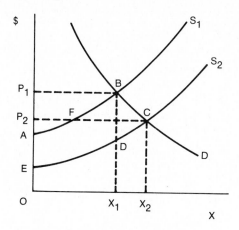

Figure 6.3. Benefits produced by a change in Q.

effect of lower cost on output. However, if the percentage reduction in marginal costs were small, or the marginal cost curve were inelastic, or both, the corresponding increase in output would be relatively small. Thus, the simple saving measure could still be used to provide a lower bound and approximate estimate of true benefits. This approach, sometimes referred to as the "damage function" approach, has been the basis of a number of estimates of the materials, household cleaning, and agricultural crop loss benefits of air pollution control and benefits to municipalities, industries, and households for reduced contamination of intake water supplies.

Second, where knowledge of cost, demand, and market structure suggests the benefits of a change in Q will accrue to producers, benefits may be estimated from observed or predicted changes in the net income of certain factor inputs. If the production unit in question is small relative to the market for the final product and for variable factors, it can be assumed that product and variable factor prices will remain fixed after the change in Q. The increased productivity then accrues in the form of a profit or in the form of a surplus income or quasi-rent to the fixed factors of production.

A modification of this approach was recently used by Mathtech, Inc. (1982) to estimate the benefits of achieving ambient air quality standards for sulphur dioxide and total suspended particulates. Mathtech used regression analysis to estimate cost functions for six 3-digit Standard Industrial Classification (SIC) industries and for the electric utility industry. The cost function gives the total cost of production of a firm as a function of the level of output, input prices, and environmental variables, including air pollution. If air pollution causes materials damages to producers, costs will be higher for those firms operating in high-pollution areas, other things being equal. There are several advantages to the cost function approach:

(1) It is not necessary to determine damage functions for specific materials.

(2) It is not necessary to estimate the stock of each material actually exposed to pollution.

(3) It is not necessary to determine specific producer's responses to air pollution – such as material substitution and preventive actions.

A pollution measure was statistically significant in five of the seven industry categories examined. Mathtech calculated benefits on the simplifying assumption that lower costs would not result in increases in output. This is equivalent to estimating the area *ABDE* in Figure 6.3. Thus, if in fact lower costs lead to higher outputs, Mathtech's calculations lead to underestimates of benefits.

Adams, Crocker and Thanavibulchai (1979) have developed and implemented a comprehensive model of producers' and market responses to changes in air quality to estimate the benefits to agriculture of controlling ozone in Southern California. The main components of their analysis are quadratic programming models for each of four agricultural subregions in California and a set of price forecasting equations for 14 crops. Yield equations giving output per acre for each crop as a function of ozone were taken from the open literature. For a specified set of air quality levels in four regions, the quadratic programming model was used to compute the profit maximizing allocation of land and other inputs to the 14 crops and the outputs of each crop by region. The price forecasting equations were then used to compute producers' profits and consumer surpluses. An improvement in ozone levels would lead to increased outputs and lower prices, thus benefiting consumers. Conceivably, with sufficiently inelastic demand functions, the price decreases could make producers worse off. But in their model, yield increases outweighed price decreases and producers reaped approximately 75 percent of the total benefits of their quality improvement.

7. Contingent choice

In contrast to the techniques described in the previous two sections, contingent choice techniques for estimating benefits involve asking people to place themselves in a hypothetical situation designed by the investigator and to respond to specific questions such as how much would they pay for a specified change, which of several alternatives would they choose, or what activities would they undertake.

The most commonly used contingent choice technique is simply to ask people through surveys and direct questions, what value they place on a specified change in environmental quality or how much quality they would "purchase" at a given price. Surveys of this type are sometimes called bidding games or willingness-to-pay-surveys. Answers to questions of this sort can be directly interpreted as estimates of benefits, subject to the qualifications discussed below.

An alternative technique known as contingent ranking has been developed and applied to estimating the benefits of improved visibility by investigators at Charles River Associates (1981). In this technique subjects are given a set of cards, each card depicting a different situation with respect to visibility and other attributes of the national park, including a postulated admission fee. Respondents are asked to place their cards in order of preference. These rankings are then analyzed with a multinomial logit model which yields a set of parameter weights on the attributes that maximizes the likelihood of realizing that rank ordering. These parameter weights can then be used to determine the increase in the admission fee required to just offset the effect of an increase in Q on the ranking of alternatives.

At least one estimate of the benefits of improved Q has been based on a contingent choice survey in which people were simply asked how their activities would change with a change in Q, in this case water quality. The report is by Heintz, Hershaft and Horak (1976). For further discussion of this study see Freeman (1982a, pp. 146–151).

There are three types of problems that arise in designing and interpreting contingent choice studies. These have to do with the potential for bias in responses, the accuracy of responses to hypothetical questions, and how to portray alternatives in a realistic and convincing manner.[27] If an individual perceives that the responses to a contingent choice survey might be used as a basis for determining environmental policy, he might attempt to influence policy by how he responds. This is called strategic bias. Opportunities for strategic bias may be more easily perceived in bidding games than in contingent ranking surveys. For example, where an individual believes that his share of the cost of providing improved Q will be in some way proportionate to his willingness to pay for it, he has an incentive to understate his willingness to pay in order to reduce his repayment obligation. This is the well-known "free-rider" problem in the public goods literature. On the one hand, where assurances are given that tax burdens will not be affected by the answers given, the individual has an incentive to overstate his willingness to pay in an effort to assure that environmental quality is provided at a high level.

In addition to strategic bias there is some evidence that certain structural characteristics of surveys have the potential for biasing responses. For example, in order to make the question seem realistic, some surveys have stated that the vehicle for payment will be an increase in the sales tax or a surcharge on electric utility bills. If respondents have some attitudes concerning the chosen means of payment, this could introduce vehicle bias into responses. Also in many willing-

---

[27] These problems are discussed in more detail in Freeman (1979a, ch. 5).

ness-to-pay surveys the questioner announces a value and then adjusts it upward or downward in fixed increments depending on response. The starting point can introduce bias.

It appears to be possible to design survey questions so as to minimize incentives for biased response. The general approach is to design the survey instrument so as to minimize the occurrence of any linkage between a subject's response and either an actual repayment or an actual outcome. But devices to eliminate incentives for biased responses also have a second effect. They reduce the incentive to provide accurate responses [Freeman (1979a, ch. 5)]. An accurate response is one that is consistent with the behavior that would be revealed if the good in question could actually be offered in a market. In the real world, an individual who takes action inconsistent with his basic preferences, perhaps by mistake, incurs a cost or a loss of utility. In the purely hypothetical survey situation, there is no cost to being wrong. Thus the incentives to undertake the mental effort to be accurate are weak at best. The more hypothetical the situation posed to the individual, that is, the farther removed the situation is from his normal everyday experience, the less likely is the answer to be accurate.

Another set of problems has to do with perceptions and how to portray accurately the hypothetical situation to respondents. For example, if the purpose of the survey is to estimate the benefits of a specified water quality improvement, the questioner must find a way to describe the improvement accurately and in sufficient detail so that all respondents are reacting to similar perceptions of water quality improvement. Some of the best survey studies have combined photographs with descriptive textual material [for example, Brookshire, Ives and Schulze (1976), Randall, Ives and Eastman (1974), and Brookshire et al. (1979)]. But there are limits to the ability of both words and pictures to convey effectively all of the aesthetic dimensions associated with environmental improvements.

The best way to resolve the questions of bias and accuracy is to conduct an experiment in which benefits are calculated both by the analysis of revealed behavior based on a properly specified model and by a contingent choice technique. If both techniques reveal similar results, then this suggests that contingent choice responses can be substituted for observations of actual behavior in benefit analysis. However, efforts to perform such experiments to date have given only mixed results [Bishop and Heberlein (1979), Brookshire et al. (1982), and Desvousges, Smith and McGiveny (1983)]. Thus, the question of the seriousness of the problems of accuracy and bias in contingent choice techniques must still be considered open.[28]

---

[28] For further discussion of the evidence on bias and accuracy, see Schulze, d'Arge and Brookshire (1981) and Rowe and Chestnut (forthcoming).

8. Conclusion

In this paper I have reviewed a variety of techniques and models developed for the purpose of measuring the benefits of environmental improvements. I think that there are two major lessons to be drawn from this review. The first is that although environmental quality has the attributes of a public good, people can often be induced to reveal their preferences for Q either through their actions in markets as they respond to price signals or through their response in contingent choice settings. The second lesson is that the correct interpretation of the signals sent by market behavior must be based on a proper model of the individual choice problem which accurately portrays the substitute or complement relationships and the range of possible individual responses to change in Q. In the context of such models it can be seen that early conjectures such as that benefits are measured by changes in defensive spending are likely to be wrong.

References

Adams, Richard M., Narongsakdi Thanavibulchai and Thomas D. Crocker (1979) *Methods Development for Assessing Air Pollution Damages for Selected Crops Within Southern California* (U.S. Environmental Protection Agency, Washington).

Bailey, Martin J. (1980) *Reducing Risks to Life: Measurement of the Benefits* (American Enterprise Institute, Washington).

Bartik, Timothy J. (1982) "Evaluating the Benefits of Neighborhood Change", unpublished Ph.D. dissertation, University of Wisconsin, Madison.

Bayless, Mark (1982) "Measuring the Benefits of Air Quality Improvements: A Hedonic Salary Approach", *Journal of Environmental Economics and Management* 9, 81–99.

Bergstrom, Theodore C. and Robert T. Goodman (1973) "Private Demands for Public Goods", *American Economic Review* 63, 290–296.

Bishop, Richard C. and Thomas A. Heberlein (1979) "Measuring Values of Extra Market Goods: Are Indirect Measures Biased?" *American Journal of Agricultural Economics* 61, 926–930.

Borcherding, Thomas E. and Robert T. Deacon (1972) "The Demand for Services of Non Federal Governments", *American Economic Review* 62, 891–901.

Bradford, David F. and Gregory G. Hildebrandt (1977) "Observable Preferences for Public Goods", *Journal of Public Economics* 8, 111–121.

Brookshire, David S., Ralph C. d'Arge, William D. Schulze and Mark Thayer (1979) *Methods Development for Assessing Air Pollution Control Benefits*, vol. 2: *Experiments in Valuing Non Market Goods: A Case Study of Alternative Benefit Measures of Air Pollution Control in the South Coast Air Basin of Southern California* (U.S. Environmental Protection Agency, Washington).

Brookshire, David S., Berry C. Ives and William D. Schulze (1976) "The Valuation of Aesthetic Preferences", *Journal of Environmental Economics and Management* 3, 325–346.

Brookshire, David S., Mark Thayer, William D. Schulze and Ralph C. d'Arge (1982) "The Valuation of Public Goods: A Comparison of Survey and Hedonic Approaches", *American Economic Review* 72, 165–177.

Brown, Gardner Jr. and Robert Mendelsohn (1983) "The Hedonic Travel Cost Method", unpublished.

Brown, James N. and Harvey S. Rosen (1982) "On the Estimation of Structural Hedonic Price Models", *Econometrica* 50, 765–768.

Cesario, Frank J. and Jack L. Knetsch (1970) "Times Bias in Recreation Benefits Estimates", *Water Resources Research* 6, 700–704.

Cesario, Frank J. and Jack L. Knetsch (1976) "A Recreation Site Demand and Benefit Estimation Model", *Regional Studies* 10, 97–104.

Charles River Associates, Inc. (1981) Benefits of Improving Visibility at Mesa Verde National Park (Charles River Associates, Inc., Boston).

Clawson, Marion and Jack L. Knetsch (1966) *Economics of Outdoor Recreation* (Johns Hopkins University Press, Baltimore).

Conley, B.C. (1976) "The Value of Human Life in the Demand for Safety", *American Economic Review* 66, 45–55.

Courant, Paul N. and Richard Porter (1981) "Averting Expenditure and the Cost of Pollution", *Journal of Environmental Economics and Management* 8, 321–329.

Cropper, Maureen L. (1981) "Measuring the Benefits from Reduced Morbidity", *American Economic Review* 71, 235–240.

Desvousges, William H., V. Kerry Smith and Matthew P. McGivney (1983) A Comparison of Alternative Approaches for Estimating Recreation and Related Benefits of Water Quality Improvements (Research Triangle Institute, Research Triangle Park, NC).

Diamond, Peter A. and Daniel McFadden, (1974) "Some Uses of the Expenditure Function in Public Finance", *Journal of Public Economics* 3, 3–21.

Feenberg, Daniel and Edwin S. Mills (1980) *Measuring the Benefits of Water Pollution Abatement* (Academic Press, New York).

Freeman, A. Myrick III (1974) "On Estimating Air Pollution Control Benefits from Land Value Studies", *Journal of Environmental Economics and Management* 1, 74–83.

Freeman, A. Myrick III (1975) "A Survey of the Techniques for Measuring the Benefits of Water Quality Improvement", in: Henry Peskin and Eugene Seskin (eds.), *Cost Benefit Analysis and Water Pollution Policy* (The Urban Institute, Washington).

Freeman, A. Myrick III (1979a) *The Benefits of Environmental Improvement: Theory and Practice* (Johns Hopkins University Press, Baltimore).

Freeman, A. Myrick III (1979b) "Hedonic Prices, Property Values and Measuring Environmental Benefits: A Survey of the Issues", *Scandinavian Journal of Economics* 81, 154–173.

Freeman, A. Myrick III (1982a) *Air and Water Pollution Control: A Benefit Cost Assessment* (John Wiley, New York).

Freeman, A. Myrick III (1982b) "The Health Implications of Residuals Discharges: A Methodological Overview", in: V. Kerry Smith and John V. Krutilla (eds.), *Explorations in Natural Resource Economics* (Johns Hopkins University Press, Baltimore).

Goldman, S.M. and Hirofumi Uzawa (1964) "A Note on Separability in Demand Analysis", *Econometrica* 32, 397–398.

Griliches, Zvi (1971) Price Indices and Quality Change (Harvard University Press, Cambridge).

Harrington, Winston and Paul R. Portney (1983) "Valuing the Benefits of Improved Human Health", unpublished.

Hausman, Jerry A. (1981) "Exact Consumer's Surplus and Dead Weight Loss", *American Economic Review* 71, 662–676.

Heintz, H.T., A. Hershaft and G. Horak (1976) "National Damages of Air and Water Pollution", A Report submitted to the Environmental Protection Agency.

Hori, H. (1975) "Revealed Preference for Public Goods", *American Economic Review* 65, 197–991.

Hurwicz, Leonid (1971) "On the Problem of Integrability of Demand Functions", in: John Chipman and others (eds.), *Preferences, Utility, and Demand* (Harcourt Brace and Jovanovich, New York).

Jackson, Clement J., Calvin R. von Buscek, Richard C. Schwing and Bradford Southworth (1976) *Benefit-Cost Analysis of Automotive Emission Reductions* (General Motors Research Laboratories, Warren, Michigan).

Jones-Lee, Michael W. (1976) *The Value of Life: An Economic Analysis* (University of Chicago Press, Chicago).

Katzner, Donald W. (1970) *Static Demand Theory* (MacMillan, New York).

Knetsch, Jack L. (1964) "Economics of Including Recreation as a Purpose of Eastern Water Projects", *Journal of Farm Economics* 46, 1148–1157.

Lave, Lester B. and Eugene P. Seskin (1977) Air Pollution and Human Health (Johns Hopkins University Press, Baltimore).

Lave, Lester B. and Eugene P. Seskin (1979) "Epidemiology, Causality and Public Policy", *American Scientist* 67, 178–186.

Liu, Ben-chieh and Eden S. Yu (1976) Physical and Economic Damage Functions for Air Pollutants by Receptor (U.S. Environmental Protection Agency, Corvallis, Oregon).

Lucas, Robert E. B. (1977) "Hedonic Wage Equations and Psychic Wages in the Returns to Schooling", *American Economic Review* 67, 549–558.

Mäler, Karl-Goran (1974) Environmental Economics: A Theoretical Inquiry (Johns Hopkins University Press, Baltimore).

Mäler, Karl-Goran and Ronald Wygza (1976) Economic Measurement of Environmental Damage (Organization for Economic Cooperation and Development, Paris).

Mathtech, Inc. (1982) Benefits Analysis of Alternative Secondary National Ambient Air Quality Standards for Sulfur Dioxide and Total Suspended Particulates (Mathtech, Inc., Princeton, NJ).

McConnell, Kenneth (1975) "Some Problems in Estimating the Demand for Outdoor Recreation", *American Journal of Agricultural Economics* 57, 330–334.

Mishan, Ezra J. (1959) "Rent as a Measure of Welfare Change", *American Economic Review* 49, 386–394.

Mohring, Herbert (1971) "Alternative Welfare Gain and Loss Measures", *Western Economic Journal* 9, 349–368.

National Academy of Sciences, Coordinating Committee on Air Quality Studies (1974) Air Quality and Automobile Emission Control, vol. 4, *The Costs and Benefits of Automobile Emission Control* (National Academy of Sciences, Washington).

Quigley, John M. (1982) "Nonlinear Budget Constraints and Consumer Demand: An Application to Public Programs for Residential Housing", *Journal of Urban Economics* 12, 177–201.

Randall, Alan and John R. Stoll (1980) "Consumer's Surplus in Commodity Space", *American Economic Review* 70, 449–455.

Randall, Alan, Berry Ives and Clyde Eastman (1974) "Bidding Games for Evaluation of Aesthetic Environmental Improvements", *Journal of Environmental Economics and Management* 1, 132–149.

Roback, Jennifer (1982) "Wages, Rents, and the Quality of Life", *Journal of Political Economy* 90, 1257–1278.

Rosen, Sherwin (1974) "Hedonic Prices and Implicit Markets: Product Differentiation in Perfect Competition", *Journal of Political Economy* 82, 34–55.

Rosen, Sherwin (1979) "Wage-Based Indices of Urban Quality of Life", in: Peter Mieszkowski and Mahlon Straszheim (eds.), *Current Issues in Urban Economics* (Johns Hopkins University Press, Baltimore).

Rowe, Robert D. and Lauraine G. Chestnut (forthcoming) "Valuing Environmental Commodities: Revisited", *Land Economics*.

Ryan, John W., et al. (1981) *An Estimate of Nonhealth Benefits of Meeting the Secondary National Ambient Air Quality Standards* (Stanford Research Institute, Inc., Palo Alto).

Saxonhouse, Gary R. (1977) "Regressions From Samples Having Different Characteristics", *Review of Economics and Statistics* 59, 234–237.

Schulze, William D., Ralph C. d'Arge and David S. Brookshire (1981) "Valuing Environmental Commodities: Some Recent Experiments", *Land Economics* 57, 151–172.

Scott, Anthony D. (1965) "The Valuation of Game Resources: Some Theoretical Aspects", *Canadian Fisheries Reports* 4.

Silberberg, Eugene (1972) "Duality and the Many Consumer's Surpluses", *American Economic Review* 62, 902–952.

Smith, V. Kerry (1979) "Indirect Revelation of the Demand for Public Goods: An Overview and Critique", *Scotish Journal of Political Economy* 26, 183–189.

Thaler, Richard H. and Sherwin Rosen (1976) "The Value of Saving a Life: Evidence from the Labor Market", in: N.E. Terleckyj (ed.), *Household Production and Consumption* (Columbia University Press, New York).

Weinstein, M., D. Shepard and J. Pliskin (1976) "The Economic Value of Changing Mortality Probabilities: A Decision-Theoretic Approach", Discussion Paper 46D, John Fitzgerald Kennedy School of Government (Harvard University, Cambridge).

Willig, Robert D. (1973a) "Consumer's Surplus: A Rigorous Cookbook", Technical Report no. 98, Stanford University, Stanford.

Willig, Robert D. (1973b) "Welfare Analysis of Quality Affecting Prices and Products", Memo no. 513, Stanford University, Stanford.

Willig, Robert D. (1976) "Consumer's Surplus Without Apology", *American Economic Review* 66, 589–597.

Willig, Robert D. (1979) "Consumer's Surplus Without Apology: Reply", *American Economic Review* 79, 469–474.

Wilman, Elizabeth A. (1980) "The Value of Time in Recreation Benefit Studies", *Journal of Environmental Economics and Management* 7, 272–286.

Zeckhauser, Richard and Anthony Fisher (1976) "Averting Behavior and External Diseconomies", unpublished.

Chapter 7

ENVIRONMENTAL ECONOMICS, INDUSTRIAL PROCESS MODELS, AND REGIONAL-RESIDUALS MANAGEMENT MODELS

DAVID JAMES

Macquarie University, Australia

1. Conceptual framework for industrial activity analysis and regional environmental quality management

1.1. Materials balance, residuals discharges, and environmental external effects

The concept of externalities associated with residuals in the environment has long standing within the discipline of economics ever since Pigou (1932) discussed the welfare implications of smoke from a railroad. But it was not until the environmental movement of the later 1960s, together with new insights gained from industrial and water research, especially in the United States, that economists were forced to consider the full significance of economic activity in terms of its effects on environmental quality. The work of Ayres and Kneese (1969) and Kneese, Ayres and d'Arge (1970) from Resources for the Future (RFF) represented a turning point in the literature. These writers applied the laws of mass balance (or conservation of mass), which were well known to chemical engineers in their design and analysis of industrial plants, to the economic system as a whole.

Within the framework of a Walras–Cassel general equilibrium model (specifically a physical Leontief system), Ayres and Kneese formulated a set of identities relating to the use and disposal of materials by the various production and consumption sectors of the economy. Without going into mathematical proofs, which can be found in the references cited, the main balances can be summarized as: the mass of all materials inputs from the environment to the economy, ignoring flows from the environment directly to the final consumption sector, equals the mass of inputs to the intermediate product sectors; the mass of inputs to the intermediate product sectors equals the mass of products supplied to the final consumption sector plus the mass of residuals discharged to the environment minus the mass of materials recycled; and the mass of all final products equals the

Handbook of Natural Resource and Energy Economics, vol. I, edited by A.V. Kneese and J.L. Sweeney
© *Elsevier Science Publishers B.V., 1985*

mass of materials recycled plus residuals generated by the final consumption sector. Assuming no accumulation or recycling, the mass of all inputs from the environment must equal the mass of all residuals discharged to the environment.

Several strands of research arose from this work. Elaborations and criticisms of the model came from Noll and Trijonis (1971), Converse (1971), and Victor (1972), among others. The welfare implications were profound. Ayres and Kneese demonstrated that, far from constituting a theoretical curiosum, environmental externalities associated with the discharge of residuals to natural systems are a normal and inevitable outcome of economic activity. Research on pollution and environmental damage functions soon followed [OECD (1974, 1976)]. At the national level, input–output models were extended to operational simulation tools capable of projecting discharges of liquids, solids, and gases to air, water, and land, under various economic growth scenarios [Ridker (1972)], and efforts were made to identify the industrial sectors most responsible for particular types of residuals discharges and environmental damage [Victor (1972), Ayres and Gutmanis (1972)].

The outcome of primary interest here is the development of multidisciplinary quantitative models designed to analyze industrial activities, the generation and discharge of residuals by activities to the environment, the effects of residuals on ambient environmental quality (AEQ) and receptors, and the actions that can be taken to manage AEQ at the regional level. Such models are described in the literature as residuals–environmental quality management (REQM) models.

The plan of the chapter is as follows. First, a set of operational concepts and definitions is provided. The construction of REQM models is then discussed in general terms. The relationship between economic activity and residuals flows is analyzed in greater detail, emphasizing the distinction between residuals generation and discharges to the environment. The behavior of residuals in the environment is dealt with next, demonstrating the use of air and water dispersion models and the role of dose–response functions. Approaches to residuals management are then presented, with an essentially theoretical treatment of alternative modeling techniques. The chapter concludes with a series of actual case studies demonstrating application of REQM models to the management of individual industrial plants, air and water quality, and integrated regional economic–environmental systems.

1.2. Concepts and definitions

Appropriate terminology for REQM modeling was established by RFF researchers in conjunction with their work on materials balance and industrial process analysis [Ayres (1972), Russell and Spofford (1972), Bower (1977), Bower et al. (1977), Kneese and Bower (1979)]. The same terminology is followed here.

Regional-residuals management begins with an analysis of industrial activities. The term "industrial" refers to the transformation of materials (or energy) to desired commodities or "product outputs". An activity is defined as a decision-making establishment (mine, plant, mill) consisting of a set of unit processes or operations with given site boundaries. This definition of an industrial activity draws heavily on the concepts of chemical engineering. As described by Ayres (1972), a unit operation is a physical transformation of materials within a plant, and a unit process involves chemical reactions. Each operation or process is distinct, and has a specific set of technological characteristics, production inputs, and product outputs. The industrial process approach to production analysis thus involves a detailed study of everything that takes place within an industrial activity. At a higher level of aggregation, activities of a similar kind may be classified as a regional production sector, although considerable variation could exist in product mixes, input requirements, and production technologies. Whether such variation is important or not will be discussed at a later stage.

Flows of materials and energy that remain from the production of product outputs are referred to as nonproduct outputs. Some nonproduct outputs have further economic use, either as marketable by-products or as recovered materials (or energy) that can be used in production processes in the same plant. In sugar refining, for example, sugarcane fiber (bagasse) can be converted to building boards or placed in combustion chambers to raise steam for process heat or electricity generation.

Recovery of nonproduct outputs is affected by economic factors. Costs usually are involved in recovery operations, and in an efficient industrial plant, recovery will proceed to the level at which the marginal recovery cost equals the economic value of the recovered materials or energy. Among other things, prices of product outputs, by-products and production inputs to an activity will govern recovery operations.

Remaining nonproduct materials and energy are defined as residuals. Materials residuals take the form of gases, liquids, and solids. Energy residuals comprise noise, heat, and vibration. Radioactive residuals are a third category with their own special characteristics. The term "residual" is clearly economic. Whether or not a nonproduct output becomes a residual depends on prevailing cost and price conditions and on process technologies. Government regulations and charges may also be important determinants. It is worth noting, finally, that residuals are not defined as "wastes" or "pollutants", since at their point of generation their subsequent economic or environmental significance is unspecified.

Residuals can be left untreated or subjected to modification processes. On-site modification of residuals may entail add-on processes (e.g. flue-gas scrubbing) or constitute an integral part of the activity's production processes. In either event, modification processes require their own materials and energy inputs and may lead to by-products, secondary materials and energy recovery, and further residuals generation, depending on particular circumstances. Disposal alternatives include discharge to the environment at site boundaries, storage on site, and conveyance to other locations for off-site storage or discharge.

The environment consists of natural systems outside economic activity boundaries. For the purpose of residuals management, AEQ can be measured in terms of the concentrations of residuals at receptor points within a region. Linkages between discharges of residuals and ambient concentrations can be quite complicated, as natural systems processes and effects are involved. For nonreactive residuals, this refers to the physical dispersion of residuals in air, water, and land systems. Critical factors are the locations of discharge points, the mass or volume of residuals discharged, the type of residuals, temporal release patterns, and physical processes in the environment, such as diffusion, sedimentation, fallout, and accumulation. Reactions among residuals such as oxidation (and reduction), biological assimilation, or transformation may, however, occur in the environment. For policy reasons, it may be necessary to consider the exposure of receptors (plants, humans, animals, materials, and structures) to ambient concentrations and assess the ultimate environmental impacts through dose–response relationships.

Management of environmental quality involves physical measures to alter the release or functions of residuals in the environment, and implementation incentives (inducements or penalties) introduced by government to control the disposal of residuals by activities. Various institutional arrangements may be established to facilitate this task. Each particular set of physical measures, implementation incentives, and institutional arrangements to control AEQ is defined as an environmental management strategy. The conceptual framework for a residuals-environmental quality management system is presented in Figure 7.1. In any situation, many alternatives usually exist as a means of reaching AEQ goals.

1.3. Components of a regional environmental quality model

Quantitative models are available to deal with all phases of the analysis and management of residuals in a regional environment. The researcher has a choice of constructing a comprehensive modeling system incorporating all possible components, or of carefully selecting the most appropriate models to tackle specific management problems.

The conceptual framework of Figure 7.1, for example, has been translated into an operational regional model by Russell and Spofford (1972) and applied to the Delaware Estuary, as discussed in Section 5.4.1. Under the Russell–Spofford approach, production decisions within an activity are simulated by means of a linear programming model that incorporates different technologies, by-products, materials recovery, and residuals modification processes. Technologies and

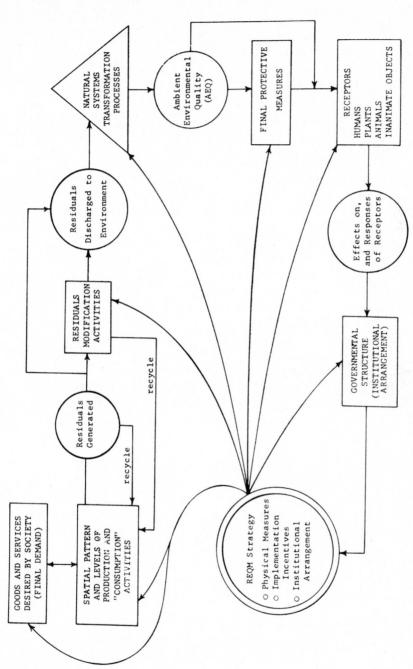

Figure 7.1. Concept of a residuals–environmental quality management (REQM) system. *Source:* Bower (1977, p. 8).

residuals handling respond to cost parameters in the objective function or to constraints imposed on residuals discharge rates.

The behavior of residuals released to the environment is analyzed by means of natural systems models, which have been surveyed by Bower (1983) and Basta and Bower (1982), among others (and briefly in Chapter 3 of this Handbook). Ambient concentrations of nonreactive residuals in air and water systems can be estimated with physical dispersion models. Reactive residuals require more elaborate analysis taking physical and chemical processes into account. Biological models combine residuals movement in the environment with ecological processes such as the transmission of toxic substances in food chains and changes in the population levels of organisms of terrestrial or aquatic ecosystems.

Environmental damage functions may play an important role in an environmental quality management model. Estimates of exposure of receptors to ambient conditions in the environment are required, and physical receptor effects determined through dose–response functions or models. Monetary estimates can, in principle, be made to obtain monetary representations of economic welfare changes (see the discussion in Chapter 6 of this Handbook).

Whether damage functions are needed in a model depends largely on the kind of management objectives pursued. As pointed out by Lesuis et al. (1980), objectives often conflict, and compromise solutions must be found. Typical goals for a regional system are the maximization of output or income, minimization of environmental damage costs and minimization of production and residuals management costs. Quantitative models, designed to assess tradeoffs between economic and environmental goals, are described later in Section 4.4. Many of these models incorporate environmental standards rather than environmental damage (or improvement) functions.

1.4. Approaches to model construction

Construction of REQM models can be approached in a number of different ways. Bower (1983) classifies approaches according to: mathematical rigor (simple empirical functions, two-variable correlation models, multivariate regression models, and analytical models); natural systems media (air, water, land, and ecosystems); and phenomena under study (natural systems or receptor effects).

Models may also be classified in terms of their mathematical form. Simulation models, static or dynamic, are useful when decisionmakers' priorities are not clearly specified. Alternative outcomes of different environmental management strategies can be presented to decisionmakers for their consideration. A drawback with simulation modeling is that the full range of management options may not be properly identified, and the results of simulations may be difficult to interpret. Optimization models, especially those based on mathematical programming techniques, offer a more systematic means of meeting management goals.

Regardless of the kind of model proposed, certain criteria should be met when setting up the analytical framework. The first is that due attention should be given to the spatial, temporal, physical, chemical, ecological, and receptor-effects aspects of the model. Second, flexibility should be maintained so that the model can be adapted to a variety of policy applications. Third, the overall framework should be decomposable so that research skills can be directed to specific modeling tasks and provision is made for the monitoring of outputs from each component of the model. Fourth, the problem of uncertainty must be addressed. One solution is to build a stochastic model. Other approaches include sensitivity analysis and the estimation of probability distributions for key explanatory variables in the model. Finally, certain logistical difficulties in constructing, operating, and applying the model need to be overcome.

1.5. Model accuracy, cost, and applications

Costs of an REQM model can be divided into several categories. Data acquisition costs comprise the first. The data requirements for a comprehensive model incorporating natural systems and dose–response effects are considerable. Unless data can be provided by existing research institutions, private industry, and government agencies, primary data collection has to be carried out, and this is a very costly operation. Models based on Leontief input–output systems may be quite expensive if a set of regional input–output accounts has to be specially compiled. Costs of research personnel may also be high. Environmental modeling is a multidisciplinary endeavor and the necessary skills, particularly those of coordination and direction, may be difficult to locate and buy. A third cost category is that of computing time (where needed) which usually rises rapidly as model complexity increases.

Problems of accuracy may create serious difficulties in implementing a REQM model. Data may be unreliable or outdated. The model itself may not be properly specified. Problems arise, for example, if an attempt is made to use a steady-state model to predict a dynamic situation, or if a linear model does not appropriately represent actual relationships. Verification may be difficult to achieve in practice; expensive simulation and monitoring may be required. Natural systems models, especially those of ecosystem behavior, are notorious for their unreliability. Statistical analyses of dose–response relationships have similarly been heavily criticized. With all of these problems, tradeoffs typically must be made between model accuracy and cost.

Communication of the results of an REQM model to users is the final logistical problem to overcome. Unless users are frequently consulted in the early stages of model construction, the wrong issues may be analyzed and irrelevant conclusions drawn. It is often necessary to simplify the results to convey the findings to environmental managers. In this respect, benefit–cost analysis is a useful approach, as a wide spectrum of effects can be condensed to a single indicator. Cost-effectiveness analysis, with environmental standards set by scientific and medical experts, is another realistic route to follow. Problems of this kind are dealt with extensively in the general economic literature, but references that are specifically concerned with REQM models are Spofford et al. (1975), EPRI (1979a), Bower (1983), Kneese (1977), and Kneese and Bower (1979).

2. Economic activity and the determination of residuals flows

2.1. Methods of determining residuals discharges

Approaches to the estimation of residuals discharges from economic activities should be guided by the kind of environmental planning or management problem to be tackled. In some situations, the aim is to find the best set of residuals management practices and technologies that meets AEQ goals while maintaining existing levels of product outputs for an established regional industrial framework. Controls may simply be required for a single major plant within a region, so that an in-depth study of a particular industrial activity is called for. In other situations, the objective might be to obtain "broad-brush" scenarios of future economic development patterns, with associated residuals discharge and AEQ effects, to identify general problem areas that subsequently can be examined in greater detail.

In principle, industrial process models of the kind developed by Resources for the Future (RFF) should yield the most accurate estimates of residuals discharges at the individual plant level and at the regional level, and the relevant methodologies are highly commended in this review. It is worth noting, nevertheless, that the RFF approach is suitable only in certain contexts. Activity levels are assumed to already exist, and an optimal REQM strategy is sought in an essentially static production situation. Future projections could of course be made, and either a comparative statics or dynamic programming approach adopted, but a commensurate increase in data requirements and modeling effort must also be expected. The costs of complex dynamic optimization models are invariably high, although they have been borne by various member countries of the OECD in their development of national energy system assessment models [International Energy Agency (1980)].

For relatively low-cost projections of regional-residuals discharges, multisectoral simulation models – in particular, generalized regional input–output models – have been a popular choice. Industrial activity levels in such models are usually quantified in terms of sectoral monetary output values. Important detail can easily be hidden on input patterns, production technologies, product mixes, discharge rates, and relative sizes of individual establishments in the same regional industrial category, but the technique nevertheless generates information on "average" conditions, which is undoubtedly better than having no information at all. Furthermore, if desired, multisectoral models featuring mixed indicators of industrial output – both monetary and physical – can be constructed, and engineering detail pursued in the industrial sectors that are the most significant environmentally. Residuals recovery and modification processes can fairly easily be incorporated. Multisectoral simulation models thus do have a role to play in REQM programs, their main contribution being to provide rough estimates of residuals discharges under different technological and economic growth scenarios.

The level of aggregation of industrial activities within an REQM model is clearly a major factor governing the approach to residuals discharge determination. This point having been made, it is appropriate to consider the methods that have been applied to individual industrial plants, linked industrial activities, and multisectoral regional production systems.

2.2. Residuals from individual plants

Residuals discharged by industrial activities can be determined by applying the laws of conservation of mass to individual plants. The mass of all inputs to a plant, including environmental inputs such as oxygen used in combustion or chemical processes, must equal the mass of all final products and by-products, materials accumulated on-site, and residuals directly discharged to the environment or transported to other locations.

To estimate residuals discharges from a given activity, one approach is to establish residuals discharge coefficients and apply these to output levels of the activity. As demonstrated by Kneese and Bower (1979), such coefficients may be obtained in two stages: first, by ascertaining the net generation of residuals within the activity, and second, by determining the actual discharge of residuals into the environment. The two concepts are quite distinct. In the absence of controls over residuals discharges, generation coefficients may be written as a simple function:

$$R_g = f(M, TP, PO, POS), \tag{1}$$

where R_g is a vector of residuals generated per unit of output or raw material input, M is a vector of raw materials used, TP is a set of process technologies, PO is product mix, and POS a set of product specifications.

It is preferable to calculate generation rates in terms of physical output levels or in relation to materials or energy inputs. As an example of the input approach, combustion emission factors can be combined with fuel-use patterns in a plant to estimate airborne emissions [U.S. EPA (1973), Stern (1976), and Tomany (1975)].

Residuals discharge coefficients depend on the same factors as generation coefficients, but new determinants must be taken into account. An appropriate expression is

$$R_d = F(M, TP, PO, POS, EC, TR), \tag{2}$$

where R_d is a vector of residuals discharged per unit of output or raw material input, EC reflects a set of controls, standards or charges imposed on specific residuals, and *TR* indicates residuals modification technology. Changes in any of these factors may result in new discharge coefficients. Other methods of estimating discharge coefficients include the use of chemical engineering analysis, plant monitoring data, plant performance specifications submitted to government authorities, international studies, or industrial surveys.

As pointed out in Chapter 3 of this Handbook, the spatial characteristics of residuals discharge are important from an environmental management viewpoint. Within a plant, discharges may occur at many points. Discharge standards imposed under the "bubble concept" [Deland (1979)] can be expected to result in engineering solutions quite different from those obtained when restrictions are applied to specific on-site locations or unit processes. As previously noted, discharges may occur at locations other than site boundaries, as with flyash from power stations or with coal washery rejects that can be discharged off-site through slurry pipelines.

Discharges also have a time dimension. Seasonal variations can occur because of fluctuating demand patterns or the effect of climate on raw material supplies. Short-term variations can be caused by peak-load demands as in electric power generation, maintenance operations, work shifts, accidents, and even the deliberate release of residuals at night to avoid detection and prosecution. Long-term variations in discharges will tend to arise from changes in the scale of production, physical depreciation of equipment, the introduction of different process technologies, and alterations in cost and price conditions.

To handle the complexities of process technologies, residuals generation and residuals discharge for individual industrial plants, mathematical programming can be applied. Programming has been commonly used in industry for management decisions, especially petroleum refining [Manne (1963)], but it was not until the work of Russell (1971, 1973) and Russell and Vaughan (1974, 1976) that specific recognition was given to the role of residuals. Russell's model offers a powerful method of assessing the effects of different economic, technological, and regulatory factors on plant operations. It is a linear programming model of the form

$$\max_{\text{s.t.}} - c_x X - c_b B - c_w W - C_t T - c_v V + c_y Y - c_d D$$

$$
\begin{bmatrix}
A_{11} & A_{12} & & & & A_{16} & \\
A_{21} & & A_{23} & & & & \\
A_{31} & & & & & & \\
A_{41} & A_{42} & A_{43} & A_{44} & A_{45} & & A_{47} \\
& A_{52} & A_{53} & A_{54} & A_{55} & & A_{57} \\
& & & & & & A_{67}
\end{bmatrix}
\begin{bmatrix}
X \\ B \\ W \\ T \\ V \\ Y \\ D
\end{bmatrix}
\geqq
\begin{bmatrix}
0 \\ b_2 \\ b_3 \\ 0 \\ 0 \\ b_6
\end{bmatrix}
\tag{3}
$$

$$X, B, W, T, V, Y, D \geq 0.$$

Vectors representing process levels in the model are: X, a set of production alternatives; B, production of by-products; W, materials recovery from residuals;

T, treatment of residuals; *V*, transport of residuals; *D*, discharge of residuals; and *Y*, sale of products. The objective function maximizes revenue from the sale of all products ($c_y Y$) where c_y is a vector of output prices, and minimizes the total costs of production ($c_x X$), by-product production ($c_b B$), raw material recovery ($c_w W$), residuals treatment ($c_t T$), and residuals transport ($c_v V$), where the subscripted c's are row vectors indicating corresponding unit costs. If charges are imposed on residuals discharges, then the vector c_d in the objective function takes on positive values. The model treats charges as costs and minimizes them together with all other production costs.

The rows of the activity matrix indicate the model's constraints. Row set 1 ensures that all products sold are actually produced. Row set 2 constrains the supplies of inputs to production activities, including those from materials recovery processes. Row set 3 controls output quality. Row set 4 is a mass balance equation for primary residuals generated by all activities. Row set 5 represents the generation and handling of secondary residuals, which can take the form of primary residuals remaining from treatment processes, new types of residuals created by a treatment process, and primary residuals at different locations. Row sets 4 and 5 ensure that all residuals generated are accounted for by means of materials recovery, production of by-products, treatment, transport or discharge. The last set of rows introduces discharge constraints. A maximum limit can be imposed on the total discharge from all activities of any particular residual. These constraints can of course be disregarded if the model is used to simulate effluent or emission charges instead of discharge standards. In a completely uncontrolled situation, the pattern of residuals discharges can be determined by setting the "costs" of discharges in the objective function equal to zero and deleting the residuals discharge constraints.

Russell's model has certain limitations because of its linear properties. It does not allow for economies of scale in production or for possible nonlinearities in residuals handling functions. The time dimension is also greatly simplified, as the model is steady state. Such models may, furthermore, be very expensive to build.

One of the earliest studies undertaken by RFF – a beet sugar production plant – is an excellent example of the principle of mass balance applied to an individual industrial plant [Löf and Kneese (1968)]. Details of the production process, with associated product outputs and residuals generated in the absence of materials recovery, are given in Figure 7.2. The process is comparatively simple, and permitted RFF to gain experience in developing a methodology that later could be applied to other industrial activities. The residual of greatest concern is biochemical oxygen demand (BOD), but considerable amounts of flue gas and lime cake slurry are also generated. The process was analyzed again with extensive recycling that removes most of the waterborne residuals. Mass balance for the improved process indicate that only a small increase of gaseous and solid residuals must be incurred to obtain a large reduction in BOD discharges. Other individual industry studies undertaken by RFF include a dairy, livestock

High Residual Beet Sugar Production Process—No Recirculation

(In pounds per ton of beets processed except where otherwise stated)
Intake: 5250 gallons/ton sliced beets—regular; 175 gallons/ton
sliced beets—Steffens additional.

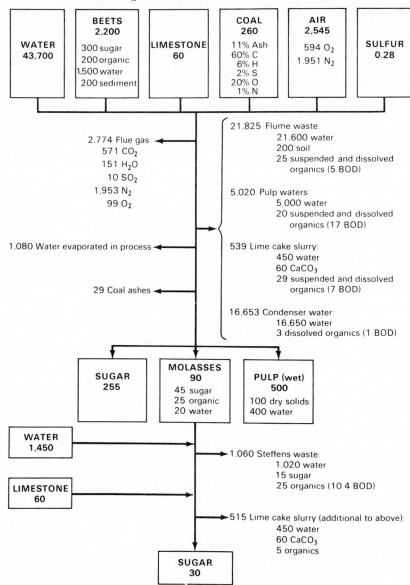

Source: Kneese et al. (1970, p. 50).

production and food processing [Kneese et al. (1970)], pulp and paper manufacture [Bower et al. (1972), Löf et al. (1973)], a brewery and lignite-fired electric power plant [Basta et al. (1978)], petroleum refining [Russell (1973)], and a steel mill [Russell and Vaughan (1976)]. Residuals generation coefficients for a wide range of industrial activities are presented in Basta et al. (1978).

Although a great deal of pioneering work was done by RFF on industrial activity analysis and residuals management, other research covered similar ground, for example, the engineering approaches to residuals discharges from energy systems followed by Brookhaven National Laboratory [Beller (1976) and Foell (1979a)].

A voluminous literature also appeared throughout the 1970s on residuals generation in input–output models, at national and regional levels [James et al. (1978)]. Most of these models use fairly aggregated economic sectors and measure output in monetary rather than physical units, thus losing much of the accuracy and detail of the RFF approach.

2.3. Regional production systems

At the regional level, residual discharges need to be identified by type, by activity or industry source, by location, and over time. The first step in the analysis is to specify a set of regional economy activity levels. Various approaches may be used. The simplest involves an exogenous estimation of output for each activity in the region for a specified time period. Regional activity levels can also be determined by "driving" the regional economic system with a national model, as in the Brookhaven model suite [Marcuse (1979)], the SEAS/RFF model [Ridker and Watson (1980)], and the Hunter Valley model [James et al. (1982)]. Other possibilities are regional, interregional, and multiregional models.

In a regional economic activity model, discharges of residuals are estimated as

$$R = P\hat{q}, \tag{4}$$

where R is a matrix of residuals discharges (residual type by industrial activity or sector), P is matrix of discharge coefficients, and $\hat{q}$ is a diagonal matrix of activity levels. Each discharge coefficient p_{kj} indicters the mass of residual k discharged per unit of sectoral output j measured in monetary or physical units. Total discharges are simply

$$z = Ri = Pq, \tag{5}$$

where z is a vector of residuals by type, discharged by all activities in the region, and i is a sum vector.

If the economic activity model includes a regional input-output matrix, sectoral outputs are found by using the Leontief inverse matrix:

$$q = (I - A)^{-1}f, \tag{6}$$

where A is the regional input–output coefficient matrix, and f is a vector of regional final demands.

Regional discharges can thus be written as a function of final demands:

$$z = P(I - A)^{-1}f. \tag{7}$$

The matrix in the above equation indicates the discharge of residuals resulting directly and indirectly from the supply of final products by economic sectors.

The basic model can be converted to a comparative statics system by adding a time dimension to the simple Leontief model:

$$z_t = P(I - A)^{-1}f_t, \tag{8}$$

where t represents time periods. If a regional capital formation matrix is available, a dynamic Leontief model can be developed, of the form

$$z_t = P(I - A - B)^{-1}f_t, \tag{9}$$

where B is a capital matrix with typical element b_{ij} indicating the output of sector i directly required to permit a one-unit production capacity expansion in sector j. Miernyk and Sears (1974) have constructed a model of this kind to analyze discharges of airborne residuals.

If a matrix of fuel use by sectors is available, regional discharges of airborne residuals can be estimated by applying combustion emission factors as in the equation

$$z = FEq, \tag{10}$$

where E is an energy-use coefficient matrix (fuel type by input–output sector) and F is a matrix of combustion emission factors (residual type by fuel type). This approach assumes that combustion processes for each fuel type are the same across all sectors and that no residuals recovery or modification occurs.

Regional input–output models have been developed by Shefer (1973), Hite and Laurent (1972), Miernyk and Sears (1974), Kohn (1975), Muller (1973), and Howe (1977), among others. Various national models of the Netherlands could also be considered as regional, such as those constructed by the Free University of Amsterdam [Jansen et al. (1978)] and DenHartog and Houweling (1974). This last reference follows the theoretical method of Leontief (1970) and incorporates residuals activities (with secondary residuals discharges) within the generalized input–output framework.

Regardless of the approach used to determine regional production levels and of the degree of aggregation that is chosen, economic activities must be allocated spatially if dispersion modeling is to be carried out. This topic is taken up in the next sections. An introductory discussion of dispersion models is found in Chapter 3 of this Handbook.

3. Environmental systems models

3.1. Air quality models

The relationship between regional air quality and the discharge of airborne residuals by industrial activities is complex. Important factors that govern ambient concentrations of residuals include classes of sources, spatial and temporal release patterns, and composition of discharges, meteorological conditions, chemical reactions in the atmosphere, the type of ground surface, and background concentrations. The airborne residuals appearing most commonly in REQM studies are sulfur oxides, carbon monoxide, hydrocarbons, nitrogen oxides, and particulates.

Because of the three-dimensional nature of air dispersion, each class of emission sources has to be modeled separately. The main classes are high-level point sources, for example, power plant stacks; medium-level point sources, such as industrial stacks; low-level area sources, such as industrial zones in which petroleum fuels are widely used; and line-source emissions that usally apply to traffic flows but may also refer to industrial activities.

The most commonly used model for high- and medium-level point sources is the Gaussian plume equation [Bach (1972)], which is of the form:

$$C(x, y, z, H) = \frac{Q}{2\pi S\sigma_y\sigma_z}\left[\exp-\frac{y^2}{2\sigma_y^2}\right]\left[\exp-\frac{(z-H)^2}{2\sigma_x^2}+\exp-\frac{(z+H)^2}{2\sigma_z^2}\right],$$

(11)

where C is the ambient concentration of the residual (g/m^3), x is the downwind coordinate (m), y is a crosswind coordinate (m), z is the vertical coordinate (m), Q is the emission rate (g/sec), S is the average windspeed (m/sec), and H is the effective stack height (m). The model assumes that, downwind from the stack, the residual will be normally distributed (in the statistical sense) in the crosswind and vertical directions. The crosswind vertical standard deviations of the plume are given (in meters) by σ_y and σ_z, respectively.

For a receptor point at a distance y from the centerline of the plume, the ground level concentration is estimated as

$$C(x, y, 0, H) = \frac{Q}{\pi S\sigma_y\sigma_z}\exp\left[-\frac{y^2}{2\sigma_y^2}-\frac{H^2}{2\sigma_x^2}\right].$$

(12)

The values of σ_y and σ_z depend on atmospheric stability conditions, as shown by Pasquill (1962) and Gifford (1961). Wind speed and direction must also be specified.

The effective stack height is given by the equation

$$H = h + \Delta h, \tag{13}$$

where h is the height of the stack and Δh is plume rise (m).

For medium-level point sources, the most commonly used formula for plume rise is that of Carson and Moses (1969) which takes the form:

$$\Delta h = A\left[-0.029\frac{V \cdot D}{S} + 5.35\frac{F^{1/2}}{S}\right], \tag{14}$$

where V is the stack exist velocity (m/sec), D is the stack diameter (m), F is heat flux (kcal/sec), S is average wind speed (m/sec), and A is an atmospheric parameter with values of 2.65, 1.08, and 0.68 for unstable, neutral, and stable conditions, respectively.

For high-level stacks, the formula of Briggs (1969) is preferred. With neutral and unstable atmosphere, the formula is

$$\Delta h = 2.5(F^{1/3}h^{2/3}), \tag{15}$$

and with stable atmosphere:

$$\Delta h = 2.96\left(\frac{F}{0.0277}\right)^{1/3}. \tag{16}$$

The heat flux is calculated from the formula

$$F = R\frac{(T_e - T_a)}{T_a} \cdot K, \tag{17}$$

where R is the volume flow rate (m^3/sec), T_e is the exit temperature (degrees Kelvin), T_a is ambient temperature, and K is a constant (84.88 kcal/m^3). When $F < 5000$ kcal/sec, the Carson–Moses formula should be used, and when $F > 5000$, the Briggs formula is more appropriate.

The Gaussian plume model has been applied to electric power plants [Mendlesohn (1979, 1980)]. Under steady-state conditions, concentrations at receptor points are proportional to discharge rates. With multiple source and receptor points, a matrix of fixed transfer coefficients can be used. For a given airborne residual, ambient concentrations can be estimated as

$$c = DR + b, \tag{18}$$

where c is a vector of ambient concentrations at different receptor points, r is a vector of discharges by source points, D is the matrix of transfer coefficients, and b is a vector of background concentrations at receptor points.

Dispersion of emissions from low-level area sources can be handled by means of a simple model developed by Gifford (1973) and Hanna (1973) of the form:

$$C = KQ, \tag{19}$$

where C is the concentration of an airborne residual in a particular grid square, Q is the level of discharges, and K is a constant that depends on meteorological factors and the size of the grid squares in the model. Howe (1977) reports use of this model in a study of the Upper Colorado River Basin.

An effective model combining Gaussian plume equations for medium- and high-level sources with a model of low-level area sources is the Smeared Concentration Approximation (SCA) model developed by Dennis (1978). The SCA model is a simplified version of the more elaborate models and can be applied using only a hand calculator. It has be incorporated in energy–environment studies [Foell (1979a)] and has been modified for the analysis of industrial emissions in the Hunter Valley [Chambers (1983)].

Gaussian models rely on analytical solution procedures to determine ambient concentrations of residuals, but other modeling approaches can be taken. In a "mixing bowl" situation, ambient concentrations depend solely on total discharges within a region, and the locations of emission sources can be ignored. This situation, however, does not occur frequently in practice. Dispersion models can be built using statistical techniques. In the Ljubljana regional study [Basta et al. (1978)], regression equations were fitted to observed values of industrial emissions and ambient concentrations. The method is straightforward, but does have obvious statistical traps. Another approach to dispersion modeling is the use of mass conservation equations, normally specified as partial differential or difference equations and solved through numerical integration techniques. The method is discussed and compared with Gaussian models for line source emissions in papers by Sistla et al. (1979) and Rao et al. (1980). Other applications are described by MacCracken and Sauters (1975) and in the U.S. Nuclear Regulatory Commission Guide 1.iii (1977).

The preceding analysis deals with conservative (nonreactive) residuals. Chemical reactions in the atmosphere may also be significant for regional air quality. The most notable case is photochemical smog, which is formed by reactive hydrocarbons, nitrogen oxides, and sunlight. Although primarily attributable to motor vehicle emissions, photochemical smog can be affected by supplementary industrial discharges, and air quality models should take both sources into account. Models used to study air pollution in Sydney, Australia, a city badly affected by photochemical smog, are described by the NSW State Pollution Control Commission (1977). Industrial emissions were handled with a Gaussian model, and the Gifford-Hanna model was applied to motor vehicle emissions.

3.2. Water quality models

Various factors need to be taken into account when modeling the effects of water borne discharges by industrial activities, the most obvious being whether the receiving water system is a stream, estuary, lake, ocean, or groundwater table. In the case of freshwater streams, flow conditions are affected by precipitation, economic activities, and reservoir operations [Howe (1979), Maass et al. (1962), Fiering (1967), Spofford (1980)]. Other systems depend also on natural conditions and economic activities. Dispersion of residuals is closely linked with the hydrologic characteristics of the system under study. Physical, chemical, and biological reactions taking place within water systems are, however, also of significance. The kinds of discharges and the spatial and temporal patterns of release are further important determinants of ambient water quality.

Some of the key concerns in regional water quality management are shown in Table 7.1.

Attempts have been made to derive general water quality indices [Brown et al. (1975), Luken et al. (1976), Jansen et al. (1978)], but for industrial discharges, the most commonly used indicators are BOD_5, TDS, and TSS [OECD (1980)].

BOD discharges involve reactive dispersion processes, as recognized by Streeter and Phelps (1925) in their study of the Ohio River. Dissolved oxygen in a stream is affected by two processes: a deoxygenation process in which oxygen is consumed by bacteria and micro-organisms as they degrade the released organic material, and a reaeration process that raises the dissolved oxygen level through surface/air interchange. Both processes are time-dependent, but a spatial determinant can be introduced by translating time into downstream distances from a given discharge point to different receptor points.

The two processes can be described mathematically as

$$\frac{\mathrm{d}D}{\mathrm{d}t} = k_1 L_t - k_2 D t, \tag{20}$$

Table 7.1
Water quality indicators

Oxygen	Pathogens
Dissolved oxygen (DO)	Fecal coliforms
5-Day biological oxygen demand (BOD_5)	
Chemical oxygen demand (COD)	
	Solids
Salinity	Total suspended solids (TSS)
Total dissolved solids (TDS)	
	Water properties
Nutrients	Temperature
	pH
Nitrates	Turbidity
Phosphates	Hardness
	Color
Toxics	Odor
	Taste
Pesticides	Electrical conductance
Heavy metals	

where D_t is the dissolved oxygen deficit below saturation concentration, L_t is BOD remaining in the flow, k_1 is a deoxygenation rate constant, k_2 is a reaeration rate constant, and t is time. L_t depends on the initial discharge of BOD (L_a) as in the equation

$$L_t = L_a e^{-k_1 t}. \tag{21}$$

Substituting for L_t and integrating the differential equation yields the classical Streeter–Phelps oxygen-sag equation:

$$D = \frac{k_1}{k_2 - k_1} L_a (e^{-k_1 t} - e^{-k_2 t}) + D_a e^{-k_2 t}, \tag{22}$$

where D_a is the initial dissolved oxygen deficit when BOD is released to the stream (that is, when $t = 0$).

In converting a steady-state discharge of BOD to DO levels at different receptor points, fixed transfer coefficients can be used. More complex versions of the Streeter–Phelps model are described by Kneese and Bower (1968). These include multiple discharge systems that can be modeled, under steady-state assumptions, by additive linear relationships, and systems that simulate non-steady-state conditions. Camp (1965) has specified a model in which dissolved oxygen depends on sedimentation or scour of organic material from the stream bed, on photosynthesis by floating plants and algae, and on deoxygenation caused by respiration of plants and animals. Camp's model has been applied by Moodie (1979). Other recent work on *DO* modeling has been carried out by Wang et al. (1979) and Wen and Kao (1980, 1982), among others.

Diffusion models for TDS can be of many different forms. The simplest case is that of a stream with constant release rates by dischargers, constant flow conditions, complete mixing of TDS, and an absence of sinks or contributing sources in the system itself. This is a case of a "conservative pollutant", in which a simple additive approach is taken to determine total mass or ambient concentrations of TDS at receptor points. The same kind of model as specified for airborne residuals in eq. (18) is appropriate.

More complex models are needed once the above assumptions are relaxed, for example, episodic release of residuals, variations in stream flow because of precipitation patterns or the operation of reservoirs, incomplete mixing, and the role of sinks [Gosz (1980)]. Industrial discharges of TDS may be supplemented by those from watercourse runoff, as modeled by Moodie (1979). Mixing zones are discussed by Neely (1982) who shows that the concentrations of a chemical in a stream can be modeled by means of a Gaussian equation, constrained by physical stream parameters such as river width, depth, and shear velocity. It is difficult to generalize about the effects of sinks on the dispersion of TDS. The type of chemical can be critical. Heavy metals, for example, usually have strong affinity for clay because of high rates of adsorption. A net loss of heavy metal salts can be expected initially through chemical reactions with stream-bed material, but over time, releases of heavy metals from saturated sinks may occur. Biological uptake by aquatic organisms can add further complications. The dynamics of such processes are likely to be quite complex, and must be modeled according to each specific set of circumstances.

Dispersion of TDS in other water systems can be mentioned only briefly here. For a discussion of estuaries, see Gameson (1973). An excellent survey of aquatic dispersion models is the U.S. Nuclear Regulatory Commission Regulatory Guide 1.113 (1976). Although designed for estimating dispersion of radioactive effluents, the models apply also to TDS discharges.

3.3. Solid residuals

Solid residuals are classified by Kneese (1977) according to the type of material and by source. Those associated with industrial activities include combustibles, noncombustibles, ashes, bulky items, hazardous materials, construction and de-molition residuals, obsolete vehicles, and tailings and overburden from mining. Solid residuals are generated also by other activities, and include food scraps, garden debris, street sweepings, dead animals, animal residues, crop residues, slush and logging residues, and sewage treatment residues. Kneese produces statistics indicating that mixed solid residuals generated by industrial processes in the United States in 1971 comprised about 2.5 percent of all solid waste (excluding mine overburden).

Mixed solid residuals generation coefficients appear in the Ljubljana regional study by Basta et al. (1978). Much of the information was obtained from salvage firms that collected waste and sold it for reuse. Nonsalable solids were estimated from municipal collection sites, but only on a volume basis. More detailed estimates of solid residuals discharges may be obtained from process analysis at different industrial activity sites. Recycling of solid residuals is discussed by Kneese, Ayres, and d'Arge (1970) and by Schlottmann (1977). Automobile scrap is dealt with by Sawyer (1974).

4. Control of regional environmental quality

4.1. Mechanisms for regional environmental quality management

The various components of an REQM system have been dealt with in the preceding sections. To manage environmental quality, three steps are required: first, an analysis of alternative physical measures or combinations of those measures that can control residuals discharge or dispersion in the environment; second, evaluation of the effects of alternative physical controls to determine the "best" or preferred plan of action; and third, selection of appropriate instruments or implementation incentives that will enable the preferred strategy to be successfully put into operation. As will be shown, management actions should ideally be directed toward the control of ambient environmental quality rather than the control of residuals discharges themselves.

4.2. Physical measures of control

At the regional level, various kinds of physical measures may be taken to control ambient environmental quality. Kneese and Bower (1979) classify them as: regulation of output; changing process technologies; modification of residuals on-site; making better use of the environment's assimilative capacity; and increasing the environment's assimilative capacity.

Output can be controlled by altering product mix or the regional economic structure. At the individual plant level, the product mix can be altered, or different product specifications introduced. Input–output models are capable of demonstrating the direct and indirect regional effects of changes in the final demand vector on total discharge of specific types of residuals. Measures can be taken to regulate categories of final demand that are responsible for residuals of major concern, as in the model of Norway developed by Førsund and Strøm (1974) (see Chapter 9 in this Handbook) a model of the Netherlands economy [Jansen et al. (1977)], and studies of the Rijnmond region [Muller (1973, 1979)].

Changes in process technologies may involve altering the input mix, the timing of production, or the introduction of completely new processes. Such measures affect the level and composition of residuals generated within industrial plants. Other measures modify residuals after they have been generated, for example, materials or energy recovery processes, production of by-products, or add-on treatment such as filtration, scrubbing, neutralization, sedimentation, and landfill. In some cases, as with fluidized bed combustion in electric power stations, changes in residuals generation and modification take place simultaneously.

The list of residuals reduction processes in industry shown in Table 7.2 is based on Kneese, Ayres and d'Arge (1970) and Luken et al. (1976), with some additions. Making better use of the environment's assimilative capacity may be achieved by controlling the spatial and temporal distribution of discharges and activities. Examples of spatial control of residuals discharges are the use of high chimney stacks or slurry pipelines. Temporal control of residuals discharges is illustrated by regulation of BOD discharges from a pulp and paper mill to maintain dissolved oxygen in receiving waters at an acceptable level. Activities may be controlled in temporal terms by appropriate production scheduling. Location of activities to regulate regional environmental quality has received a great deal of attention. The literature includes studies of power plant siting [Mendelsohn (1979,

1980), EPRI (1979b), Guldman and Shefer (1977)] and mathematical programming models of spatial planning [Nijkamp (1977), Mastenbroek and Nijkamp
(1974)].

The assimilative capacity of the environment can be increased in many ways.
One is the addition of water to effluents to increase the dilution of residuals in the
environment. Artificial mixing can be carried out in water bodies to improve
dispersion and aeration. Direct oxygenation of water is also possible through air
pumps or by churning in air with ship propellers. In some cases, as with
freshwater lakes affected by acid rain, chemical buffers can be added to raise the
pH level.

From a modeling viewpoint, restrictions on physical alternatives for AEQ
management are of major significance in setting up an appropriate mathematical
structure. If the temporal aspects of a problem are emphasized, a comparative
static or dynamic model needs to be built. Even for a static optimization model,
difficulties may be encountered. For example, if all physical measures can coexist

Table 7.2
Residuals treatment processes

Waterborne residuals

Sedimentation	Stripping
Screening	Biological filtration
Filtration	Chemical coagulation
Flotation	Emulsion breaking
Separation	Neutralization
Centrifuging	Equalization
Holding pond	Carbon adsorption
Spray irrigation	Chemical oxidation
Landfill	Chemical reduction
Drying beds	Wet oxidation
Incineration	Fermentation
Evaporation	Activated sludge
Distillation	Anaerobic digestion

Airborne residuals

Two-stage combustion	Recycling
Fluidized bed combustion	Electrostatic precipitation
Afterburning	Cyclones
Condensation	Fabric filters
Absorption	Wet scrubbing
Adsorption	Dry scrubbing

Solid residuals

Incineration	Ocean dumping
Pyrolysis	Recycling
Landfill	Compaction
Road ballast	

and be operated at nonnegative levels, linear programming is an acceptable method for optimizing residuals management alternatives. Frequently, however, only one or a limited number of activities within a given set of alternatives is permissible, and integer programming may have to be used. In siting an electric power plant, for example, only one location can usually be chosen. Indivisibilities can also occur within industrial plants. One might choose a fluidized bed combustion process or a conventional boiler with a wet scrubber, but not both. Some of the economic implications of such restrictions are discussed in the next section.

4.3. Evaluation criteria for environmental quality goals

Baseline simulation modeling of residuals discharges, dispersion, and dose-response effects produces a given set of physical, economic, and environmental characteristics. Changes in the system, such as would occur with implementation of physical measures to control environmental quality, will result in new sets of characteristics. Rational environmental quality management implies selection of the "best" outcome.

Evaluation criteria are clearly necessary for the best outcome to be determined. Bower et al. (1977) take a general view of evaluation criteria for environmental quality management and list the main considerations as: physical effects; economic effects, including distributional aspects, administrative simplicity and flexibility; timing; political preferences and institutional factors; intermedia and resource use effects; and accuracy of estimates.

4.4. Operational REQM models

Analytical methods can be applied with some, but not all, evaluation approaches. The most widely used modeling techniques can be listed as: simulation modeling combined with multiattribute utility analysis; simulation modeling supplemented by full benefit–cost analysis, including monetary damage functions for adverse environmental effects (for a discussion of benefit–cost applications, see Chapter 6 of this Handbook); cost-minimization models incorporating penalty functions if prescribed AEQ standards are transgressed; cost-minimization models designed to fulfill prescribed output constraints and environmental standards for either emissions or ambient concentrations of residuals; and income maximization models with resource restrictions and ambient concentration or emission standards. All these options are available in static or dynamic modes.

Multiattribute utility analysis [Keeney and Raiffa (1976)] has been advocated by the Wisconsin energy modeling group in their work on energy–environment management [Buehring et al. (1978), Foell (1979b)]. The technique is designed to elicit decisionmakers' preferences and assist them to choose the scenario that generates the highest level of expected utility. The method does have limitations. It may be difficult for decisionmakers to reach consistent preferences if a large spectrum of effects needs to be considered. The process can, furthermore, be very time-consuming. Finally, decisionmakers often prefer to assess outcomes in terms of community values rather than their own subjective values, and require information obtained by more objective methods. Multiattribute utility analysis is therefore likely to be useful as an evaluation technique only in rather rare situations.

Benefit–cost analysis has recently received much attention as a means of evaluating environmental impacts and guiding environmental quality management [Hufschmidt and Hyman (1982), Hufschmidt et al. (1983)]. Early work in this area concentrated on environmental damage functions [OECD (1974, 1976)]. Further work on the economic valuation of environmental effects has been carried out in the United Kingdom [Pearce (1978)] and in the United States [Freeman (1979), Sinden and Worrell (1979)]. It is inappropriate to enter a full discussion of benefit–cost analysis in this chapter, but several difficulties should be briefly mentioned. Aside from awkward value judgements underlying the method (for example, discounting long-run irreversible ecological damage costs or placing monetary values on human life and health), many practical problems need to be overcome in applying it in a REQM context. Bower and Brady (1981) report numerous difficulties in quantifying damages caused by air pollution. Another problem is that, with so many alternatives available for measures to control AEQ, estimation of all associated damage functions could be an almost unmanageable task. The net benefit response surface may contain nonlinearities and the global optimum may be difficult to find, although mathematical techniques have been applied to this problem for water resource systems [Hufschmidt (1962)] and hydroelectric power schemes [Holling (1978)].

A more realistic REQM approach is cost-effectiveness analysis combined with standard-setting. As a practical technique, cost-effectiveness has several advantages. The procedure forces decisionmakers to carefully specify the objectives they are trying to reach, for example, control of discharges at source, ambient concentrations (by residual type or location), indoor or outdoor concentrations, health levels, etc. Standards must be properly specified also with respect to time – daily, weekly, monthly, or annual averages, or perhaps short-term peak levels.

Regional cost-minimization models range from simple discharge control models to those involving ambient concentrations standards and spatial planning of activities. The Russell–Spofford model incorporates penalty functions if AEQ standards are exceeded. This approach is discussed in detail in the Delaware Valley case study (Section 5.4.4).

The model developed by Kohn (1971) features regional discharge constraints. The theoretical form of the model is presented here, and its empirical applications in Section 5.2. The model can be written as

$$\min_{\text{s.t.}} c'x \tag{23i}$$

$$Px \le z^*, \tag{23ii}$$

$$Ux = q, \tag{23iii}$$

$$x \ge 0, \tag{23iv}$$

where x is a vector of unit processes for all activities in the region; P is a residuals discharge matrix; c is a vector of associated (incremental) costs; z^* is a vector of permissible regional discharges, by residual type; q is a vector of prescribed output targets; and U is an elementary matrix.

Each product output volume, say q_h, is producible with several processes. Restrictions on the relevant process levels, $x_{h1}, x_{h2}, \ldots x_{hm}$ can be written

$$q_h = \sum_j u_{hj} x_{hj}. \tag{24}$$

The typical element of the matrix U is u_{hj}, which takes a value of one if the jth activity can produce the hth product, and otherwise a value of zero.

Kohn later incorporated an input–output matrix in the model [Kohn (1975)]. The dual problem generates shadow prices for the discharge standards, so that tradeoffs can be assessed between discharge constraints on specific residuals and regional environmental control costs.

Discharge constraint models do not in general lead to control of AEQ. (An exception is a mixing bowl situation when location of dischargers and receptors does not matter.) Dispersion models must be added to estimate ambient concentrations. If a set of fixed transfer coefficients is appropriate, ambient concentrations at receptor points can be found by means of a diffusion matrix. Ignoring background concentrations, a separate matrix can be used for each residual, as follows:

$$c^k = D^k r^k, \tag{25}$$

where c^k is a vector of ambient concentrations of the kth residual at different receptor points, D^k is the diffusion matrix, with typical element d_{jn}^k indicating transfer of the kth residual from activity j to receptor n, and r^k is a vector of discharges from activities.

As discharges depend on activity levels,

$$r^k = \hat{p}^k q, \tag{26}$$

where $\hat{p}^k$ is a diagonal matrix of discharge coefficients for the kth residual. AEQ constraints enter the model as

$$D^k \hat{p}^k q \le c^{k*}, \tag{27}$$

where c^{k*} is a vector of permissible ambient concentrations (which may, of course, be uniform) at receptor points.

The air quality management model developed by Muller (1973, 1979) places environmental restrictions on ambient concentrations of airborne residuals. Unlike Kohn's model, which uses a cost-minimization approach, Muller's model maximizes regional income. The objective function is

$$\max v'q, \tag{28}$$

where v is a vector of value-added coefficients and q is a vector of sectoral activity levels. In the absence of environmental constraints, output levels are restricted by maximum labor use and prescribed minimum supplies of final products:

$$(I - A - B - M)q \geq f^*, \tag{29i}$$

$$n'q \leq w^*, \tag{29ii}$$

$$q \geq 0, \tag{29iii}$$

where I is an identity matrix, A is the regional input–output coefficient matrix, B is a capital formation matrix, M is a matrix of inputs to antipollution investments, and f^* is a vector of prescribed final supplies. The region's workforce is represented by the scalar w^*, and n is a vector of labor input coefficients.

Muller uses the same diffusion matrix for all residuals. Discharge points, furthermore, are allocated to grid positions by subdividing regional sector outputs. Ambient concentrations are estimated as

$$C = P\hat{q}SD, \tag{30}$$

where $\hat{q}$ is a diagonal matrix of sector outputs, P is a residuals discharge coefficient matrix (residual type by sectoral output), S is a matrix that distributes outputs to grid positions, D is the diffusion matrix transferring residuals from discharge to receptor points, and C is the required matrix, indicating concentrations of residuals, by type, at different receptor points. AEQ restrictions take the form:

$$P\hat{q}SD \leq c^*, \tag{31}$$

where c^* is a vector of ambient concentration standards for different residuals, applied at a particular receptor point.

The models discussed so far permit all activities, even unit processes within activities, to enter the optimal solution. If the number of unit processes has to be limited, integer variables must be introduced. For example, in the Kohn model, if x_1, x_2, and x_3 are three alternative methods of producing q_1, and only one of the three is permissible, an extra set of constraints must be added to the model, for example

$$x_1 - v_1 x_1 \geq 0, \tag{32i}$$

$$x_2 - v_2 x_2 \geq 0, \tag{32ii}$$

$$x_3 - v_2 x_3 \geq 0, \tag{32iii}$$

$$v_1 + v_2 + v_3 = 1, \tag{32iv}$$

$$0 \leq v_j \leq 1, \quad v_j \text{ an integer,} \tag{32v}$$

The overall result is a mixed linear-integer programming model. Burton and Sanjour (1970) used integer programming methods to model air pollution control. Optimal siting of electric power stations could be assessed with this method, for the formulation is similar to that for the selection of unit processes within plants. One disadvantage of the method is that shadow prices cannot be obtained.

Dynamic optimization models of regional-residuals management are described by Guldmann (1978) and Parvin and Grammas (1976), among others. Such models have not been used as frequently as static optimization models.

4.5. Implementation methods

An extensive literature has appeared on alternative institutional and administrative approaches to implementation of regional environmental quality management strategies. Bower et al. (1977) list the main alternatives as: regulatory, comprising laws, ordinances, and permits controlling production processes, performance, location, timing, and procedures; economic, applied to residuals, inputs, product outputs, and residuals modification processes; administrative; judicial; and educational/informational.

Effluent (or emission) charges have been strongly advocated on economic efficiency grounds. The OECD (1980) refers to "incentive" charges that are high enough to induce dischargers to introduce residuals modification schemes, and "redistributive" charges that raise revenue – without necessarily altering discharge patterns – that can be diverted to municipal sewerage works, research on pollution abatement, and subsidization of new investment in residuals modification technologies in private industry.

Uniform incentive charges can be shown to achieve a given reduction of discharges at minimum direct economic cost to the region. Consider a situation involving only one residual and many dischargers. Initially, the jth activity discharges an amount of r_j^*. The amount of residual removed by the jth activity is y_j. Actual discharge by the jth activity is thus

$$r_j = r_j^* - y_j. \tag{33}$$

Suppose the abatement cost function for the jth discharger is

$$TC_j = f_j(y_j).$$ (34)

Substitution of eq. (33) in (34) leads to

$$TC_j = f_j(r_j^* - r_j).$$ (35)

Finally, suppose that, for all dischargers together, the permissible total discharge rate is r^*.

The problem takes the form:

$$\min \sum TC_j, \quad \text{for all } j,$$ (36i)

s.t.

$$\sum r_j = r^*, \quad \text{for all } j.$$ (36ii)

The optimal conditions can be found by minimizing the Lagrangian function:

$$L = \sum f_j(r_j^* - r_j) + \lambda\left(\sum r_j - r^*\right).$$ (37)

The first-order conditions of direct interest are

$$\partial L/\partial r_j = -f_j' + \lambda = 0,$$ (38)

or that

$$f_j' = f_i', \quad \text{for all } i, j, i \neq j.$$ (39)

Equation (39) implies equalization of marginal treatment costs, which can be achieved by imposing a uniform charge. Each discharger will carry out abatement up to the point where the marginal abatement cost equals the charge, so a uniform charge will, in principle, achieve a given total reduction at minimum cost.

This argument is valid for total discharges, but does not necessarily hold true for control of ambient concentrations. To demonstrate this, a linear dispersion model can be introduced. The same objective function is minimized, but the new constraint, which is assumed to apply at only one receptor point, becomes

$$c_n^* = \sum d_{nj} r_j,$$ (40)

where c_n^* is the prescribed ambient concentration of the residual at receptor point n, and d_{nj} is a transfer coefficient from source point j to receptor point n.

A new Lagrangian function should now be minimized:

$$L_0 = \sum f_j(r_j^* - r_j) + \lambda_0\left(\sum d_{nj} r_j - c_n^*\right),$$ (41)

which leads, among other results, to

$$\frac{\partial L_0}{\partial r_j} = -f_j' + \lambda_0 d_{nj} = 0$$ (42)

or

$$f_j' = f_i' \frac{d_{nj}}{d_{ni}}, \quad \text{for all } i, j, i \neq j. \tag{43}$$

Only if the transfer coefficients are the same for all dischargers ($d_{nj} = d_{ni}$) should marginal abatement costs be equalized and a uniform change imposed; otherwise a set of differential charges is required. If ambient concentrations are imposed at several receptor points, the Kuhn–Tucker theorem is needed to determine the optimal conditions.

Kneese (1977) cites the Delaware estuary water quality study to show that in a real situation a system of uniform charges would produce a result very close to the minimum cost solution. However, completely opposite conclusions are drawn in a study of nitrogen oxide control in the Chicago air quality control region [U.S. Council on Environmental Quality (1979)] which revealed that a uniform charges approach to meeting an ambient concentration standard of 250 micrograms per cubic meter could involve a total cost twelve times that of the least-cost strategy. Differential charges to bring about the least-cost solution, furthermore, ranged from $60 per pound per hour to $40000 per pound per hour. These studies indicate that it is quite dangerous to generalize about the most efficacious method of policy implementation. Each case should be considered separately.

The above exercises deal only with the direct costs of residuals management. The total costs of any implementation scheme include costs of acquiring information, enforcement, monitoring, and administration. Charges supposedly offer a low-cost approach, which may be true for uniform charges. However, if differential charges are needed, the same amount of administrative effort will probably be involved as any other method. The OECD (1980) points out that, in practice, charges have never been used on their own, but always in conjunction with direct regulations. Very little attempt has been made to manage air quality by means of charges. The main application has been in the area of water quality management. Actual cases are covered by the OECD (1981), Harrington (1981), and Bower et al. (1981), among others (for further discussion of these policy issues, see Chapter 10 of this Handbook).

5. Case studies of model applications

5.1. Control of individual industrial plants

Results of the petroleum refinery study by Russell (1973) are too extensive to be reported fully. A sample is sufficient, however, to illustrate the application of linear programming to problems of residuals management in an industrial plant. The basic refinery modeled by Russell is a plant handling 150000 barrels of crude

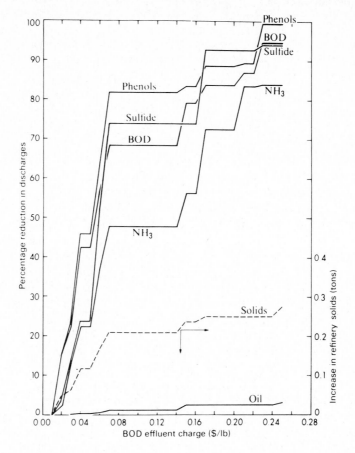

Figure 7.3. Response to BOD effluent charge, 150 000 barrels per day petroleum refinery. *Source*: Russell (1973, p. 139).

oil per day. In the uncontrolled situation, the only residuals management processes consist of oil-water separation and sour-water scrubbing.

The effects of an effluent charge on BOD discharges are shown in Figure 7.3. Because of the properties of a linear programming model, the relationship between the charge and the response is not continuous. The charge needs to increase over a range before a jump from one process technology to another occurs. Figure 7.3 reveals that as the BOD charge rises from $0.01 to $0.07, there is rapid reduction of BOD discharges, almost 70 percent. Raising the charge produces no further response until $0.16 per pound, where 80 percent BOD removal occurs. A 95 percent reduction is achieved when the charge is $0.25. The power of the model in demonstrating the interdependence of residuals is evident in the response curves for residuals other than BOD. Even though the charge is imposed on BOD itself, the consequent shifts in process technologies lead to significant reductions in ammonia, sulfides, and phenols. There is, however, a large increase in the discharge of solids, occurring principally as sludge from BOD treatment, but including particulates from incineration.

Equal moderate charges on other residuals yield disparate results. For sulfur dioxide, oil, sulfides, and residual heat, the charge has virtually no effect; positive responses are obtained for phenols, BOD, and ammonia; and dramatic reductions occur for particulates.

Other technological options for the plant include hydrocracking and *H*-oil (both processes involving introduction of excess hydrogen into the reaction vessel). A new model is developed for an "advanced" refinery using these processes. In both the basic and advanced plants, the total and marginal costs of BOD reduction rise dramatically when high levels of control are sought. These costs are, however, quite small in comparison with total refining costs (approximately 0.045 percent when a 75 percent reduction of BOD is achieved). Similar results are obtained for other residuals.

The methodological approach applied by Russell and Vaughan (1976) to residuals management in a steel production plant is the same as in Russell's model of a petroleum refinery. The main processes in a steel mill are: coking; sintering; ironmaking; steelmaking; and rolling and finishing. Steelmaking itself can be carried out with an open hearth furnace, basic oxygen furnace, or electric arc. Residuals from iron and steel production occur in large quantities, especially particulate emissions and wastewater discharges.

In the base case, the only gas cleaning controls assumed, with removal rates for particulates shown in brackets, are: dry cyclone on the sinter plant (90 percent); dry cyclone plus wet scrubber and electrostatic precipitator on the blast furnace (99 percent); electrostatic precipitator on an open hearth furnace (97 percent); electrostatic precipitator on a basic oxygen furnace (94 percent); and fabric filters on an electric arc furnace (97 percent).

Changes in the specification of the kind of steel produced have little effect on residuals discharges. A more significant factor is the type of furnace used, and the technically feasible level of added scrap metal. The electric arc and open hearth furnaces can use up to 100 percent scrap, although in practice, only the electric arc fully utilizes scrap capacity; blast furnaces have been operated on about 50 percent scrap. The basic oxygen furnace can accept only 30 percent scrap and thus is responsible for the highest levels of residuals discharges – approximately 45 percent more than an open hearth as a result of higher coke consumption. Although the electric arc typically uses 100 percent scrap, it may generate the same particulate load as the basic oxygen furnace and more sulfur dioxide than the other two kinds. The reason for this in the Russell–Vaughan model is that electricity for the furnace is generated on-site from residual fuel oil. Only if electricity is brought in is the electric arc furnace the cleanest, but then, of course, discharges occur off site.

The price of scrap metal clearly has a major influence on the choice of process technology and hence on the pattern of residuals generation. If the price of scrap is doubled, there is a 45 percent increase in iron ore used by blast furnaces, and much higher levels of discharge occur for all residuals: particulates 24 percent; sulfur dioxide 22 percent; solids 29 percent; and 1.5–25 percent for various waterborne residuals (BOD, oil, phenols, and ammonia). Residual waterborne heat increases by 5.5 percent.

Other changes analyzed with the model include the introduction of continuous casting, which changes raw material costs; variation in the cost of water; changes in by-product prices; the use of cooling towers to dissipate waste heat; the introduction of modification and recovery processes for waterborne residuals, which results in only modest increases in costs; and adoption of more effective particulate control technologies, which adds substantially to total costs.

5.2. Air quality models

A good example of a model dealing with control of regional discharges of airborne residuals is Kohn's model of the St. Louis airshed in Missouri [Kohn (1971, 1975)]. The model has been constructed and applied in several versions. The first version has been described in Section 4.4. It minimizes the total incremental regional cost of process technologies that meet output targets and discharge standards. It uses linear programming and treats sectoral activities as economically independent. The vector of prescribed product outputs has 94 elements. Outputs are set for the year 1975. The vector of possible unit processes covers the 94 already in existence plus another 215 processes, given 309 altogether. Control costs are measured in 1968 prices. The five residual types in the model are carbon monoxide, hydrocarbons, nitrogen oxides, sulfur dioxide, and particulates. Permissible discharges are calculated from ambient concentration standards, but the model described assumes that ambient concentrations are proportional to discharge, so it is relatively easy to estimate permissible discharge levels. The results of this model showed that an extra $35.3 million would need to be spent on abatement to meet regional air quality goals.

A later version of Kohn's model includes an input–output matrix based on an existing 23-sector input–output model of the region developed by Liu (1968). Outputs are supplied to activities to meet ordinary production requirements and also to implement residuals reduction measures, thus indirect sectoral discharges attributable to residuals control measures are accounted for in the model. Regional final output levels are specified so that both types of final demand must be met. Incremental abatement costs are then minimized subject to output and emission constraints. The input–output system is simplified to identify sectoral inputs to antipollution activities and to estimate the elements of the cost function. Liu's model is reduced to a rectangular system with six rows and seventeen columns. The first six sectors interact in usual input–output fashion, but the remaining eleven draw direct inputs only from the first six.

Only some of the results of the second version of the model are presented here. By adding an input–output matrix and capturing indirect residuals control costs, the total incremental cost to the region of meeting the same output and emission goals as in the first version is $36.1 million, an increase of only 2.3 percent. Unit processes do not change equiproportionally. One major change is a 15 percent overall increase in the use of natural gas to control emissions. A large substitution of gas for coal occurs in grate stokers fitted with cyclone collectors. As regards activity levels, the largest response is from the electricity generation sector which has to supply extra power for residuals-control processes, but this is only a 1.4 percent change. These results suggest that inclusion of an input–output model does not radically change the outcome obtained with an ordinary linear programming model. Given the relatively small numbers of interacting sectors, however, this finding is not altogether surprising. Finally, it is worth noting the shadow prices obtained for the different residuals discharged, which turn out to be: carbon monoxide, 0.4 cents per pound; hydrocarbons, 2.5 cents per pound; nitrogen oxides, 33.3 cents per pound; sulfur dioxide, 2.2 cents per pound; and particulates, 7.9 cents per pound.

In yet another version of the model, Kohn derives emission constraints from ambient concentrations by means of Gaussian dispersion formulae [Kohn (1974)].

The air quality model developed by Muller (1973, 1976) was designed for management of ambient concentrations of airborne residuals in the Rijnmond region in the Netherlands. The model, without environmental restrictions, is described by the linear programming problem in (28) and (29). The model has ten sectors, and uses 1965 as a reference year for all economic data. The optimal solution to the problem yields a regional income of 16 184 million guilders (Dfl), higher, in fact, than the actual 1965 income of Dfl 7614m.

Discharge coefficients for each of the ten sectors are introduced for sulfur dioxide, nitrogen oxides, carbon monoxide, hydrogen fluoride, and small particulates. Dispersion is simulated with a Gaussian model which has 23 emission points, 5 receptor points, and 16 wind directions, giving 1840 diffusion coefficients. Ambient concentrations are determined according to eq. (30). With no controls, the model indicates that standards would be exceeded for nitrogen oxides, hydrogen fluorides, and sulfur oxides at all locations, and particulates at two locations.

Ambient concentration standards are added to the model as in eq. (31), and initially it is assumed that the only method of reducing discharges is by adjusting output levels. Full employment can still be maintained, but regional income falls to Dfl 7889m. The "cost" of reaching environmental quality goals is thus Dfl 8295m. In the environmentally constrained solution, the model shows also that the highest shadow price occurs with the standard for nitrogen oxides at Rotterdam.

The model is then extended by achieving residuals control through antipollution investments. The pollution abatement investment cost function has a rectangular hyperbola form, which converts the model to a nonlinear system. With antipollution investments, discharges are reduced, environmental targets and full employment are reached, and regional income is Dfl 13 113m. This solution is attainable if environmental investments in the oil and chemical industries are 16 times the 1965 levels, 5 times greater for public utilities (mainly electric power stations), and 2 times greater for real estate and other industries. A six-fold increase in output of the oil and chemicals sector is indicated. The shadow price for nitrogen oxides at Rotterdam falls to almost zero. Price increases generated by the antipollution investments are simulated through the input-output model. The largest is a 7.8 percent rise for the public utilities sector, but increases of 3.7 and 3.1 percent occurs for the oil and chemicals and real estate sectors, respectively.

5.3. Water quality modeling

A good example of reactive residuals management in a stream can be found in the work carried out by the U.S. Army Corps of Engineers and by RFF on dissolved oxygen in the Potomac River. This research is described by Kneese and Bower (1968), Kneese (1977), and Davis (1968).

The Potomac River Basin has a total area of 14 000 square miles and is situated in the states of Pennsylvania, West Virginia, Maryland, Virginia, and in the District of Columbia. In the 1960s, population in the watershed was 3 million, most of which was located in the Washington metropolitan area. Dissolved oxygen levels in the river frequently fell to low levels, to a large extent attributable to urban sewage releases, but also upstream BOD discharges.

In 1963, the Corps of Engineers proposed a water management plan for the river after projecting water demands and waste discharges up to the year 2010. A standard of 4 parts per million (ppm) for DO was established. The recommended means of achieving this standard was 90 percent removal of BOD from discharge points through secondary sewage treatment and increased flushing in low flow conditions. To provide the necessary water, the Corps suggested construction of sixteen major dams and 400 headwater structures. Although the primary aim was to control dissolved oxygen levels, secondary objectives related to water supply for municipal and industrial use, flood mitigation, and regulation of water quality for recreational activities.

The plan, unfortunately, had several serious deficiencies. The 4 ppm standard was arbitrarily selected so there was no indication of whether an alternative standard might have yielded higher net benefits or if indeed the project should have been undertaken. Other alternatives were not investigated. Questions could be asked about the discount rate employed. Perhaps the most critical aspect of the plan was that only a fairly crude method (the mass curve approach) was used to estimate the storage capacity required to meet the minimal flow standard. The mass curve or Rippl diagram approach is a simple deterministic hydrologic model that indicates minimum reservoir capacity in relation to cumulative flow over a preceding historical period; in the case of the Potomac study, the preceding thirty years.

It was found that the low-flow augmentation method of achieving a 4 ppm dissolved oxygen standard would cost $115 million over a fifty year period (in 1965 prices) using a four percent discount rate. Some waste treatment methods, such as carbon adsorption could cost $127 million, but other single process approaches were much less expensive, for example, $29 million for reoxygenation. The lowest attainable cost was $22 million, entailing combinations of low-flow augmentation, reoxygenation, polymer precipitation, and step aeration.

The minimal cost could be reduced to only $8 million by lowering the standard to 2 ppm. Even with the economically inefficient method (low-flow augmentation) advocated by the Corps of Engineers, dramatic cost savings could be achieved by lowering the standard. The total cost fell to $27 million with a 3 ppm standard, and $8 million with 2 ppm. The plan proposed by the Corps of Engineers was rejected partly as a result of the RFF study, and a more flexible water quality management approach was subsequently adopted.

5.4. Integrated models

5.4.1. The Lower Delaware Valley

Few regions have received as much attention as the Delaware estuary in the states of Pennsylvania, Delaware, and New Jersey. Management of water quality began with formation of the Delaware River Basin Commission in 1936 to tackle the problems of residuals discharges and low levels of dissolved oxygen. A study of the region was undertaken in 1957–58 by the U.S. Public Health Service following a request by the U.S. Army Corps of Engineers. A more detailed analysis of the estuary was initiated in 1961 by state and interstate agencies, leading to a report released by the Federal Water Pollution Control Administration in 1966. The contents of this report are discussed by Kneese and Bower (1968) and Kneese (1974, 1977). Briefly, the study used a linear programming model to find the least-cost method of meeting prescribed water quality objectives at different points on the estuary, examined alternative systems of charges and regulations, and attempted to assess the relevant economic benefits of the water quality goals.

Development and applications of an integrated model of the Lower Delaware Valley, probably the most detailed and comprehensive REQM model ever built, took place in the 1970s at RFF, representing the culmination of years of research on industrial activities, residuals generation, and management of the environment. Similar studies have since been carried out in other parts of the world, although few have reached the complexity of the RFF model itself.

The most complete description of the RFF model can be found in Spofford et al. (1976). Briefer accounts have been written by Spofford, et al. (1975, 1977) and Kneese and Bower (1979). The conceptual basis of the model appears in a noteworthy paper by Russell and Spofford (1972). Voting mechanisms were considered in a didactic version of the model. [Russell et al. (1974)], but were not actually incorporated in the final formulation.

The Lower Delaware Valley region consists of the counties: Bucks, Montgomery, Chester, Delaware, and Philadelphia in Pennsylvania; Mercer, Burlington, Camden, Gloucester, and Salam in New Jersey; and New Castle in Delaware. The region covers an area of 4700 square miles, and in 1970, had a population of 5.5 million concentrated mostly in the urban areas of Philadelphia, Trenton, Camden, and Wilmington. The region is heavily industrialized, with 7 petroleum refineries, 5 large steel mills and many smaller mills, 13 large pulp and paper mills and numerous smaller ones, 15 large and 2 small thermal power stations, and other industrial plants including chemicals and petrochemicals, foundries, automobile manufacture, and electronic assembly. Sewage is discharged into the system by 140 treatment plants. There are also 17 municipal incinerators and numerous landfill sites.

The model was built with several objectives in mind. The first was to establish a framework for the analysis of solid, gaseous, and liquid residuals, their interrelationships, and their disposal in environmental media of air, water, and land. A second was to gain experience in the collection of data, the construction of models, computational problems, and derivation of policy-relevant conclusions and recommendations. A third objective was to discover whether an optimization model, incorporating a natural ecosystem model, could be developed to determine least-cost ways of meeting AEQ goals instead of the more commonly used recursive simulation models. A fourth was to explore ways of incorporating noneconomic constraints (distributional goals or political factors) in a model based essentially on an economic efficiency (cost-minimization) criterion. A final objective was to derive policy prescriptions on regional residuals management for the Lower Delaware Valley. It will be noted that four of the five research objectives are methodological rather than case-specific.

The model is a mathematical optimization model with deterministic variables. A unique feature is that it contains a nonlinear dynamic ecosystem model. Steady state solutions from the ecosystem model are fed back into the main system. Thus, the model as a whole is basically a static-equilibrium nonlinear system, which is solved through iterative procedures.

The general structure of the model is shown in Figure 7.4. The key components of the system are: an economic activity model, with residuals handling functions, including inputs, outputs, costs, and environmental modifications; natural sys-

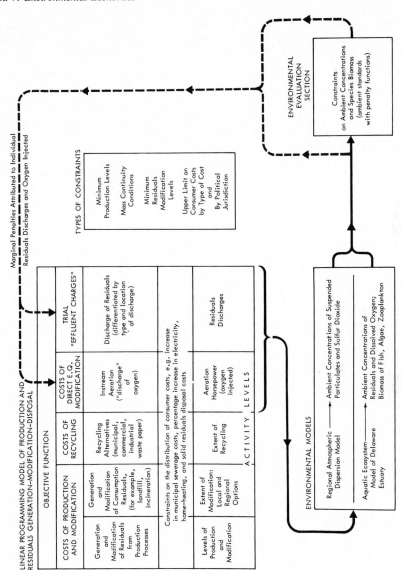

Figure 7.4. Schematic diagram of the Lower Delaware Valley residuals–environmental quality management model. *Source:* Spofford et al. (1976, p. 22).

tems models, comprising an air quality model and an aquatic ecosystem model; and an environmental evaluation module which compares environmental quality variables with predetermined standards and generates penalty functions for particular discharges in the activity model. The system also has various additional constraints (minimum product output levels, cost distribution constraints) and an objective function. These components can now be discussed in greater depth.

The main "driver" of the system is the linear programming model of activities in the region, with residuals generation, physical measures to alter discharges, recycling possibilities, and alternative methods of altering the environment to improve assimilative capacities. The objective function for the activities model includes the social costs of residuals discharged to environment, and the resource costs of alternative process technologies and environmental management options. Individual activity models are derived from separate studies carried out by RFF for different industries, as described in Section 2.2.

The air dispersion model is based on a model developed for the U.S. Environmental Protection Agency. It used the Gaussian plume approach and is a steady-state, deterministic model. Transfer matrices are obtained for 240 dischargers and 57 receptors for SO_2 and suspended particulates. Ambient concentrations are measured at ground level in average annual values. Necessary point-source data comprise stack coordinates, discharge rates, stack height, stack diameter, gas exit temperature, and gas exit velocity. To simplify the analysis, multiple stacks in a specific location were combined to obtain an "average" stack, to which the Gaussian plume equation was applied. Meteorological data required are mean annual temperature and pressure, mean annual atmospheric mixing depth, and frequency distributions for wind speed, wind direction, and atmospheric stabilities.

The aquatic ecosystem module is described in detail by Kelly (1976) and Kelly and Spofford (1977). This part of the model represents an attempt to go beyond the usual analysis of water quality in terms of dissolved oxygen and ambient concentrations of salts and solids, to simulate the effects of ambient conditions on interacting populations of aquatic organisms. Endogenous variables in the model comprise algae, zooplankton, bacteria, fish, dissolved oxygen, BOD, nitrogen, phosphorous, toxics, suspended solids, and temperature. Discharges affecting the ecosystems are BOD, nitrogen, phosphorous, toxics, suspended solids, and heat. Management goals are specified for algae, fish, and dissolved oxygen. The ecosystem model is nonstochastic and nonlinear and generates a set of results following a dynamic simulation process.

The objective function minimizes the total cost of meeting environmental quality targets (ecosystem variables and ambient concentration standards). Costs include annualized capital and operating costs of different process technologies, recycling and environmental modification, and social costs reflecting damages of residuals in the environment. This last category of costs is derived from a set of penalty functions, such that when ambient concentration standards are exceeded, values of the cost parameters for the relevant residuals in the objective function are raised. Minimum levels of product outputs have to be met, thus the model optimizes the quantities of residuals discharged, the physical control measures used, and the allocation of abatement burdens to dischargers in the region.

The solution procedure is described by Spofford et al. (1975). The penalty function is quadratic, necessitating nonlinear solution techniques. An iterative gradient method is utilized. An additional term is included in the penalty function, however, that results in a cut-off for computations when the solution is close to the full optimum. For each iteration, an ordinary linear programming algorithm is employed. The model is quite expensive to operate. Bower and Kneese (1979) comment that a typical 30-iteration run of the model would cost, at 1975 rates, $1220. After 30 iterations, ambient standards would be met and a fairly constant pattern of total discharges would be established, but the optimal levels of residuals control by individual dischargers would still not be completely determined.

The findings of the study can be evaluated in two ways: first, as regards the appropriateness of the methodology for REQM modeling in general, and second, in terms of the results on the Delaware region itself.

Several conclusions were drawn for the management of environmental quality in the Lower Delaware Region. First, it appears that air quality raises more problems than water quality because of technological difficulties and the high associated costs. Second, by using combinations of on-site residuals discharge reduction, sewage treatment and in-stream aeration, water quality standards could be met. Third, solid wastes can most effectively be disposed of by landfill in the region, but in the future, recycling and export of residuals by rail will probably be required. Municipal incinerators are not a cost-effective method of dealing with solid wastes. Finally, a wide variety of physical measures to handle residuals in the region could be used without much variation in total cost, but different combinations selected involved substantially different patterns in the incidence of management costs.

The conclusions on methodology should be of wider interest to the modeling community. Only a brief summary can be given here. There is no doubt that the research resources, data requirements, and computer time for the RFF model presented considerable difficulties for those engaged in the project. Nevertheless, if construction of such a model is contemplated, it is worthwhile identifying all the linkages among solid, liquid, and gaseous residuals rather than considering each in isolation. Computations with the nonlinear programming algorithm proved to be very costly and probably did not satisfactorily indicate the true optimum. This arose because an iterative solution method was employed and computations had to be stopped (for cost reasons) well before the optimum was reached. RFF has converted from the aquatic ecosystem model to a simple, linear Streeter–Phelps model to simplify the computations. Finally, the model was difficult to operate when distributional constraints on the incidence of costs were imposed. This, however, is a common problem in mathematical programming. If the model is overconstrained, feasible solutions may not be found.

5.4.2. *The Upper Colorado River Basin*

The Upper Colorado River Basin has been the subject of several regional environmental quality studies. It consists of the Green, Upper Main Stem, and San Juan sub-basins of the main Colorado River system, covers an area of 102 000 square miles, and contains sections of five states: Wyoming, Colorado, Utah, New Mexico, and Arizona. Precipitation reaches 50 inches per year in the headwaters and is below 6 inches in downstream desert areas. The outflow per unit area of 60 acre-feet per square mile is the lowest of any river basin in the United States. The region nevertheless is an important ecological resource and contains a large number of rare and endangered fish and wildlife species.

Human activities have already had major environmental impacts on the region. The population in 1970 was 346 000, engaged mostly in agriculture, grazing, and metal mining. About 70 percent of the area of the basin is owned by the federal government and used for a wide variety of recreational pursuits. Water supply and quality present difficult management problems. The river has many dams, reservoirs, and aqueducts, and water flows are carefully regulated. Downstream flows are fully utilized; typically, no water reaches the Colorado's end point in the Gulf of California. Salinity is of major concern. Natural processes (release of salts from shales, evapotranspiration, concentration of salts by vegetation) produce high background levels of dissolved solids, and this is exacerbated by irrigation practices, acid drainage from mines, use of cooling water by power stations, and discharge of sewage into the river system.

The newest threat to the basin's environment is the proposed development of the extensive deposits of coal and oil shale that underlie the region. This will result in large strip mines, oil shale refining operations, and the construction of electric power stations. Air quality in the region has already deteriorated from power station activity. The proposed energy developments will contribute further airborne residuals and place added stresses on water resources, raising the consumptive use of water and increasing salinity loadings. Uranium mining and milling in the basin will add to these problems.

The study reported by Howe (1977) represents one attempt to model the Upper Colorado River Basin, undertaken by the University of Colorado under sponsorship of the Economic Development Administration, U.S. Department of Commerce. The model has three main components: a set of regional input–output tables for the Upper Basin; a hydrologic model that simulates surface and groundwater flows and their uses in the basin; and an air dispersion model that determines ambient concentration of airborne residuals discharged from point and area sources. The model is a classic example of a generalized input–output model applied at the regional level.

The University of Colorado model was designed for several applications. The first was analysis of the effects of a large reduction in the use of water for irrigation in the Upper Main Stem sub-basin on the regional economy, hydrology, and water quality. The second application was to assess the effects of two possible coal development patterns in the Gunnison River sub-basin – either increased coal mining for export purposes, or extended coal mining accompanied by power station construction and operation. A third aim was to estimate the damage costs of uncontrolled salinity and examine the regional significance of alternative irrigation techniques and agricultural practices. Finally, the model was designed to determine whether energy developments in the Upper Basin might be constrained by environmental factors and what the tradeoffs are between environmental quality and different patterns of economic activity.

Economic scenarios for the Upper Basin are generated with input–output tables for the three subregions: Upper Main Stem (33 sectors); Green River (24 sectors); and San Juan River (30 sectors). The input-output models are not formally linked in an interregional system. Howe comments that the data were over ten years old so that the reliability of the model was somewhat in doubt. It is interesting to note also that the tables took eighteen months to compile and cost $500 000.

The hydrosalinity model uses monthly data and is driven by precipitation, temperature, and water inflows. Incoming water and total dissolved solids entering the basin establish the initial conditions. Flows within the basin are affected by tributary inflows, reservoir storage, water releases, water use by industry and municipal activities, agricultural practices, evaporation, imports and exports of water, groundwater use, and reservoir operation within the basin. Water flows and salinity are calibrated against data for a 25-year period. The model generates not only average values, resulting from hydrometeorological data driving the system, but frequency distributions of the key variables.

Air quality is analyzed by means of APGDM, a computerized air pollution generation and discharge model. The model determines ground level concentrations of airborne residuals on a quarterly basis, given the levels of economic activity indicated by the input–output model or from independent surveys. Each of the sub-basins is fairly self-contained as regards airborne residuals because of the high mountain ridges in the region; thus the sub-basin input–output models can be used separately to determine residuals discharge and dispersion. Area and point sources of discharges are distinguished. Ambient concentrations are reported on a grid system or as an isopleth mapping. An accuracy of ± 20 percent for the air dispersion model is claimed.

One of the frustrations of the University of Colorado's exercise was the failure to establish close working relationships with state and federal government agencies responsible for development decisions in the region. According to Howe, because of vested interests of the individual states involved, little progress toward efficient management of air and water quality was apparent.

A second study of the Upper Colorado River Basin was conducted by the University of New Mexico and RFF at the request of the Office of Biological Services of the U.S. Fish and Wildlife Service as part of the Southwest Region Under Stress Project. The results of the study, a collection of papers based on an RFF forum held in Albuquerque, New Mexico, 1976, are reported by Spofford et al. (1980). The interesting feature of this study is that, even though a formal REQM model was not developed from the inputs available, the papers do interrelate closely and provide an ideal basis for constructing a simulation model at some future stage. Moreover, the sequence in which the separate analyses are presented in the final report offers a valuable guide to the methodology that can be followed in gathering and organizing the information required to establish an operational, analytical structure. The study is noteworthy also in pushing beyond a consideration of ambient air and water quality to dose–response relationships for animal and fish species in the region.

Energy developments in the region are assessed in two ways: an autonomous study of possible energy expansion, emphasizing coal mining, power generation, synthetic natural gas, synthetic crude oil, and uranium mining; and with the aid of a 40-sector interregional input–output model driven by a demographic module. Feedbacks from the economic model determine employment and immigration. Environmental impacts resulting from energy developments, industrial production, and recreational activities are identified.

The impacts are assessed initially in terms of water quantity and quality. Particular properties of water systems, of significance to aquatic organisms, are shown to be: concentrations of dissolved gases; levels of toxic compounds; supply of nutrients; turbidity; physical characteristics of the river system; and temperature. The effects of changes in these characteristics are then traced for fish populations in the Colorado River. Impacts of energy developments on big game in the region are dealt with, although this analysis is not integrated with the economic and water resource scenarios. Separate papers are also included on energy developments in the Yampa Basin, with effects on water quality and trout populations. The study concludes with a discussion of institutional approaches to water quality management, with implications for fish and wildlife populations.

5.4.3. Hunter Valley

The Hunter Valley is situated in southeast Australia about 100 miles north of Sydney. It is approximately 130 miles from east to west and 75 miles north to south. The Hunter River rises in the north and reaches the coast at Newcastle, the major city in the region. The Hunter is joined by its western tributary, the Goulburn River, in the center of the valley.

The main population centers are situated in the city of Newcastle, and in surrounding towns and smaller villages. Lake Macquarie is located south of Newcastle and forms an extension of the metropolitan area.

The main activities in the region are black coal mining, electric power generation, iron and steel production, aluminum smelting, and metal fabrication. There are 52 active coal mines, producing about 35 million tonnes each year, or roughly one-third of Australia's total black coal output. Electricity generation is around 22 000 gigawatt hours.

Environmental concerns were expressed in the later 1970s with the impending natural resource boom, as projections indicated a trebling of coal output from the Hunter Valley, especially from new open cut mines. Plans were also made for an expansion of electricity generation and aluminum smelting. Much of the growth impetus has now slowed as a result of the world recession, but a further expansionary phase is very likely in the late 1980s and many of the same problems will need to be addressed once again.

A model is currently being constructed within the Centre for Environmental Studies at Macquarie University under sponsorship of the National Energy Research Development and Demonstration Council [James et al. (1982)]. The model combines a national energy-economic input–output model with an environmental input–output model for the Hunter region based on a set of transactions tables prepared by Garlick (1979). Aims of the exercise include: integration with MARKAL, an engineering-economic model of energy use in Australia developed by the Commonwealth Scientific and Industrial Research Organisation [Musgrove et al. (1983)]; simulation of national economic and energy scenarios, tracing the implications for coal-related developments in the Hunter region; simulation of the air and water quality effects of economic scenarios in the Hunter region; and investigation of possible regional environmental constraints on regional or national development.

The regional input–output model has 23 sectors, with all transactions flows measured in dollars, except for raw coal, washed coal, and electricity, which are measured in physical units. Regional economic scenarios will be driven by the national energy model or obtained from autonomous studies of the regional economy and its future prospects. The main airborne residuals under examination are sulfur oxides and fluorides. Sulfur oxides are a reasonable general indicator of air quality, and fluorides are important because of their potential damaging effects on vineyards in the region. An improved version of the Dennis model is being used to simulate average monthly concentrations of these residuals, and to determine the meteorological conditions under which peak concentrations can arise [Chambers (1983)].

A water supply model is being constructed, based on data supplied by the NSW Water Resources Commission. Water demands will be projected by means of the input–output model, together with appropriate assumptions about irrigation practices in the agricultural sector. A major problem is salinity, as the coal fields have been formed from ancient marine sediments. Salinity occurs naturally through groundwater extrusion, but as yet the impact of mining on salinity levels, especially during times of low river flow, is not properly known. These problems are being investigated by the Macquarie group.

Preliminary results suggest that the water supply/demand pattern and salinity levels will be the main environmental quality problems to tackle. When this is established with greater certainty, more detailed analysis of environmental management alternatives, together with their economic costs, can be undertaken.

5.4.4. RIM

RIM is the acronym for "Reken-en Informatiesysteem Milieuhygiene", a multi-sectoral economic–environmental model of the Netherlands currently under development at the Institute for Environmental Studies, Free University, Amsterdam. The Institute's English language version is ECIS (Environmental Computation and Information System). RIM is discussed here as an example of an REQM model, as it contains all the elements of a regional environmental model, and even though RIM is designed to provide information for the management of residuals at the national level, the Netherlands itself is so small and compact geographically that the entire country can be treated as a single region.

RIM has evolved from several lines of research over the last ten years, but the common thread has been a residuals-generation and modification input–output model of the Netherlands economy that has been successively improved and expanded to its present form. Much of this research, including current development of the model, has been sponsored by the Ministry of Environment and Public Health. Very little documentation is available, unfortunately, in the English language.

The origins of RIM can be traced to early work on combustion emissions associated with energy use in a paper written by Jansen and Stapel (1974) that made use of a 23-sector input–output model. By 1977, the system had been enlarged to a 60-sector model, and linear programming was applied to assess tradeoffs between economic variables and energy-related residuals discharges [Jansen et al. (1977)]. A brief description of this work can be found in James et al. (1978).

In the next stage of development, process residuals were added to the model [Jansen et al. (1978)] and, for each of the 60 sectors, discharge coefficients were calculated for four environmental indicators: an air quality index obtained by weighting different airborne residuals and aggregating them, a water quality index reflecting heavy metals discharges, a BOD water quality index, and chemical wastes measured by mass. The model was used to create alternative scenarios for 1985, analyzing policies emphasizing economic goals, such as income and employment, or environmental quality as measured by the four indicators just described.

The feasibility study for RIM was carried out in 1980 [Hordijk et al. (1980)] after a research tour of the United States where detailed discussions were held on the U.S. EPA SEAS (Strategic Environmental Assessment System) model. The conclusion was reached that a much simpler model would need to be constructed for the Netherlands given the proposed manpower and funding. The most recent

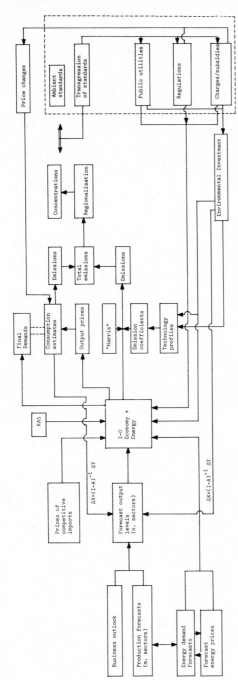

Figure 7.5. RIM. *Source:* Hordijk et al. (1980, p. 13).

description of the model appears in Olsthoorn and Jansen (1982). The first phase of the project, producing an inventory of nitrogen oxide emissions in the Netherlands and possible emission patterns for the period 1978–2000 under different technologies for NO_x control has now been completed [Olsthoorn et al. (1982)].

The general structure of RIM appears in Figure 7.5. Economic forecasts from the Central Planning Bureau and the Ministry of Economic Affairs, together with assumptions about energy prices and energy demands, are translated into a set of final demands that drive the 60-sector input–output model. The RAS method is proposed for updating and forecasting the input–output coefficients. It is possible also that these coefficients will be modified according to the results of econometric studies already underway in the Netherlands on energy use and technical change [Lesuis et al. (1980)].

Emission coefficients in the model apply to specific processes within each sector, as far as possible from physical emission factors rather than from monetary data. NO_x emissions, for example, are estimated for stationary and mobile sources. The stationary source emissions are based on fuel use patterns, including different combustion processes and emission control technologies, and on process emissions from the outputs of products such as nitric acid and fertilizers. With mobile sources, emissions are estimated separately for private automobiles driven in different modes and using different fuels, commercial vehicles, taxis, motorcycles, rail transport, and special vehicles. The calculations reflect earlier work carried out on NO_x emissions in the Netherlands [METRA (1977)]. Future research on sulfur oxides emissions will likewise be assisted by existing studies [Ministerie van Volksgezondheid en Milieuhygiene (1980)].

Emission coefficients are affected in the model by new technological profiles created through environmental investment. This part of the model follows from the implementation of environmental quality standards. National emissions, once determined, are translated into ambient concentrations at different receptor points through a regionalization program. Ambient concentrations are then compared with selected standards. If the standards are transgressed, management actions are simulated. These may take the form of residuals discharge controls for public utilities such as water and sewage plants, or regulations and subsidies/charges to control residuals discharges from the private sector. Price effects from these measures lead to changes in final demands, requiring an iterative adjustment of the model. In addition, environmental investment may take place, affecting sectoral outputs and emission coefficients as previously mentioned.

RIM will perform a number of functions in the Netherlands. It will be used to obtain advance warnings of environmental pollution by comparing predicted ambient concentrations of residuals with existing standards. In the longer term, it will simulate patterns of economic growth and energy use, and indicate the requirements for new standards before environmental damage actually occurs. A time span of twenty years is proposed. RIM will assist general evaluation of government policies and will be particularly useful in integrating environmental goals with other socioeconomic goals. RIM will also be a valuable information-gathering system. Data will be collected and analyzed as on ongoing process. Another function is publicity. Regular reports can be issued to advise the community of trends in the economy and environmental quality, encouraging critical public discussion of environmental policies and establishing a rational basis for future action. Finally, RIM will help to coordinate institutions involved in managing the economy, energy use, and environmental quality. All participants in the planning and management process will have common use of a detailed data and modeling base.

6. Concluding remarks

Sufficient experience has now been gained in the industrial process/REQM area for a number of conclusions to be drawn, and for various challenges to be identified in future research. Perhaps the most important fact to emerge is that if REQM modeling is to have practical relevance – in terms of analyzing alternative industrial process technologies, assessing their effects on ambient environmental quality, and indicating guidelines for environmental managers to follow – economists need access to detailed physical and engineering models and data. Is multidisciplinary teamwork the best way to achieve this goal? Should economists endeavor to take over relevant branches of engineering and environmental science? Can the physical systems analysts provide reference guides with appropriate model descriptions and areas of application that economists and environmental managers can incorporate in an REQM framework? Answers to these questions must be found if REQM modeling is to maintain credibility in future years.

The relationship between modelers and users is crucial. Above all, modelers must realize that the object of analysis is not the construction of theoretically elaborate mathematical systems, but the solution of specific problems. Methodology is, to a certain extent, transferrable from one set of problems (or geographic region) to another, but continued sponsorship by policymakers can be expected only if practical results are achieved. Modelers accordingly need to make careful judgments about the directions of research before data collection and analysis begin. For example, what is the scope of the problem? Is pollution in a region associated with all activities, or only a few? Is is necessary to study all residuals discharged, or are only certain residuals of prime significance? How many classes of receptors must be analyzed? Should dose–response relationships be considered, or are widely used ambient concentration standards acceptable proxies for environmental goals? If institutional and environmental boundaries (airsheds, watersheds, ecosystems) do not coincide, how can policymakers be shown the value of a broad-ranging modeling exercise? Institutional constraints on management strategies may be just as important as economic, environmental and technological parameters.

For future research on industrial activities, physical measures of inputs, commodity outputs and residuals discharges associated with specific process technologies are clearly superior to monetary measures. Compilation of commonly used industrial technologies and residuals modification processes would be extremely useful to REQM modelers. Cost functions specific to countries and regions could be readily constructed by economists by applying financial data to engineering process models, permitting tradeoff analysis of the costs of residuals discharge management and levels of control. Where multiactivity REQM models are involved, as in linked activity models or input–output systems, the prospects of identifying intersectoral or interactivity flows measured in physical units should be carefully explored, as this approach lends itself readily to mass balance and energy balance analysis. Less significant regional production flows may be modeled in monetary values if other data are unavailable.

Nonreactive dispersion modeling appears to have reached a satisfactory stage of development, especially for steady-state calculations. Further work remains to be done, however, in several areas. So far, only a limited number of residuals have been studied. Much more needs to be known about types of residuals discharged from industrial activities, particularly toxic substances. Although acid rain and photochemical smog have recieved much attention, reactive residuals modeling is still in a state of infancy. The dynamics of residuals behavior in the environment is a topic of emerging interest. Very little is understood about the accumulation of substances in physical (and biological) systems. Compilation of emission inventories, increased field monitoring, and model verification are important requirements in future REQM work.

Probably the weakest link in the entire chain of analysis is dose–response modeling and the construction of damage functions. According to recent studies a large component of damage resulting from air pollution may be human health, yet estimates vary by orders of magnitude. Much better data on dose–response relationships are urgently needed. Concern is also expressed by medical researchers about the paucity of reliable data on long-term exposure of humans to low-level concentrations of various substances. In this respect uncertainty exists even about the more commonly studied air-borne residuals such as sulphur oxides and carbon monoxide. Effects of residuals on ecosystems is another area which, as yet, remains largely unexplored. Work on the economic valuation of environmental effects has progressed rapidly in the last few years. Delays in specifying damage functions are the result of inadequate physical modeling rather than valuation methodologies. Deficiencies in damage function estimation should not preclude further REQM research. What can be expected in the foreseeable future is an emphasis on standard-setting and cost-effectiveness analysis. Mathematical programming and simple tradeoff models can make important contributions in this area. When more experience in environmental systems modeling has been gained, full benefit–cost analyses of regional industrial development programs and environmental quality management may evolve.

References

Ayres, Robert U. (1972) "A Materials-Process-Product Model", in: Allen V. Kneese and Blair T. Bower (eds.), *Environmental Quality Analysis: Theory and Method in the Social Sciences* (Johns Hopkins University Press, Baltimore) pp. 35–67.

Ayres, Robert U. and Ivars Gutmanis (1972) "Technological Change, Pollution and Treatment Costs in Input–Output Analysis", in: Ronald G. Ridker (ed.), *Population, Resources and the Environment*, U.S. Commission on Population Growth and the American Future (U.S. Government Printing Office, Washington) pp. 313–337.

Ayres, Robert U. and A.V. Kneese (1969) "Production, Consumption and Externalities", *American Economic Review* 59, 282–297.

Bach, Wilfred (1972) *Atmospheric Pollution* (McGraw-Hill, New York).

Basta, Daniel J. and Blair T. Bower (eds.) (1982) "Analyzing Natural Systems: Analysis for Regional Residuals-Environmental Quality Management", Research Paper (Resources for the Future, Washington).

Basta, Daniel J., James L. Lounsbury and Blair T. Bower (1978) "Analysis for Residuals–Environmental Quality Management", RFF Research Paper R-11 (Resources for the Future, Washington).

Beller, M. (ed.) (1976) "Energy Systems Studies Program Annual Report", BNL 50539, Brookhaven National Laboratory, Upton, New York.

Bower, Blair T. (1967) "The Economics of Industrial Water Utilization", in: Allen V. Kneese and Stephen C. Smith (eds.), *Water Research* (Johns Hopkins University Press, Baltimore).

Bower, Blair T. (1975) "Studies of Residuals Management in Industry", in: Edwin S. Mills (ed.), *Economic Analysis of Environmental Problems*, National Bureau of Economic Research (Columbia University Press, New York) pp. 275–324.

Bower, Blair T. (1977) "The Why and What of Regional Residuals Environmental Quality Management Modeling", in: Blair T. Bower (ed.), *Regional Residuals Environmental Quality Management Modeling*, Research Paper R-7 (Resources for the Future, Washington), pp. 1–32.

Bower, Blair T. (1983) "Analyzing Effects on Natural Systems and Receptors", in: Maynard M. Hufschmidt, David E. James, Anton D. Meister, Blair T. Bower and John A. Dixon (eds.), *Environment, Natural Systems and Development: An Economic Valuation Guide* (Johns Hopkins University Press, Baltimore).

Bower, Blair T., Remi Barre, Jochen Kuhner and Clifford S. Russell (1981) "Incentives in Water Quality Management: France and the Ruhr Area", Research Paper R-24 (Resources for the Future, Washington).

Bower, Blair T., Charles N. Ehler and Allen V. Kneese (1977) "Incentives for Managing the Environment", *Environmental Science and Technology* 11, 250–254.

Bower, Blair T., George O.G. Lof and W.M. Hearon (1972) "Residuals Management in the Pulp and Paper Industry", *National Resources Journal* 11, 605–623.

Brady, Gordon L. and Blair T. Bower (1981) "Air Quality Management: Quantifying Benefits", Research Report no. 7, East–West Environment and Policy Institute, Honolulu.

Briggs, G.A. (1969) "Plume Rise", Atomic Energy Commission Critical Review Series, TID 25075.

Brown, F. Lee and A.O. Lebeck (1976) *Cars, Cans and Dumps: Solutions for Rural Residuals* (Johns Hopkins University Press, Baltimore).

Brown, Robert M., Nina I. McClelland, Rolf A. Deininger and Michael F. O'Connor (1975) "A Water Quality Index—Crashing the Psychological Barrier", in: William A. Thomas (ed.), *Indicators of Environmental Quality* (Plenum/Rosetta, New York) pp. 173–182.

Buehring, William A. and Wesley K. Foell (1976) *Environmental Impact of Electrical Generation: A Systemwide Approach* (International Institute for Applied Systems Analysis, Laxenburg, Austria).

Burton, Ellison S. and William Sanjour (1970) "A Simulation Approach to Air Pollution Abatement Program Planning", *Socio-Economic Planning Sciences* 4, 147–159.

Camp, T.R. (1965) "Field Estimates of Oxygen Balance Parameters", *Journal of Sanitary Engineering Division*, American Society of Civil Engineers, 91, 1–16.

Carson, J.E. and H. Moses (1969) "The Validity of Several Plume Rise Formulas", *Journal of the Air Pollution Control Association* 19, 862–966.

Chambers, John A. (1983) "A Dispersion Model for the Prediction of Ambient Air Pollution Concentrations in the Hunter Region, NSW", Center for Environmental and Urban Studies, Macquarie University, North Ryde, NSW.

Cherniavski, E.A. (1974) "Brookhaven Energy System Optimization Model", Report no. BNL 19569 Brookhaven National Laboratory, Upton, New York.

Converse, A.O. (1971) "On the Extension of Input–output Analysis to Account for Environmental Externalities", *American Economic Review* 61, 197–198.

Davis, Robert K. (1968) *The Range of Choice in Water Management* (Johns Hopkins University Press, Baltimore).

Deland, Michael R. (1979) "The Bubble Concept", *Environmental Science and Technology* 13, 277.

Den Hartog, H. and A. Houweling (1974) "Pollution, Pollution Abatement and the Economic Structure: Empirical Results of Input–output Computations for the Netherlands", Occasional Papers no. 1/1974 Central Planning Bureau, The Hague.

Dennis, R.L. (1978) "The Smeared Concentration Approximation Method: A Simplified Air Pollution Dispersion Methodology for Regional Analysis", IIASA Research Paper RR-78-9 International Institute for Applied Systems Analysis, Laxenburg, Austria.

EPRI (1979a) "Workshop Proceedings: Integration of Environmental Considerations Into Energy-Economic System Models", Report no. WS-78-95 Electric Power Research Institute, Palo Alto.

EPRI (1979b) "Modeling Future Power Plant Location Location Patterns", Report no. EA-1063 Electric Power Research Institute, Palo Alto.

Fiering, Myron B. (1967) *Streamflow Synthesis* (Harvard University Press, Cambridge).

Foell, Wesley K. (1979a) *Management of Energy/Environment Systems: Methods and Case Studies* (Wiley, New York).

Foell, Wesley K. (1979b) "The Wisconsin/IIASA Energy/Environment Models: An Overview and Recent Applications", in: Workshop Proceedings: Integration of Environmental Considerations Into Energy-Economic System Models, Report no. WS-78-95 (Electric Power Research Institute, Palo Alto) pp. 4.37–4.50.

Foell, W.K., J.W. Mitchell and J.L. Pappas (1975) "The Wisconsin Regional Energy Model: A Systems Approach to Regional Analysis", Report no. 56 (Energy Systems and Policy Research Group, University of Wisconsin, Madison).

Forsund, Finn R. and Steinar Strom (1976) "The Generation of Residual Flows in Norway: An Input–output Approach", *Journal of Environmental Economics and Management* 3, 129–141.

Freeman, A. Myrick (1979) *The Benefits of Environmental Improvement: Theory and Practice* (Johns Hopkins University Press, Baltimore).

Gameson, A.L.H. (1973) *Mathematical and Hydraulic Modelling of Estuarine Pollution*, Water Pollution Research Technical Paper no. 13 (Her Majesty's Stationery Office, London).

Garlick, S. (1979) "New Input–output Tables for the Hunter Region", (Hunter Valley Research Foundation, Tighes Hill, N.S.W.).

Gifford, Jr., F.A. (1961) "Use of Routine Meteorological Observations for Estimating Atmospheric Dispersion", *Nuclear Safety* 2, 47–51.

Gifford, Jr., F.A. (1973) "The Simple ATDL Air Pollution Model", rev., ATDL Contribution File no. 78 (Oak Ridge, NOAA Atmospheric and Diffusion Laboratory).

Gosz, James R. (1980) "The Influence of Reduced Stream Flows on Water Quality", in: Walter O. Spofford, Jr., Alfred L. Parker and Allen V. Kneese, (eds.), *Energy Developments in the Southwest*, RFF Research Paper R-18 (Resources for the Future, Washington).

Green, A.E.S. (ed.) (1980) *Coal Burning Issues* (University of Florida Press, Gainsville).

Guldmann, Jean-Michel (1978) "Industrial Location, Air Pollution Control and Meteorological Variability: A Dynamic Optimization Approach", *Socio-Economic Planning Sciences* 12, 197–214.

Guldmann, Jean-Michel and Daniel Shefer (1977) "Optimal Plant Location and Air Quality Management Under Indivisibilities and Economies of Scale", *Socio-Economic Planning Sciences* 11, 77–93.

Hafkamp, Wim and Peter Nijkamp (1980) "An Integrated Interregional Model for Pollution Control", in: T.R. Lakshmanan and P. Nijkamp (eds.), *Economic-Environmental-Energy Interactions: Modeling and Policy Analysis* (Martinus Nijhoff, The Hague).

Hanna, Steven R. (1973) "A Simple Dispersion Model for the Analysis of Chemically Reactive

Pollutants", *Atmospheric Environment* 7, 803–817.

Harrington, Winston (1981) "The Regulatory Approach to Air Quality Management: A Case Study of New Mexico", Research Paper R-25 (Resources for the Future, Washington).

Hite, James C. and Eugene A. Laurent (1972) *Environmental Planning: An Economic Analysis* (Praeger, New York).

Holling, C.S. (1978) *Adaptive Environmental Assessment and Management* (Wiley, New York).

Hordijk, L., H.M.A. Jansen, A.A. Olsthoorn and J.B. Vos (1980) "Reken-en Informatiesysteem Milieuhygiene, Een Studie Naar Haalbaarheid" (Institute for Environmental Studies, Free University, Amsterdam).

Howe, Charles W. (1977) "A Coordinated Set of Economic, Hydro-salinity and Air Quality Models of the Upper Colorado River Basin with Applications to Current Problems", in: Blair T. Bower (ed.), *Regional Residuals Environmental Quality Management Modeling*, RFF Research Paper R-7 (Resources for the Future, Washington) pp. 108–138.

Howe, Charles W. (1979) *Natural Resource Economics* (Wiley, New York).

Hufschmidt, Manyard, M. (1962) "Analysis by Simulation: Examination of Response Surface", in: Arthur Maass, Maynard M. Hufschmidt, Robert Dorfman, Harold A. Thomas, Jr., Stephen A. Marglin and Gordon Maskew Fair (eds.), *Design of Water Resource Systems* (Macmillan, London).

Hufschmidt, Maynard M. and Eric L. Hyman (eds.) (1982) *Economic Approaches to Natural Resource and Environmental Quality Analysis* (Tycooly, Dublin).

Hufschmidt, Maynard M., David E. James, Anton D. Meister, Blair T. Bower and John A. Dixon (1983) *Environment, Natural Systems and Development: An Economic Valuation Guide* (Johns Hopkins University Press, Baltimore).

International Energy Agency (1980) *A Group Strategy for Energy Research, Development and Demonstration* (Organisation for Economic Cooperation and Development, Paris).

James, David, Alison Gilbert and John Chambers (1982) "An Integrated Energy-Economic-Environmental Model for Australia: Background, Conceptual Framework and Research Design" (Centre for Environmental Studies, Macquarie University, North Ryde, N.S.W.).

James, D.E., H.M.A. Jansen and J.B. Opschoor (1978) *Economic Approaches to Environmental Problems* (Elsevier, Amsterdam).

Jansen, H.M.A. et al. (1978) "Milieuverontreiniging en Productiestructuur in Nederland" (Institute for Environmental Studies, Free University, Amsterdam).

Jansen, H.M.A., J.B. Opschoor, J.H.A. Stapel, A.A. Olsthoorn, J.B. Vos and J.L. ten Broek (1977) "Luchtverontreiniging en Economische Struktuur" (Institute for Environmental Studies, Free University, Amsterdam).

Jansen, H.M.A. and J.H.A. Stapel (1974) "Vuil uit Nederlands Pijpen" Werknota no. 40 (Institute for Environmental Studies, Amsterdam).

Keeney, Ralph L. and Howard Raiffa (1976) *Decisions with Multiple Objectives* (Wiley, New York).

Kelly, Robert A. (1976) "Conceptual Ecological Model of the Delaware Estuary", in: B.C. Patten (ed.), *Systems Analysis and Simulation in Ecology* vol. IV (Academic Press, New York).

Kelly, Robert A. and Walter O. Spofford, Jr. (1977) "Application of an Ecosystem Model to Water Quality Management: The Delaware Estuary", in: C.A.S. Hall and J.W. Day, Jr. (eds.), *Ecosystem Modeling in Theory and Practice: An Introduction with Case Histories* (Wiley, New York).

Kneese, Allen V. (1974) "The Application of Economic Analysis to the Management of Water Quality: Some Case Studies", in: J. Rothenberg and Ian G. Heggie (eds.), *The Management of Water Quality and the Environment* (Macmillan, London) pp. 73–103.

Kneese, Allen V. (1977) *Economics and the Environment* (Penguin, Harmondsworth, Middlesex) pp. 151–194.

Kneese, Allen V., Robert U. Ayres and Ralph C. d'Arge (1970) *Economics and the Environment: A Materials Balance Approach* (Resources for the Future, Washington).

Kneese, Allen V. and Blair T. Bower (1968) *Managing Water Quality: Economics Technology, Institutions* (Johns Hopkins University Press, Baltimore).

Kneese, Allen V. (1977) "Issues Surrounding Regional Residuals-Environmental Quality Management Modelling", in: Blair T. Bower, (ed.), *Regional Residuals Environmental Quality Management Modeling*, Research Paper R-7 (Resources for the Future, Washington) pp. 33–51.

Kneese, Allen V. and Blair T. Bower (1979) *Environmental Quality and Residuals Management* (Johns Hopkins University Press, Baltimore).

Kohn, Robert E. (1971) "Optimal Air Quality Standards", *Econometrica* 39, 983–995.

Kohn, Robert E. (1974) "Industrial Location and Air Pollution Abatement", *Journal of Regional Science* 14, 55–63.

Kohn, Robert E. (1975) "Input–output Analysis and Air Pollution Control", in: Edwin S. Mills (ed.), *Economic Analysis of Environmental Problems*, National Bureau of Economic Research (Columbia University Press, New York) pp. 239–274.

Leontief, Wassily W. (1970) "Environmental Repercussions and the Economic Structure", *Review of Economics and Statistics* 52, 262–271.

Lesuis, P.J.J., F. Muller and P. Nijkamp (1980) "Operational Methods for Strategic Environmental and Energy Policies", in: T.R. Lakshmanan and P. Nijkamp (eds.), *Economic-Environmental-Energy Interactions: Modeling and Policy Analysis* (Martinus Nijhoff, The Hague).

Liu, Ben-chieh (1968) *Interindustrial Structure of the St. Louis Region, 1967* (St. Louis Regional Industrial Development Corporation).

Lof, George O.G., W.M. Hearon and Blair T. Bower (1973) "Residuals Management in Pulp and Paper Manufacture", in: Walter S. Kaghan (ed.), *Forest Products and the Environment*, American Institute of Chemical Engineers Symposium Series, vol. 69, no. 133.

Lof, George O.G. and Allen V. Kneese (1968) *The Economics of Water Utilization in the Beet Sugar Industry* (Johns Hopkins University Press, Baltimore).

Luken, Ralph A., Daniel J. Basta and Edward H. Pechan (1976) *The National Residuals Discharge Inventory* (National Research Council, Washington).

Maass, Arthur, Maynard M. Hufschmidt, Robert Dorfman, Harold Thomas, Jr., Stephen A. Marglin and Gordon Maskew Fair (1962) *Design of Water-resource Systems* (Macmillan, London).

MacCracken, M.C. and G.D. Sauters (eds.) (1975) *Development of an Air Pollution Model for the San Francisco Bay Area: Final Report to the National Science Foundation* (Lawrence Livermore Laboratory, Livermore, California).

Manne, Alan S. (1963) *Scheduling of Petroleum Refinery Operations* (Harvard University Press).

Marcuse, William (1979) "A Hierarchial Decomposition Analysis to Environmental Policy Analysis", in: Workshop Proceedings: Integration of Environmental Considerations Into Energy-Economic Systems Models, Report no. WS-78-79 (Electric Power Research Institute, Palo Alto) pp. 4.77–4.86.

Mastenbroek, A.P. and P. Nijkamp (1974) "Een Multi-Regional Milieumodel Voor Een Ruimtelijke Allocatie Van Investeringen", in: P. Nijkamp (ed.), *Milieu En Economie* (Universitaire Pers, Rotterdam).

Mendelsohn, Robert O. (1979) *Towards Efficient Regulation of Air Pollution from Coal-Fired Power Plants* (Garland, New York).

Mendelsohn, Robert O. (1980) "An Economic Analysis of Air Pollution from Coal-Fired Power Plants", *Journal of Environmental Economics and Management*, 7, 30–43.

Mendelsohn, Robert O. and Guy Orcutt (1979) "An Empirical Analysis of Air Pollution Dose Response Curves", *Journal of Environmental Economics and Management* 6, 85–106.

Metra Consulting Group (1977) "Long-term Consequences of NO_x and SO_2 Abatement", Report to Ministerie van Volksgezondheid en Milieuhygiene, Metra Consulting Group, London.

Miernyk, William H. and John T. Sears (1974) *Air Pollution Abatement and Regional Economic Development* (D.C. Heath, Lexington).

Ministerie van Volksgezondheid en Milieuhygiene (1980) SO_2 *Beleidskaderplan* (Zitting 1979–80, 15834, Nrs. 1-2, Tweede Kamer).

Moodie, A.R. (1979) "Modeling of Water Quality and Hydrology in an Urban Watercourse", Australian Water Resources Council, Technical Paper no. 45 (Australian Government Publishing Service, Canberra).

Muller, Frederik (1973) "An Operational Mathematical Programming Model for the Planning of Economic Activities in Relation to the Environment", *Socio-Economic Planning Sciences* 7, 123–138.

Muller, Frederik (1976) "An Integrated Regional Environmental Economic Model", in: P. Nijkamp (ed.), *Environmental Economics*, vol. 2, Methods (Martinus Nijhoff, The Hague).

Muller, Frederik (1979) *Energy and Environment in Interregional Input–output Models* (Martinus Nijhoff, The Hague).

Musgrove, A.R. de L., K.J. Stocks, P. Essam, D. Le and J.V. Hoetzl (1983) "Exploring Some Australian Energy Alternatives Using MARKAL", Technical Report TR-2 (Division of Energy Technology, CSIRO, Lucas Heights, N.S.W.).

Neely, W. Brock (1982) "The Definition and Use of Mixing Zones", *Environmental Science and Technology* 16, 518–521.

New South Wales State Pollution Control Commission (1977) "Report on Air Pollution Constraints in the Sydney Region" (State Pollution Control Commision, Sydney).

Nijkamp, P. (1977) *Theory and Application of Environmental Economics* (North-Holland, Amsterdam).

Noll, Roger G. and John Trijonis (1971) "Mass Balance, General Equilibrium and Environmental Externalities", *American Economic Review* 61, 730–735.

OECD (1974) *Environmental Damage Costs* (Organisation for Economic Cooperation and Development, Paris).

OECD (1976) *Economic Measurement of Environmental Damage* (Organisation for Economic Cooperation and Development, Paris).

OECD (1980) *Pollution Charges in Practice* (Organisation for Economic Cooperation and Development, Paris).

OECD (1981) *The Costs and Benefits of Sulphur Oxide Control: A Methodological Study* (Organisation for Economic Cooperation and Development, Paris).

Olsthoorn, A.A. and H.M.A. Jansen (1982) "RIM: Reken-en Informatiesysteem Milieuhygiene", in: H. Aiking, P. Ester, L. Hordijk and H.E. van de Veen (eds.), *Mozaiek van de Mileuproblematiek* (VU Boekhandel/Uitgeverij, Amsterdam) pp. 65–79.

Olsthoorn, A.A., R. Thomas, J.B. Vos, J.P. Hettelingh, L. Hordijk and H.M.A. Jansen (1982) *Drie Scenarios Voor de Ontwikkeling van de NO$_x$ Emissies in Nederland 1978–2000* (Institute for Environmental Studies, Free University, Amsterdam).

Pasquill, F. (1962) *Atmospheric Diffusion* (Van Nostrand, New York).

Parvin, Manoucher and Gus W. Grammas (1976) "Optimization Models for Environmental Pollution Control: A Synthesis", *Journal of Environmental Economics and Management* 3, 113–128.

Pearce, David W. (ed.) (1978) *The Valuation of Social Cost* (Allen and Unwin, London).

Pearce, David W. (1978) "Air Pollution", in: David W. Pearce (ed.), *The Valuation of Social Cost* (Allen and Unwin, London) pp. 54–67.

Pigou, A.C. (1932) *The Economics of Welfare*, 4th Edition (Macmillan, London).

Rao, S. Trivkrama, Gopal Sistla, Michael T. Keenan and John S. Wilson (1980) "An Evaluation of Some Commonly Used Highway Dispersion Models", *Journal of the Air Pollution Control Association* 30, 239–246.

Ridker, Ronald G. (ed.) (1972) *Population, Resources and the Environment*, U.S. Commission on Population Growth and the American Future (U.S. Government Printing Office, Washington).

Ridker, Ronald G. and William D. Watson (1980) *To Choose a Future* (Johns Hopkins University Press, Baltimore).

Russell, Clifford S. (1971) "Models for the Investigation of Industrial Response to Residuals Management Actions", *Swedish Journal of Economics* 73, 134–156.

Russell, Clifford S. (1973) *Residuals Management in Industry: A Case Study of Petroleum Refining* (Johns Hopkins University Press for Resources for the Future, Baltimore).

Russell, Clifford S. and Walter O. Spofford, Jr. (1972) "A Quantitative Framework for Residuals Management Decisions", in: Allen V. Kneese and Blair T. Bower (eds.), *Environmental Quality Analysis: Theory and Method in the Social Sciences* (Johns Hopkins University Press, Baltimore) pp. 115–179.

Russell, Clifford S., Walter O. Spofford, Jr. and Edwin T. Haefele (1974) "The Management of the Quality of the Environment", in: J. Rothenberg and Ian G. Heggie (eds.), *The Management of Water Quality and the Environment* (Macmillan, London) pp. 224–277.

Russell, Clifford S. and William J. Vaughan (1974) "A Linear Programming Model of Residuals Management for Integrated Iron and Steel Production", *Journal of Environmental Economics and Management* 1, 17–42.

Russell, Clifford S. and William J. Vaughan (1976) *Steel Production: Processes, Products and Residuals* (Johns Hopkins University Press, Baltimore).

Sawyer, James W., Jr. (1974) *Automotive Scrap Recycling: Processes, Prices and Prospects* (Johns Hopkins University Press, Baltimore).

Schlottmann, Alan (1977) "New Life for Old Garbage: Resource and Energy Recovery from Solid Wastes", *Journal of Environmental Economics and Management* 4, 57–67.

Shefer, Daniel (1973) "Forecasting Industrial Air Pollution in the Haifa Bay Area with an Input–output Model", *Socio-Economic Planning Sciences* 7, 397–406.

Sinden, John A. and Albert C. Worrell (1979) *Unpriced Values: Decisions Without Market Prices* (Wiley Interscience, New York).

Sistla, Gopal, Perry Samson, Michael Keenan and S. Trivikrama Rao (1979) "A Study of Pollutant Dispersion Near Highways", *Atmospheric Environment* 13, 669–685.

Spofford, Jr., Walter O. (1980) "Potential Impacts of Energy Development on Streamflows in the Upper Colorado River Basin", in: Walter O. Spofford, Jr., Alfred L. Parker and Allen V. Kneese (eds.), *Energy Development in the Southwest*, RFF Research Paper R-18 (Resources for the Future, Washington) pp. 351–429.

Spofford, Jr., Walter O., Alfred L. Parker and Allen V. Kneese (eds.) (1980) *Energy Development in the Southwest*, RFF Research Paper R-18 (Resources for the Future, Washington).

Spofford, Jr., Walter O., Clifford S. Russell and Robert A. Kelly (1975) "Operational Problems in Large Scale Residuals Management Models", in: Edwin S. Mills (ed.), *Economic Analysis of Environmental Problems*, National Bureau of Economic Research (Columbia University Press, New York) pp. 171–238.

Spofford, Jr., Walter O., Clifford S. Russell and Robert A. Kelly (1976) *Environmental Quality Management: An Application to the Lower Delaware Valley*, RFF Research Paper R-1 (Resources for the Future, Washington).

Spofford, Jr., Walter O., Clifford S. Russell and Robert A. Kelly (1977) "The Lower Delaware Valley Integrated Residuals Management Model: A Summary", in: Blair T. Bower (ed.), *Regional Residuals Environmental Quality Management Modeling* RFF Research Paper R-7 (Resources for the Future, Washington) pp. 52–106.

Stern, Arthur C. (1976) *Air Pollution*, vol. III (Academic Press, New York).

Streeter, H.W. and E.B. Phelps (1925) "A Study of the Pollution and Natural Purification of the Ohio River—III: Factors Concerned in the Phenomena of Oxidation and Reaeration", Public Health Bulletin no. 146.

Tomany, James P. (1975) *Air Pollution: The Emissions, the Regulations and the Controls* (American Elsevier, New York).

Turner, R.K. (1978) "Water Pollution", in: David W. Pearce (ed.), *The Valuation of Social Cost* (Allen and Unwin, London) pp. 97–119.

U.S. Council on Environmental Quality (1979) *Environmental Quality: Tenth Annual Report* (Council on Environmental Quality, Washington).

U.S. Environmental Protection Agency (1973) "Compilation of Air Pollutant Emission Factors", Publication no. AP-42 (Environmental Protection Agency, Washington).

U.S. Environmental Protection Agency (1979) *Energy from the West: Impact Analysis Report* (U.S. Environmental Protection Agency, Washington).

U.S. Nuclear Regulatory Commission (1976) *Estimating Aquatic Dispersion of Effluents from Accidental and Routine Reactor Releases for the Purpose of Implementing Appendix I*, Regulatory Guide 1.113 (U.S. Regulatory Commission, Washington).

U.S. Nuclear Regulatory Commission (1977) *Regulatory Guide 1.111: Methods for Estimating Atmospheric Transport and Dispersion of Gaseous Effluents in Routine Releases from Light-Water Cooled Reactors* (U.S. Nuclear Regulatory Commission, Washington).

U.S. Office of Technology Assessment (1979) *The Direct Use of Coal* (Government Printing Office, Washington).

Victor, Peter A. (1972) *Pollution: Economy and Environment* (Allen and Unwin, London).

Wang, Mu Hao, Lawrence K. Wang, Jao-Fuan Kao, Ching-Gung Wen and David Vielkind (1979) "Computer-aided Stream Pollution Control and Management", Part I, *Journal of Environmental Management* 9, 165–183.

Wang, Lawrence K., Mu Hao Wang, Jao-Fuan Kao and Ching-Gung Wen (1979) "Computer-aided Stream Pollution Control and Management", Part II, *Journal of Environmental Management* 9, 185–204.

Wen, Ching-Gun and Jao-Faun Kao (1980) "Mathematical Modeling of Stream Water Quality by a New Moment Method: Theoretical Development", *Journal of Environmental Management* 10, 1–11.

Wen, Ching-Gun and Jao-Fuan Kao (1982) "Determination of Sensitivity of Water Quality Parameters for Stream Pollution Control", *Journal of Environmental Management* 74, 17–34.

Chapter 8

INPUT–OUTPUT MODELS, NATIONAL ECONOMIC MODELS, AND THE ENVIRONMENT

FINN R. FØRSUND

University of Oslo

1. Introduction. A general equilibrium setting

As pointed out in the previous chapter, externalities have emerged as the rule rather than the exception in the economic activities of man. Pervasive environmental spillovers are replacing the now outmoded bees and apple orchards as the economists' examples of external effects.

A basic consideration underlying environmental pollution analysis is, as also indicated in the previous chapter, the materials balance: the input of materials and energy in economic activities must eventually be disposed of in the environment as residuals (gaseous, liquid, solid, heat, and noise) or accumulated within the activities as machinery, buildings, consumer durables, etc. [cf. Ayres and Kneese (1969), Kneese et al. (1970)]. The "materials balance" approach clearly underlines the generality of residuals as the normal outcome of the throughput of materials in the course of production and consumption activities. Residuals measured in weight are defined by the difference between the weight of the total material inputs to an activity and the weight of the products which are the objective of the activity, plus the weight of net accumulation of tangible assets in the activity.

The receiving bodies of Nature, the environmental receptors, play a decisive role in the economic analysis of pollution. The view adopted here is that the receptors provide man with two types of services: residual disposal services and environmental services. The former type relates to the inherent generation of residuals by the materials-processing economy of an industrialized state; the latter type is an omnivorous category of recreation activities like sport fishing, boating, skiing, etc., amenity services, aesthetic values, including the intrinsic value of Nature, and the provision of extraction possibilities from mineral deposits, water, air, etc.

Handbook of Natural Resource and Energy Economics, vol. I, edited by A.V. Kneese and J.L. Sweeney
© *Elsevier Science Publishers B.V., 1985*

A residual is defined as a pollutant if the corresponding disposal service of receptors negatively affects, quantitatively or qualitatively, the raw materials or recreation services "produced" by the receptors. The discharge of residuals does not of necessity generate pollution. The natural environment has an assimilative capacity. Owing to dilution, decay, decomposition, chemical transformation, etc. occurring in nature, there are certain threshold values of ambient residual concentrations that must be exceeded before harmful effects appear.

Pollution problems are often stated in terms of different kinds of damages, e.g. health effects, wear and tear of buildings. In our context, damages are conceived as reducing the levels of flows of raw materials or recreation services. Such reduction can take place at the same time as the residuals are discharged, or in the future.

The policy problem posed by pollution is quite simple to state in general terms: it is just the classical economic problem of utilization of scarce resources. The task is to strike a balance among the competing uses of the receptors, i.e. to determine an optimal compromise on the possibility frontier for residual disposal services and all other goods and services.

The nature of pollution problems necessitates policy measures both across and along the time axis. The time dimension is essential when the negative effects of residuals are due not to current flows, but to stocks of accumulated flows of residuals. There are two different categories. In the first place we have residuals which are accumulating in the environment due to their own chemical nature, i.e. they are persistent. This holds, for example, for heavy metals, fluorine, pesticides, halogenated hydrocarbons, and plastics. Some of these residuals may of course pass through different receptors in the environment before they reach the final receptor where accumulation takes place. It is a common characteristic of these residuals that they adversely affect the extraction of raw materials; that is, the quality and/or quantity of future flows of fish, meat, vegetables and so on is reduced, thereby, for instance, causing human health problems.

In the second place, the residuals can accumulate owing to discharges of residuals in excess of receptors' assimilative capacity.

Where negative effects result only from current flows of residuals, the environment regains its natural conditions in a comparatively short time after "closing the tap". Such situations can be dealt with "across the time dimension", unlike where accumulated stocks matter. At a given point in time the negative externalities from the stocks of residuals cannot be optimally adjusted by myopic considerations about current discharge rates only (provided the time horizon of society is not negligible).

The implementation of optimal control measures requires empirical information on several aspects of pollution problems. Empirical effort in the field of environmental pollution can be organized along the following main lines [cf.

Russell and Spofford (1972)] taking the receptors as reference:

(a) The generation of residuals in production and consumption and discharge to receptors.

(b) The natural processes taking place in the receiving environmental medium due to discharge of residuals, e.g. diluting, decay, decomposing, transportation between and among receptors, and transformation of residuals.

(c) Defining the environmental services "produced" by the environmental medium and establishing the impact on these of ambient concentrations of residuals.

(d) Evaluating the preferences attached to changes in environmental services, including the time perspective (of the "present generation").

A general equilibrium analysis must show the trade-offs open to rational decisions. Significant sources for change as regards point (a), discharges to receptors are:

(i) the scale of the activities and thereby the output mix among activities;

(ii) the input mix in an activity;

(iii) process techniques of production and consumption;

(iv) the product characteristics, including durability;

(v) modification of primary residuals ("end of pipe treatment") [Following Russell and Spofford (1972) the concept of "modification" is used instead of "waste treatment" to underline the conservation of mass. The residuals do not physically disappear by waste treatment];

(vi) recycling of residuals;

(vii) the location of activities.

As regards points (b) and (c), it is possible to influence the natural processes of dilution, decay, transportation of discharged residuals among receptors, by measures such as low flow augmentation and aeration of water, and to take protective measures like chlorination of drinking water, double glazing against noise, etc.

A general equilibrium (static) setting appropriate for recognizing the major interdependencies between man's economic activities and their effects and interaction on the natural environment may be of the following highly stylized type. The variables are (read as vectors):

U = utility levels of consumers,

Z = primary residuals from consumption and/or production,

Y = input of man-produced goods in consumption,

E = input of environmental services to consumption "produced" by environmental media in question,

X = production of consumer goods,

V = resources available for production, residual modification and/or recipient management,

S = secondary residuals (after modification),
R = ambient concentrations of residuals in the natural environment.

The general relationships between these variables are represented as follows:

$$W(U, Z; Y, E) = 0, \tag{1}$$

$$F(X, Z; V) \leqq 0, \tag{2}$$

$$Y \leq X, \tag{3}$$

$$M(S, Z; V) = 0, \tag{4}$$

$$D(R; S) = 0, \tag{5}$$

$$N(E; R, V) = 0, \tag{6}$$

$$V \leqq V(R). \tag{7}$$

The semicolons distinguish between outputs from, and inputs to, activities.

Residuals are generated as joint products in consumption and production [eqs. (1) and (2)]. These primary residuals are – together with the usual recourses – inputs to modification activities [eq. (4)]. Modification is conceived of as end-of-pipe treatment, or add-on activity giving the primary residuals different physical forms and/or discharging them to other receptors than those implied by the basic activity techniques. The purpose of modification is to substitute for residual disposal services causing harmful effects other disposal services with less harmful effects. The output from modification is either recycled as resource inputs in activities or discharged to the environment as secondary residuals. Eq. (5) represents the natural processes taking place in the receptors, i.e. dilution, decomposition, transportation, etc. The decisive assumption here is that discharge of residuals results in certain ambient concentrations of residuals in the various geographically located environmental media. Accumulation of residuals is not accounted for in this static equilibrium setting. Eq. (6) relates the flow of environmental services to ambient concentration of residuals. The general specification allows interaction between residuals. By the use of resources harmful effects of residuals can be modified.

Consumers derive utility both from consumption of man-made goods and from environmental services. The discharge of residuals generates cost in the model by reducing the amount and/or quality of the environmental services and thereby decreasing utility levels of affected consumers.

The notion of the concept "environmental service" is somewhat vague. How are these services to be measured? One approach adopted in Førsund (1972) is to define the services as potential goods, i.e. the possibility of swimming in water of certain quality dimensions, the possibility of breathing air of a certain standard, etc. This option demand approach leads to treating the environmental services as public goods, and thus reflects the public good nature of environmental pollution. The variable E can be interpreted as a quality indicator for the respective services.

Another approach is to define the services as those being actually consumed, i.e. the number of man-hours spent on sport fishing, viewing scenery, etc. The environmental services can then also be private goods or there are private costs of utilizing public goods [cf. Meyer (1971)]. But one cannot escape the fundamental quality dimensions of environmental services. An hour's sport fishing, for example, must also have attributed to it a quality indicator; for example, the number of catches [see Stevens (1966)].

Extraction activity is not explicitly accounted for in the model; the raw materials, labor, capital goods, etc. are just there in given amounts. Extensions within the limits of a static equilibrium model are, however, straightforward and do not bring in new elements that affect the model in principle.

Equation (7) shows how residuals generate cost on the side of production. The additional resource requirements to producers caused by residuals are represented by a general decrease in the amount of resources available for productive use. It is, perhaps, natural to specify the generation of costs on the production side in as detailed form as on the consumption side, but this is not attempted here.

Summing up, the general equilibrium model outlined here accounts for (i) generation of residuals from production and consumption with possibilities of input substitution and scale changes, (ii) modification possibilities, (iii) diffusion in the environment, (iv) effects on the services provided by the environment, and (v) the evaluation of environmental changes through utility functions and impact on available resources.

Although the analysis is built upon residuals measurable in physical units as generating disutility, the Z-vector in the utility function can be given a broader interpretation of "generic congestion" suggested in Rothenberg (1970) [see also Førsund (1972)].

This model overcomes some of the shortcomings of the mass balance model in Kneese et al. (1970) [cf. criticism in Converse (1971) and Noll and Trijonis (1971)], e.g. fixed coefficients in production and no generation of costs by residual discharges.

Identifying consumers, producers, locations, etc., one could now proceed to derive Pareto-optimal rules for allocation of resources [see Førsund (1973)]. The purpose of this chapter, however, is to evaluate the usefulness of environmental analysis carried out on an aggregate national level within the framework of standard national economic planning models.

2. Macroeconomic models and the environment

2.1. Introduction

Pollution problems are locally experienced problems in the sense that it is the environmental services of geographically located environmental media that are negatively affected by the discharge of residuals. It follows, then, that regional empirical studies are called for to implement policy measures in the "problem sheds" of a river basin, an estuary, the air over a city, etc. (see Chapters 3 and 7 of this Handbook).

On a national level models of the interactions of economic activities have become useful and important tools of macroeconomic policymaking in most countries [see, for example, Brody and Carter (1972), Polenske and Skolka (1976)]. The pervasive nature of residuals generation brought out by the material balance approach of Ayres and Kneese (1969) and portrayed in a general equilibrium setting in the previous section, made it quite natural to investigate the possibility of exploring the usefulness of incorporating environmental services like residuals disposal and extraction into comprehensive national economic model frameworks. As an abstraction it is, of course, straightforward to envisage environmental service categories at the same level as economic activities in national models. It remains to be argued, however, that such an aggregation serves more than pedagogical purposes.

2.2. Input–output approach

"One of the most important responses by economists to environmental problems has been to extend the application of input–output models to the examination of relationships between economic activity and the emission of pollutant materials" [Cumberland and Stram (1976, p. 368)].

The natural extension of input–output (I–O) models to represent interactions between the environment and economic activities was pointed out by several economists in the late sixties–early seventies [see, for example, Cumberland (1966), Daly (1968), Isard (1969), Victor (1972), Hite and Laurent (1972)]. The extension proposed by Leontief (1970, 1973) has received special attention [Leontief and Ford (1972), Flick (1974), Steenge (1978), Lowe (1978), Moore (1980), Lee (1982), Rhee and Miranowski (1984)].

The generation of primary residuals in the economy may be represented as

$$Z = g(V, Y), \tag{8}$$

by combining eqs. (1) and (2), and reinterpreting vectors V and Y as intermediate delivery and final demands, respectively. In addition to entering a linearized version of (8), Leontief (1970, 1973) also entered a pollution abatement sector, i.e. a representation of the modification function (4) with secondary residuals as outputs and primary residuals and intermediate deliveries as inputs. This latter extension has not been followed up empirically. Representing basically end-of-pipe treatment, such a representation may lose empirical relevance as a certain catch-up phase of existing industries is over and pollutant generation is more and more influenced by changing the basic production technologies when new production capacity is installed. Also, Leontief's emphasis on "pollutant elimination" does not convey satisfactorily the materials balance principle of preservation of matter.

Basing the accounting framework on the recommended U.N. classification of make and absorption matrices [United Nations (1968)], Victor (1972) has presented a most comprehensive extension of the *I–O* model. The basic layout is presented in Table 8.1. [See also Daly (1968).]

The commodity–industry approach is the most appropriate one for modeling residuals as byproducts of production and consumption activities. The general question of whether to adopt a commodity or sector technology structure [Armstrong (1975)] also applies here. In the case of residuals being linked to specific inputs a commodity technology is the most appropriate, i.e. a residual has

Table 8.1
An extended input–output table

Delivering \ Receiving	Commodities	Industries	Final demand	Totals	Environment: Air, land, water
Commodities		Input of commodity by industry	Input of commodity to final demand		Discharge of residuals by use of commodity in final demand
Industries	Output of commodities by industry				Discharge of residuals by industry
Primary inputs, imports					
Totals					
Environment: Air, land, water		Input of extraction and recreation services to industry	Input of extraction and recreation services to final demand		

the same input structure of commodities in whichever industry it is generated. The industry technology assumption means that all residuals generated by an industry have the same input structure irrespective of which commodity is produced.

The more disaggregated the commodity industry is, the more realistic the assumption of fixed coefficients in residuals generations. A detailed data set is, however, not easy to obtain. Empirical studies have so far been restricted to an industry-by-industry format of the $I\!-\!O$ model, except for the commodity–industry approach in Victor (1972) [but with residuals linked to *industry* output by fixed discharge coefficients; see Leontief and Ford (1972), Hite and Laurent (1972), Cumberland and Stram (1976), Førsund and Strøm (1976), den Hartog and Houweling (1976), and an excellent survey and evaluation of $I\!-\!O$ models and environmental applications in James et al. (1978)].

The industry–industry $I\!-\!O$ model is extended to cover generation of residuals by assuming that each industry generates residuals in fixed proportions to sector output, and the same applies to final demand categories. The generation of residuals is assumed identical to the discharge of residuals, i.e. modification activities are internalized in the sector production technologies. A matrix, D^a, of such coefficients, d_{ij}^a, transferring the discharge to receptor type a (a = air, land, water) of residual type i generated per unit of output in industry j and a matrix F^a of coefficients, f_{ik}^a, transferring discharge to receptor of type a of residual type i generated by final demand category k, can be directly plugged into the standard solutions of $I\!-\!O$ models yielding the total amount of residuals accompanying menus of final demand:

$$Z^a = D^a (I - A)^{-1} Y + F^a Y = T^a Y, \tag{9}$$

where

Z^a = vector of residuals, with element Z_i^a,
  a = air, land, water, i = type of residual,
D^a = matrix of fixed discharge coefficients with elements d_{ij}^a computed as Z_{ij}^a / X_j for the base year,
X^j = gross production of industry j,
A = technology matrix of fixed input–output coefficients with elements a_{ij} computed as V_{ij}/X_j, where V_{ij} is the intermediate delivery from sector i to sector j,
Y = final demand vector (including imports) with element Y_k,
F = matrix of fixed discharge coefficients with elements f_{ik}^a computed as Z_{ik}^a / Y_k for the base year,
T^a = matrix of total final demand discharge coefficients, t_{ik}^a, showing total discharge of residual i to receptor a per unit of final demand category k.

It has been suggested that economic growth should be slowed down, or even stopped (ZEG), in order to protect the quality of the environment. Utilizing eq.

(9) we may calculate the costs of reducing discharge levels of residuals. Keeping the composition of final demand fixed "residual reduction cost coefficients", S_i^a, can be calculated as follows:

$$S_i^a = 1 \Big/ \sum_k t_{ik}^a \cdot \gamma_k = S/Z_i^a, \tag{10}$$

where γ_k is the share of final demand k, of total available bill of goods, S (i.e. gross national product plus imports).

Reducing discharges of residuals by a uniform reduction of final demands was one of several possibilities mentioned in Section 1. It would probably be the most expensive way of reducing discharge of residuals [see Førsund and Strøm (1976) for an empirical illustration].

2.3. Projection studies

"Input–output economic models, because of their logical structure and consistency with the physical concept of mass balance provide a promising basis upon which to build models needed to evaluate alternative economic-environmental options for the future" [Cumberland and Stram (1976, p. 381)].

Equation (9) may be used as a basis for projecting future levels of discharge of residuals. Inserting a projected vector of final demands directly yields the corresponding levels of residuals discharged. Such point-of-time projections are found in Leontief and Ford (1972), Cumberland and Stram (1976) and Kneese and Bower (1979). Leontief and Ford also identify the impact of a change in the *composition* of final demand from a base year to a future year. In such projection exercises it is also straightforward to include changes in the *I–O* coefficient matrix, A [done in Leontief and Ford (1972)] and the discharge coefficient matrices D^a and F^a.

In general, residuals discharge matrices can be plugged into any national multisectoral growth model and pollution consequences of different growth paths traced. In countries where input–output coefficients are updated yearly (as in Norway), repeated computations of final demand "menus" will show up any trend in the accompanying residuals generation.

A projection study is done in Førsund and Strøm (1974) on the basis of a multisectoral growth model. The interdependencies among the 26 production sectors through intermediate deliveries are treated in an *I–O* framework, but as regards input of capital and labor the assumption of fixed coefficients are replaced by neoclassical production functions of the Cobb–Douglas type. The allocation of exogenously given *total* labor force and capital on the sectors is governed by the rule of value of marginal products equal to factor prices. The demand for sectoral outputs is partly exogenous, e.g. exports and government demand, and partly endogenous. Private consumption functions for goods composed of sectoral outputs are specified.

The main outputs of the model are exogenously determined growth rates for sectoral production, product prices and allocation of labor and capital on the sectors. The model typically generates nonproportional expansion of industries. This latter feature has important consequences for the pattern of residuals generation in the future. Due to the relative decline of primary sectors and an increased share of service industries in the economy several important pollutants increase at a rate significantly less than the average growth rate of the national economy.

2.4. Macroeconomic impacts of abatement activities

The environmental protection programs undertaken in recent years in most of the industrialized countries have been of such magnitude that their macroeconomic impacts have become of some concern, especially effects on inflation, employment, productivity, and economic growth. [See OECD (1982) and Chapter 9 of this Handbook.]

Analyses of price effects of abatement activities may be undertaken within an *I–O* model by means of the standard static value-added price equations:

$$p_j = \sum_i p_i a_{ji} + \sum_h q_h b_{hj}, \tag{11}$$

$$P = QB(I - A)^{-1}, \tag{12}$$

where

p_j = product price of sector j,
q_h = price of primary factor h,
b_{hj} = unit requirement of primary factor h in sector j.

Yearly capital costs of abatement equipment, maintenance, and running costs shift the value-added coefficients, QB [see Leontief and Ford (1972), Evans (1973), Hollenbeck (1979), Mutti and Richardson (1976, 1977), Pasurka (1984)]. (In principle, running operation of abatement equipment using intermediate deliveries should be registered as changes in input–output coefficients, a_{ij}.) The assumption of complete passing on of costs implied by (11) may, of course, be modified to accommodate actual mark-up behavior.

In order to study employment effects of pollution abatement, it is necessary to introduce demand functions for final demand categories and make assumptions about the degree to which abatement investments crowd out other investment. Price increases reduce demand, and thereby employment, while if abatement investment crowds out other investment activities completely, employment effects are bound to be adverse.

3. The generation of residuals in the Norwegian economy 1978[1]

At present, data on discharge of residuals are not collected in such a way that they can readily be utilized in an economic model; partly due to the fact that residuals generating units when collecting residuals data differ from the basic establishment unit of the national accounts, and partly due to excessively detailed information as regards residuals. In total, 37 types of residuals have been constructed for the Norwegian economy. The establishment of discharge coefficients for 1978 has thus involved solving a number of aggregation problems and filling in information by intuition, hunch, and rule of thumb rather than factual measurement. There are three sets of discharge coefficients relating to the receptors air, water, and land.

The sector classification of the input–output model of the Norwegian economy developed by the Central Bureau of Statistics, MODIS IV, is rather detailed, consisting of 123 production sectors. The I–O model is organized on a commodity–sector basis. However, data did not permit establishing commodity discharge coefficients. The discharge coefficients are related to the production sectors instead, implying that the commodities produced by a sector generate the same amount of residuals per unit of output.

Table 8.2

Main categories of final demand. Discharges to air caused by and increase of 100 million N.cr. in final deliveries to each of the main final demand categories (in tons)

	Total export	Government consumption	Total gross asset formation	Total private consumption
Mercury	0.000	0.000	0.000	0.000
Lead	0.098	0.118	0.039	0.216
Sulfur oxides	129.486	7.857	19.977	13.578
Hydrochloric acid	0.133			
Nitrogen oxides	12.814	0.623	2.393	1.720
Other acids	0.039	0.047	0.008	
Fluorine	1.873	0.001	0.067	0.000
Chlorine	1.899	0.001	0.004	0.001
Carbon monoxide	6.272	7.472	2.727	13.634
Nitrogen compounds	7.421	8.396	2.835	15.380
Mine tailings, inorganic sludge and dust	199.724	68.692	28.263	125.421
Aliphetic halogenated hydrocarbons	1.385	0.094	0.170	0.197
Oil and products of oil	18.021	18.169	6.221	33.285
Taste- and smell-producing substances	0.167	0.042	0.089	0.050
Organic solvents	0.132	0.022	0.066	0.100

[1] The empirical work was carried out by Miss Rønnaug Teige.

3.1. The pollution content of final demand

An $I-O$ model is traditionally solved to yield the relationship between a given vector of final demands and the level of sector products. By multiplying the latter with the discharge matrices the accompanying pollution levels are readily found.

Table 8.3

Main categories of final demand. Discharges to water caused by an increase of 100 million N.cr. in final deliveries to each of the main final demand categories (in tons)

	Total export	Government consumption	Total gross fixed asset formation	Total private consumption
Mercury	0.000	0.000	0.000	0.000
Lead	0.932	0.000	0.000	0.000
Cadmium	0.004	0.000	0.000	0.000
Zinc	1.555	0.001	0.005	0.001
Copper	0.529	0.000	0.001	0.000
Iron	24.306	0.984	3.004	0.991
Chrome	4.580	0.000	0.004	0.032
Sulfur oxides	117.799	4.584	10.217	3.805
Hydrochloric acid	6.106	0.002	0.006	0.002
Nitrogen oxides	1.237	1.037	0.173	0.125
Other acids	3.144	0.094	0.082	0.044
Soda lye	1.722	0.045	0.301	0.156
Other bases	27.673	0.001	0.008	0.000
Fluorine	5.252	0.061	0.309	0.061
Cyanide	0.181	0.017	0.068	0.017
Chlorine	0.259	0.000	0.016	0.016
Arsenic	0.175	0.000	0.001	0.000
Phosphorus compounds	0.632	0.006	0.021	0.102
Nitrogen compounds	10.015	0.572	0.502	0.199
Mine tailings, inorganic sludge and dust	13.644	31.469	205.447	12.829
Aliphetic halogenated hydrocarbons	0.004		0.001	0.000
Other halogenated hydrocarbons	3.858	0.003	0.241	0.249
Bark	5.309		0.201	0.201
Fiber	36.365	1.161	3.409	3.042
Biologically decomposable organic substances	171.960	2.311	14.103	23.082
Oil and products of oil	4.674	0.495	0.705	2.164
Disperging agents	0.233	0.010	0.145	0.130
Taste- and smell-producing substances	0.050	0.007	0.029	0.007
Substances with acute poisonous effect	0.615			
Organic solvents	0.303	0.145	0.019	0.087
Waste, unspecified	149.884			2.415

Table 8.4

Main categories of final demand. Discharges to land caused by an increase of 100 million
N.cr. in final deliveries to each of the main demand categories (in tons)

	Total export	Government consumption	Total gross fixed asset formation	Total private consumption
Mercury	0.035			
Lead	1.149		0.000	
Mine tailings, inorganic sludge and dust	868.824	57.845	510.514	30.046
Pesticides	0.009		0.009	
Bark	134.052	9.028	18.945	15.799
Plastic substances	0.127	0.029	0.049	0.039
Oil and products of oil	0.004		0.002	
Waste, unspecified	88.082	3.433		62.501

As regards foreign trade fixed import coefficients are assumed, and final
demand is calculated inclusive of imports.

The final demand categories are organized in four main categories: total
export; government consumption; total gross fixed asset formation; and total
private consumption. Total export may then be further split in seven categories
and private consumption in fourteen categories. The results presented in Tables
8.2–8.4 are all based on an increase of 100 million Norwegian crowns (N.cr.) in
each of the final demand categories at a time, i.e. the resulting discharge of the
residuals in question when *one* final demand category is increased by one unit
(100 million N.cr.) and all other final demand levels are kept constant.

3.2. Discharge to air

Of the four main categories, Table 8.2 shows that Export has the highest unit
discharges of most of the residuals. This is especially the case for Sulfur oxides,
Nitrogen oxides, and Dust. Notable exceptions are Carbon monoxide and Hydrocarbons where Private consumption takes the lead.

The splitting up of Export reveals that Pulp and paper with Metals in second
position have substantial "unit discharges" of sulfur oxides. Metals has the lion's
share of Fluorine, Chlorine, and Dust. Chemicals has the highest unit discharge of
Nitrogen oxides and compounds and Hydrocarbons. The strength of the *I–O*
approach is to reveal unexpected results due to the interactions in the economy.
We may note when splitting up Private consumption that the category Schooling,
etc. generates substantial amounts of Sulfur oxides, Dust, and Hydrocarbons due
to intermediate deliveries from Pulp and paper, and that "Medical care" generates more Dust than, for instance, Tobacco.

3.3. Discharge to water

There is a considerably higher number of residuals discharged to water than to the other two receptors. When looking at the four main categories, the unit levels are in general smaller than for air; the notable exception being Sludge.

Total export has, again, a totally dominating position, having the highest unit discharge for all residuals. Disaggregation shows that Pulp and paper account for nearly all of the discharge of Fiber and decomposable organic substance, whereas Chemical products has the highest unit discharge of Iron, Sulfur oxides, Nitrogen compounds, and Metals the highest by far for Mine tailings, Sludge, etc.

Private consumption generates residuals on a very moderate scale. The dominating residual (in weight) is Decomposable organic substances, where Edible fats, etc. has the highest unit discharge. One may, again, note that Schooling, etc. has relatively high discharges of several residuals due to inter-mediate deliveries from Pulp and paper. A relatively large unit discharge of Iron from beverages stems from intermediate deliveries from the chemical sector.

3.4. Discharge to land

The discharges to land are rather limited, the most important being Mine tailings, etc. and Bark. Again, Exports dominates for all residuals, but Gross fixed asset formation has also a substantial unit discharge of Mine tailings. Within Exports, a disaggregation reveals that Metals has the dominating unit discharge of Mine tailings, etc. and Pulp and paper has the dominating unit discharge of Bark.

Intermediate deliveries from the corresponding production sectors show up in the unit discharges from Private consumption categories when disaggregated. Schooling, etc. now gets the highest unit discharge of Bark.

3.5. Concluding remarks

The most dominating final demand categories of the Norwegian economy 1978 turned out to be the export categories Pulp and paper, and Metals. These correspond directly to production sectors. Intermediate deliveries from these production sectors account for much of the residuals generated when increasing other categories of final demand.

4. The usefulness of extending national economic models to cover interactions between the environment and economic activities

It is, of course, to be expected that the proponents of an *I–O* approach to analyze environmental repercussions offer favorable arguments for such approaches.

Leontief (1970, p. 262), for example, claims that "...conventional input–output computations can yield concrete replies to some of the fundamental factual questions that should be asked and answered before a practical solution can be found to problems raised by the environmental effects of modern technology and uncontrolled economic growth".

As pointed out in Section 2.1, practical problems have to be found on a quite more disaggregated level than national economic models (this aspect is developed in Chapters 3 and 7 of this Handbook). However, Leontief's point concerns the planning phase prior to such decisions.

A basic point to be made is that it is necessary to put environmental considerations on the map when macroeconomic decisions, which have environmental repercussions, are made. Various environmental impact data collected by environmental management bodies can be systematized and organized in a meaningful way linking economic activities and the environment. Such linking efforts can in themselves increase the awareness of possible environmental consequences of economic activities.

As regards the actual utilization of environmental data on the national level, the "overriding superiority of the input–output approach lies in its systematic description of the environmental and economic repercussions..." [Lowe (1978, p. 110)]. The basic use of an $I-O$ model is to show the residuals generation (and use of extraction and recreation services if these are linked to economic activities) accompanying alternative patterns of final demand. Thus, returning to Section 1 about possibilities for influencing generation of residuals, reducing the amounts of polluting residuals by reducing levels of economic activity can be thoroughly investigated by changing scale and composition of final demand.

Final demand categories posing potential pollution problems can be identified. As regards the case study of Norway, Export had the highest "pollution content" of the final demand categories for almost all types of residuals. Following the direct and indirect deliveries to final demand yields the industries with the most significant contributions. The more pervasive the generation of residuals the more necessary is the $I-O$ approach.

The various actions possible to reduce pollutant generation will change the discharge coefficients (d_{ij}^a and f_{ik}^a in Section 2.2). An $I-O$ model offers a consistent framework for assessing impacts of changing discharge coefficients due to modification activities, investments in new technology, etc. To come closer to a more realistic assessment of pollution problems, the generation of residuals within the national model may be a point of departure for more refined analyses based on disaggregated regional, or problem shed, ecological models reviewed in Chapter 7 of this Handbook.

As regards abatement policy in general, the $I-O$ model traces the impact of abatement activities on the other economic magnitudes, e.g. employment levels and price increases [see OECD (1982)]. The magnitude involved when dealing with pollution problems is clearly revealed in macroeconomic terms by means of the $I-O$ analysis. As regards Norway, the reduction of pollution from existing industry found politically satisfactory by the Ministry of Environment required about 1 percent of industry investment over a ten-year period, increasing inflation by maximum one percent and having a very small impact on net employment [OECD (1982)].

References

Armstrong, A.G. (1975) "Technology Assumptions in the Construction of U.K. Input–Output Tables", in: R.I.G. Allen and W.F. Gossling (eds.), *Estimating and Projecting Input–Output Coefficients* (Input–Output, London).

Ayres, R.U. and A.V. Kneese (1969) "Production, Consumption and Externalities", *American Economic Review* 59, 282–297.

Brody, A. and A.P. Carter (eds.) (1972) *Input–Output Techniques* (North-Holland, Amsterdam).

Converse, A.O. (1971) "On the Extension of Input–Output Analysis to Account for Environmental Externalities", *American Economic Review* 61, 197–198.

Cumberland, J.H. (1966) "A Regional Interindustry Model for Analysis of Development Objectives", *Regional Science Association Papers* 17, 65–94.

Cumberland, J.H. and B.N. Stram (1976) "Empirical Results from Application of Input–Output Models to Environmental Problems", in: K.R. Polenske and J.V. Skolka (eds.), *Advances in Input–Output Analysis* (Ballinger, Cambridge) 365–382.

Daly, H.E. (1968) "On Economics as a Life Science", *Journal of Political Economy* 76, no. 1, 392–406.

Den Hartog, H. and A. Houweling (1976) "Pollution, Pollution Abatement and the Economic Structure: Empirical Results of Input–Output Computations for the Netherlands", in: K.R. Polenske and J.V. Skolka (eds.), *Advances in Input–Output Analysis* (Ballinger, Cambridge) 389–408.

Evans, M.K. (1973) "A Forecasting Model Applied to Pollution Control Costs", *The American Economic Review, Papers and Proceedings* 63, no. 2, 244–252.

Flick, W.A. (1974) "Environmental Repercussions and the Economic Structure: An Input–Output Approach: A Comment", *The Review of Economics and Statistics* 56, 107–109.

Førsund, F.R. (1972) "Allocation in Space and Environmental Pollution," *The Swedish Journal of Economics*, 74, no. 1, 19–34.

Førsund, F.R. (1973) "Externalities, Environmental Pollution and Allocation in Space: A General Equilibrium Approach," *Regional Urban Economics*, 3, 3–32.

Førsund, F.R. and S. Strøm (1974) "Industrial Structure, Growth and Residual Flows," in: J.G. Rothenberg and I.G. Heggie (eds.), *The Management of Water Quality and the Environment* (Macmillan, London) pp. 21–69.

Førsund, F.R. and S. Strøm (1976) "The Generation of Residual Flows in Norway: An Input–Output Approach", *Journal of Environmental Economics and Management* 3, 129–141.

Hite, J.C. and E.A. Laurent (1972) *Environmental Planning: An Economic Analysis* (Praeger, New York).

Hollenbeck, K. (1979) "The Employment and Earnings Impacts of the Regulation of Stationary Source Air Pollution", *Journal of Environmental Economics and Management* 6, no. 3, 208–221.

Isard, W. (1969) "Some Notes on the Linkage of the Ecologic and Economic Systems", *Regional Science Association, Papers and Proceedings*, 22, 85–96.

James, D.E., H.M.A. Jansen and J.B. Opschoor (1978) *Economic Approaches to Environmental Problems* (Elsevier, Amsterdam–Oxford–New York).

Kneese, A.V., R.U. Ayres and R.C. d'Arge (1970) *Economics and the Environment: A Materials Balance Approach* (The Johns Hopkins Press, Baltimore).

Kneese, A.V. and B.T. Bower (1979), *Environmental Quality and Residuals Management* (The Johns Hopkins University Press, Baltimore–London).

Lee, K.-S. (1982) "A Generalized Input–Output Model of an Economy with Environmental Protection", *The Review of Economics and Statistics* 64, no. 3, 466–473.

Leontief, W. (1970) "Environmental Repercussions and the Economic Structure: An Input–Output Approach", *The Review of Economics and Statistics* 52, 262–271.

Leontief, W. (1973) "National Income, Economic Structure, and Environmental Externalities", in: M. Moss (ed.), *The Measurement of Economic and Social Performance* (National Bureau of Economic Research, New York) pp. 565–576.

Leontief, W. (1974) "A Reply", *The Review of Economics and Statistics* 56, 109–110.

Leontief, W. and D. Ford (1972) "Air Pollution and the Economic Structure: Empirical Results of Input–Output Computations", in: A. Brody and A.P. Carter (eds.), *Input–Output Techniques* (North-Holland, Amsterdam–London) 9–30.

Lowe, P.D. (1978) "Pricing Problems in an Input–Output Approach to Environment Protection", *The Review of Economics and Statistics* 60, 110–117.

Meyer, R.A., Jr. (1971) "Private Costs of Using Public Goods", *The Southern Economic Journal* 37, no. 4, 479–488.

Moore, S.A. (1980) "Environmental Repercussions and the Economic Structure: Some Further Comments", *The Review of Economics and Statistics* 62, 139–142.

Mutti, J.H. and J. Richardson (1976) "Industrial Displacement through Environmental Controls", in: I. Walter (ed.), *Studies in International Environmental Economics* (John Wiley & Sons, New York) pp. 57–102.

Mutti, J.H. and J. Richardson (1977) "International Competitive Displacement from Environmental Control", *Journal of Environmental Economics and Management* 4, no. 2, 135–152.

Noll, R.G. and J. Trijonis (1971) "Mass Balance, General Equilibrium an Environmental Externalities", *American Economic Review* 61, no. 4, 730–735.

OECD (1982) "Macro-Economic Effects of Environmental Policies", Environment committee group of economic experts (Paris).

Pasurka, C.A. Jr. (1984) "The Short-Run Impact of Environmental Protection Costs on U.S. Product Prices", *Journal of Environmental Economics and Management* 11, no. 4, 380–390.

Polenske, K.R. and J.V. Skolka (eds.) (1976) *Advances in Input–Output Analysis* (Ballinger, Cambridge).

Rhee, J.J. and J.A. Miranowski (1984) "Determination of Income, Production and Employment under Pollution Control: An Input–Output Approach", *The Review of Economics and Statistics* 64, no. 1, 146–150.

Rothenberg, J. (1970) "The Economics of Congestion and Pollution: An Integrated View", *The American Economic Association, Papers and Proceedings* 60, 114–121.

Russell, C.S. and W.O. Spofford, Jr. (1972) "A Quantitative Framework for Residuals Management Decisions", in: A.V. Kneese and B.T. Bower (eds.), Environmental Quality Analysis: Theory and Method in the Social Sciences (The Johns Hopkins Press, Baltimore–London) pp. 115–179.

Steenge, A. (1978) "Environmental Repercussions and the Economic Structure: Further Comments", *The Review of Economics and Statistics*, 60: August, 482–486.

Stevens, J. (1966) "Recreation Benefits from Water Pollution Control", Water Resources Research, 2: 167–182.

United Nations (1968) "A System of National Accounts", *Studies in Methods*, series F, no. 2 (New York).

Victor, P.A. (1972) *Pollution: Economy and Environment* (Allen and Unwin, London).

PART 3

THE ECONOMICS OF ENVIRONMENTAL POLICY

Chapter 9

DISTRIBUTIONAL AND MACROECONOMIC ASPECTS OF ENVIRONMENTAL POLICY

G.B. CHRISTAINSEN

California State University, Hayward

and

T.H. TIETENBERG*

Colby College, Waterville

1. Introduction

1.1. An overview of the chapter

The achievement of an efficient balance between the economic system and the environment is just one of many societal objectives. How environmental policy affects these other objectives is important because these impacts may serve to constrain the set of politically feasible policies, may recommend some approaches over others or may provide guidance as to the most appropriate timing of policy implementation.[1]

Two effects of environmental policy have been singled out in the literature as deserving special attention – distributional effects and macroeconomic effects. The former concerns how the costs and benefits of environmental policy are distributed among socioeconomic groups and among geographic regions. The latter concerns the impact of environmental policy on important national aggregates such as inflation, unemployment and productivity.

In this chapter we shall survey what is known (and not known) about these effects. This survey includes an examination of the theoretical models which serve to identify the channels of influence, the data which provide the raw material for the estimates and the methods used to quantify the impacts. Our objective is to convey a sense of the magnitude of the impacts along with an appreciation for the reliability of these estimates for policy purposes. We begin with a brief description of the policies which have triggered the effects being estimated.

---

* Though this chapter is truly co-authored, Tom Tietenberg assumed the major responsibility for writing the first three sections while Greg Christainsen assumed the major responsibility for writing the macroeconomic section.

[1] Conceptual models of the environmental policy-making process which support the importance of these factors include those by Downing (1981) and Zeckhauser (1981). Empirical support can be found in Leone and Jackson (1977).

Handbook of Natural Resource and Energy Economics, vol. I, edited by A.V. Kneese and J.L. Sweeney
© *Elsevier Science Publishers B.V., 1985*

1.2. The policy context

Though the methods conventionally used to measure the impacts of environmental policy are widely applicable to a large array of potential policies, the numerical estimates relate to a very specific set of policies. To place those estimates in context, it is necessary to understand at least the broad outline of the policies being analyzed. Our discussion also serves as an introduction to the treatment of alternative policy instruments in the following chapter.

Most of the existing English language work has concentrated on the effects of U.S. air and water pollution control policies. Therefore to avoid spreading ourselves too thin we shall limit our focus to this literature.

1.2.1. Air pollution

For each of eight conventional pollutants (called "criteria" pollutants) the U.S. Environmental Protection Agency (EPA) has established ambient air quality standards. These standards set legal ceilings on the allowable concentration of the pollutant in the outdoor air averaged over some time period. Many pollutants have the standard defined both in terms of a long-term average (defined normally as an annual average) and a short-term average (e.g. a three-hour average). Compliance with the standard usually requires that these short-term averages be exceeded no more than once a year. These standards have to be met everywhere, though as a practical matter they are monitored at a large number of specific locations.

The *primary standard* is designed to protect human health. It is supposed to be set at a sufficiently stringent level that even the most sensitive members of the population are protected. This is the first standard to be determined and it has the earliest deadlines for compliance. All pollutants have a primary standard. For some pollutants a *secondary standard*, designed to protect aspects of human welfare other than health for those pollutants where such separate effects have been observed, has also been established. Currently only sulphur oxides and particulates have separate secondary standards. Forms of human welfare protected by the secondary standard include aesthetics (particularly visibility), damage to physical objects (e.g. houses and monuments) and damage to vegetation. The secondary standard is more stringent than the primary standard whenever the pollutant has effects on welfare; it is never less stringent. Therefore, once the deadline for compliance with the secondary standard has been reached, it, rather than the primary standard, tends to govern the degree of required control.

EPA has the responsibility for defining the ambient standards, but the primary responsibility for ensuring that the ambient air quality standards are met falls on state air pollution control agencies. They exercise this responsibility by developing and executing an acceptable state implementation plan (SIP), which must be approved by the EPA. This plan divides the state up into separate air quality control regions. (There are special procedures for handling regions which cross state borders such as Metropolitan New York.) The SIP spells out, for each control region, procedures and time tables for meeting local ambient standards and for abatement of the effects of locally emitted pollutants on other states. The degree of control required by these plans depends on the severity of the pollution problem in each of the control regions.

By 1975 it had become apparent that despite some major gains in air quality, many areas (called "nonattainment" areas) had not met, and would not meet, the ambient standards for certain pollutants by the statutory deadlines. Subsequent statutes call for revised implementation plans for these regions providing for implementation of all "reasonably available control measures as expeditiously as practicable" on all existing sources and for "reasonable further progress" demonstrated on an annual basis toward meeting the standards. The former requirement mandates the specification of emission standards for existing sources, while the latter requires annual reductions in emissions of sufficient magnitude to guarantee compliance by the deadline.

Regions which were in attainment became subject to another set of controls known collectively as the PSD policy. This policy derives its name from its objective, namely the Prevention of Significant Deterioration of the air in cleaner regions. The PSD regulations specify maximum allowable increases or increments in pollution concentration beyond some baseline. In essence these regulations establish more stringent ambient standards for regions with relatively little pollution.

In addition to defining the ambient standards and requiring states to control sources in nonattainment and PSD regions, the EPA has itself established national, uniform emission standards for (1) hazardous pollutants, (2) new sources (or major modifications of existing sources) of criteria pollutants and (3) motor vehicles. The preemptive establishment of nationally uniform standards was seen as a way to prevent states from caving in under industry pressure. These standards serve as a floor on the regional degree of control placed on affected sources. The standards are much more stringent for new or modified sources than for existing sources.

Three major reforms have taken place recently which have the effect of reducing some of the regulatory burden by moving current policy closer to a market approach. These are the alternative emission reduction approach (known popularly as the "bubble" concept), the emissions offset policy, and emission reduction banking.

The "bubble" concept specifically allows existing emitters to trade a more relaxed degree of control on one source for a more stringent degree of control on another source of the same pollutant as long as total emissions are not increased by the substitution. These trades can, under certain circumstances, occur between plants or even between firms. The object, of course, is to allow a firm to meet its emission reduction goal as flexibly and cheaply as possible while insuring that air quality is not degraded by the trade.

The emission offset policy was originally designed as a means for allowing economic growth in nonattainment areas while insuring no further degradation of their air quality. It allows potential new entrants to a nonattainment area to procure sufficient reductions from existing firms (over and above their previous legal requirements) so as to offset the increases in pollution which would otherwise occur upon the initiation of production in the area by the new source.

Emission reductions banking is a system for allowing sources to reduce their emissions more than required and to bank the excess for subsequent sale. This portion of the program is designed to stimulate a market for newer, cheaper control techniques and to assure the availability of reductions which can be traded.

1.2.2. Water pollution

There are three major aspects of water pollution control legislation which are important for our purposes. The first aspect concerns the clean water goals established by Congress. The preamble of the Clean Water Act calls for the achievement of two goals: (1) "...that the discharge of pollutants into the navigable waters be eliminated by 1985" and (2) "...that wherever attainable, an interim goal of water quality which provides for the protection and propagation of fish, shellfish, and wildlife and provides for recreation in and on the water be achieved by July 1, 1983".

There were two main programs created to pursue these goals, though, as was recognized at the time, these programs would not be sufficient to eliminate discharges. The first involved EPA-determined effluent standards for discharges. This was implemented by requiring sources of pollution to secure permits. These permits would be granted only when the discharges met certain technology-based effluent standards.

According to the 1972 Water Pollution Control Amendments the effluent standards were to be implemented in two stages. By 1977 industrial sources, as a condition of their permit, were required to meet effluent limitations based on the "best practicable control technology currently available" (BPT). In addition all publicly-owned waste treatment plants were to have achieved secondary treatment by 1977. By 1983 industrial sources were required to meet effluent limitations based on the presumably more stringent "best available technology economically achievable" (BAT) while publicly-owned waste treatment plants were required to meet effluent limitations which depended upon the "best practicable waste treatment technology".

The second prong in the two-pronged U.S. water quality control strategy involved federal financial support for the construction of waste treatment plants.

Under this program municipalities could receive federal grants to cover up to 55 percent (subsequently raised to 75 percent in 1972 and lowered again to 55 in 1981) of the construction of municipal sewage treatment plants. This approach not only lowered the cost to the local government of constructing these facilities, it also lowered the cost to any who used them. The key aspect of this program for the purposes of this chapter was that, in contrast to other strategies for pollution control, this program was directly funded by tax revenues. This creates a rather different incidence of the burden of control than policies funded by wage decreases, dividend reductions or price increases. Alternative environmental policy instruments are discussed in the following chapter.

2. The incidence of pollution control costs on individual industries

2.1. The initial incidence

The initial incidence of much of the current pollution control policy falls on industry. In order to comply with environmental regulations industries have had to invest a considerable amount of capital in pollution-control equipment. The proportions of new plant and equipment expenditures allocated to this purpose by industry are recorded in Table 9.1.

The data in that table suggest that the proportion of new plant equipment expenditures going to pollution control in the average industry is large, though it has diminished since the middle 1970s. These data also suggest that according to this way of measuring it the distribution of the cost burden among industries is quite uneven.

The ultimate incidence of this burden will depend on the ability of firms to shift this initial cost burden to consumers by raising prices or to workers in the form of lower employment, lower wages, or both or to shareholders through smaller dividends. The ability of the analyst to estimate the magnitudes of these shifts will depend on a knowledge of the variables which are relevant and their impact on the ultimate incidence.

2.2. Incidence shifting

In order to understand the conditions under which costs can be passed forward or backward we begin with a simple partial equilibrium model of how an industry reacts to a change in its cost structure when faced by a stable demand schedule. To get at the essence of the problem without unnecessary details consider a perfectly competitive, constant cost industry which is composed of a large number of identical firms. We assume that this industry is initially in long run equilibrium as pictured in Figure 9.1. Faced with the market determined price of P^0 the representative firm would maximize profits by producing q^0. Since the price is

Table 9.1

Percent of new plant and equipment expenditures by nonfarm business on
pollution control

	1975[a]	1980[b]	1981[b]	Planned 1982[b]
Total nonfarm business	5.8	3.1	2.8	2.7
Manufacturing	9.3	4.8	4.3	4.2
Durable goods	8.1	3.9	3.2	3.3
Primary metals[c]	17.2	12.7	9.6	9.7
Blast furnaces, steel works	13.5	18.5	15.5	12.5
Nonferrous metals	24.1	8.7	6.6	8.8
Fabricated metals	NA	2.4	2.4	2.1
Electrical machinery	5.8	1.7	1.7	1.9
Machinery, except electrical	1.8	1.3	1.1	1.2
Transportation equipment[c]	3.4	2.9	2.5	2.6
Motor vehicles	3.9	4.3	3.5	4.0
Aircraft	2.8	1.4	1.6	1.4
Stone, clay and glass	14.3	6.5	5.1	5.3
Other durables[d]	5.3	2.8	2.8	3.2
Nondurable goods	10.3	5.7	5.3	5.2
Food including beverage	5.2	3.7	3.6	3.3
Textiles	4.6	4.3	3.2	3.3
Paper	16.8	5.7	5.7	7.1
Chemicals	10.9	5.8	6.5	6.3
Petroleum	11.8	8.3	6.6	5.9
Rubber	4.0	1.7	2.3	3.0
Other nondurables[e]	2.8	0.7	0.6	0.6
Nonmanufacturing	3.2	2.1	1.8	1.7
Mining	1.9	3.6	2.7	3.3
Transportation	NA	0.9	0.7	1.0
Railroad	1.4	0.9	0.9	1.3
Air	0.6	0.2	0.3	0.5
Other	1.4	1.8	1.3	1.2
Public utilities	8.4	8.1	7.3	6.7
Electric	9.7	10.0	9.1	8.3
Gas and other	1.5	1.0	1.0	0.8
Trade and services	NA	0.2	0.1	0.1
Communication and other[f]	0.6	0.1	0.1	0.1

[a]*Survey of Current Business* Vol. 58 (June 1978), p. 34.

[b]*Survey of Current Business* Vol. 62 (June 1982), p. 18. Percentage was derived by dividing total pollution abatement expenditure by total new plant and equipment expenditures.

[c]Includes industries not shown separately.

[d]Consists of lumber, furniture, instruments, and miscellaneous.

[e]Consists of apparel, tobacco, leather, and printing-publishing.

[f]Consists of communication, construction, social services and membership organizations, and forestry, fisheries and agricultural services.

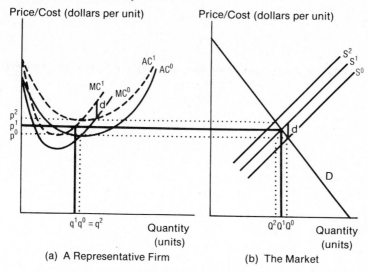

Figure 9.1. Market reactions to pollution control costs.

equal to average cost at q^0, economic profits are zero. There would be no incentive for firms to enter or exit the industry.

Suppose that this equilibrium was disturbed by an EPA regulation forcing each firm to reduce its pollution. Suppose further that the effect of this regulation on the industry can be reflected as a uniform upward shift in the marginal and average cost curves by a vertical distance d. The market supply curve would shift up by d as well. The market price would rise from P^0 to P^1, an increase less than d. Since revenues would fall short of costs, the exit of some firms in the industry would result.

This departure is reflected in market supply as a further shift leftward. The magnitude of the shift is determined by the amount of exit needed to restore the equality of price and average cost. This occurs at price P^2, which is exactly d greater than P^0. The market produces the smaller amount Q^2, but each remaining firm produces the same amount it did before the increase in cost.

2.2.1. The effect of economies of scale and market power

The result that all remaining firms produce the same amount arises from our assumption that the marginal cost curve shifts uniformly upward by d. If the marginal cost curve were not uniformly shifted upward, the firm would not produce the same amount before and after the increase in costs because its economies of scale would have been affected. It appears that there are economies of scale in water pollution control [see Hanke and Gutmanis (1975) and Pittman

(1981)] so that the remaining firms may be larger after pollution control measures
are implemented than before. To some unknown extent this effect may be offset
by the EPA tendency to concentrate enforcement on larger sources.

The effect of pollution control expenditures on any industry also depends on
the market structure of that industry. In a monopoly, the entry of new firms
would not occur with or without environmental controls. The absence of this
pressure changes the way in which a typical firm would react to pollution control
regulations. As long as the competitive industry and the monopoly face identical
market demand curves the monopoly would reduce production by a smaller
amount than would the competitive industry. Thus the effect on employment
would be smaller in a monopoly than in a comparable competitive industry. To
some extent, a monopolist insulates its workers from cost shocks.

2.2.2. The effect of the new source bias

As was discussed in the policy section of this chapter, the current regulatory
approach focuses mainly on new sources; as a result of this focus the costs for
new sources are typically raised by more than the costs for old sources. Under the
conditions of stable demand studied above this would not make any difference,
since firms would be exiting, not entering. However, if demand were increasing
over time, in the absence of pollution control regulations firms would normally be
entering, rather than exiting, the industry. Due to their higher costs (resulting
from the new source bias of the regulations) the entrance of new firms would be
delayed and their market share would be smaller than would be the case with
regulations affecting old and new plants to the same degree. Existing plants
benefit from this new source bias in the regulations. Since the new firms are
higher cost producers (due to their higher pollution control costs), their profits
would be bid to zero, but the existing firms will receive a form of Ricardian rent
which would not be eliminated by competition.

Koch and Leone (1979) have shown that the tissue industry has experienced
precisely this kind of circumstance. They found that in the long run the high costs
of compliance for new facilities led to an eventual price increase that exceeded the
increase in average cost. In addition to eliminating the normal equivalence
between price and average cost found in the simple model this differential
regulation effect would tend to make the burden of labor in existing plants
smaller than it would otherwise be.

Other studies seem to confirm the fact that current regulations have increased,
rather than reduced, the value of existing firms by limiting competition from
potential entrants. Maloney and McCormick (1982), for example, found evidence
of this in several different industries. When OSHA imposed a standard limiting
the amount of cotton dust workers in textile plants could be exposed to, new and
old firms faced very different compliance costs. The authors' examination of stock

prices revealed that a number of textile firms affected by the standard registered an increase in value at the same time as OSHA announced its proposed standards. Moreover, the value increases were positively related to the fraction of cotton used by the firms in their production. This finding suggests that the worth of existing plants was increased, not reduced, by the regulation.

Maloney and McCormick also found that an increase in stock prices of companies owning smelters occurred soon after a 1973 Supreme Court decision to uphold the PSD program. This decision had the effect of limiting competition from new smelters which would otherwise have located in PSD regions, increasing the market value of existing firms. Thus, it seems clear that environmental regulations have rather complicated effects within as well as among industries.

The magnitude of the respective burdens borne by consumers and by labor are determined to a large extent by the elasticity of demand for the product as well as by the importance of the new source bias. Imagine, for example, that the demand curve for the product was perfectly inelastic. In this case the short run price increase would equal d and short run economic profits would be 0. There would be no effect on the level of production and no resulting effect on the demand for labor. Consumers would bear the entire burden.

The more elastic is the demand curve, the larger the impact on production and, hence, labor. This is important because it suggests the impact of pollution control depends not only on the degree of labor intensiveness of the industry (which determines how severely labor would be affected by declines in production), but also by the elasticity of demand (which determines how large the declines in production would be). Thus, for example, industries which face severe competition from imports not subject to the same controls would face greater threats of employment declines than those producing products with no effective substitute, domestic or foreign.

The new source bias suggests that the detrimental impact on employment in existing plants should be rather small and the evidence seems to confirm this. The "Economic Dislocation Early Warning System" was set up by EPA to monitor plant closings and associated job losses where pollution control was alleged to be a factor in the closing. The data collected by this monitoring system [U.S. Environmental Protection Agency (1982)] from January 1971 through September 1982 suggest that a total of 154 plants were closed involving a total of 32 749 jobs. Twenty three percent of the plant closings and 34 percent of the jobs lost were in the primary metals industries. An additional 14 percent of the closings and 20 percent of the jobs were lost in the chemicals and allied products industries. From Table 9.1 it can be seen that both of these industries are among the leaders in terms of the percent of new plant and equipment expenditures going toward pollution control. In addition steel, one of the primary metals industries, has faced heavy import competition, making the demand for its product more price elastic.

The adverse employment impacts have been geographically concentrated as well as sectorally concentrated. About 62 percent of the plant closings and 66 percent of the associated job losses were concentrated in the Northeast and the Midwest. Over one half of these were in the Midwest.

2.2.3. The bubble and offset policies

Control authorities have a substantial degree of flexibility in how they distribute the cost of pollution control among industries. Prior to the implementation of the bubble and offset policies the traditional approach was to specify a separate emission standard for each pollutant source. As is now well known,[2] this approach led to an expensive allocation of the control responsibility.

The bubble and offset policies allow air quality objectives to be met with a much lower expenditure on abatement equipment. However, permit markets also involve expenditures on the permits themselves, an expense sources do not encounter when emission standards are administratively imposed. Thus, whether compliance cost, defined as the sum of abatement and permit expenditures, is higher for sources (individually as well as collectively) with permit systems or without them cannot be determined analytically; it must be determined empirically.

Most of the existing literature examining even a subset of these issues involves water pollution. In an early paper Rose (1973) investigated the conceptual properties of auction systems while a more recent and complete theoretical treatment of these issues can be found in Dewees (1983). Because these papers are theoretical, however, they could not address any of the more fundamental aspects of choice which are, by their very nature, empirical.

A recent paper by David et al. (1980) uses a detailed empirical model to evaluate the consequences for the total compliance costs faced by individual firms of a scheme which initially allocates permits in proportion to an individual source's effluent discharge. Their paper does not, however, compare this allocation with other options available to the control authority. Other recent articles by Lyon (1982) and Palmer et al. (1980) suggest that permit expenditures are a significant proportion of total compliance costs, and, for this reason, schemes which distribute permits free of charge may well create a substantially lower financial burden on sources than auction markets.

The offset and bubble policies fall within this class of lower financial burden strategies for existing sources. The permits are given away to existing firms, not auctioned off. As a result the bubble and offset policies should result in lower expenditures by sources than the traditional policy approaches. Indeed, a recent

---

[2] See the description of this literature in Tietenberg (1983).

case study of particulate control in St. Louis[3] found that due to the inefficiency of the historical regulatory approach substantial improvements in air quality are possible with relatively small increases in cost. The existence of the bubble and offset policies would mean smaller cost increases and smaller upward pressure on prices and smaller adverse employment impacts on existing sources than would previously have been the case. For potential new sources (which have to purchase the permits) these reforms mean even higher costs, since the additional cost of the permits could be expected to outweigh the savings from purchasing smaller amounts of abatement equipment.

2.2.4. General equilibrium studies

The partial equilibrium analysis of distribution of the impact of pollution control policy is incomplete because it examines only one market at a time. It assumes that prices of all other factors and commodities are not affected by the policies so that an isolated examination of the effects on a single market is not misleading. Given that environmental policy can affect so many industries simultaneously this assumption is suspect.

Theoretical general equilibrium models attempt to broaden the scope of the analysis, although, usually, only to two sectors. In these models generally there are two outputs and two inputs. Pollution can either be treated as an undesirable additional output [e.g. Siebert (1981)] or as an input [e.g. Yohe (1979) and Yu and Ingene (1982)]. In the latter case the models assume that compensation is to be paid by the firm for its use of the environment.

In general these models support the findings of the partial equilibrium models. Following the imposition of pollution control regulations output in the pollution-producing industry would be reduced and the products produced by that industry would carry relatively higher price tags. Resources previously used to increase output would be committed to abating pollution. Meanwhile the nonpolluting industry would expand production and its products would be favored by a relative price decline. In these full employment models national income (measured in terms of the value of two output commodities only) would decline.

When the full employment assumption is changed, however, a rather different impact is obtained. Yu and Ingene (1982) show that in a model with a rigid wage structure more stringent pollution controls would not necessarily reduce national income, even if the economy was subject to unemployment. In particular, if the polluting sector operates with a higher capital/labor ratio than the nonpolluting sector, more restrictive controls would lead to an expansion in total employment and the payments to labor. National income would rise if the increased payments to labor in this expanding sector exceed the payments made as compensation for the use of the environment in the contracting sector.

[3] Atkinson and Tietenberg (1984).

2.3. Technological progress

Regulations can also have effects on the rate and the direction of technological progress. Magat (1978, 1979) has modelled the influence of regulations on innovation using a simple induced-innovation model which ignores uncertainty. From this model he derives a theorem stating:

> An effluent standard induces the firm to bias its technological advance toward abatement technology innovation, while the firm's R&D expenditure rate may either decrease or increase. If without an effluent standard, the firm devotes no R&D effort to abatement technology improvement, then an effluent standard will cause it to invest in abatement technology innovation. Imposing an effluent standard is likely to reduce a firm's rate of output technology innovation, but it need not have this effect for all firms (1979, p. 13).

In general the available empirical evidence supports this theory, though our knowledge of the magnitude of these impacts is very limited. There is no overall estimate of the effects on the industrial sector as a whole. There are, however, some interesting case studies funded by the National Science Foundation which deal with the impact of environmental policy on specific industries, with the chemical industry receiving particular emphasis. These studies allow the opportunity to examine how regulations affect the various phases of the research and development process.

2.3.1. The basic research phase

Regulations can affect the basic research phase by having an impact on the magnitude and the distribution of research and development funds. By increasing the amount of time required to bring products to market and the risks associated with those which do go to market the rate of return on research and development can be adversely affected. On the other hand, environmental regulations tend to emphasize different product characteristics than might normally be emphasized in the absense of these regulations. Therefore new opportunities are created for the development of new products or new production techniques. Those firms which pioneer the effort to bring these new products or techniques to market can reap first-mover profits. Thus the sign of this effect could potentially be either positive or negative.

The earliest of the empirical studies [Iverstine, Kinard and Slaughter (1978)] examined the impact of environmental protection regulations on Research and Development (R&D) activities in the industrial chemical industry. Completed in 1978 this study was based almost exclusively on personal interviews with Research and Development officers in 15 of the largest U.S. chemical companies. It found that a significant part of the research and development budgets (13.521

percent on average) was allocated toward projects labelled as environmental protection programs. Yet despite this the R&D budgets had fallen over the period 1970–76 as a percentage of sales, indicating that the share of R&D funds committed to raising productivity fell in this industry. There was no offsetting increase in R&D budgets to compensate for the amount allocated toward environmental protection.

This study also contained some interesting data on how the environmental protection R&D funds were spent. Approximately 34 percent were spent developing pollution containment systems, 18 percent on improvement to the manufacturing processes to reduce pollution and 26 percent on the development of new products to replace those harmful to the environment. Interestingly very little was spent developing new products to reduce currently unregulated environmental damage, even if such regulations were anticipated. The R&D officers apparently felt that the regulatory process represented such a "moving target" that it was too risky to spend much time, effort or financial resources in anticipation of potential outcomes of that process.

2.3.2. The development phase

The development phase involves taking the ideas discovered during the basic research phase and translating them into a marketable product. Regulations tend to lengthen this phase, particularly for those products for which premarket testing is required. This additional testing will increase the cost of development and reduce the number of products brought to market. Only those having sufficiently large markets that the development cost can be recouped will survive this phase of the innovation cycle. Those which do survive should pose less environmental and health risks. Nine of the 15 firms surveyed in the Iverstine, Kinard and Slaughter study reported delays in product development from a few weeks to five years as a result of the additional burden required to meet environmental regulations.

2.3.3. The commercialization phase

The commercialization phase involves bringing the new product or the new production technique into the market. Regulations can affect this phase both by reducing the set of permissible entries and by the new source bias inherent in some of the regulations. Many potential new products would not be brought onto the market because they could pose health or environmental risks which would be unacceptable under the new laws or because the cost of compliance could not be recouped. The Iverstine, Kinard and Slaughter study found that in their sample of 15 firms several had cancelled new products because of the regulations.

This study also discovered, however, that the regulations led to unanticipated discoveries which might, to some extent, offset the costs of research and development. Ten out of 15 firms reported discovering marketable products or processes as a result of their research. All firms agreed that the revenues from the sale were not sufficient, by themselves, to pay their development costs, but one firm estimated that for every dollar spent on environmental protection research and development 50 cents was received in revenues. This means that studies which assume that there are no offsetting benefits probably tend to overestimate the impact of pollution control expenditures on prices. Furthermore, according to other studies [e.g. Allison (1977) and Brashares et al. (1980)], there are industries which have actually reduced their costs after implementing newly developed pollution reduction processes.

Other studies using larger samples, a smaller, more focused set of environmental regulations and more sophisticated statistical techniques have tended to corroborate those initial findings. For example, Ashford et al. (1979) conducted both personal and telephone interviews with a sample of some 50 U.S. chemical companies. The particular regulations examined dealt with the control of lead, mercury, polychlorinated byphenyls (PCBs) and vinyl chloride.

They found that because the regulations were created with a substantial industry input, the four standards that were actually promulgated were, in most instances, based on existing available technology. It was rare to find a standard requiring technology not already existing in the industry. Despite this, several very important innovative responses were seen to have arisen from new entrants to the industry. Their entrance was made possible by the regulation, particularly when existing products were banned or severely restricted. For example, successful PCB substitutes were developed by large oil and chemical companies, transformer/capacitor manufacturers and foreign corporations – none of whom had been in the PCB manufacturing business. In one case, the worker exposure and emissions problems of PVC fabricators were essentially solved by their suppliers.

Some 20 percent of the firms interviewed admitted that there had been ancillary innovations resulting from regulation which had market potential. These included development of a new catalyst for petroleum refining, the initial development of a new chlorine manufacturing process, increased yields of polyvinyl chloride resin, better process monitoring techniques and new paint formulations. Twenty percent is probably an understatement. Not only would those interviewed tend to have an interest in overstating compliance cost, but the innovations tended to be so diffuse and indirect that they were not likely to be fully appreciated by any single individual in the corporation.

2.4. Productivity

The effect of environmental regulations on the productivity of specific industries has received substantially less attention than it should have. Despite the fact that it is easier to interpret the results of industry studies and to tie them to specific regulatory actions, most work has been focused on cross industry studies.

Just how useful the insights derived from industry studies can be is illustrated by a study of the electric utility sector over the 1973–79 period by Gollop and Roberts (1983). Using a translog cost function they were able to estimate the effects of sulphur dioxide emission standards, scale economies and technological progress on productivity growth.

In their model they develop a firm-specific measure of regulatory intensity which depends on the severity of the emission standard, the extent of enforcement of those standards and the unconstrained emission rate relevant to each utility. This combined measure rises steadily over the period due largely to an increase in enforcement as emission rates fall toward the legally mandated rates. Very little of the increase is due to a tightening of the standards.

In their sample of 56 privately-owned utilities 11 were not constrained at all by the regulations over the period. Using these unconstrained utilities as a benchmark Gollop and Roberts calculate that for the rest, environmental regulations were responsible for a 0.59 percentage point reduction in utility productivity growth. Stated in other terms, they found that annual average productivity growth in the electric utility sector would have been 0.44 percent higher in the absence of the sulphur dioxide regulations.

3. The incidence on households

As the preceding sections have indicated, the market reactions to pollution control regulations are complex. In spite of an obvious attempt by Congress to apply many of the standards uniformly the cost burdens have not been uniformly distributed among industries much less among firms. The ultimate incidence of this cost burden depends on a number of factors. The elasticity of demand for the product affects the degree to which production (and, hence, employment) is affected. The existence of market power, the new source bias and the bubble and offset policies affect the degree to which prices are affected by the imposition of the regulation.

These relationships take time to evolve and, therefore, to capture the full impact the analysis must have a dynamic component. The evidence suggests, for example, that environmental regulations have affected not only the rate of technological progress, but the direction as well. The results of this redirection seem to mean that less research and development money is being spent on enhancing productivity and more is being spent on environmental improvement. To some extent these expenditures have produced new saleable products which tend to offset the expenditures. Since these offsets are not included in the official cost data, their neglect will produce an overestimate of the true cost of the regulations to the affected industries.

A complete picture of household incidence must include not only the manner in which the cost burden is transmitted to households by firms through price increases, or employment and wage decreases, it must also include the manner in which the benefits are transmitted. Environmental policies improve the quality of the the nation's air and water resources and households reap the benefits of this improvement. The ultimate effect of environmental policies on households must weight these benefits against the costs of obtaining them. In this section we shall review the work that attempts to quantify these impacts.

3.1. Air pollution

Households receive rather different net benefits (total household benefits minus total household costs) from stationary source and mobile air pollution control because of the rather different way in which their respective cost burdens are shared. Therefore, we shall consider each of these separately, prior to putting the results together to study the combined effects of the air pollution control policy package as a whole.

3.1.1. Automobile air pollution control

In the early 1970s, the U.S. EPA (1972) put out a study suggesting that the costs of automobile air pollution control were probably progressively distributed. In essence, the argument was that since the poor had lower rates of auto ownership, and the control policy was focused on new cars, the largest burdens would fall on the middle and upper income groups.

Subsequent studies have not supported that conclusion. These more recent studies suggest that the problem is more complex than realized by the early EPA study. In particular, the increase in the cost of emission controls on new cars would cause secondary effects in the used car market.

These secondary effects create a fairly complicated incidence pattern. While new car buyers would clearly face higher prices, the owners of used cars when the policy was imposed would receive a gain from the policy in the form of a higher resale value for their cars. This gain, however, is transitory. All future purchasers of automobiles would pay higher prices regardless of whether they buy new cars or used cars. The future used car cost would depend on the rate of depreciation in new car prices.

Studies by Dorfman (1975), Harrison (1975) and Freeman (1977) attempt to trace out these effects using a depreciation model developed by Wykoff (1970). Only Freeman attempts to capture the short-term effects. He derives two rather interesting results: (1) the gain to used car owners within each income group (caused by the increased resale value of the used car) is on balance larger than the loss (caused by the cost of the emission controls) to new car owners in that same income group, and (2) the gains are progressively distributed. Thus, in the short run, the automobile pollution control costs are more .than offset by used car capital gains and the largest capital gains are received by lower income groups.

As interesting as this result is, one should not make too much of it. The offsetting capital gain is a one-time benefit, not to be repeated. Furthermore, it can only be realized when the automobile is sold. And as soon as another car is purchased, the higher cost associated with the emission controls would have to paid regardless of whether a new or used car were purchased.

For these reasons the most interesting aspect of automobile air pollution control cost incidence concerns the long run when all cars cost more. Once again there will be several factors to consider: (1) the increase in cost to new car purchasers; (2) the increase in cost to used car purchasers; and (3) the number of new and used car purchasers in each income group.

All three studies have found that automobile pollution control costs are regressively distributed. Harrison (1975) has the most complete description of the incidence. He finds, for example, that costs are higher in the suburbs than in the central city, and are higher in smaller cities than in larger cities. He also finds the degree of regressivity higher in the suburbs and generally in smaller cities (Los Angeles is an exception, being a large city with a highly regressive incidence).

This evidence addresses only part of the story. In order to determine the ultimate incidence it is necessary to complement these estimates of cost incidence with some estimate of the incidence of benefits. To complement his analysis of the distribution of the cost burden Harrison (1975) also conducted a detailed study of the incidence of the benefits of automobile pollution control policy. Because of the difficulties of estimating a generally accepted monetary value for benefits, he measured benefits solely in terms of improvements in the concentrations of three automobile pollutants (CO, NO_x, and O_x). These improvements were calculated for each geographic area and, using data on the income levels of people in those areas, he calculated the degree of reduced exposure experienced by each of these groups.

He found that the benefits from improvement in air quality were progressively distributed *for those living in urban areas.* Furthermore, the most progressive distribution of the benefits occurred in the very largest cities. This results from the disproportionate representation of the poor in the most heavily polluted areas in our largest cities.

When his cost and benefit estimates are combined, Harrison concludes:

Households living in suburban areas, small urban areas, and nonurban areas – which make up two-thirds of United States households – do poorly under the current scheme. Households in these areas gain quite modest air quality benefits while paying large costs. Lower income groups in these areas fare particularly poorly since the costs fell quite heavily upon them under the current scheme (p. 109).

In a general sense the Harrison study suggests that the automobile air pollution control policy, which was so carefully designed to be uniformly applied, has led to a highly unbalanced distribution of the net benefits. The imbalance appears both in the distribution of net benefits among geographic areas and among socioeconomic groups. According to his estimates those living in rural areas, particularly the poor, seem to be relatively more burdened than other segments of society.

Other studies of the distribution of automobile air pollution control benefits and costs, such as the one by Grad et al. (1975), have been conducted on a more local scale. Funded by the National Science Foundation this multidisciplinary, multiuniversity study examined the emissions payoff and costs of implementing various local automobile air pollution control strategies. The analysis was based on a model designed to simulate the transportation system of Boston, Massachusetts and to forecast how that system would respond to changes in the various policies available to local authorities. The model was based on a large amount of data on the origins and destinations of trips in the Boston area and contained equations which simulated the choice of mode (e.g. bus or auto) as a function of factors such as travel time, cost, etc. Once the travel patterns were simulated the model projected the effects of these travel patterns on aggregate emissions and, finally, on the concentrations of pollutants which could be expected in each of 123 different receptor locations in the city. The model kept track, not only of the size of the emission reductions, but also the locations where the pollutant concentrations were reduced. This latter piece of information can be important because some parts of the city were more heavily polluted than others and, therefore, reductions in those areas would make a particularly valuable contribution to meeting the ambient air quality standards.

This model serves as a useful contrast to the models previously discussed. The others provide conclusions which are national in scope while this model provides conclusions which are specific to Boston. Yet this model provides information not available from others. Pollution control policy has an important local dimension which is, of necessity, ignored by national models. How the various policies affect benefits depends on their effect on the exposure of the population to pollutant concentrations. The change in exposure depends not only on the amount of emission reduction, but on the location of the emission reduction. The spatial detail necessary to capture these effects is possible only in the more local models.

3.1.2. Stationary source air pollution control

Stationary source controls would also result in higher prices, but, because different commodities are affected, the incidence would not necessarily be the same. While the rate of automobile ownership is quite low among the poor (particularly the urban poor), they are less insulated from increases in other commodity prices.

The studies which estimate the incidence of industrial air pollution control costs on households depend on a proportionality assumption. Industrial costs are presumed to be passed forward to households in different geographic regions or different income groups on a dollar for dollar basis in proportion to the average household expenditures for that group. No account was taken of the potential differential effects on income groups of the specific commodities which could be expected to experience price increases. Furthermore, other costs such as employment or wage declines were not considered. For example, if the industrial pollution control costs are represented by C, then the cost burden borne by the ith family in the jth income class in the kth region (C_{ijk}) would be given as

$$C_{ijk} = W_{ijk} \cdot C \tag{1}$$

In practice the W_{ijk} are usually estimated using only national data [see Gianessi, Peskin and Wolff (1980)]. Regional differences are ignored. Thus, every family in the kth income class is assumed to bear the same share of total industrial control costs regardless of where they live. Furthermore, this share is insensitive to the distribution of the industrial cost burden. A dollar cost increase in any industry is presumed to have the same impact on any family in a given income class as a dollar increase in cost for any other industry. These are obviously very strong assumptions.

Since the poor spend a higher proportion of their income, it is not surprising that those who have derived estimates [e.g. Gianessi, Peskin and Wolff (1979) and Dorfman (1975)] have found the costs to be regressively distributed. The approach dictates the conclusion. It is not obvious that a more detailed consideration of the specific industries (and, hence commodities) affected would yield the same conclusion. Most authors have relied on the work of Dorfman (1975, p. 114), who reports that the use of an input–output matrix to trace the effects of industry-specific cost increases on the consumption expenditures by different income groups produced a result similar to the result achieved using the proportionality assumption. This finding is by no means universal, however. One study [Yan et al. (1975)] which used an input–output table to test the validity of this finding in the Philadelphia region found no particular pattern emerging. In certain ranges the cost of pollution control policy was progressively distributed while in others it was regressive. In short, in this study the commodity bundles consumed by different income groups were affected differently, but no simple pattern was evident.

Studies of the benefits of air pollution control tell a rather different story. A study by Asch and Seneca (1978) examined how the exposure to air pollution was distributed in the United States. They wanted to know whether exposure to air pollution was systematically related to the economic and social characteristics of the population.

To answer this question, they constructed two different samples of data. The first sample consisted of observations on the annual geometric mean concentrations of particulates taken from 284 cities. Socioeconomic variables such as income levels, age composition and education levels, were collected for these cities. Doing separate computations for each state, the particulate pollution levels were correlated with these socioeconomic characteristics. Their results indicated that in virtually all states, high pollutant concentrations were found in cities with higher percentages of lower income people, higher percentages of the aged and higher percentages of nonwhites.

They complemented this analysis with another sample which examined the intra-city variation in air quality. For this second sample the exposure to three air pollutants (sulphur dioxide, nitrogen dioxide and particulates) was correlated with socioeconomic characteristic within three U.S. cities: Chicago, Cleveland and Nashville. The fact that the pollution levels and socioeconomic characteristics were measured at a number of sites within each city allowed for a much more precise link between local pollution levels and the immediately affected pollution to be established.

The income distribution measures consistently confirmed that the poorest portions of these cities experienced higher pollution levels. Similar patterns were associated with property values. Higher pollution levels were generally found in neighborhoods with lower property values. The results for racial exposure were mixed. In Chicago higher pollution levels were found in neighborhoods with a high percentage of nonwhites, but in Cleveland the opposite was true – higher concentration of nitrogen dioxide were found in neighborhoods containing relatively high proportions of whites.

Asch and Seneca also examined whether the improvements in air quality achieved during the early 1970s were progressively, proportionally, or regressively distributed. On balance they found that the physical improvements were progressively distributed – the lower income portions of the cities received the greatest reductions in pollutant concentrations. In fact they found many high income areas actually became more polluted during the period. Similar results were obtained by Zupan (1973) who studied the New York Region.

3.1.3. A combined assessment

The Asch and Seneca (1978) and Zupan (1973) studies deal with exposure, rather than economic benefits. The two are not the same because the concept of economic benefits deals with the worth of reducing exposure, not merely the exposure reduction. Gianessi, Peskin and Wolff (1977) attempted to bridge this gap by distributing to local areas the national damage estimates computed by the EPA and then prorating the benefits among socioeconomic groups on the basis of exposure.

Once again proportionality was assumed. Per capita benefits (which are equal to per capita pollution damage reduction) were computed as

$$\frac{D_i}{P_i} = \frac{1}{P_i}\sum_j D_{ij} = \frac{1}{A_i}\sum_j \frac{D_j T_{ij}}{\sum_i \left[(P_i/A_i)T_{ij}\right]}, \tag{2}$$

where D_i is the pollution damage reduction in the ith geographic region, P_i is the population in that region, D_{ij} is the reduction in damage caused by the jth pollutant in the ith region, A_i is the size of the ith region in square miles, D_j is the total national damage from pollutant j (taken from EPA estimates), and T_{ij} is the total emissions of pollutant j by all sectors in geographic area i.

Household benefits are calculated merely by multiplying the per capita benefits by the number of people in the household. This approach implicitly assumes that wealthier individuals in a given geographic area derive the same per capita benefit as others with lower income.

There are two reasons for believing this assumption is heroic. As the Asch and Seneca (1978) results suggest, each income group is typically exposed to a different improvement in concentration by virtue of its unique residential location. Even if each income group was willing to pay the same amount as every other income group for a unit of concentration reduction, household benefits would still vary among income groups because improvements in exposure would vary. Furthermore, the public goods literature makes it quite clear that higher income groups should be willing to pay more for a given concentration reduction.[4]

Combining these estimates with comparably distributed cost estimates demonstrates that the variability of the per family benefit estimates across regions and income groups was several times larger than the variability in costs. Thus, while the average family in large urban areas received many times the benefits from the program than did the average suburban or rural family, their costs differed by a much smaller amount. Therefore it is not surprising that the heavily industrialized, highly populated areas of the Eastern United States lead the list of the largest gainers, while the more rural and agricultural areas are among the largest losers.

---

[4] See, for example, the discussion in Baumol and Oates (1975, pp. 201–202) and the study by Johnson (1980) discussed below.

Gianessi, Peskin and Wolff also list the specific areas calculated as receiving positive net benefits and those receiving negative net benefits. For automobile air pollution they found only four areas of the country (Jersey City, New York, Patterson, and Newark) that enjoyed positive net benefits. For stationary source air pollution they found 61 (out of 274) areas receiving positive net benefits. When the mobile and stationary source estimates were combined, they found 24 areas experiencing positive net benefits. Thus, according to this study, the majority of the areas and the majority of the population are paying costs for air pollution control which are higher than the benefits they receive.

With respect to the distribution of net benefits among income classes the Gianessi, Peskin and Wolff study estimated the net benefits from stationary source pollution to be progressively distributed, and the net benefits from mobile source control to be regressively distributed. The combination of policies yielded ambiguous results with no clear pattern emerging. Generally the poor and lower middle class appeared to be somewhat harder hit, although the poorest of the poor end up with the smallest net burden.

One should not make too much of any listing of areas, such as the one described above, which are net beneficiaries or net losers because the magnitude of net benefits is subject to such a great deal of uncertainty, particularly in the calculation of benefits. It does seem clear, however, that automobile air pollution control policy violates some conventional norms of equity. Persons of similar economic means in different parts of the country are not treated equally and, furthermore, the net benefits of air pollution control policy are distributed in a mildly regressive manner.

An interesting counterpoint to the assumption that benefits are proportional to exposure is provided in a study by Johnson (1980). He attempts to estimate a general equilibrium model in which (1) all markets are cleared by new prices after environmental policies have been imposed and (2) the benefit valuation depends upon income level. Using Swedish data he values the collective good environmental benefits using a procedure suggested by Aaron and McGuire (1970) and extended by Maital (1973). In this procedure the value of benefits received from a collective good by an income class is computed as

$$B_j = B/MU_j(Y_j),$$ \hfill (3)

where B is the total benefits received, B_j is the value accruing to income class j and $MU_j(Y_j)$ is the marginal utility of income to the group standardized such that

$$\sum_j MU_j(Y_j) = 1.0.$$ \hfill (4)

The marginal utility of income is computed as

$$MU_j(Y_j) = Y_j^{-\phi},$$ \hfill (5)

where ϕ is set equal to 1.5, based on three independent econometric estimates.[5]

[5] See Maital (1973).

Though the author quite properly cautions against using his empirical results as anything but suggestive, the conclusion that the benefits of air pollution control are quite regressively distributed comes through loud and clear. This is a natural consequence of the approach. Unfortunately this study suggests that our conclusions about the magnitude of the regressivity of the benefits of environmental policy are rather sensitive to an unsettled methodological argument about the role of income in valuing public goods. The existing studies, however, leave little doubt that the benefits are regressively distributed.

3.2. Water pollution

3.2.1. Point sources

Water pollution presents an interesting contrast. The program of control erected to combat water pollution includes not only industrial effluent standards (which are similar to the industrial emission standards used to combat air pollution), but also federal subsidies to waste treatment plants. Since these subsidies are financed through the tax system, their impact could conceivably be quite different from measures financed chiefly by higher product prices.

These tax costs are typically imputed to households in two steps. First the local and federal portions of the cost associated with the construction of municipal waste treatment plants are isolated. Then these are apportioned among households on the basis of local and federal average tax rates for each income class. In general the local taxes turn out to be regressive and the federal taxes progressive.[6]

Three separate national studies – Dorfman (1975), Gianessi and Peskin (1980), and Lake, Hanneman and Oster (1979) – were undertaken to find the distribution of the costs of federal point source water pollution control policy. All three studies came to similar conclusions.

In general they conclude that the distribution of the costs of water pollution control was regressive. The industrial effluent standards were found to impose quite a large regressive burden while the burden of the municipal treatment plant subsidies was distributed progressively. The industrial effluent standards were found to be regressive because the resulting higher consumer prices affect the poor disproportionately. The progressivity of the municipal waste treatment plant subsidies results from their major source of financing – the progressive federal tax system.

To place these results into perspective Gianessi and Peskin compare the incidence of the water pollution control costs to the incidence of the air pollution control costs. They find water pollution cost incidence less regressive due both to the form by which the municipal treatment plant subsidies are financed and the

---

[6] See Dorfman (1975, Figs. 2 and 3).

lack of any component in the water pollution control policy which resembles the highly regressive automobile control policy.

The conclusion that the municipal waste treatment subsidies are progressive has not gone unchallenged. In an examination of the incidence of these subsidies in EPA region VII (Iowa, Missouri, Kansas and Nebraska) Collins (1977) found that they tended to redistribute income from the middle income classes primarily to the very rich. This conclusion depends critically on one particular assumption in the analysis and characteristics which may be somewhat unique to the region studied.

This study assumes that the subsidies received by industrial users of the waste treatment plants is not passed forward to consumers in lower prices, but rather is retained by the owners. Since the owners of capital, in general, tend to be in the upper portion of the income distribution, this assumption results in a major gain by that group. As the author demonstrates (p. 553) if this assumption were changed to distribute the subsidy to industrial customers rather than owners, the burden of municipal waste treatment subsidy would be quite progressive.

Assuming that the owners of capital retain the subsidy turns out to be particularly important in the Collins study because over one-half of the subsidies in the region studied accrue to industrial users. Using exactly the same methodology as Collins to estimate the distributional burden of waste treatment subsidies within the Boston metropolitan area Ostro (1981) found the burden to be quite progressively distributed. This rather different finding results from the fact that in Boston the industrial share of the subsidy was only 7.85 percent, making the results less sensitive to the assumption about the incidence of the industrial subsidy.

The literature on the distribution of the benefits of water pollution control is very thin. In one study Winston Harrington (1981) investigated the distribution of water-based recreation benefits resulting from the implementation of the BPT portion of the 1972 Water Pollution Control Amendments. Using the RFF Water Network Model to simulate the effects of the policy on water quality and an econometric model to estimate the change in recreational demand resulting from the improvement in water quality, Harrington found the benefits to be very unequally distributed. In particular he found whites favored relative to nonwhites, middle income families favored relative to the poor, city-dwellers favored relative to those living in the country, and Northeast residents relative to those residing in other regions.

3.2.2. Nonpoint sources

The studies described above deal with pollution caused by point sources.[7] It is now becoming clear in the United States that as point sources are becoming

[7] One exception was Gianessi and Peskin (1980) which considered the costs of controlling urban storm runoff, conventionally treated as a nonpoint source.

increasingly controlled, nonpoint sources are becoming relatively more important. The RFF Water Network Model has also been used by Gianessi and Peskin (1981) to analyze the geographic distribution of the benefits of agricultural sediment control.

The basic approach was to supplement county-by-county industrial pollution inventories with county-by-county inventories of sediment related pollutants. The model was then used to simulate water quality under a variety of point and nonpoint control strategies. The main conclusion derived from this exercise was that only approximately one-third of the nation's river points would experience significantly improved water quality with the adoption of cropland sediment control policy as a supplement to point source control policy. For this reason the authors suggested that nonpoint control policies should be focused on those agricultural regions where they would make a difference. The simulations also indicated, however, that approximately one-half of the nation's rivers would still experience violations of the total phosphorus and total nitrogen standards unless more stringent controls were established for other nonpoint sources such as pastureland, rangeland and urban runoff.

3.3. An overview

From a methodological point of view the art of estimating the distribution of benefits and costs is still in a period of infancy. There are many reasons for this. Perhaps the most important is the complexity of the task. The policies being evaluated are complex, and not surprisingly, they produce complex reactions in the market.

Among the analytical dilemmas created by complexity is the issue of the most appropriate scale at which to conduct the analysis. On the one hand both the household and industrial incidence relationships are best modeled on a local scale. For example, the translation of emissions into air or water quality has an important local spatial dimension. The way households value improvements depends heavily on where the concentrations are improved, on how these improvements affect the exposure of various socioeconomic groups, and on the willingness of these various income groups to pay for those exposure improvements. Furthermore, the manner in which firms react to pollution controls depends on whether they have been producing for some years or are newly established.

On the other hand, the policies being evaluated are largely national in origin, if not always national in implementation. This creates a need for information which is comparable on a national scale. No national study can be conducted using the level of detail possible on a local scale. Though computers can handle massive amounts of data, the data are not likely to be comparable or of uniform quality.

Heroic simplification is necessary to derive national estimates. Confidence intervals, though frequently not amenable to calculation, are certainly large.

Complexity and data limitations, however, are not the only barriers to the development of a completely satisfying approach to estimating the distribution of the benefits and costs. We have shown that the distribution of the benefits among socioeconomic groups is quite sensitive to assumptions about how different groups value reductions in pollutant exposure. Two distinct approaches have been taken. The first assumes that each group values exposure reduction the same. Its chief virtue is simplicity and, hence, feasibility. The second conditions the valuation on estimates of the marginal utility of income. Though more elegant and probably closer to the true distribution, these estimates have been derived only in very simple numerical exercises.

The point is not that refinement is infeasible or undesirable, it is neither. There are, however, limits to just how that refinement can proceed without being impeded by limits on complexity and data availability.

4. Macroeconomic aspects of environmental policy

4.1. Post-War macroeconomic performance

Beginning in the mid-1960s, the performance of the U.S. economy in terms of its key macroeconomic indicators deteriorated. Statistics on the growth rate of output, inflation, unemployment, and capital formation all combined to paint a

Table 9.2
Performance of key macroeconomic indicators

	1947–66	1966–73	1973–78	1978–82
Real GNP (average annual growth rate)	3.89%	3.46%	2.71%	0.63%
Inflation (consumer price index)	1.97%	4.49%	7.68%	9.79%
Unemployment rate (average rate weighted by size of each year's labor force)	4.81%	4.23%	6.67%	7.30%
Real gross private domestic investment (average annual growth rate)	4.45%	4.12%	1.09%	−4.60%

Source: Economic Report of the President (1983). All growth rates have been computed by calculating the year-to-year changes in the natural logarithms of the variables in question.

gloomy picture. Table 9.2 summarizes the post-War behavior of these variables in the United States.

The deterioration in macroeconomic performance depicted in Table 9.2 occurred at the same time that the environmental movement began to gain strength. A plausible hypothesis, then, is that the increasing scope and volume of environmental regulations promulgated after the mid-1960s contributed to the country's poor macroeconomic performance.

As Sections 2 and 3 made clear, environmental policy has had pronounced effects on certain industries and households. The issue addressed in this section is how significant these effects have been at an aggregate (or "macroeconomic") level.

Of particular interest is the impact of environmental policy on the aggregate performance of *productivity*. Most macroeconomic variables refer to outputs or inputs, but not both at the same time. A convenient way to assess an economy's efficiency, however, is to consider its *output per unit of input* – both the output of goods and services and the inputs used to produce them must be considered. In concept, a nation's productivity can be defined simply as its aggregate final output per unit of input. Because of difficulties in aggregating the diverse outputs and inputs of a modern economy, however, the measurement of productivity performance is not a straightforward matter. The most common procedure has been to measure productivity by obtaining an estimate of final aggregate private sector output divided by an estimate of the number of hours of labor input employed. This concept can be called a *single-factor* (i.e. *labor*) productivity measure, and because it does not reflect in its denominator the full set of inputs, it has clear weaknesses. Recently, however, economists have attempted to compile series for private sector output per *total* input (labor, capital, raw materials, etc.) and several related measures. These are designed to avoid some of the weaknesses of the standard labor productivity measure.

By any of these measures, productivity growth in the United States dropped significantly after the mid-1960s. As Table 9.3 indicates, the growth rate of labor productivity in the private sector as a whole was, from 1973 to 1978, only about one-third of the rate of the immediate post-War years.

Table 9.3
Average annual growth rate of labor productivity

	1947–66	1966–73	1973–78	1978–82
Private business sector	3.23%	2.32%	1.03%	0.10%
Private nonfarm business sector	2.65%	2.08%	0.92%	−0.15%

Source: Economic Report of the President (1983).

It is difficult to evaluate the underlying trend in productivity growth since 1978 because the U.S. economy has not yet fully recovered from the recessions which have occurred since that time. Productivity growth tends to decline during recessions because businesses tend to refrain from dismissing skilled laborers in proportion to the decline in the demand for their output, due to the costs of hiring and training new workers when conditions improve. Thus, output per unit of input tends to suffer during recession periods. As the U.S. economy recovers from the most recent recession, a clearer picture of its growth potential should emerge. In any event, Table 9.3 shows that the average growth rate of labor productivity in the private sector was 0.10 percent from 1978 to 1982. It was −0.15 percent in the private nonfarm sector.

4.2. The effects of environmental policy on productivity growth and inflation

During the late 1960s and 1970s government regulations required that an increasing proportion of the labor and capital employed by business be devoted to the protection of employee health and safety and to pollution abatement. While such regulations may involve substantial benefits, their contribution to *measured* output – marketed goods and services – is often minimal. It can be argued that certain regulations designed to protect worker health do enhance well-being, morale, and ultimately, measured productivity, but more often than not, it has been argued that environmental regulations have *impaired* measured productivity performance. Consider the following assertions.

(1) As noted in Section 2 pollution control regulations require abatement investments, which compete with normal investments in productive plant and equipment, crowding out the latter to some unknown extent. Hence, labor has less conventional capital with which to work than it would otherwise have, and, as a result, its output may be reduced.

(2) Also as noted in Section 2, pollution control regulations subject new sources of pollution to much more stringent standards than existing sources. This uneven treatment encourages business to use existing – and lower-productivity – plant and equipment longer than otherwise and to delay the introduction of new capital with more advanced technology.

(3) Pollution control equipment, once installed, requires manpower for its operation and maintenance. This manpower adds to labor input with no addition to saleable output.

(4) For business to conform to environmental regulations, it must secure information regarding them, obtain information regarding options to meet them, and undertake legal and administrative activities to avoid, delay, or change them. These activities require labor services that yield no saleable output.

(5) Uncertainty regarding (a) future regulatory requirements, (b) interpretation of current regulations, and (c) security of proprietary information demanded by regulators tends to inhibit investment.

As noted in Section 2.2, however, environmental regulations can either retard or *enhance* technological progress. In what follows, the relationships among regulation, technological progress, productivity growth, and inflation are made more explicit, and studies which have attempted to assess the impact of environmental regulations on productivity growth are reviewed.

4.2.1. Regulation, technological progress, and productivity growth: A simple model[8]

In order to identify the formal channels through which environmental regulations can affect productivity growth, we begin from a microeconomic model of a representative firm's technology. We impose no restrictions on the technology's returns to scale, the marginal rates of substitution among the variables in the production function, the *form* of technological progress, or the manner in which regulatory policy affects productivity growth. While the primary sources of productivity growth identified by this model are themselves functions of prior variables, the sources are emphasized because of their central role in the production process and their relationship to regulatory policy.

Consider a twice differentiable production function *F*:

$$Q = F(X_1, X_2, \ldots, X_n, R, T), \tag{6}$$

where Q is output, the X_i are inputs, R is a measure of regulatory intensity, and T is time. We assume all factor markets are competitive, but we do not require competitive output markets.

The regulatory intensity variable R is of primary interest. In our model, R is an index number bounded from below by zero. The variable would take a zero value only in the unlikely instance that absolutely no regulations applied to the firm. Otherwise, R has some positive value whose magnitude is determined by the scope and severity of the regulations imposed on the firm. The measure R takes successively higher positive values as the number of regulations increase, the standards of existing regulations become more strict, and/or the compliance requirements (e.g. reporting) become more complex.

Logarithmically differentiating (6) with respect to time decomposes the rate of growth in output (economic growth) into its source components

$$\frac{d \ln Q}{dT} = \sum_i \frac{\partial \ln Q}{\partial \ln X_i} \cdot \frac{d \ln X_i}{dT} + \frac{\partial \ln Q}{\partial R} \cdot \frac{dR}{dT} + \frac{\partial \ln Q}{\partial T}. \tag{7}$$

In eq. (7), the rate of growth in firm output equals the output elasticity weighted

---

[8] An extended version of this model was developed by Frank Gollop in Christainsen et al. (1980).

sum of rates of growth of inputs, plus the elasticity weighted rate of change in regulatory intensity, plus the rate of technological progress.

The logarithmic partial derivatives appearing in (7) have particular economic interpretations. Given competitive factor markets and optimizing behavior by the firm, each logarithmic marginal product equals the product of the corresponding input's cost share and the degree of scale economies

$$\frac{\partial \ln Q}{\partial \ln X_i} = \frac{\partial Q}{\partial X_i} \cdot \frac{X_i}{Q} = \frac{P_i X_i}{P_Q Q \left(1 - \frac{1}{\varepsilon}\right)} = \frac{P_i X_i}{\left(\frac{\partial C}{\partial Q}\right) Q}$$

$$= \frac{P_i X_i}{C} \left(\frac{\partial \ln C}{\partial \ln Q}\right)^{-1}$$

$$= \frac{P_i X_i}{C} \left(\sum_i \frac{\partial \ln Q}{\ln X_i}\right), \tag{8}$$

where P_Q is the product's market price, ε is the price elasticity of demand, C is total production cost, and

$$P_i = P_Q \left(1 - \frac{1}{\varepsilon}\right) \frac{\partial Q}{\partial X_i} \qquad (i = 1, 2, \ldots, n),$$

$$P_Q \left(1 - \frac{1}{\varepsilon}\right) = \frac{\partial C}{\partial Q}, \tag{9}$$

$$\sum_i \frac{\partial \ln Q}{\partial \ln X_i} = \left(\frac{\partial \ln C}{\partial \ln Q}\right)^{-1}.$$

The sum of these output elasticities equals the conventional measure of returns to scale

$$v_Q = \sum_i \frac{\partial \ln Q}{\partial \ln X_i} \qquad (X_1, X_2, \ldots, X_n, R, T). \tag{10}$$

If v_Q equals unity, output proportionally responds to changes in all inputs. This condition characterizes constant returns to scale. If v_Q is greater (less) then unity, output responds more (less) than proportionally with increases in all inputs, thus implying the existence of increasing (decreasing) returns to scale. Regardless of its value, v_Q isolates that change in output which is related to changes in all inputs. It is independent of technological progress and changes in regulatory policy.

The partial derivatives of output with respect to regulatory intensity v_R and time v_T define the rates of regulatory effect and technological progress, respectively:

$$v_R = \frac{\partial \ln Q}{\partial R} \qquad (X_1, X_2, \ldots, X_n, R, T), \tag{11}$$

$$v_T = \frac{\partial \ln Q}{\partial T} \qquad (X_1, X_2, \ldots, X_n, R, T). \tag{12}$$

Holding all inputs and time constant, v_R measures the effect of changes in regulatory intensity on the level of output. A positive (negative) value indicates that increased regulations induce higher (lower) production. Similarly, if v_T is greater (less) than zero, then, holding all inputs and regulations constant, technological progress leads to increased (decreased) rates of production.

Given this characterization of economic growth, the sources of productivity growth can be identified. Formally defined, the growth rate of total factor productivity v_G equals the rate of growth in output less the constant returns to scale weighted average of rates of growth in inputs:

$$v_G = \frac{d \ln Q}{dT} - \sum_i \frac{P_i X_i}{C} \cdot \frac{d \ln X_i}{dT}, \tag{13}$$

since, from (8):

$$\frac{\partial \ln Q}{\partial \ln X_i} = \frac{P_i X_i}{C} \qquad (i = 1, 2, \ldots, n). \tag{14}$$

Consequently, any nonproportional change in output that cannot be explained by a proportional change in all inputs is modeled as the firm's productivity growth.

Subtracting the cost share weighted average of input growth rates from both sides of (8) permits us to express the rate of productivity growth as the sum of its three source components:

$$\begin{aligned} v_G &= \frac{d \ln Q}{dT} - \sum_i \frac{P_i X_i}{C} \cdot \frac{d \ln X_i}{dT} \\ &= \sum_i \frac{P_i X_i}{C} (v_Q - 1) \frac{d \ln X_i}{dT} + v_R \frac{dR}{dT} + v_T. \end{aligned} \tag{15}$$

Eq. (15) states that the rate of productivity growth equals the sum contribution of scale economies, regulatory intensity, and technological progress.

If the technology exhibits constant returns, v_Q equals unity and (15) reduces to

$$v_G = v_R \frac{dR}{dT} + v_T; \tag{16}$$

that is, productivity growth is affected only by changes in regulatory policy and technical change. If, however, v_Q is greater (less) than unity, there are increasing (decreasing) returns and scale economies (diseconomies) are a positive (negative) source of productivity growth; that is, given $d \ln X_i/dt > 0$ for all i:

$$\sum_i \frac{P_i X_i}{C}(v_Q - 1)\frac{d \ln X_i}{dT} > 0, \quad \text{for } v_Q > 1,$$

and

$$\sum_i \frac{P_i X_i}{C}(v_Q - 1)\frac{d \ln X_i}{dT} < 0, \quad \text{for } v_Q < 1.$$

Similar interpretations apply to regulatory effects and technological progress. If v_R equals zero, changes in regulatory intensity have no *direct* impact on productivity growth. If v_R is greater (less) than zero, increased regulation generates a positive (negative) contribution to productivity growth v_G. Analogously, if v_T is zero, there is no technological progress. Technological change exists (makes a positive or negative contribution) only if v_T is greater or less than zero.

4.2.2. Direct and indirect regulatory effects

The rate of productivity growth v_G defined in (13) is expressed as the sum of three source components

$$v_G(\cdot) = \sum_i \frac{P_i X_i}{C}\big[v_Q(\cdot) - 1\big]\frac{d \ln X_i}{dT} + v_R(\cdot)\frac{dR}{dT} + v_T(\cdot), \qquad (17)$$

where v_Q, v_R, and v_T, defined in (10), (11), and (12), respectively are each functions of all input levels (X_i), the degree of regulatory intensity (R), and time (T). Consequently, changes in the intensity of regulation can affect a firm's productivity growth in direct and indirect ways.

Regulation's direct or first-order effect is modelled by the partial derivative v_R. Holding the firm's inputs and level of technology constant, changes in regulation can impact productivity growth directly. Increased regulations, for example, may shift managerial attention from the production of the firm's "conventional" output to the filing of detailed government reports. The expected *direct* effect in this case is negative.

Important indirect effects also can result since regulation can influence the contribution of *each* source of productivity growth. These indirect or second-order effects are captured by the partial derivatives of scale economies and the rates of regulatory effect and technological progress with respect to regulatory intensity. Complying with regulations might, for example, divert resources away from research and development activities and thereby retard technological progress. The result would be an indirect effect of regulation on productivity growth, a second-order effect transmitted through a change in the rate of technological progress.

In summary, regulation can affect the growth rate of total factor productivity (v_G) directly, or, indirectly, by affecting the existence of scale economies and/or the rate of technological progress.

Two important limitations of the above model should be made explicit. First, the model takes the type of output produced by a representative firm as given. In fact, however, regulation might affect the economy's aggregate productivity performance by altering the *composition* of output. It has been argued, for example, that shifting production away from manufactured goods and toward services retards productivity growth. Second, the model refers to *total factor* productivity and not *labor* productivity. The latter could be affected by the *ratio of nonlabor to labor inputs* as well as the influences mentioned above.

The flowcharts in Figure 9.2 attempt to encapsulate a more complete view of the possible first- and second-order effects of regulation on productivity growth.

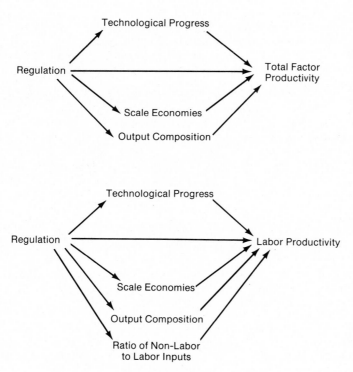

Figure 9.2. The effect of regulation on productivity.

4.2.3. The relationship between productivity growth and inflation

Declining productivity growth reflects a fundamental problem in macroeconomic performance and underlies other symptoms of economic malfunction as well. The problem of inflation and the productivity slowdown are related in a number of ways. For example, the dislocations caused by unpredictable changes in the rate of inflation may well generate inefficiencies that contribute to a decline in productivity growth. Conversely, to the extent that inflationary pressures result from a deficiency in the aggregate supply of output relative to aggregate demand, low rates of productivity growth will contribute to these pressures.

A simple way of looking at the effect of productivity growth on inflation is to consider the following identity: $\dot{P} = \dot{W} - \dot{w}$, where $\dot{P}$ is the rate of inflation, $\dot{W}$ is the growth rate of *nominal* wages, and $\dot{w}$ is the growth rate of *real* wages. If, over time, it can be assumed that the growth rate of real wages will equal the growth rate of labor productivity ($\dot{LP}$), then given the growth rate of nominal wages, inflation and productivity growth can be seen to be inversely related; $\dot{P} = \dot{W} - \dot{LP}.$[9]

As noted above, however, there may be two-way causality between productivity growth and inflation, and any econometric model of one or the other must take into account this simultaneity. The point to be stressed here is that regulation may affect the rate of inflation through its effect on productivity growth.

The extent to which past increases in regulation caused productivity to decelerate – and price increases to accelerate – remains controversial, however. The test is in the strength of the linkage between such regulations and economic growth and efficiency. The next section discusses some of the studies which have attempted to address this issue and to establish the strength of this linkage.

4.2.4. Studies of the impact of environmental policy on productivity growth

4.2.4.1. Macroeconometric studies. An important approach to estimating the effect of environmental regulations on productivity is through adoption of standard, intermediate-term, macroeconometric models. With these models, the impact of aggregate expenditures or cost changes induced by environmental policy can be traced through the economy over time.

An attractive feature of the macroeconometric models is that the predictions they generate are integrated and simultaneously determined. While the model outlined earlier in this section captures the primary channels through which

---

[9] During the 1960–64 period, the growth rate of nominal wages in the United States was 4.5 percent. Because labor productivity increased at a 3.5 percent clip, the rate of inflation was only 1 percent as measured by the Consumer Price Index. In 1974, on the other hand, nominal wages increased at a 9 percent rate, twice the pace of the 1960–64 period, but productivity growth fell by 3 percent; there was thus an inflation rate of *12 percent* that year, and a decline in material living standards.

regulation can affect productivity growth, the subsequent discussion revealed that there are other channels through which regulation might operate – by altering the composition of output and prices, for example. In principle, macroeconometric models can capture *all* of the important channels through which regulation might operate. The equations of the models are linked so that price increases in one sector are translated into cost and price increases in other sectors. These secondary effects may involve changes in employment levels, which in turn may influence aggregate demand. Similarly, the many other feedbacks inherent in macroeconometric models ensure at least a crude approximation to the simultaneous and interdependent decision-making characterizing a market economy.

The general approach taken in the macroeconometric simulation studies is easy to describe. Beginning with estimates of the expenditures necessitated by regulation, it is first determined how these expenditures will manifest themselves in the economy (or how their absence would be felt). By adjusting the appropriate equations in the model, one can characterize an economy without regulation and the spending it entails. For example, any jobs related to the manufacturing of mandated pollution control equipment must be deleted in the "without controls" case. Similarly, investment in pollution control equipment must be removed, as must state and local spending for pollution abatement. State and local taxes must be reduced by the amount of expenditures in the "without" case, as well. Finally, a basic set of assumptions must be made about the future values of the variables determined outside the model, the so-called exogenous variables. For example, how much will the three levels of government spend for goods and services in the years to come? At what rates will income be taxed? How fast will the money supply expand? What will be the rate of population growth?

Once appropriate adjustments have been made to the model and the exogenous variables have been specified, the model can be solved to produce a picture of the economy operating over some period of time first in the presence, and then in the absence of environmental regulation. The only difference between the two simulations is that one includes spending and other changes induced by regulation, while the other does not. The difference between the time paths of the important variables is then taken to be the measure of the effect of regulation. This is the basic approach that has been used in all the simulation studies to date.

The Data Resources (DRI) macroeconometric study (1979, 1981), one of the most important of this type, indicates that environmental policy measures in the United States reduce productivity as the induced pollution control investment "crowds out" alternative capital investments in plant and equipment. In describing the results of their simulation analysis of labor productivity, DRI (1979) stated:

The increased factor demands associated with the operation and maintenance of pollution abatement equipment resulted in a drop in labor productivity. Any given firm would now require additional employees to produce the same level of output. Further, the capital stock, which helps make the workers produce more, had been diluted with a portion which made no contribution to production. The DRI model solution results indicate that productivity was 0.5 percent lower by 1978 and 1.4 percent lower in 1986, given the pollution requirements. Over the entire period (1970–86), productivity growth averaged 0.1 percentage point a year less. The reduction in productivity growth produces higher unit labor costs (the cost of labor associated with the production of a given unit of output). Initially these produce reduced profit margins, eroding corporate profits, but over time they get passed on in the form of higher prices.

The conclusion of this and other macroeconometric studies [e.g. Evans (1978)], then, is that environmental regulations have had an adverse effect on economic performance in the United States, but that it has not been large in magnitude. Employment, output, inflation, and productivity have all been affected, but the effects are consistent with the fact that environmental control expenditures have represented only about 1.5–2.0 percent of GNP in the United States. These studies, however, do have weaknesses, and their results should not be taken as definitive. For one thing, the higher prices to which environmental regulations contribute may trigger responses by labor and other factor suppliers to recoup the price increases in the form of higher wages and other factor payments. Second, environmental regulation (and the uncertainties surrounding it) may delay the installation of facilities and new technologies, or indeed, ultimately lead to a decision not to install some of them at all. These two effects have not been captured in the estimates yielded by the macroeconometric models to date and lead to caution in interpreting their conclusions. A full evaluation of the impact of environmental regulations should include studies based on alternative approaches as well.

4.2.4.2. Growth accounting studies. A relatively straightforward, yet comprehensive, approach to understanding the effect of various factors on the growth of GNP or productivity is the "growth accounting" approach. The work of Edward Denison (1978, 1979a, 1979b) exemplifies this approach. See also, for example, Kendrick (1978), Norsworthy, Harper and Kunze (1979), and Thurow (1980).

In it, separate estimates of the role of various determinants are made, often on the basis of rough, ad hoc analyses along with a good dose of judgment. Then the remaining, unaccounted-for residual is assigned to a broad, catch-all category. In Denison's framework, output in the nonresidential business sector serves as the numerator in the productivity index. The input denominator is a combined measure of labor, capital and land, in which relative earnings are used to weight the inputs. This measure is consistent with national product accounts usage. To evaluate the impact of environmental regulations on the productivity index,

Denison estimates the incremental costs of production made necessary by environmental regulations. These costs as a percentage of the total costs of the three inputs are then used as an estimate of the percentage reduction in output per unit of input ("productivity") attributable to regulation. This procedure, in effect, assumes that the inputs required by environmental policy would, in the absence of these regulations, be used in the production of measured output.

Crucial to Denison's estimates is the definition of the incremental costs attributed to environmental policy. First, total environmental costs are defined as the annual operation, maintenance and repair (OMR) costs for environmental purposes, plus the sum of depreciation on pollution abatement equipment and an estimate of the *opportunity cost* of the stock of pollution abatement equipment. The opportunity cost refers to what this capital *could* have earned if it were conventional capital rather than pollution abatement equipment. Denison computes this to be the product of the net stock of pollution abatement equipment and the *average* rate of return on the net capital stock observed in the economy. (Both the OMR and capital stock estimates are U.S. Department of Commerce series.) Then an estimate of the level which these environmental costs would have attained in the *absence* of regulations is subtracted from actual environmental costs to yield an estimate of the *incremental* costs attributable to environmental policy.

Using the incremental environmental cost estimate so derived, Denison constructs an index indicating the impact of post-1967 regulations on productivity growth. From 1967 to 1969 the average annual impact was -0.05 percentage points; from 1969 to 1973 it was -0.1 percentage points; during 1973–1975 the effect peaked at -0.22 percentage points; in 1975–1978 it decreased to -0.08 percentage points.

While not an unreasonable approach, Denison's procedure is open to question on several counts. First, the data employed in estimating environmental costs are taken from employer surveys and may reflect the incentive in such data collection procedures for exaggerated claims of required costs. For example, new equipment which is *both* more efficient and which generates fewer residuals is likely to be recorded as pollution abatement equipment. The reliability of the underlying data series has been questioned by Peskin (1980) on other grounds as well. Second, as described above, Denison's procedure implicitly assumes that, for a given level of inputs, marketed output is reduced by pollution-control-mandated investments on a dollar-for-dollar basis. If, in fact, because of input substitution, pollution control expenditures do not divert equivalent expenditures on standard inputs, output would not fall to the extent estimated by Denison. In other words, input usage could be changed in such a way as to ensure compliance with regulations, but the loss in output from changing the way in which inputs are used might be *less* than the reported costs of pollution abatement expenditures themselves. Denison's estimate may therefore overstate the negative impact of environmental policy on productivity growth. Third, Denison assumes that inputs displaced by environmental regulations would have generated the *average* rate of return observed in the economy. This presumes that business firms do not displace marginal, low-return activities first (if displacement is required). Again, the direction of the bias is to overstate the productivity-reducing impact of environmental policy.

Finally, the growth accounting estimates, by being tied to the national income and product accounts, disguise the fact that the source of the expenditure mandated by regulations determines the estimated effect of the regulations on *measured* output. For example, if increased expenditures for mandated environmental protection are made by government or consumers, *measured* productivity is *not* adversely affected. These expenditures *are* directly reflected as *outputs* in the national accounts. In other words, purchases of pollution abatement equipment by consumers or government contribute to real gross national product as presently measured. Expenditures for pollution abatement equipment made by *businesses*, on the other hand, *do not*. They are viewed by the Department of Commerce as increases in production costs which contribute to the value of the GNP implicit price deflator and *nominal* GNP, but *not* real GNP. The estimates by Denison, by neglecting induced governmental and consumer expenditures and focusing only on the effect of the regulations on *measured* output, could then *understate* the true adverse effect on productivity growth.

Taken at face value, Denison's estimates, like those of Data Resources, imply that environmental regulations have reduced productivity growth, but that they in no way account for a major portion of the productivity slowdown. As we have seen, however, much uncertainty surrounds these estimates.

4.2.4.3. Other studies. In addition to the macroeconometric and "growth accounting" studies, there have been a wide variety of other analyses designed to measure the impact of environmental regulations on measured productivity growth in the United States. Some of these studies have adopted a cross-section approach, in which the burden of environmental regulations (as measured by pollution control expenditures) by industry is compared with industry productivity performance. By holding constant other factors, it has been hoped that the contribution of environmental regulations to productivity change could be established. Other studies have compared the productivity performance of industries heavily impacted by environmental controls, both before and after the controls went into effect, with the performance of industries not heavily impacted by regulations. If the heavily impacted industries showed a more rapid decrease in productivity growth than the others, a causal link would again be established [Crandall (1979, 1980, 1981)].

Yet another approach for establishing this linkage is a statistical analysis of the time series of productivity growth. As noted for the United States, this series appears to have significant breaks in the time pattern of growth – for example, 1966 or 1967 and 1973. The question posed in these analyses, then, is: Can factors be identified as accounting for these breaks in trend? The intensity of environmental controls has been included among these factors [Siegel (1979)].

All of these U.S.-based studies are subject to important caveats and reservations. The data are less than ideal, the number of observations is limited (in both the cross-section and time series studies), potentially important contributors to the productivity slowdown have not been included in the analyses, and the specification of the models has, in some cases, been inconsistent with economic theory. Nevertheless, each of them has added some insight into the environmental regulation-productivity slowdown puzzle for the United States. Given the importance of the issue, an overall assessment of the quantitative importance of the linkage between environmental regulations and productivity growth is in order. Two propositions follow directly from these findings:

(1) All of the studies noted find a distinct relationship between environmental regulations and the productivity slowdown in the United States. Although many other factors have also contributed to the slowdown, environmental regulations have played a role.

(2) It has been impossible to establish a single quantitatively reliable estimate of the magnitude of the contribution of environmental controls to the productivity slowdown. Based on the full set of studies of this linkage and considering the post-1970s pattern to that before 1970, a reasonable minimum estimate of the contribution of environmental regulations to the slowdown in the United States would be 5 percent of the slowdown. A maximum estimate would be 15 percent, although one or two studies assign a contribution as high as 20 percent. An appraisal of all of the studies would support a conclusion that approximately 8–12 percent of the slowdown in measured productivity growth from the 1960s to the 1970s was due to environmental regulations.

4.3. The effects of environmental policy on unemployment

4.3.1. The "bottom-up" approach

There are two basic techniques that have been used to measure the consequences of environmental policies on employment. One can be called a "bottom-up" approach, since it initially attempts to measure the impact of a specific policy change on individual households and businesses, and then to trace in a very detailed way the changes in demand, output, and prices that this change induces. The numerous individual responses are added to calculate the aggregate impact of the policy. The second technique, discussed later, is a "top-down" approach. The bottom-up approach is often referred to as a microsimulation technique; in recent years, it has been widely used by researchers to evaluate policy measures in a number of areas, especially in the tax and income-transfer areas.

The first step is to identify a population of individual firms or households that will be affected by the policy in question. Each unit in this population is differentiated according to a number of individual characteristics, such as income level, family size and composition, age, sex, and educational and racial characteristics. Similarly, firms might be classified by sector, size, and age of equipment. Then, the impact of a specific policy on each household or firm is estimated. The magnitude and nature of the impact will, of course, depend on both the nature of the policy and the characteristics of each firm or household. The next step is to evaluate how specific environmental policies will effect decisions that the household or firm reaches. That is, the behavior of the various agents must be incorporated in a model which builds on a theoretical framework such as that described earlier in this chapter. Will any additional consumption or investment be undertaken? Will the demand for or supply of labor change? If so, by how much?

Once these questions have been answered satisfactorily, the final step is to determine whether these "induced" decisions will affect other households or firms, inducing still more responses. In turn, supply and demand in various markets will be affected, and hence prices and wage rates. When all these effects have been worked out, according to the rules of the economic model, the ramifications of the policy can be evaluated and described by classes of units, as for example, income groups for households, industries for firms, and regions for both firms and households.

Clearly, the larger the number of variables, the more complex the modelling task. Grouping by class makes the effort more manageable, but some detail is lost in the process. In such cases, the effect of environmental policy on a group of firms is estimated, and the induced effect on unit production costs, prices, and input demand for the group is simulated. These changes are passed on through the economy, thereby altering relevant economic variables – prices, costs, sales, and incomes – concerning other groups. Ultimately, such changes will result in an altered mix of goods and services produced in the economy, different relative prices, and new output allocations, as each of the affected markets reaches a new equilibrium.

Perhaps the most comprehensive microsimulation model for evaluating the economic impact of environmental policy was developed by Hollenbeck (1976, 1979), who applied his model to the stationary-source regulations of the amendments to the Clean Air Act of 1970. Hollenbeck used estimates of the actual air-pollution-abatement expenditures made in 1973, and the investment required to achieve and maintain compliance over the 1971–79 period.

Hollenbeck merged a microsimulation model of household decisions with a 17-sector, input–output model of industry behavior. Four occupations and five income classes are distinguished in the study. The structure of the combined model incorporates several fundamental economic relationships that are necessary for estimating the full economic effects of the policy. These relationships include, among others: (1) the effect of pollution control investment induced by policy on the final demand for goods in each sector of the economy; (2) the effect of the policy on the price level of the goods produced by polluting industries; (3) the effect of relative price changes on the composition of consumer demand; (4) the effect of price changes on wage rates and, in turn, the effect of changes in wage rates on the quantity of labor supplied; (5) the effect of changes in the demand for goods on the outputs of industries which directly supply these goods, and on industries which are second, third, and later round suppliers of the directly affected industries; (6) the effect of industrial output changes on the demand for labor, employment, the wage rate, earnings, and household incomes; and (7) the effect of household income changes on the level and composition of household consumption. When the economy receives the direct impacts of the policy, responses occur which reflect these relationships and the economy adjusts until a new equilibrium is achieved.

The net result of this simulation was an estimate that employment declined 0.21 percent as a result of the amendments to the Clean Air Act of 1970, with employment prospects for low-skilled workers most seriously affected. In the aggregate, he estimated there could be an annual reduction of nearly 160000 jobs because of the imposition of stationary-source regulations.

Microsimulation techniques make it possible to analyze in detail the economic effects of various policies by identifying such effects by category of household and firm. However, these techniques are not without limitations. One major disadvantage is that they give no indication of the timing of the impact. In a sense, the microsimulation approach represents an opportunity to compare two snapshots of the structure of the economy, one affected by environmental policy, and one not affected by environmental policy. Another problem is that the elaborate detail that characterizes these models sometimes impedes their reliability and reduces confidence in the estimates they yield, placing the value of the ultimate results in doubt.

4.3.2. The "top-down" approach

The second type of approach to assessing the effect of environmental policies on employment is a top-down approach. The strategy here is first to specify a system of aggregate relationships in the economy, then to identify how a given policy change will affect one or more of the key aggregate economic variables in the system – for example, the demand for investment goods – and, finally, to predict the performance of the economy in both the presence and the absence of the policy change in question. Only after measuring the impact of the policy on the variables in the aggregate is an effort made to estimate the probable effects on individual sectors of the economy.

This approach has been conducted with macroeconometric models such as that constructed by Data Resources. In the analyses discussed here the primary factors presumed to be altered by environmental policy include the level of investment (representing the purchase of pollution abatement equipment by business firms) and the level of government spending for pollution abatement. The level of these expenditures in various years was first estimated. These estimates were then entered into the model as a description of changes in investment spending induced by environmental policy. The analyses discussed also assumed that environmental policy altered some of the basic relationships that are a part of the model. For example, new pollution control investment was presumed to be nonproductive. As a result, the value of industrial assets (against which returns are measured) increased, with no concomitant increase in total productive capacity. Hence, the rate of return was reduced. Moreover, it was assumed that required maintenance of the equipment would add to the production costs of the affected industries and to the prices charged for their output. Both of these adjustments to the model were difficult to specify accurately in advance; as a result, a good deal of judgment and ad hoc estimation was involved.

The first comprehensive evaluation of the macroeconometric implications of environmental regulations was conducted by Chase Economeric Associates (1975), with support from the Environmental Protection Agency. Subsequently, the Chase analysis has been replicated several times, and has been included in the annual report of the Council on Environmental Quality (CEQ).

The Chase model forecasted that, until 1981, environmental measures served to *reduce* the unemployment rate from the levels that would have existed in the absence of environmental policies. Beyond 1981, the model predicted small increases in the unemployment rate because of environmental legislation. By 1983, Chase predicted that the unemployment rate would be about 4 percent higher than would otherwise be the case. Thus, if the rate without the policy were 6 percent, with the policy it would be about 6.25 percent. Analyzing the data, the employment-generating effects outweigh those that tend to reduce employment during periods when investments to protect the environment are larger. However, effects taper off and finally reverse as investment demands are offset by the loss in productivity and slowdown in the rate of growth of real GNP, caused in part by higher prices.

As previously mentioned, Data Resources (1979, 1981) has employed incremental abatement cost estimates (provided by CEQ) to evaluate the macroeconometric impacts of U.S. pollution control legislation for 1970–86. The DRI model is optimistic with respect to the employment effects of pollution control legislation. Employment opportunities show an increase throughout the 1970–86 period. As one might expect, the pollution control sector accounts for most of the gains in employment. Jobs are created in manufacturing and installing pollution control equipment and in operating and maintaining this extra capital investment. From 1982 to 1986 – even when real GNP falls below DRI's estimate of what otherwise would have occurred – the unemployment rate is consistently about 0.2 to 0.3 percentage points below what it would otherwise have been. This is explained by the finding that the incremental abatement costs have a negative effect on the productivity of employed labor. Because of this, more workers are required to produce any given level of GNP, and, as a result, GNP can fall, employment rise, and unemployment fall all at the same time.

4.3.3. *Summary of employment effects*

In estimating the effects on employment of environmental policies, the overriding importance of methodology cannot be overemphasized. Many studies have considered only the direct impact of the policies in question [Hannon and Bezdek (1973), U.S. Department of Labor (1975)]. A more complete analysis, however, must also consider the indirect effects of these policies, with the realization that these may at least partially offset the direct effects.

Thus, there is a need for studies based on a general equilibrium (Hollenbeck) as well as on a macroeconometric (Chase, DRI) model, though each has its limitations. Based on these studies, a reasonable statement of the relationship between employment and environmental policy would appear to be: the overall employment impact of environmental policies, though perhaps negative, is not very severe. The impact is likely to be positive in periods when there is substantial investment in pollution abatement equipment. Whether positive or negative, the empirical work to date indicates that the absolute value of the effect on the nation's unemployment rate is probably less than 0.25 percentage points.

4.4. *The macroeconomic effects of environmental policy: Some best-guess estimates and their policy implications*

By any measure, there was a slowdown in productivity growth in the United States during the 1970s. This slowdown was accompanied by higher rates of inflation and unemployment. It is also clear that environmental regulations cannot escape some of the blame for the slowdown in the rate of productivity growth. However, little evidence exists to suggest that as much as 15 percent of the slowdown in labor productivity in the economy's private business sector can be attributed to them. A reasonable estimate would attribute, say, 8–12 percent of the slowdown in productivity growth to environmental regulations. This amounts to a reduction in the growth rate of labor productivity of 0.2–0.3 percentage points. Taking the growth rate of nominal wage rates as given, environmental regulations have probably been responsible for an increase in the rate of inflation of a similar magnitude.[10] As for the nation's unemployment rate, environmental regulations may have either raised it or lowered it. In either case, the overall impact has probably been less than 0.25 percentage points.

It should be noted that these bottom-line assessments attempt to account for both the *direct* and *indirect* effects of environmental regulations. As a result, whatever effects environmental regulations have on capital investment and the capital/labor ratio are included in assessing their ultimate impact on economic performance. In this vein, the evidence on the adverse impact of environmental regulations on the capital stock and its productivity appears very weak [Christainsen et al. (1980)]. As Sections 2 and 3 pointed out, environmental regulations can have major adverse output and productivity impacts on certain sectors or industries (e.g. copper). These impacts tend to be localized, however, and because of the small size of these sectors relative to the national economy, they appear to have a rather trivial impact on macroeconomic performance.

One basic and overriding point should be made with respect to environmental regulations. The contributions to economic welfare which they are intended to make are, by and large, not reflected in marketed or measured output. These effects include improved health (implying less demand for medical services), longer lives, expanded outdoor recreation opportunities, greater enjoyment of existing recreation opportunities, and reduced demands for cleaning and other "defensive" activities. Were the standard productivity measures effective indicators of economic welfare, these outputs would be included in the numerator of the measure. Although they are difficult to quantify, let alone value, numerous studies have indicated marked increases in these outputs from environmental policy. Some evaluations which have been made of them suggest benefit–cost ratios in excess of one [Lave and Seskin (1977), Freeman (1979)]. If this is in fact the case, the effect of these regulations on "true" productivity would be positive and not negative, and the inclusion of the outputs of these regulations in the numerator of standard productivity measures would both offset the negative effects of other factors on productivity growth and change the *sign* of the effect attributable to environmental regulations.

In any event, there are clear indications that the measured level of productivity in the United States will improve for the foreseeable future. Some of the key factors which contributed to the productivity slowdown of the 1970s – increases in energy prices and the changing age–sex composition of the labor force, for example – have reversed themselves or moderated. Whether sizable increases in capital investment will make a significant contribution to future productivity growth depends largely on the portion of the nation's savings which is pre-empted

---

[10] On this, see Chase (1975) and Data Resources (1979, 1981) once again.

by federal budget deficits. Many economists view capital investment as a key determinant of labor productivity.

5. Conclusions

This chapter has examined some of the economic theory and empirical work pertaining to the distributional and macroeconomic effects of environmental policy. Perhaps the most general conclusion that can be drawn is that no one can say with certainty what these quantitative impacts of environmental policy have been in the past or will be in the future. The barriers to the development of precise, accurate estimates include the complexity of the policies being analyzed and the market reactions to them, the lack of key data and the quality of some of those which are available, the importance of local conditions in determining the magnitude of the impacts, and unsettled methodological disputes.

The available evidence does permit, however, some rather broad conclusions to be drawn about the impacts of environmental policy. The new source bias of the regulations has reduced their impact on existing firms. Adverse employment and productivity impacts have apparently been small, though those which have occurred have been both geographically and sectorally concentrated.

The research and development process has apparently been affected by environmental regulations, at least in those few industries studied so far. There has been a redirection of research and development budgets toward production techniques and products which have fewer environmental side effects.

The distribution of the net benefits of automobile pollution control policy seems unambiguously regressive. Conclusions about the stationary source air pollution control policy are less clear because they are sensitive to the manner in which income levels are assumed to affect the valuation placed on improvements in air quality. In general the cost of water pollution control seems less regressively distributed than the costs of mobile or stationary source air pollution control. What limited evidence we have suggests that the benefits of water pollution control policy may be quite regressively distributed.

The macroeconomic impacts of environmental policy seem to be uniformly small. The available evidence suggests that the adverse effects on the inflation rate and the growth rate of productivity have been no more than 0.3 percentage points. As previously mentioned, adverse employment impacts have also been small, and it is even arguable that policy has acted so as to *increase* employment.

There can be no doubt that refinements can be made in our procedures and, therefore, in our understanding of the quantitative impacts of environmental policy. Yet it would be a mistake to fail to heed what these studies are telling us now because they fail some test of perfection. They afford a valuable chance to understand the impacts of past policies, at least in broad terms, and offer a menu of opportunities for reform. Decisions have to be made with the best information available and the studies we have discussed have added useful, if limited, information to the policy process.

References

Aaron, Henry and Martin McGuire (1970) "Public Goods and Income Distribution", *Econometrica*, 907–920.

Allison, Gail (1977) *Are Jobs Really the Price of a Clean Environment?* (League of Women Voters, Washington).

Asch, Peter and Joseph J. Seneca (1978) "Some Evidence on the Distribution of Air Quality", *Land Economics* 54, 278–297.

Ashford, Nicholas A., Dale Hattis, George R. Heaton, Adam Jaffe, Sally T. Owen and W. Curtiss Priest (1979) *Environmental/Safety Regulation and Technological Change in the U.S. Chemical Industry*, Report to the National Science Foundation, Grant No. PRA 76-21368.

Atkinson, S.E. and T.H. Tietenberg (1984) "Approaches for Reaching Ambient Standards in Non-Attainment Areas: Financial Burden and Efficiency Consequences", *Land Economics* 60, 148–159.

Baumol, William J. (1974) "Environmental Protection and Income Distribution", in: Harold M. Hochman and George E. Peterson (eds.), *Redistribution Through Public Choice* (Columbia University Press, New York).

Baumol, William J. and Wallace E. Oates (1975) *The Theory of Environmental Policy* (Prentice-Hall, Inc., Englewood Cliffs).

Brashares, Edith N., C. Winston Harrington, Wesley A. Magat and Henry M. Peskin (1980) *Industrial Air and Water Pollution Regulations and Innovation*, Report prepared for the Office of Technology Assessment (Resources for the Future, Inc., Washington).

Chase Econometric Associates (1975) *The Macroeconomic Impacts of Federal Pollution-Control Programs*, Report prepared for the U.S. Council on Environmental Quality and the U.S. Environmental Protection Agency (Washington).

Christainsen, G., F. Gollop and R. Haveman (1980) *Environmental and Health-Safety Regulations, Productivity Growth, and Economic Performance: An Assessment*, Joint Economic Committee, 96th Congress, 2nd Session (U.S. Government Printing Office, Washington).

Collins, Robert A. (1977) "The Distributive Effects of Public Law 92-500", *Journal of Environmental Economics and Management* 4, 344–354.

Crandall, R. (1979) "Is Environmental Policy Responsible for Declining Productivity Growth?", Paper prepared for Annual Meeting of Society of Government Economists, Atlanta, Georgia.

Crandall, R. (1980) "Pollution Controls and Productivity Growth in Basic Industries", in: T. Cowing and R. Stevenson (eds.), *Productivity Measurements in Regulated Industries* (Academic Press, New York) 347–368.

Crandall, R. (1981) Regulation and Productivity Growth, Brookings Institution Reprint No. 375 (The Brookings Institution, Washington).

Data Resources Incorporated (1979) *The Macroeconomic Impact of Federal Pollution Control Programs: 1978 Assessment*, Report submitted to the Environmental Protection Agency and the Council on Environmental Quality.

Data Resources Incorporated (1981) *The Macroeconomic Impact of Federal Pollution Control Programs: 1981 Assessment*, Report submitted to the Environmental Protection Agency.

David, M., W. Eheart, E. Joeres and E. David (1980) "Marketable Permits for the Control of Phosphorus Effluent into Lake Michigan", *Water Resources* 16, 263–70.

Denison, E. (1978) "Effects of Selected Changes in the Institutional and Human Environment Upon Output Per Unit of Input", *Survey of Current Business* 58, 21–44.

Denison, E. (1979a) "Pollution Abatement Programs: Estimates of Their Effect Upon Output Per Unit of Input, 1975–1978", *Survey of Current Business* 59, 58–59.

Denison, E. (1979b) *Accounting for Slower Economic Growth* (The Brookings Institution, Washington).

Dewees, Donald N. (1983) "Instrument Choice in Environmental Policy", *Economic Inquiry* 21, 53–71.

Dorfman, N.S. (1975) "Who Will Pay for Pollution Control? The Distribution by Income of the Burden of the National Environmental Protection Program", 1972–1980, *National Tax Journal* 28, 101–115.

Downing, Paul B. (1981) "A Political Economy Model of Implementing Pollution Laws", *Journal of Environmental Economics and Management* 8, 255–271.

Economic Report of the President, (1982) (U.S. Government Printing Office, Washington).

Economic Report of the President (1983) (U.S. Government Printing Office, Washington).

Evans, Michael "Testimony before the Congressional Joint Economic Committee, Special Study on Economic Change: Hearings Before the Joint Economic Committee", Congress of the United States, Part 2 (U.S. Government Printing Office, Washington) 596–615.

Freeman, A. Myrick III (1977) "The Incidence of the Cost of Controlling Automobile Air Pollution", in: F.T. Juster (ed.), *The Distribution of Economic Well-Being* (Ballinger Publishers, Cambridge).

Freeman, A. Myrick III (1979) *The Benefits of Environmental Improvement* (Johns Hopkins University Press, Baltimore).

Giannesi, Leonard P. and Henry M. Peskin (1980) "The Distribution of the Costs of Federal Water Pollution Control Policy", *Land Economics* 56, 85–102.

Gianessi, Leonard P. and Henry M. Peskin (1981) "Analysis of National Water Pollution Control Policies, 2. Agricultural Sediment Control", *Water Resources Research* 17, 803–821.

Gianessi, L.P., Henry M. Peskin, and Edward Wolff (1977) "The Distributional Implications of National Air Pollution Damage Estimates", in: F. Thomas Juster (ed.), *The Distribution of Economic Well-Being* (Ballinger, Cambridge, Mass.).

Gianessi, L.P., Henry M. Peskin, and Edward Wolff (1979) "The Distributional Effects of Uniform Air Pollution Policy in the United States", *Quarterly Journal of Economics* 93, 281–301.

Gollop, Frank M. and Marc J. Roberts (1983) Environmental Regulations and Productivity Growth: The Case of Fossil-Fueled Electric Power Generation, *Journal of Political Economy* 91, 654–74.

Grad, Frank P., Albert J. Rosenthal, Laurie R. Rocket, James A. Fay, John Heywood, John F. Kain, Gregory K. Ingram, David Harrison, Jr. and Thomas Tietenberg (1975) *The Automobile and the Regulation of Its Impact on the Environment* (University of Oklahoma Press, Norman).

Hanke, Steve H. and Ivars Gutmanis (1975) "Estimate of Industry Water-borne Residuals Control Costs: A Review of Concepts, Methodology and Empirical Results", in: Henry M. Peskin and Eugene P. Seskin (eds.), *Cost Benefit Analysis and Water Pollution Policy* (Urban Institute, Washington), 231–268.

Hannon, B. and R. Bezdek (1973) "Job Impact of Alternatives to Corps-of-Engineers Projects", Engineering Issues – *Journal of Professional Activities* 99, 421–531.

Harrington, Winston (1981) "The Distribution of Recreational Benefits from Improved Water Quality: A Micro Simulation", Discussion Paper D-80, Quality of the Environment Division, Resources for the Future.

Harrison, David Jr. (1975) *Who Pays for Clean Air: The Cost and Benefit Distribution of Automobile Emission Standards* (Ballinger Publishers, Cambridge).

Haveman, Robert H. (1978) *The Results and the Significance of the Employment Studies in Organization for Economic Co-operation and Development, Employment and Environment* (Organization for Economic Cooperation and Development, Paris) 48–53.

Hollenbeck, K. (1976) "The Employment and Earnings Incidence of the Regulation of Air Pollution", Unpublished doctoral dissertation, University of Wisconsin-Madison.

Hollenbeck, K. (1979) "The Employment and Earnings Impact of the Regulation of Stationary Source Pollution", *Journal of Environmental Economics and Management* 6, 208–221.

Iverstine, Joe C., Jerry L. Kinard, and William S. Slaughter (1978) *The Impact of Environmental Protection Regulations on Research and Development in the Industrial Chemical Industry*, Report to the National Science Foundation, Grant No. PRA 76-21321, May.

Johnson, F.R. (1980) "Income Distributional Effects of Air Pollution Abatement: A General Equilibrium Approach", *Atlantic Economic Journal* 8, 10–21.

Kendrick, John (1978) "Testimony before the Congressional Joint Economic Committee, Special Study on Economic Change: Hearings Before the Joint Economic Committee", Congress of the United States, Part 2 (U.S. Government Printing Office, Washington), 616–636.

Koch, C. James and Robert A. Leone (1979) "The Clean Water Act: Unexpected Impacts on Industry", *Harvard Environmental Law Review* 3, 84–111.

Kopp, R. and V. Smith (1980) "Productivity Measurement and Environmental Regulation: An Engineering-Econometric Analysis", in: T. Cowing and R. Stevenson (eds.), *Productivity Measurements in Regulated Industries* (Academic Press, New York) 249–281.

Lake, Elizabeth, William M. Hanneman and Sharon M. Oster (1979) *Who Pays for Clean Water? The Distribution of Water Pollution Control Costs* (Westview Press, Boulder).

Lave, L. and E. Seskin (1977) *Air Pollution and Human Health* (Johns Hopkins University Press, Baltimore).

Leone, Robert A. and John E. Jackson (1977) "The Political Economy of Federal Regulatory Activity: The Case of Water Pollution Controls", in: Gary Fromm (ed.), *Studies in Public Regulation* (The MIT Press, Cambridge, MA.), 231–271.

Lyon, Randolph (1982) "Auctions and Alternative Procedures For Allocating Pollution Rights", *Land Economics* 58, no. 1, 1–15.

Magat, Wesley A. (1978) "Pollution Control and Technological Advance: A Dynamic Model of the Firm", *Journal of Environmental Economics and Management* 5, 1–25.

Magat, Wesley A. (1979) "The Effects of Environmental Regulation on Innovation", *Law and Contemporary Problems* 43, 4–25.

Maital, Schlomo (1973) "Public Goods and Income Distribution: Some Further Results", *Econometrica* 41, 561–68.

Maloney, Michael T. and Robert E. McCormick (1982) A Positive Theory of Environmental Quality Regulations, *Journal of Law and Economics* 25, 99–123.

Norsworthy, J., M. Harper, and K. Kunze (1979) *The Slowdown in Productivity Growth: Analysis of Some Contributing Factors* Brookings Papers on Economic Activity 2, 387–421.

Organization for Economic Cooperation and Development (1978) *Employment and Environment* (Organization for Economic Cooperation and Development, Paris).

Ostro, Bart D. (1981) "The Distributive Effects of Public Law 92-500", *Journal of Environmental Economics and Management* 8, 196–198.

Palmer, Adele R., William E. Mooz, Timothy H. Quinn and Kathleen A. Wolf (1980) *Economic Implications of Regulating Chlorofluorocarbon Emissions from Nonaerosol Applications*, Report prepared for the U.S. Environmental Protection Agency (Rand, Santa Monica).

Peskin, H.M. (1978) "Environmental Policy and the Distribution of Benefits and Costs", in: Paul Portney (ed.) *Current Issues in U.S. Environmental Policy* (Johns Hopkins University Press for Resources for the Future, Baltimore), 144–163.

Peskin, H. (1980) *Environmental Gains and Economic Losses: A Connection?* Report for the Environmental Assessment Council of the Academy of Natural Sciences.

Pittman, Russell W. (1981) "Issues in Pollution Control: Interplant Cost Differences and Economies of Scale", *Land Economics* 57, 1–17.

Portney, P. (1981) "The Macroeconomic Impacts of Federal Environmental Regulations", *Natural Resources Journal* 21, 459–488.

Rose, Marshall (1973) "Market Problems in the Distribution of Emission Rights", *Water Resources Research* 5, 1132–44.

Siebert, Horst (1981) *Economics of the Environment* (Lexington Books).

Siegel, R. (1979) "Why Has Productivity Slowed Down?", *Data Resources U.S. Review* March, 1.59–1.65.

Tietenberg, Thomas H. (1983) "Regulatory Reform in Air Pollution Control: The Role of Economic Analysis", in: Robert H. Haveman and Julius Margolis (eds.), *Public Expenditure and Policy Analysis*, 3rd edn. (Houghton Mifflin Company, Boston) 458–472.

Thurow, L. (1980) "The Productivity Problem", *Technology Review* 83, 40–51.

U.S. Department of Labor, Bureau of Labor Statistics (1975) *Impact of Federal Pollution Control and Abatement Expenditures on Manpower Requirements*, Bulletin 1836 (U.S. Government Printing Office, Washington).

U.S. Environmental Protection Agency (1972) *The Economics of Clean Air–1972* (Environmental Protection Agency, Washington).

U.S. Environmental Protection Agency (1982) *Third Quarter Report of the Economic Dislocation Early Warning System* (Environmental Protection Agency, Washington).

Weisbrod, B.A. (1979) "Distributional Effects of Collective Goods", *Policy Analysis* 5, 67–95.

Wykoff, Frank C. (1970) "Capital Depreciation in the Postwar Period: Automobiles", *The Review of Economics and Statistics* 52, 168–172.

Yan, Chiou-Shuang, An-Min Chung, Edward C. Kaziara and Andrew G. Verzilli (1975) "Air Pollution Control Costs and Consumption Pattern Effects: A Regional Analysis", *Journal of Environmental Economics and Management* 2, 60–68.

Yohe, G.W. (1979) "The Backward Incidence of Pollution Control–Some Comparative Statics in General Equilibrium", *Journal of Environmental Economics and Management* 6, 187–98.

Yu, Eden S.H. and Charles A. Ingene (1982) "The Backward Incidence of Pollution Control in a Rigid-Wage Economy", *Journal of Environmental Economics and Management* 9, 304–310.

Zeckhauser, Richard (1981) "Preferred Policies When There is a Concern for Probability of Adoption", *Journal of Environmental Economics and Management* 8, 215–237.

Zupan, Jeffrey M. (1973) *The Distribution of Air Quality in the New York Region* (Resources for the Future, Inc., Washington).

Chapter 10

COMPARATIVE ANALYSIS OF ALTERNATIVE POLICY INSTRUMENTS

PETER BOHM

University of Stockholm

and

CLIFFORD S. RUSSELL*

Resources for the Future, Washington

1. Introduction

The choice of instruments for environmental policy implementation has had a special place in applied economics since the 1920s, when Pigou suggested the use of taxes on negative external effects and subsidies on positive external effects to correct allocative distortions. This is understandable, for at least at first glance it is a problem that appears to offer a nearly perfect target for our skills. Because of the importance here of external effects and public goods, and because the policies and thus the associated implementation strategies have had to be devised *de novo*, it has seemed an area to which economic insights, independent of other disciplines and unfettered by tedious historical baggage, could make very great contributions.

To some extent, of course, this has been true. Sophisticated theoretical work has contributed to the understanding of the characteristics of particular instruments. Empirical studies have produced estimates of the actual cost advantages to be expected from the adoption of instruments favored by economists instead of those being put in place by policy-makers. But therein lies the rub; those policy-makers have for the most part stubbornly refused to accept and act on the basis of the theory offered and the supporting empirical work. Overall, economists seem to have been perceived as gadflies, ignoring or misunderstanding the real situation and thus producing largely irrelevant criticisms of the instruments actually chosen, along with impractical, even politically dangerous, prescriptions for change. (Although see the comments on European experience below.)

* The second author is grateful for support from the Alfred P. Sloane and Andrew W. Mellon Foundations for his work on alternatives to direct regulation in environmental policy. Both authors wish to thank Alan Kneese, John Mullahy, and especially T.H. Tietenberg for helpful critiques of earlier drafts.

Handbook of Natural Resource and Energy Economics, vol. I, edited by A.V. Kneese and J.L. Sweeney
© *Elsevier Science Publishers B.V., 1985*

As with all such standoffs between the research and policy worlds, some truth resides with both sides. As this review will seek to show, economists have achieved some of their fundamental results by ignoring crucial features of the physical world and by abstracting from the full complexity of the economic world. These concessions to simplicty have made most of the arguments that are easiest to explain, and hence potentially easiest to sell, if not wrong at least seriously misleading. Further, and whether rightly or wrongly, economists seem to have refused to take seriously the political implications of some of their favorite prescriptions. These implications include both straightforward matters of cost distribution and more subtle problems of ethical content. At the same time, the developers and supporters of the regulatory systems currently in place in the United States and many other industrial countries have themselves been guilty of misleading arguments, and some of these will be pointed out in what follows. The core of good sense in economic criticisms of command and control regulation and in economic prescriptions for more flexible incentive systems should not permanently be obscured by the rhetorical flourishes of those who favor systems with strong and explicit moral overtones or who have narrower interests in the evolving status quo.

The structure of this chapter is designed to accomplish four specific goals as part of our broader aim of clarifying the contribution of economic analysis to the debate over the instruments of environmental policy. First, we shall describe the general situation in which environmental policy goals must be achieved. An appreciation of the complexity of this situation will provide a base from which to consider both past error and actual special cases. Second, we shall define a set of dimensions along which policy instruments may usefully be judged. These include: static efficiency, centralized information and computation requirements, enforceability, dynamic incentive effects, flexibility in the face of exogenous change, and implications for goals other than efficiency. In the process, we intend to make explicit the irreducible political content of choices among policy instruments and thus the reasons that technical arguments on the other dimensions will not be decisive in the political arena. Third, we shall briefly review both some major non-economic attempts to evade the complexity of the general case and the record of adoptions of explicitly economic prescriptions.

Finally, following this background tour, we shall return to examine more carefully some of the economic complexities associated with a variety of instruments and problems.

Section 2 will concentrate on administratively (or legislatively) set prices and taxes designed to influence behavior.

Section 3 will be devoted to instruments that complete the set of markets – that is, where commodities or rights are administratively defined and prices are set by decentralized bargains among the actors subject to the policy (owning or wishing to own the rights).

Section 4 will deal with various forms of deposit–refund systems and performance bonds, as well as liability rules.

Section 5 will take up specifications of behavior and other instruments involving direct intervention in the behavior of the actors subject to the policy.

Section 6, finally, will discuss moral suasion as a policy instrument, primarily in contexts where there are significant constraints on the set of policy alternatives.

1.1. Some definitions and background assumptions

The position adopted in this chapter is that choice of policy goal and choice of instrument or implementation system are essentially separable problems. And, for the most part, the discussion here will take as given goals or standards for ambient environmental quality (air, surface or groundwater, landscape or whatever). The conceptually preferable position, that both goal and instrument must be chosen simultaneously in a grand meta-benefit/cost analysis, is for now operationally quite hopeless. Further, we shall usually assume the existence of an agency of government charged with meeting the standards.

The essence of the agency's problem of attaining chosen ambient quality standards is that the actions of many individual and independent actors (firms, households, other government units) affect actual environmental quality. The actors will differ among themselves in production technologies and product mixes (where these words are interpreted broadly enough to include such activities as home space heating and sewage treatment plant operation). In the most general case, the environmental effect of each actor is different from that of every other actor and more than one combination of actions by all the actors will result in meeting the standard.[1] The combinations will differ both in total cost to society and in the way any particular cost is distributed across the set of actors.

These actors are all assumed to be "rational" and self-interested.[2] For the agency to succeed in attaining the ambient environmental standard it must in

---

[1] The most common environmental policy problems involve as "actions" discharges of pollution into part of the natural environment. The effects of each source's actions depend on the characteristics of the environment (stream flow, water temperature, and so forth for water pollutants; wind speed and direction, terrain, hours of sunlight and so forth, for air pollutants). More generally, "actions" can include such diverse matters as the construction of ugly buildings, the use of farming methods that disrupt natural terrestial ecosystems, or the placing of radioactive wastes into trenches or caverns. We usually will take "effects" to be measured relative to the ambient environmental quality standards at specified monitoring points. A more elegant treatment would involve measuring effects as damages (to human health and welfare, the ecological support systems, and so forth, but such an approach to policy implementation is not yet practically significant.

[2] Some criticisms of policy instruments that allow the actors flexibility, such as charges per unit of emissions of pollutant, appear to arise from the opposite assumption – that dischargers of pollution will act in an economically irrational way and pay a higher charge bill than would be optimal just for the pleasure of polluting. It seems possible that these critics have confused the position of a wealthy person confronted by a consumption tax with that of a firm.

some way induce at least some of the actors to take actions contrary to their narrow self-interests as defined in the pre-policy world of relative prices and constraints. The costs of these actions may involve both real resource use and transfers that are costs only to the payors, not to the larger society. The assumptions imply that when an actor, more particularly a firm, is faced with orders or charges ordained by the agency, it will respond in a way to maximize its present value in the long run. In the short run, we can usually capture all that is important by assuming the minimization of costs for given output, location, technology and factor prices, but subject to the new constraint or taking account of the new price, as on pollution discharge.[3] The difference between short and long run is the range of adjustments available. In the long run, the discharger can seek a new location, production process and pollution control technology, even entirely new products to make.

A full description of the background setting for the discussion of environmental policy instruments must include the fact that the agency cannot costlessly know

---

[3] Again it will be useful to tie this notion down by reference to the most common problem, pollution discharge. The cost to an actor of adjusting to orders or prices imposed by the agency will be captured in a cost-of-discharge-reduction function. This function shows the marginal (or total) cost of reducing discharge by an amount, R, below its level in the absence of any agency initiative. For many short run purposes it will be convenient to assume that this function is defined for fixed output, though more generally, output and all factor input decisions are made simultaneously with the decision about R. Thus, more generally, the two problems, one for an emission charge and one for an emission limit, may be written as follows:

Charge

$$\max_{\text{s.t.}} p'Z - q'Y - e(X - R)$$

$$0 = F(Z, Y, X - R),$$

$$Z, Y, X - R, R \geq 0.$$

Limit

$$\max_{\text{s.t.}} p'Z - q'Y$$

$$0 = F(Z, Y, X - R),$$

$$X - R \leq L,$$

$$Z, Y, X - R, R, \geq 0,$$

where Z is a vector of outputs, with prices p'; Y is a vector of inputs other than pollution discharge services, with prices q'; X, uncontrolled discharges; R, discharge reduction; e the emission charge; and L the emission limit.

In the short run, X is implicitly defined by the problem:

$$\max_{\text{s.t.}} p'Z - q'Y$$

$$0 = F(Z, Y, X),$$

$$Z, Y, X \geq 0.$$

This notion of "discharge reduction" can be expanded just as we expanded the notion of "discharge".

what each of the actors is actually doing at any particular time or on average over any period. Checking the behavior of the actors against applicable regulatory orders, or determining what is owed by way of emission charges is another resource-using problem, one we shall refer to as the monitoring problem. The subsequent matter of punishing violators of orders, or those in some way abusing the charge system, we call the enforcement problem. The monitoring problem is made especially difficult, again in the most general case, by the character of "pollution discharges". These are for the most part invisible to the unaided human senses. Furthermore, once a unit of discharge has left the discharge point it is in general not attributable to any particular discharger. Thus, measurement must occur at the point of exit (or before) if it is to occur at all.[4]

Finally, the entire problem of environmental policy implementation is embedded in changing natural (atmospheric land surface, and aquatic) and economic worlds. These changes occur on the short run, stochastic scale of wind and weather shifts as well as the secular scale of changing tastes and technology. As the world changes, with ambient quality standard held constant, the implementation problem changes. If a particular set of actions by dischargers results in meeting the ambient quality constraint under conditions A, those actions may fail to produce an acceptable result under conditions B, perhaps because sources have moved or production levels have changed in response to changing tastes or resource prices, or simply because the natural systems involved do not dilute and disperse the discharges in the same way under B as under A.

1.2. Dimensions for judging environmental policy instruments

The above description of the general situation in which environmental policies must be achieved suggests several dimensions along which potential instruments for achievement may be judged.

(1) *Static efficiency.* The efficient implementation system achieves the chosen goal at least resource cost. This dimension is almost always interpreted in a static sense and that will be the approach here. "Static" means, as a practical matter, that we assume an unchanging environmental goal and allow only for the first round of reaction to the implementation orders or incentives; that is, discharge reductions with fixed technology and location for each discharger.

(2) *Information intensity.* This dimension involves the attempt to measure, at least qualitatively, how much data and what level of predictive modeling skills must be available to the pollution control agency to use the implementation system in question. Its importance lies in the desire for efficiency coupled with our assumption of many different actors affecting the environment differently. As a

---

[4] This, we repeat, is the general case and may be qualified in a number of ways. See below, footnote 47.

general matter, efficiency will require that each actor be given an individually tailored order (such as a discharge reduction order) or be faced with an individually tailored price for discharges or subsidy for discharge reductions. Finding the full set of such tailor-made instruments requires either an information- and computation-intensive "model" of the situation to be regulated or a very difficult trial and error process.

(3) Ease of monitoring and enforcement. This refers to the relative difficulty of making and interpreting the measurements of discharges necessary to judge compliance, prepare bills, or audit self-reporting. These measurements are complicated not only by the features of invisibility and inherent "fugitiveness" already mentioned, but by the variability of discharges with production levels, equipment malfunctions and operator actions; by the imprecision of measurement devices and the discrete sampling techniques used in many such devices; and by the awkwardness involved in obtaining entry to a discharger's premises and setting up elaborate equipment in order to take the samples. The overall effect is to make it very expensive for the agency to use common measurement methods frequently enough to produce any reasonable probability of detecting a true violation of a time-averaged discharge standard (or to check the payment for an emission charge over a similar period).

Enforcement actions to prod violators back into line may include administrative fines, civil or criminal court proceedings and penalties, or more indirect actions, such as blacklisting. The relation between the enforcement penalties and methods and the monitoring activities (and hence the probability of detection) is important in defining the incentives for compliance with the chosen instruments, but the choice of enforcement methods may reasonably be seen as a second-order version of the choice of the instruments themselves and is therefore treated only cursorily in what follows.

(4) Flexibility in the face of economic change. Here the interest is in the ease with which the implementation system adjusts to maintain the given ambient goal when exogenous changes occur in tastes, technologies, resource use, or other features of economic activity. The fundamental distinction is between a system that adjusts through decentralized actions of the regulated dischargers – firms, households, and other government units – and one that must be adjusted through recalculation and imposition by the agency of the new discharge standards or required emission charges. The advantages of flexibility in this sense include the avoidance not only of information gathering and computations, but also of the inevitable political interference with changes in the system.[5]

(5) Dynamic incentives. This involves the actions encouraged by the instrument in the longer run. One important distinction here is between instruments that

---

[5] This judgement assumes that the ambient quality standard is a legitimately chosen policy goal. Tinkering with the implementation system, while aimed at changing only cost shares, may affect the society's ability to achieve the goal itself.

encourage the search for and adoption of new, environment-saving technology and those that encourage retention and operation of existing plants. Another is between instruments that distort relative factor prices, as by making capital-intensive methods artificially cheap, and those that do not. A third distinction of some interest is between instruments that provide incentives for dischargers to move and those that do not.[6]

(6) Political considerations. Several political considerations affect society's choice of policy instrument at least as much as cogent arguments about their relative merits on the above dimensions. Three are especially important. The first is distributional, the second ethical, and the third relates to broader economic stabilization concerns.

At the simplest level, it is clear that the matter of cost distribution is intimately linked to the political viability of alternative ways of meeting collective environmental goals. Because we choose a distribution of benefits when we choose the goals, and because we have no mechanisms (other than the very creakiest mechanisms) for redistributing incomes (and thus benefits), a choice of cost distribution implies a fixed pattern, of net benefits for that broad area of environmental policy.[7] If an analysis of the distribution of costs and benefits shows that a majority of voters or the members of some powerful or vocal voting block will probably incur net costs from the policy, one would certainly be tempted to predict at least a rocky road for it.[8] Note further that, from the point of view of the payor, "mere transfers", such as emission charge payments, are part of the cost of an instrument.

The ethical features of environmental policy instruments include, most prominently, the message conveyed and the extent to which the actors in the system are allowed to choose among alternative actions. One widely held view is that environmental policy should involve stigmatizing pollution, whether as a crime against nature or against other persons. [See, for example, the arguments in Kelman (1981) and those of Railton (1984).] In this view, regulatory orders backed up by criminal sanctions have the proper flavor, while charge systems that make "buying pollution" just like buying labor services, are immoral. A related matter is that of choice. While freeing up discharger choices is usually at the heart

---

[6] This distinction may be illustrated by the difference between an efficient emission charge system, which must be based on individual charges, tailored to location, and a uniform charge system. Under the former there necessarily are possibilities for movement to lower charge locations. (Though, as a practical matter, the anticipated savings might only rarely be large enough to justify the cost of moving.)

[7] As already discussed, in the longer run, by changing residence, job, asset portfolio, or habits, individuals can change their own net benefits from a particular policy (goal plus method of accomplishment).

[8] Because neither costs nor benefits of environmental quality improvements are easy for individuals to determine, most may find it hard to judge where their self interest stands once any option is operating. Thus, predictions may create opposition that would not otherwise exist. Indeed, the idea that opposition *ought* to exist may be itself enough to do in a plan.

of economists' arguments for the efficiency properties of economic incentive instruments, the very provision of such choice appears ethically undesirable to others. If pollution discharge is wrong *per se* (as opposed to being wrong only when done in excess of a discharge standard or as part of a fraud in the context of an emission charge system) then there should at least be no choice about how much of the wrong each actor is allowed to produce. And, indeed, there should be no confusion about "allowable" being equivalent to "acceptable". For those who hold discharge to be wrong, there is no acceptable discharge goal this side of zero, and the only acceptable dynamic incentive is one aimed at that goal. (On ethical questions in environmental policy more broadly, see Chapter 5 of this Handbook.)

Aspects of stabilization policy may also play an important role. At least, this was the case in certain European countries during the 1970s, where municipal waste water treatment installations were improved partly for reasons of environmental policy, partly to counteract recession in the building industry. [See, for example; OECD (1978).]

1.3. Avoiding the complications: Shortcuts from goals to behavior

The practical difficulties of the general case, which imply that advancing along one of the above dimensions usually means giving up something on another (or on several others), may be seen as the inspirations for attempts to construct shortcuts for society to follow. Some of the features of these shortcuts will reappear in later discussions, but for now they may be viewed simply as special cases, in which goal and instrument collapse into a single entity.

One such case involves pure technology standards. The actors in the situation are required to adopt particular treatment (or production) technologies. Whatever discharges result from the adoption are accepted, and the ambient goal implicitly becomes whatever is achieved when all sources comply. This approach has the advantage of appearing easy to monitor (though operation is different from installation and the "easy" monitoring only applies to installation).

The technology standard may be extended to the long run and in the process appear to capture some of the ethical high ground while at the same time seeming to provide desirable incentives. This shortcut amounts to the injunction to "do your best" at all times – in particular to adopt better technology as it becomes available. This seems to force each discharger inexorably toward zero discharge. But, of course, since much technical change is endogenous to the system of incentives, and since this policy implies fresh costs for new technologies with no rewards, "do your best" seems very likely to have the effect of slowing progress toward lower discharges.

A third shortcut is to use an emission charge as a revenue-raising device for a program of environmental quality improvement based on government projects or subsidies. Here, the charge is related to some characteristic of the discharger that will be relatively insensitive to it – for example, output – with the actual unit charge usually based on a rule of thumb relation between output and discharge. In this case, the expectation is that output, and hence charge payments will remain unchanged. In such plans the revenue collected is usually intended to be used for projects such as regional sewers and treatment plants, or treatment plant subsidies to individual dischargers, designed to improve environmental quality. The facilities become, *de facto*, the policy goal, and the environmental quality they produce is accepted willy nilly. Another possibility is to treat the revenue as part of the state's general revenue. For a discussion of the reduction in excess burden from a tax system achievable under this second alternative, see Terkla (1984).

1.4. Historical perspective: Notes on chosen approaches

The residuals from human production and consumption activities have always found their way to the natural environment. And even in long-vanished ages of sparse populations and small scale production units the disposal of these residuals could create local pollution problems in the sense of significant negative externalities. There is no lack of anecdotal evidence of the seriousness of these problems, especially in large cities [Baumol and Oates (1979)]. What does appear to be lacking is evidence that prices (charges) or markets were invited to play any role in dealing with these problems. Regulatory orders backed by fines, imprisonment, or physical punishment, seem to have predominated as policy instruments, though certainly those orders could be quite sophisticated.[9]

What changed over time was the source and geographic scope of pollution problems; not the method of trying to correct them. In the nineteenth century, when rapid industrialization was producing very large air and water pollution problems all over Europe, and in the northeastern United States, it seems that slightly more modern versions of the ancient prohibitions were the medicine first prescribed [e.g. the historical sections in Johnson and Brown (1976) dealing with France, Germany, Hungary, Great Britain and Sweden]. When these manifestly failed, an effort was made to require licenses (permissions, consents, contracts) by the terms of which some limits could be placed on private and municipal dischargers [Richardson et al. (1983.)].

The first significant move away from simple prescription of particular activities in pollution control policy seems to have come very early in this century in Germany, when the first water management cooperatives or Genossenschaften

---

[9] For example, Parker (1976) reports that the record of the manorial court for the Chatteris Manor, including the village of Foxton (in England) contains a number of rules constraining pollution of the brook that ran through the village. Householders were prohibited from allowing ducks or geese to "frequent" the brook, from washing linen "clothes" in the brook, and from draining household wastes into the brook except after 8 at night. All rules were backed by specified fines per offense.

were authorized for river basins in the North Rhine-Westphalia state [Johnson and Brown (1976), Kneese (1964)]. Instead of attempting to forbid the inevitable waste disposal, these organizations set out to deal with it collectively, through sewer and treatment-plant construction, assessing the costs of these efforts to their members. Of even more interest to latter day economists, the method of cost assessment was (and still is) based on the waste load each member generated. Because of the units (money per unit waste) this charge-back method looks very like an effluent charge and has been described as such by many commentators. But, as we shall see below, the common arguments for the social desirability of an effluent or emission charge are based on quite different goals and system design. Therefore, however much we may admire the audacity of the Germans who broke with at least 1000 years of traditional approaches, we really must wait even longer to see a charging scheme designed with incentive rather than revenue-raising effects in mind.[10]

Implementation programs closely related to the pioneering work of the German Genossenschaften exist now in several European countries, including the Netherlands, France and Hungary [Johnson and Brown (1976)]. Sewer services charges, which are a narrower version of the same approach are widely used in the United States and the United Kingdom [Elliott (1973), Urban Systems (1979), Webb and Woodfield (1981)]. But it appears that only in the Federal Republic of Germany has a national system of charges, designed explicitly to have an incentive effect, been put in place. This system was created by the national law passed in 1976 which will take full effect in 1986 [Bower et al. (1981), Brown (1982)]. This charge is linked to permit terms and compliance therewith, but is *not* based on the costs of collective treatment works.

These European countries are exceptions, however. The United States, for example, has not adopted an emission charge system for dealing with any pollution problem (a sketch of the approaches actually adopted is found in the previous chapter). While any number of proposals for charge applications have been made, both at federal and state levels, none has survived to the stage of implementation. Examples of these failed initiatives include [Baumol and Oates (1979) and Zeckhauser (1981)]:

(1) A 1970 proposal for a national tax on lead in gasoline.

(2) A 1970 citizen's initiative in Maine that put a BOD effluent charge on the ballot as a referendum item [Freeman (1970a), (1970b)].

(3) A 1971 proposal for a national effluent charge based on biochemical oxygen demand (BOD).

---

[10] Arguments along this line are made by Johnson and Brown (1976) and by Bower et al. (1981). The collective decision-making process of the Genossenschaften is of some considerable interest in its own right, with the dischargers themselves dominating the boards that decide on quality levels, treatment efforts, and hence necessary charges [Klevorick and Kramer (1973)].

(4) A 1972 SO_2 Emissions Tax Proposal. [This proposal was resurrected by Senator Durenberger of Minnesota, as another alternative for dealing with the problem of acid rain. *Inside EPA* (1983).]

(5) The 1972 Vermont law establishing effluent charges for organic discharges to natural waters. (This law was never put into effect, though neither was it, to our knowledge, repealed.)

Rather, the U.S. system of pollution control developed since the Second World War, and very largely since the late 1960s, contains modern versions of the consent or permit approach.[11] At the present time, however, administrative initiatives are creating many of the features of a *marketable* permit system out of the raw material of the original legislation. These new features will be mentioned below when we discuss marketable permits generally.

It is perhaps too extreme to say that the new German national effluent charge law is the only economic incentive system for pollution control ever successfully legislated. A major exception is the so-called "bottle bill" or deposit–refund system aimed at litter pollution by drink containers. Such laws (and similar ones concerning waste lubrication oil, junked cars, etc.) have been successfully put in place in several states of the United States and many European countries and do constitute explicit attempts to influence polluting behavior through economic incentives [Bohm (1981)]. The fact remains, however, that over the long sweep of history direct regulations (prohibitions, specifications of behavior, nonmarketable permits to discharge) have been the instruments of actual choice for dealing with pollution, whether from geese in village brooks or petroleum refineries on major rivers. Unlike commodity prices and markets, which existed before economists began analyzing them, administratively set prices or legistatively created markets do not appear to have sprung up as intuitive responses to externality problems. Quite the reverse; even after sustained intellectual development of these concepts during the period from 1960, we can find few examples of their application.

Let us turn now to more careful consideration of what that development has been about and to the ongoing debate over whether these newer instruments are or are not to be preferred to one or another version of the traditional approaches.

2. Instruments in the form of prices

The use of prices as instruments of environmental policy began to receive serious, and for the most part favorable, attention from economists in the mid 1960s. The most important early work is generally acknowledged to be that of Kneese

---

[11] More will be said about this system below, but for a reasonably full description, see for water pollution control, Freeman (1978) and for air pollution control, Lave and Omenn (1981).

[especially Kneese (1964)].[12] The theme of this section will be to show how the extremely attractive and compelling case made by Kneese has had to be modified as inconvenient elements of reality were explicitly recognized and dealt with. Because the literature on charges is enormous, matching the broad range of specific questions that has captured the interests of economists, we shall be forced to choose only a few of many lines of argument we might trace. Our choices are based on judgements about practical importance, not necessarily on number of pages devoted to the issue in the literature. We do, however, in the footnotes refer the reader to other disputes.

After we have discussed effluent or emission charges in principle, we shall turn to the design of models for the calculation of optimal charges in realistically complex situations. We shall then be able to report some of the results obtained from those models when they are directed to questions of the relative costs of alternative implementation systems.

To this point, the section will have been couched in static terms, and even our complications of the Kneese model will have assumed away a number of further important considerations relevant to instrument choice. The remainder of the discussion will be devoted to these other matters and will parallel the list of dimensions of judgement offered in the introduction. That is, we consider enforceability, flexibility in the face of exogenous change, dynamic incentive effects, and political implications of alternative instruments.

2.1. Arguments in the static case

For expository convenience in this and certain other sections let us construct a very simple model of an environmental policy problem involving two dischargers of a single residual, a natural environment receiving their discharges, receptors (unspecified in number) suffering damage from the resulting environmental degradation, and two potential monitoring stations at which that degradation can be measured.[13] We shall call the dischargers 1 and 2, and the potential monitoring

---

[12] As a matter of intellectual history, it would be interesting to trace the development of the emission-charge idea from Pigou's statements to Kneese's influential book, with its very practical air. This is not attempted here, but we do note in passing that an even earlier RFF book contained a paper by Gulick (1958) in which the use of prices to "determine interrelationships, priorities, and comparative needs and desires" was advocated in the context of resource problems, including pollution, in the modern city.

[13] A first judgement is implicit in our choice of model structure. It is that a partial equilibrium model can be a useful tool in examining questions of instrument performance. It is not a judgement that will receive universal assent, for general equilibrium treatment allows consideration of the consumption effects of output reductions due to a tax and can thus provide important perspectives about the appropriate instrument for controlling a monopolist and about the symmetry or asymmetry of charges and subsidies. Thus, Mäler's (1974a) comprehensive and insightful treatment of issues related to instrument choice is couched in terms of a general equilibrium model. So is Fisher's (1981)

stations A and B. The following quantities and functions will be central to our purpose:

X_1, $X_2 \equiv$ raw waste loads generated per unit time at the two sources,

R_1, $R_2 \equiv$ reductions in the raw waste loads achieved at the sources, as for example by recycling,

D_1, $D_2 \equiv$ discharges from the two sources per unit time,

so that $D_i \equiv X_i - R_i$, $\hspace{6cm}$ (1)

$C_1(R_1)$, $C_2(R_2) \equiv$ costs of pollution reduction at the two sources $\left(\text{assume } dC_i/dR_i > 0; \ d^2 C_i/dR_1^2 \geq 0 \right)$,

$f(D_1, D_2) \equiv$ damages suffered by receptors of the pollution $\left(\text{assume } \partial f/\partial D_i > 0 \text{ and } \partial^2 f/\partial D_i^2 \geq 0 \right)$.

Sometimes we shall wish to consider ambient quality standards rather than assuming a damage function is known. For this purpose we define:

S_A, $S_B \equiv$ ambient environmental standards at the monitoring points.

The pollution control agency's problem for our simple region may be written in general terms as:

$$\min f(D_1, D_2) + C_1(R_1) + C_2(R_2) \hspace{4cm} (2)$$

or, by (1):

$$\min f(D_1, D_2) + C_1(X_1 - D_1) + C_2(X_2 - D_2). \hspace{2.5cm} (2a)$$

With this apparatus in hand it is possible easily to explore the "Kneese case" for charges and several of the most important qualifications to it. The classic case for emission charges depends on two assumptions: that f is linear and that the locations of the sources does not matter to their relative roles in damage production. Then the problem in (2a) becomes

$$\min a(D_1 + D_2) + C_1(X_1 - D_1) + C_2(X_2 - D_2). \hspace{2.5cm} (3)$$

The first-order conditions for an optimum are:

$$a - dC_1/dR_1 = 0 \quad \text{and} \quad a - dC_2/dR_2 = 0.$$

Thus, if the authority knows the linear damage function it can announce the optimal charge, a, without knowledge of the sources' cost functions. It is easy to see that if each firm minimizes cost, its response to this charge a will be the "proper" one, and $dC_i/dR_i = a$ will be true for $i = 1, 2$. The emission charge

more recent and much simpler discussion. Examples of papers addressing specific issues in a general equilibrium framework include: Burrows (1981) on controlling the monopolistic polluter; Sims (1981) on the asymmetry of subsidies and charges in the short run; Meselman (1982) also on subsidies and charges; and Harford and Ogura (1983) on charges and standards.

approach therefore boasts a powerful combination of static efficiency and information economy.

The first part of this case that we shall examine is the assumption that $D_1 + D_2$
is the appropriate argument for the damage function. Consider, for example, the
possibility that damages are measured at a particular point (say a riverside park)
and that one source is farther upstream from the park than the other. If the
residual involved is not entirely conservative, the appropriate (still linear) damage
function form should be $a(\alpha_1 D_1 + \alpha_2 D_2)$ with $0 \le \alpha_1$, $\alpha_2 < 1$ and $\alpha_1 \ne \alpha_2$.[14]

Then the first order conditions are:

$$a\alpha_1 - dC_1/dR_1 = 0 \quad \text{and} \quad a\alpha_2 - dC_2/dR_2 = 0. \tag{4}$$

They tell us that the optimal charges must be tailored to the location of each
source (location matters) but that the authority can still announce optimal
charges without knowledge of the cost functions *if* it knows both the damage
function and the action of the environment on the discharges (captured in the α_i,
often referred to as "transfer coefficients"). This result holds even if damages are
measured at more than one point and added to get total regional damages, and if
the sources affect the damage function arguments differently at each such location. Thus, if total damages are given by

$$a_A(\alpha_{1A}D_1 + \alpha_{2A}D_2) + a_B(\alpha_{1B}D_1 + \alpha_{2B}D_2) + \cdots a_N(\alpha_{1N}D_1 + \alpha_{2N}D_2),$$

then the optimal charge for source 1 is

$$a_A\alpha_{1A} + a_B\alpha_{1B} + \cdots + a_N\alpha_{1N}$$

The generalization to M sources is also straightforward.

The classical case for charges begins to unravel as soon as we drop the
assumption of linear damage functions. Then the optimal charge is not independent of the optimal discharge levels and, in general, cost functions must be known
to the agency. In the simplest such case, the damage function is non-linear in
$D_1 + D_2$, and the sources have identical cost functions so that if $D_1 = D_2$, then
$C_1(R_1) = C_2(R_2)$. Then it can be shown that at the optimum $D_1 = D_2$, and
$dC_1/dR_1 = dC_2/dR_2$, and a single emission charge is optimal. But the optimal

---

[14] Notice that the form $\alpha_1 D_1 + \alpha_2 D_2$ arises whenever *either* the residual in question is noncon-
servative in the environment (e.g, is chemically changed or physically settles out between source and
receptors) *or* where we are not in a position to measure the total contribution of a source to ambient
quality by looking at a finite number of monitoring points. This latter condition differentiates the
general air pollution problem from the general water pollution problem, because diffusion in the
atmosphere results in the "loss" of discharged residuals.

Notice also that we are assuming a particularly simple form of the environmental model implicitly
embedded in our problem. In general the effect of D_1 on the ambient quality at the damage
measurement point may depend both on the level of D_1 and on the levels of all the other discharges.
In this general case, things are even more difficult than we shall see them to be below for linear
transfer functions.

D_1 and D_2, and hence the optimal charges depend on the cost function parameters. The agency's information requirement is immediately vastly greater.[15]

If either the cost functions are not identical or the locations of the sources matter, then the optimal charges must be source specific and depend on knowledge of the cost functions.

Any number of commentators in the early charges literature pointed out that not only was the assumption of *linear* damage functions unrealistic, but the very idea of any known and accepted damage function was more than economic knowledge could (perhaps ever) support. The point was certainly valid when made, and the reader is free to reach a conclusion on its current validity on the basis of the relevant chapters in this Handbook; our interest is in the line of analysis inspired by it (see especially Chapters 7 and 16). This is the line that takes ambient quality standards, chosen by some exogenous (probably political) process as representing the goals of environmental policy and sees charges as instruments for realizing those goals.

In this context, the agency's problem becomes:

$$\min_{\text{s.t.}} \left[C_1(X_1 - D_1) + C_2(X_2 - D_2) \right] \tag{5}$$

$$g(D_1, D_2) \le S_A$$

for two dischargers and a standard defined at a single point. For M dischargers and N standards, the problem becomes:

$$\min_{\text{s.t.}} \sum_i C_i(X_i - D_i)$$

$$g_A(D_1, D_2, \ldots, D_M) \le S_A$$
$$\vdots \tag{6}$$
$$g_N(D_1, D_2, \ldots, D_M) \le S_N.$$

In the simplest case, location is assumed not to matter, and only one standard is specified. Then on the basis of our other assumptions we can assume that the standard will be exactly satisfied, and a simple Lagrangian formulation suffices. The agency's problem is:

$$\min L = C_1(X_1 - D_1) + C_2(X_2 - D_2) - \lambda(D_1 + D_2 - S_A). \tag{7}$$

---

[15] The fact that, in the simpler case, a single emission charge applies might suggest that a trial and error process for seeking the optimum would work. The problem is that only by being able to measure costs and benefits at each trial would the agency be able to decide whether its last trial produced an improvement. Certainly measuring costs and benefits at a point does not require knowledge of the functions over their ranges, but the distinction in terms of required centralized data seems minor.

The first-order conditions are:

$$\frac{\partial L}{\partial D_1} = -\frac{dC_1}{dR_1} - \lambda = 0,$$

$$\frac{\partial L}{\partial D_2} = -\frac{dC_2}{dR_2} - \lambda = 0,$$

$$D_1 + D_2 = S_A,$$

from which we see that $dC_1/dR_1 = dC_2/dR_2 = -\lambda$. Thus, a single charge is optimal, but it can be found only on the basis of knowledge of costs or through a trial and error process. The latter is possible because after each trial the result can be observed at the monitoring point and there is no necessity for the agency actually to measure costs at all. (Of course, even though the proper charge could in principle be found via trial and error, the "errors" imply higher overall costs because of lumpy and at least partially irreversible investments. Thus, the results of proper charges set on the first try are not the same as those achieved without the knowledge necessary to that accomplishment.)

The introduction either of location differences or of a non-conservative residual complicates matters, but not fatally in principle, so long as a single standard (one monitoring point) is still all we have to worry about. The constraint in the agency's problem becomes $\alpha_1 D_1 + \alpha_2 D_2 \le S_A$, and the first-order conditions from the Lagrangian problem are:

$$\frac{\partial L}{\partial D_1} = -\frac{dC_1}{dR_1} - \lambda\alpha_1 = 0,$$

$$\frac{\partial L}{\partial D_2} = -\frac{dC_2}{dR_2} - \lambda\alpha_2 = 0, \tag{8}$$

$$\alpha_1 D_1 + \alpha_2 D_2 = S_A,$$

so that, for example,

$$\frac{dC_2}{dR_2} = \frac{\alpha_2}{\alpha_1} \cdot \frac{dC_1}{dR_1}.$$

This result leaves us with some hope for trial and error, because even though charges must be individually tailored, the ratio of any two optimal source-specific charges is the ratio of the sources' transfer coefficients. Thus, trial and error could proceed on the basis of a single "numeraire" charge.

Similarly, if there is more than one standard to be met, but every source affects every monitoring point exactly the same, a single charge for all sources is still optimal. The agency's monitoring problem is more difficult because it must check each point at which a standard is defined, but it can still, in principle at least, perform a simple trial-and-error exercise based on iterations on one charge.

As soon as we both introduce multiple monitoring points and allow location to matter, however, any practical possibility of trial and error disappears. Thus, in this most realistic case, an optimal effluent charge system depends on the agency having knowledge of source cost functions and calculating a set of individually tailored charges. To see why this is so, consider our simple example with a second standard (monitoring point). The agency's problem is:

$$\min L = C_1(X_1 - D_1) + C_2(X_2 - D_2) - \lambda_A(\alpha_{1A}D_1 + \alpha_{2A}D_2 - S_A)$$
$$-\lambda_B(\alpha_{1B}D_1 + \alpha_{2B}D_2 - S_B), \tag{9}$$

and from the first-order conditions:

$$\frac{dC_1/dR_1}{dC_2/dR_2} = \frac{\lambda_A\alpha_{1A} + \lambda_B\alpha_{1B}}{\lambda_A\alpha_{2A} + \lambda_B\alpha_{2B}}. \tag{10}$$

Thus, even if both constraints could be exactly satisfied so that the shadow prices, λ_j, were non-zero, those shadow prices would not be known without a full solution. And without the shadow prices as weights, the ratio of the marginal costs cannot be calculated, even when the agency knows the transfer coefficients. Thus, trial and error cannot proceed on the basis of a single numeraire related in a known and constant way to each other optimal marginal cost (charge). This difficulty is compounded when there are many sources and monitoring points, because quality at some of the latter will inevitably be better than specified by the standard when the standard is not violated at any monitoring point. The corresponding λ's are zero, but which are zero is not known in advance.[16] Thus, while an actual trial-and-error process could lead to a feasible charge set (one that produced the desired ambient quality), it will not in general produce the cost effective outcome.

2.2. Modeling of the realistic static case

These last observations carry us to the end of our discussion of the simple static case and its complication. Overall we have seen just how restrictive are the assumptions that support the classical case for charges – that static regional efficiency can be attained with no knowledge by the agency of the cost functions of individual sources. Two natural enough questions are: If calculation of individually tailored charges is usually going to be necessary, just how hard is it likely to be? And how much difference will various charging systems make? For example, if individually tailored charges are optimal, but a single region-wide charge were actually to be applied to all sources, how much additional cost would be incurred?

The answers to these questions turn out to be specific to particular regions (because specific locations and the nature of the local environments matter); and

---

[16] Trial and error is difficult because of the large number of "knobs" available to twist in a multi-source region. If each of only 10 sources could control to each of only three levels of discharge, there would be over 59 000 possibilities for an initial trial. That first trial might eliminate some fraction of the options as either infeasible or unnecessarily strict, but finding a feasible and even modestly efficient option might easily involve many very expensive trials.

to particular pollution problems (because the cost-of-control functions differ among residuals as does the behavior of the discharges in the environment).[17] We shall confine ourselves, however, to two examples of modeling efforts designed to mimic realistic regional environmental quality management problems, attempting thereby at least to give an indication of the variations likely to be encountered.[18] These models were chosen because they can be compared both here, where effluent charges are at issue, and in Section 3, where our attention turns to marketable permits of various kinds. After the very briefest of descriptions of the models, we shall summarize some of the lessons learned from them.

The two models we shall use for comparison were both constructed in the early 1970s when enthusiasm for such exercises, and the regional efficiency solutions to which they might lead, was sufficiently great to sustain the costs of development and computation. One, the Atkinson and Lewis model, is of major point sources of particulates in the St. Louis region [Atkinson and Lewis (1974a, 1974b)]. The other is a multimedia, multiresidual model of the Lower Delaware Valley region (referred to here for brevity as Philadelphia) [Spofford et al. (1976)]. The differences and similarities of the models are highlighted in Table 10.1; and there we can see that the biggest differences are in size and complexity. The RFF model contains many more point sources, other residuals discharged both to water and air, and interactions among residuals in treatment processes.[19] In structure, however, and in the important matter of atmospheric dispersion modeling, the two models are similar.

In Table 10.2 some key comparisons are summarized. A policy of uniform percentage reduction orders for all sources sufficient to achieve the desired standard at the worst polluted monitoring station is taken to be the benchmark for compliance costs. (This policy is close enough to that embodied in most U.S. State Implementation Plans (SIP) for air pollution control that we shall follow the studies and refer to it by this acronym.) The other two policy instruments are a regionally (or zonally) uniform emission charge and an optimal effluent charge set. The latter, of course, involves different charges at each source reflecting their different locations relative to the binding ambient quality constraints. Atkinson and Lewis look at primary and secondary particulate standards, while Spofford examines only primary standards, but has results for both particulates and SO_2.

---

[17] In actual cases, removal processes often display such complications as economies of scale and joint removal of two or more residuals, so that the seeking of optimal regional management solutions, including optimally tailored charges, is much more difficult than our simple example hints at. See, for example, Russell (1973) and Russell and Vaughan (1976) on industrial pollution reduction costs.

[18] See, for other examples: on organic water pollution control in the Delaware estuary, Kneese and Bower (1972) and Johnson (1967); On water pollution control in Wisconsin's Fox River, O'Neil (1980); On SO_2 control in Nashville, Tennessee, Teller (1967); On nitrogen oxide emissions control in Chicago, Seskin, Anderson and Reid (1983); On chlorofluorocarbon control, Palmer et al. (1980); On phosphorus runoff control, Jacobs and Casler (1979).

[19] The sources of cost function data also differ for the major sources. The RFF model uses specially constructed industrial LP models to derive the regional model control vectors for steel mills, petroleum refineries and power plants.

Table 10.1
Summary of model structures and data bases

Model	Basic structure	No. of sources	Residuals included	Sources of cost data	Date of cost data	Basis for air pollution dispersion model	Number of monitoring points
Atkinson & Lewis (St. Louis)	Separable LP	27 point sources (All industrial: 9 power plants, 2 pet. refineries, 4 feed & grain mills)	Particulates	IPP Model[b]	Unclear (probably 1970)	Steady-state Gaussian diffusion (Martin & Tikvart)	9
Spofford (Philadelphia)	LP[a]	183 point sources (124 industrial: 17 powerplants, 7 pet. refineries, 5 steel mills; 57 Area sources home & commercial heating)	*Air* Particulates SO$_2$ *Water* Biochemical Oxygen Demand (nitrogeneous and carbonaceous)	Specially constructed plant LPs[c] IPP model[b]	Roughly 1970	Steady-state Gaussian diffusion (Martin & Tikvart)	57

[a] The original version was non-linear but the results reported in Table 10.2 come from a new, linear version.

[b] The Implementation Planning Program was designed to operate on air quality control region inventories and to allow the user to specify different control options, producing an estimate of control costs for the region and predicting resulting levels of ambient quality.

[c] See Russell (1973) and Russell and Vaughan (1976) for published examples.

Sources: Scott E. Atkinson and Donald H. Lewis (1974) *A Cost Evaluation of Alternative Air Quality Control Strategies*, Report No. EPA 600/5-74-003 (USEPA, Washington Environmental Research Center, Washington). Walter O. Spofford, Jr., Clifford S. Russell, and Robert A. Kelly (1976) *Environmental Quality Management* Washington: Resources for the Future, Washington).

Walter O. Spofford, Jr. (forthcoming) "Properties of Alternative Source Control Policies: Case Study of the Lower Delaware Valley", unpublished manuscript in progress, Resources for the Future.

When particulate matter is the residual of concern, both models produce similar results. Compliance costs are highest for the uniform roll-back approach and lowest (of course) for the optimal charge set. A regionally uniform charge produces intermediate compliance costs in each model. Notice also that as the number of zones increases in Spofford's model, the costs for a zonally uniform charge fall toward the optimal charge result. For the primary standard (75 μg/m^3) there is even surprising agreement between the models on the relative costs under each of these instruments, though the absolute size of Spofford's costs are very much higher, reflecting a larger number of sources and worse initial quality level. The same pattern holds when Atkinson and Lewis examine the costs of meeting the secondary standard (60 μg/m^3). The cost savings achievable by

Table 10.2
Compliance costs and emission charges under different emission charge systems in two regional models

| Policy instruments | Atkinson and Lewis (St. Louis) Particulates | | | | Spofford Lower Delaware Valley[d] | | | |
| | Secondary Std. | | Primary Std. | | Particulates Primary Std. | | SO$_2$ Primary Std. | |
	10^6/yr	Relative to SIP	10^6/yr	Relative to SIP	10^6/yr	Relative to SIP[e]	10^6/yr	Relative to SIP[e]
				Compliance costs				
SIP/uniform percent reductions[a]								
Single regional zone	$8.3		$2.0		$158.0		210.5	
Three zones[b]					115.9	0.73	202.6	0.96
Eleven zones[b]					63.9	0.40	167.5	0.80
Uniform emission charge								
Single regional zone	3.8	0.46	0.3	0.15	14.2	0.09	252.0	1.20
Three zones					12.8	0.08	193.5	0.91
Eleven zones					10.4	0.06	138.5	0.66
Optimal charges[c]	1.9	0.23	0.07	0.03	7.2	0.05	118.5	0.56
			Total out-of-pocket costs (including effluent charges)					
SIP/uniform percent reduction								
Single regional zone	$8.3		$2.0		158.0		210.5	
Three zones					115.9	0.73	202.6	0.96
Eleven zones					63.9	0.40	167.5	0.80
Uniform emission charge								
Single regional zone	6.7	0.81	1.3	0.64	54.7	0.34	504.1	2.39
Three zones					49.7	0.31	431.7	2.05
Eleven zones					32.7	0.21	295.9	1.40
Optimal charges	3.5	0.43	0.3	0.15	[Optimal charge payments not available.]			

[a] The two models have slightly different versions of this option. Atkinson and Lewis begin with industry-specific, technology-based emission standards and then reduce all discharges uniformly to reach the ambient standards. Spofford begins from the actual 1970 emission levels and reduces all discharges by uniform percentages (regionally or by zone) until the standard is met.

[b] Spofford's zones correspond to political jurisdictions: 3 states and 11 counties.

[c] The optimal charge solution corresponds to the least-cost solution when applied to both the point and area sources in the region.

[d] The Lower Delaware Valley region, which stretches from Wilmington, Del. to Trenton, N.J., includes eleven counties in Delaware, Pennsylvania, and New Jersey.

[e] The numbers in this column are calculated relative to the region-wide SIP alternatives.

going to a more efficient policy instrument are sufficiently great in both models (and for both standards in the Atkinson and Lewis work) that, even allowing for the out-of-pocket emission charge payments, it would be possible to make every discharger in the region better off through a suitable transfer arrangement.

When, however, we look at Spofford's results for SO_2 primary standards (80 $\mu g/m^3$), a very different pattern emerges. The regionally uniform emission charge produces a less efficient outcome than the uniform roll-back. Under zonally uniform charges, the more familiar pattern reasserts itself, but in all cases the call is a close one. In no case is the cost saving enough that the sum of compliance costs and emission charges is less than the compliance cost under the uniform roll-back instrument. This pattern of results happens to depend on Spofford's inclusion of home and commercial sources (the area sources) of SO_2 emissions among those subject to the charge. It can be shown, however, using a simple model like the one used in our earlier discussion of effluent charge properties, that the uniform emission charge is more likely to produce a costlier regional solution whenever sources with high marginal costs of discharge reduction have large impacts on ambient concentrations at the monitoring (standard) point. This is true in the Delaware model, where petroleum refineries with very steep marginal costs of SO_2 reduction (at the high reduction levels required) are also sited very close to the critical monitoring point. The addition of the relatively low marginal cost home and commercial heating sources far from the critical monitoring point accentuates this tendency and produces the result observed by Spofford.

Thus, how seriously one takes the Spofford results depends to some extent, though by no means entirely, on how seriously one takes the idea of applying an emission charge to small dispersed sources. (Note that such application could be via a fuel sulphur-content charge, so need not depend on unrealistic assumptions about monitoring and enforcement capabilities.) Nonetheless, the fact that in particular circumstances such results *can* be observed should make us cautious about general rule ranking policy instruments. While it is true that a tailored charge set can produce large savings, it is not always true that a uniform charge can improve on a simple regulator approach – even when we confine our attention to compliance costs. When we add in potentially massive transfer payments produced by the charge we can understand why sources might be extremely reluctant to see this instrument adopted. The only general rule would seem to be that if we want to explore alternatives in real settings we ought to do so with models first and only after we have an idea of the range of useful options, propose policy changes.[20]

2.3. Other dimensions of judgement

As important as static efficiency and economy of centralized information may be in the economic literature on environmental policy instruments, we must consider

[20] However, on the legal issues surrounding actual use of models for computing optimal or other charge sets, see Case (1982).

other dimensions of judgement as well. And these dimensions can well be more important to the adoption and long-term success of an instrument than the more familiar arguments.

2.3.1. Ease of monitoring and enforcement

Monitoring pollution sources to ascertain that they are paying the proper emission charge is a difficult problem. But a central point, as we see it, is that the monitoring problem is no harder if an emission charge is involved than if compliance with emission standards or permit terms is the concern. Thus, criticisms of emission charges based on the claim that compliance is harder to monitor are incorrect when the alternatives are also concerned with limiting the discharge of residuals per unit time. However, in a richer model including not only the statistical nature of the monitoring problem but also the decentralization of monitoring and enforcement activities and the possibility of polluter actions to conceal true discharge levels, Linder and McBride (1984) have identified certain drawbacks to a charge system not shared by a discharge standard. These include possible encouragement for less aggressive monitoring.

2.3.2. Flexibility in the face of exogenous change

It is first necessary to be clear about what counts as "flexibility". We shall use that word to mean the ease with which the system maintains the desired ambient standards as the economy changes. The most important measures of "ease" are first the amount of information the agency has to have and the amount of calculation it has to do to produce the appropriate set of incentives for a new situation and, second, the extent to which adjustments involve a return to a politically sensitive decision-making process.

In the restricted situation in which charges are both efficient and independent of costs (known, linear damage functions) the case for charges remains impressive. In fact, the same charge remains optimal after the addition of a new source or the expansion or shutdown of an existing source so long as change does not shift the marginal damage function. This automatic adjustment is thus based on allowing changes in discharges and ambient quality levels while maintaining marginal damage equal to marginal cost at each source.

If the policy goal is to maintain an ambient standard at a single monitoring point, after a change the charge must be adjusted, but the convenient relationship among optimal charges based on transfer coefficients is still there to take advantage of.

In the general case, where location matters and ambient standards are the goal of environmental policy (or where damage functions are either unknown or non-linear) emission charges do not protect ambient quality unless they are adjusted by the agency as change occurs. Such adjustment requires new calculations if the charges are to be· efficient. (And then, because the charges are individually tailored, each charge is a fresh chance for political action.)[21] If the actual charges used are uniform and set by trial and error, adjustment will involve the expense of error, and, in addition, static efficiency will not be achieved.

2.3.3. Dynamic incentives

In the matter of incentive to technical change, the simple general rule may be summarized as follows. If compliance with an order is costly and if there is some choice of how to comply (what equipment or technique to use) then there will be an incentive for the source faced with the order to seek cheaper ways of complying in the long run. It is also true that for any particular source, an incentive system that puts a value on the discharge remaining after control will create a greater incentive to change than will a regulation specifying that same level of discharge.[22] We shall return to this matter when discussing the regulatory approach in Section 5.

2.3.4. Political considerations

Two broad questions should be dealt with here: distributional problems and ethical arguments. As for the first, it is obvious that emission charges in their pure form are bound to cost any particular source more than would a simple emission standard designed to achieve the same discharge at that source. Such evidence as that from cost models, both simple and complex [e.g. Vaughan and Russell

---

[21] For a discussion of the inevitability of political bargaining over emission charges, see the fine discussion by Majone (1976).

[22] This is easy to show. In the figure below, the firm's initial marginal cost-of-discharge-reduction cure is MC_0. Assume it is complying with an order to discharge no more than D_0. This could also be achieved by the agency charging a *fee* of e_0 per unit of discharge. The order costs the firm area A, the cost of control to D_0. The charge would cost it area $A + B$, the control cost *plus* the total fee paid on remaining discharges. If, as shown in the second panel, the firm can find a way to reduce its costs to MC_1, it saves C under the order system and $C + G$ under the charge.

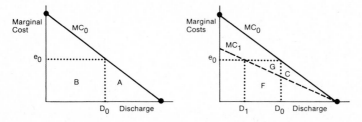

The new discharge, D_1, under the charge system is lower as well. This result also applies to marketable permits, for the permit price corresponds to the charge even though it may not be paid out of pocket by the originally permitted source. This argument is set out more fully and formally by Wenders (1975). For a slightly different view, see Magat (1978). And for another analytical approach, see Reppetto (1979).

(1976)], suggest that out-of-pocket costs of achieving a particular emission level at a source may easily be doubled by charge payments. On the other hand, the appropriate comparison should be the regional setting for a given ambient standard and real policy instrument alternative. Thus, if the efficient set of charges is contrasted with an inefficient set of emission standards, such as that obtained by imposing uniform percent reduction requirements on all dischargers, it is, as we have seen, an open and region-specific empirical question whether or not the savings from better distribution of pollution control effort will leave none, some, or all of the sources better off under the efficient charge, even after allowing for the charge payment itself. The real political problem here may be that dischargers doubt that the efficient charge set would ever be found or applied and see that an inefficient charge has a much increased chance of just costing them more money for the same results in the short run.[23]

One response to this political problem has been the proposal to use the revenue from charges to subsidize other acts of environmental protection. Another response has been concern over whether or not those revenues should be used to compensate the sufferers of damages from the remaining pollution. Certainly the idea has political appeal and seems to provide a symmetry otherwise lacking in the charges approach. But economists appear to have agreed after some debate that this symmetry would in fact be undesirable from an efficiency point of view; that while polluters should in principle pay charges equal to the marginal social damages they cause, damaged parties should absorb those damages without compensation and not be subjected to the incentive to increase exposure to pollution to collect (additional) compensation. [See, for example, Baumol and Oates (1975), Fisher (1981) and Olsen and Zeckhauser (1970). For a discussion of some ethical aspects of the compensation issue see Chapter 5 of this Handbook.] Only slightly more palatable to economists, but politically attractive, is the alternative already mentioned of using charge receipts to finance pollution control investments, especially those of an inherently collective nature such as in-stream aeration facilities or low flow augmentation dams.

The second political question, that of ethical stance, will be mentioned only briefly. The question arises because to many people pollution is wrong, not morally neutral.[24] These people do not want to see decisions about pollution placed on a footing symmetric with the firm's decisions about purchasing "normal" inputs such as labor services or packing cases. They want pollution stigmatized by strongly worded laws with strictly defined discharge limitations and criminal penalties for violations. The polluter's ability to choose how to react to a charge, the heart of the economist's efficiency case, is also the heart of the

---

[23] Distributional impacts on competitive industries are analyzed under a variety of assumptions by Dewees (1983).

[24] There is no evidence about what part of the general population feels this way, but Kelman's interviews with congressional staff members and active Washington environmentalists reveal a preponderance of this view among Democratic staffers and the environmentalists [Kelman (1981)].

environmentalist's opposition (for further discussion see Chapter 5 of this Handbook).[25]

A summary of this discussion of emission charges as a policy instrument for pollution control reveals a distinctly mixed bag of features. Certainly the classical position, in which static efficiency, information economy, and automatic adjustment to exogenous change can all be obtained at once, rests on very restrictive assumptions. In the more general case, static efficiency must be purchased at the cost of both information economy and flexibility in the face of change. Beyond that, emission charges suffer in the political arena from their distributional disadvantages (potentially large transfers imposed on polluters) and their ethical "flavor", which is apparently entirely too neutral to suit those who judge pollution to be a moral rather than a technical problem of market failure. In later sections we shall see how other instruments look under the same light.

3. Incentives to complete the set of markets: Tradeable rights

In practice the commonest form of policy instrument for environmental policy is the pollution permit, the terms of which usually embody either technological specifications or discharge limitations. We have explored some of the advantages and disadvantages of replacing such specifications with administratively set prices on discharges. Another possibility is to create a situation in which prices are attached to discharges by a decentralized, market-like process. To achieve this permits must be tradable among the interested parties, and the supply of permits must be less than the potential demand at zero price.

The idea of a marketable permit system appears to have occurred first to Crocker (1966) and to have been set out more completely by Dales (1968a, 1968b). It amounts to the dual of the emission charge idea – quantities instead of prices are set administratively; prices instead of discharge totals result from the free choices of those subject to the system. Its development in the literature has roughly paralleled that of charges. Early formulations were simple and compelling but later analysis showed that introducing complications reflecting features of reality reduced that apparent attractiveness. [For an excellent recent review, see Tietenberg (1980).] Just as with the charges, alternative versions of marketable

[25] It is worth noting in passing that the early writers may have unwittingly encouraged the views that those who favor economic instruments are basically insensitive to the health of the environment. For example, Kneese in his classic 1964 work, gives as examples of policies leading, potentially at least, to more efficient regional policies, the dedication of an entire river to waste disposal (the open sewer idea) and the storage of residuals for discharge in times of high assimilative capacity. In an illustrative example he also appears to sanction pollution-caused fish kills if the costs of cleanup are not exceeded by the damages to downstream commercial fishing interests. None of these are intrinsically wrapped up with emission charges and any or all might or might not be justifiable on the basis of efficiency analysis in a particular situation. But the political realities in the United States at least have made it clear that these are unacceptable alternatives. Their appearance in a fundamentally important statement of the value of emission charges probably tainted the latter.

permits have been defined, having different static properties and different implications for information and calculation loads. In discussing these cases and their
properties the idea of duality will provide a useful benchmark, though in some
cases this must be interpreted broadly.

Moving beyond the simple static context to complex (but still static) regional
models, we shall observe as expected that employing marketable permit systems
can lead to substantial costs savings compared to regulatory methods.[26] When we
expand the horizon to include other dimensions of judgement, such as flexibility
in the face of exogenous change, we shall continue to find a broad notion of
duality useful for putting our findings in perspective. We shall, however, find that
in some respects charges and marketable permits have the same properties while
in others they are different without being dual. As before, at each stage we shall
pick and choose among the many issues that have interested economists but shall
endeavor to provide citations where we avoid discussion.

3.1. Simple static cases: Efficiency and information

Strictly speaking the benefit-based arguments for charges do not have duals in the
set of marketable permit systems. It is when we introduce constraints on quality
that we find price- and quantity-setting systems to be dual. But it is worthwhile
nonetheless to observe that some early (and even not so early) statements of the
case for marketable permits introduced an assumption that was conceptually
equivalent to assuming knowledge of the benefit functions. This was the assumption that environmentalists (those with tastes for a clean natural environment)
could and would combine to buy and retire pollution rights, thus carrying the
system toward a socially optimum level of pollution analogous to that reached by
the optimal benefit-based emission charge set.[27] But this assumption is fully as
unrealistic as that involving benefit functions. The problems of public goods and
free riders that imply no markets in environmental services, hence no demand or
benefit functions available from directly observable behavior, imply that such
combinations would be very difficult to establish. Even the analogy of the
environmental groups, which combine thousands of individuals into potent forces
for pollution control, cannot help us here. These groups succeed through highly

[26] In modeling studies of permit systems the model is almost always asked to produce the optimal
(post trade) allocation of a fixed supply of permits and not to mimic the set of trades that leads there.
As we shall see, it is not necessary for the control agency to have a complete model to introduce a
statically optimal permit system even in the general case when such modeling *is* necessary to find an
optimal emission charge set.

[27] Emphasis should be placed on "analogous". Because the social choice process contemplated by
this argument for marketable permits is completely different from that involved in voting for
standards or even calculating an optimal result using costs and benefits "to whomsoever they may
accrue", there is no reason to expect the same quality levels to be thrown up by the three
processes – assuming for the moment that environmentally minded citizens *could* combine to purchase
and retire rights.

leveraged lobbying and litigation, not competition in the market. Rough calculations strongly suggest that all the national environmental groups in combination could make only a small dent in the pollution problem of any single large urbanized region if they had to do it by purchase of rights [Oppenheimer and Russell (1983)].[28]

More realistically, marketable permit systems are seen as potential instruments for achieving chosen ambient quality goals.[29] Corresponding to the single regional emission charge, which we saw was optimal only in very special circumstances, the simplest marketable permits system involves a single regional total emission limitation and a market for emission rights equally valid at any location in the region. These permits trade at a single regional price. Such a system can produce the desired ambient quality at least cost when location of discharge does not matter. The optimum level of total discharge for the given ambient standard could in principle be found by trial and error – the largest total just allowing the standard to be met.

In other situations, specifying a regional emission total and permitting trades among all dischargers on a pound-for-pound basis is not optimal, just as the single charge is not. While market transactions would result in an allocation of the permits such that resource costs were minimized for that total, one of the following would be unavoidable.

(a) the ambient quality goal would not be met; or

(b) if the initial total were chosen so that no conceivable set of trades could result in violation of the ambient standard, then the cost of meeting the standard would certainly be higher than necessary; or

(c) even if the total were greater, so that the standard were met only after some particular predicted trades, there would in general be a cheaper way of meeting it.

Trial and error could, however, be used to find a total allocation such that after trading the ambient standard was nowhere violated.[30] The trials would involve specification of the total permits to be allocated and observation of resulting quality. The same problems of extra cost arising from irreversible investment decisions arise here as in the use of trial and error with a charge system.

At the other end of the scale is the ambient rights system where the rights specified and traded are rights to cause pollution by particular amounts (usually assumed to be steady state concentrations) at the specified monitoring points. In

---

[28] Another reason that rights markets are unlikely to achieve a socially efficient outcome is that interfirm pollution effects may produce nonconvexities in production sets of nonpolluters who are allowed to buy and sell permits. Multiple optima then exist and the final result will be sensitive to the amount of rights issued initially. See Crone (1983) and Tietenberg (1983).

Rose (1973) analyzed systems of permit allocation using iterative bids and responses keyed to a known non-linear damage function. This provides another link to the optimal charge literature.

[29] We postpone for now the matter of how the permits might be initially distributed. This is discussed briefly under distributional matters in Section 3.3 below.

[30] How carefully the standard is protected depends on how many monitoring points are specified. The fewer of these the higher the chance that an after-trade allocation will result in an undetected violation (a "hot spot").

the ideal ambient rights system the agency simply defines rights totals at each ambient monitoring point equal to the difference between the desired standard and the contributions of all sources not subject to the system.[31] It has been shown by Montgomery (1972) that from any original allocation of these ambient rights the least cost regional solution can be reached by decentralized trading.

This system, then, sounds very appealing. Virtually nothing need be known by the agency except what amount of ambient quality "capacity" is available to be allocated. The market does the rest, without central calculation. The problem is that the *decentralized* information problem is formidable. Each source must simultaneously decide its optimal moves in each of the several markets, because any changes in its discharge rate simultaneously affects its need for ambient rights in every market.[32] If each source can be assumed to be a price taker in every market, the system looks like a set of competitive factor markets and we can invoke familiar market stability theorems to reassure ourselves that the optimal trading *could* go on. With only a few large buyers and sellers in each market, however, the practical chances for optimal decentralized results fall substantially. Thus, the centralized information intensity of the optimal charge system has its "dual" in the decentralized information problem of multiple markets in ambient quality permits.

Compromises between the extremes have been proposed. In zoned emission permit systems [e.g. Tietenberg (1974), Atkinson and Tietenberg (1982)] the region is divided into subregions, emission permit subtotals are allocated to subregions, and within subregions to sources. A source can trade pound-for-pound within its subregion and not at all outside it. If the initial allocation does not violate the standard, the zoned system raises the chances that no allowable set of subsequent trades will do so.

The zoned system raises in a more insistent way a problem we have so far ignored: market thinness. Tradable permit systems depend for their desirable properties on trades taking place and on these trades being sufficiently frequent to

---

[31] Such sources are usually termed "background", meaning such contributions as those blowing (or flowing) in from other regions or those from natural, uncontrollable sources in the region. More completely, however, the allocated permit totals can only equal whatever is left at each station when all sources not required to hold permits are operating in accordance with assumed regulatory requirements. Thus, the contribution of home heating discharge to regional SO_2 and particulates could be estimated using assumptions about fuel quality requirements.

[32] For a given initial allocation of ambient quality rights, q_{ij}^0 to each source i at each point j, each source must solve the problem:

$$\min_{\text{s.t.}} C_i\left(X_i - D_i^1\right) + \sum p_{q_j}\left(\Delta q_{ij}\right)$$

$$\alpha_{ij} D_i^1 \le q_{ij}^0 + \Delta q_{ij}, \quad \text{for all } j,$$

where $C(\cdot)$, D, X, and α are as defined in Section 2 and superscripts denote before and after trading situations, q_{ij} is the initial allocation of ambient quality permits at point j to source i, Δq_{ij} is the change through trade in the number of permits held at j by i, where purchases are plus and sales are minus and p_{q_j} is the price of permits at point j.

establish a market clearing price (regional emission permits) or a number of market clearing prices (ambient permits, zoned emission permits). If there are only a few sources in each market there may be no transactions for many periods because of capital commitments in particular production or discharge control process. Or transactions may be distorted by monopolistic or monopsonistic (duopolistic or duopsonistic) behavior by a dominant source or sources. These problems are major concerns of Hahn and of Cass et al., who have worked on designing an SO_2 discharge permit system for the South Coast Air Basin in California [Hahn (1980), Cass et al. (1980) and Hahn and Noll (1981)]. See also Russell (1981) for some preliminary evidence on numbers of sources and the supply and demand for permits. Several workers in this field, for example Tietenberg (1974) and David et al. (1980) have advocated periodic expiration of rights, making them like leases rather than freehold properties, with the idea that when some or all of a source's permits expired it would be forced into the market to obtain replacements.[33]

Another compromise emission permit system depends on "trading ratios" related to the source-specific transfer coefficients. If it is possible to identify a hot spot in advance, the coefficients relating all source discharges to that point can be used. Then, if source i sells to source j e_i units of emission permits, source j can use (discharge) α_{ik}/α_{jk} (e_i) units where k is the designator of the potential hot spot.[34]

3.2. Evidence from regional models

It will be useful here, as it was in our discussion of emission charges, to introduce some evidence from realistic regional models. In order to maintain comparability

---

If the p_{q_j} were exogenously given, this calculation would be straightforward for any source. But for the decentralized system the p_{q_j} are only implicitly defined by the market-clearing relations:

$$\sum_i \Delta q_{ij} = 0, \quad \text{for all } j,$$

and

$$\sum_i \sum_j p_{q_j} \Delta q_{ij} = 0.$$

[33] This strategy is also liked by some writers to the maintenance of agency "flexibility" – the ability to retire permits without the cost or fuss of litigation over the taking of property. See the discussion below under flexibility.

[34] A complete system of implicit trading ratios constraining trades has been suggested by Krupnick and Oates (1981) and Krupnick, Oates and Van de Verg (1983) who refer to it as an "offset system". This scheme protects ambient quality at all monitoring points (points for which transfer coefficients are available). In fact, however, the constraints faced by each source in deciding how to trade seem to be equivalent to those involved in the ambient permit system when source-specific constraints are combined with the zero net creation of permits at each monitoring point. For a system aimed at maintaining the status quo quality if that is better than the standard, see McGartland and Oates (1983).

Table 10.3
Compliance costs under different marketable permit systems in two regional models

| | Atkinson and Tietenberg (St. Louis) Particulates | | | | Spofford (Philadelphia) | | | |
	$2\ \mu g/m^{3d}$ $10^6/yr$	Rel to SIP	$10\ \mu g/m^{3d}$ $10^6/yr$	Rel to SIP	Particulates Primary Std $10^6/yr$	Rel to SIP	SO_2 Primary Std $10^6/yr$	Rel to SIP
SIP/uniform percent reduction[a]	$9.8		$6.2		$158.0		$210.5	
Emission permits[b]								
Single zone	8.0	0.82	1.5	0.24	16.0	0.10	199.4	0.95
Three zones[a]	6.9	0.70	1.5	0.24	16.1	0.10	204.6	0.97
Six zones	8.6	0.88	1.8	0.29				
Eleven zones					23.3	0.15	215.2	1.02
Ambient permits								
Single Market	3.5	0.36	0.6	0.10	–		–	
Multiple Markets	3.1	0.32	0.5	0.08	9.7	0.06	177.1	0.84

[a] The Atkinson and Tietenberg SIP strategy involved first assigning to each of 27 sources an emission level based on application of control strategies represented in SIP guideline documents. To produce the level of ambient pollution at the worst receptor point shown in the table, further necessary reductions were made on an equal-percentage-reduction basis. Spofford's version of this policy involves equal percentage reductions at all sources from a base of 1970 inventory emissions.

[b] For the emission permit and ambient permit systems, Spofford imposes fuel quality regulations on home and commercial heating activities. These activities do *not* participate in the permit markets.

[c] Atkinson and Tietenberg report on two slightly different versions of a three-zone permit system. The costs reported here are a rough average of those reported in their article (Figure 4) for the two versions.

[d] Contribution to annual average concentration of suspended particulates at receptor location with worst quality of the 27 point sources modeled. Nothing is said about what value of this indicator might correspond to the primary air quality standard of 75 $\mu g/m^3$. Results are given for levels of this indicator from roughly 2 to 12 $\mu g/m^3$.

Sources: Scott E. Atkinson and T.H. Tietenberg (1982) " The Empirical Properties of Two Classes of Designs for Transferable Discharge Permit Markets", *Journal of Environmental Economics and Management* 9, no. 2, 101–121.

Walter O. Spofford Jr. (1983) "Properties of Alternative Source Control Policies: Case Study of the Lower Delaware Valley", Resources for the Future, unpublished report.

across instruments, we shall again concentrate on two such modeling projects: Atkinson and Tietenberg's work on particulate control in the St. Louis region;[35] and Spofford's analysis of particulate and SO_2 control in the Lower Delaware Valley Region (Philadelphia).[36]

Some control-cost results from these two modeling exercises are summarized in Table 10.3. These must be interpreted with caution, because the ambient stan-

[35] The Atkinson/Tietenberg work is based on the same model as that of Atkinson and Lewis (1974), used in the emission charge section.

[36] Again, this by no means exhausts the possibilities. Other studies providing modeling evidence include: deLucia (1974) on BOD discharge permits for the Mohawk River in New York; Cass et al. (1980) and Hahn and Noll (1981) on SO_2 discharge permits in the South Coast Air Basin in California; Eheart (1980) on BOD discharge permits for the Willamette River in Oregon; David et al. (1980) on phosphorus discharge permits for Lake Michigan; O'Neil et al. (1981) on BOD discharge permits for the Fox River in Wisconsin.

dards imposed on the models were not the same. Atkinson and Tietenberg (A&T) report the contribution of 27 major point sources to quality degradation at the receptor location with the worst air quality. Spofford imposes the primary air quality standards at each of 57 monitoring points in the region.

Subject to this caveat, however, the pattern of results is of some interest. Most obviously, the A&T results for the less strict "standard" ($10 \ \mu g/m^3$) look very like Spofford's results for the primary particulate standard. Either type of permit represents a very large improvement over the SIP/uniform percentage reduction policy, with the ambient permit system costing 10 percent or less of the strictly regulatory approach (in terms of real compliance costs only).

For both the stricter particulate standard in A&T's work and in the SO_2 example from Spofford, however, the relative cost differences change. In the former these drop off less dramatically. In the latter, the emission permit systems represent either no cost improvement or only the tiniest of improvements, and even the ambient permits are well over 80 percent as expensive as the SIP policy.

Thus, again it appears that the rankings of policy instruments, even in static efficiency terms, will in general depend on the residual in question, the strictness of the ambient standard being contemplated, and the characteristics of the regional economy and environment. We cannot even be certain that the theoretically best ambient permit system will be the lowest cost alternative because of the important of such small sources as home heating, for which permit requirements and trading seem completely out of the question.

3.3. Other dimensions of judgement

Marketable permit systems display both similarities to and differences from emission charges when judged on such dimensions as ease of monitoring and enforcement, flexibility in the face of exogenous change, dynamic incentives, and political attributes. We consider these in turn in this section.

3.3.1. Monitoring and enforcement

Monitoring an emission permit, marketable or not, defined in terms of allowable emissions per unit time, is the same problem as monitoring for emission charge billing. When permits are marketable, the problem may be compounded by the necessity of being current with completed trades. And this extra difficulty might be exploited by dischargers trading in the short run to stay one jump ahead of agency monitoring teams.[37] Problems are compounded if trades are allowed between conventional sources such as stacks and hard-to-monitor sources such as dirt roads and refuse piles.

[37] This strategy could be foiled by requiring long minimum holding periods, but this would have to be backed up by a complete, real-time inventory of all permits. David et al. (1980) propose that all trades take place only at quarterly auctions as another strategy to assist in monitoring for compliance.

One extra fillip accompanies an ambient permit system, however. The current state of technology does not in general allow us to differentiate the contributions of specific dischargers to concentrations of pollutants observed at an ambient monitoring point.[38] This means that monitoring for compliance in this case must also involve monitoring of discharges. That is, a portfolio of ambient permits must be translated into an effective discharge permit by use of an agreed-on regional environmental model.

3.3.2. Flexibility in the face of change

This is a dimension on which a marketable permit system seems to have a distinct advantage. Once established, and assuming necessary monitoring and enforcement effort, a permit system maintains either discharge totals (regional or zonal) or ambient quality standards without constant intervention and recalculation by the agency. If the demand for permits shifts because of regional growth or decay, this will be reflected in the market prices of permits. Permit reallocation takes place as firms find it in their interest to reduce discharges and sell permits to new entrants or expanding resident firms.

With reallocation through trading of emission permits goes the continued danger of new hot spots.[39] This danger, plus the thought that the initial allocation might be regretted for other reasons, has inspired several analysts to push for a different kind of flexibility – bureaucratic ability to reduce the total of emission permits outstanding without compensation [e.g. Tietenberg (1974), deLucia (1974)]. This flexibility would be obtained by automatic and periodic expiration of rights (e.g. one-fifth might expire every year). There would be no obligation to reissue the same number that expired, and in some systems, all new rights would be auctioned. This particular form of flexibility seems to threaten the real long run advantages of permit systems, however, for decisions to buy and sell permits would become shorter run matters if expropriation after only 5 years were a real possibility.

3.3.3. Dynamic incentives

In principle, the incentives for technical change provided by permits correspond to those produced by charges. In either case, reducing discharges produces a

---

[38] But see footnote 47 on inferring discharges from the multiple sources affecting multiple monitoring points on the basis of knowledge of the elements in each discharge stream.

[39] Notice that by a suitably conservative choice of initial allocation the agency could avoid all possibility of hot spots no matter what the pattern of trading. This would in general imply a very severe restriction on total permits and thus a high control cost. One place for modeling, then, as in our empirical section, is to identify the efficient post-trade pattern of discharges so that the initial total allocation can be such as to produce the desired ambient standard under that spatial pattern of discharge. Thus, costly information again can substitute for costly discharge control.

monetary gain to the source. However, it may be difficult to sell any substantial number of permits, especially if the market is thin; hence, a (full) monetary gain may not be captured as easily under the permit system as under the charge system. Moreover, for very strict initial allocations of emission permits designed to avoid hot spots under any possible set of trades, the permit price will be higher than that implied, for example, by an ambient quality permit system. Thus, static inefficiency can produce larger long-run incentives to reduce discharges.

3.3.4. Political considerations

The distribution of costs under a marketable permit system depends on both the number of permits originally allocated and on how the allocation is done. Auction systems are conceivable [e.g. Rose (1974), Repetto (1979) and, for a "Vickrey Auction", Collinge and Bailey (1983)] and produce a result similar to emission charges, with all sources being out of pocket for both control costs and permit costs. More likely would seem to be free initial allocation, either in proportion to original, uncontrolled emissions or to a projected equilibrium allocation. In either case, the value of the issued permits is a windfall to the existing sources. This may purchase their acceptance of such a system, where they seemed likely (though not certain) to oppose an emission charge. The other side to this coin is the opposition such a windfall is likely to create among environmentalists – and, indeed, others.

The other political consideration we have mentioned is the extent to which the instrument stigmatizes polluting activity and appears to give the polluter no choice but to clean up. On this scale, the marketable permit looks modestly preferable to the charge. The chance to pay and pollute without committing a "violation" is limited by the total number of available permits, not merely by the arguments of economists who assume rational cost-minimizing behavior. While permit violations are possible the very use of the word "violations" indicates that such behavior is considered wrong and presumably subject to punishment.

3.4. A real-world approximation

More significant than intricate efficiency arguments, modeling exercises, and speculation about political considerations is the fact that an approximation to a marketable emission permit system is now in place for air pollution control in the United States. This system has been developed out of a combination of necessity and imagination by the USEPA and certain of its contractors. It has three major components:

(1) *Offsets* – arrangements that allow a new or expanding source to buy into an area by paying for the reduction of emissions at other sources. The reductions must more than balance the new source's emissions, and the new source must

meet applicable regulatory requirements such as new source performance standards. [See, for example, Liroff (1980).]

(2) *Bubbles* – originally designed to let a single complex plant balance its pollution control effort among its several stacks in such a way as to reduce its costs while simultaneously reducing its emissions. The idea is basically to relax specific regulatory requirements at one or another high cost process in return for extra effort at a place where extra removal comes cheap. The idea has subsequently been expanded to allow multiplant bubbles which amount to permit trades among existing sources (e.g. Brady and Morrison, (1982)].

(3) *Emission Reduction Credit Banking* – This feature allows sources that have opportunities to reduce emissions but no current markets in which to sell the freed up "permits" to bank them for later use or sale [Brady and Morrison (1982)]. The system represented by these related features is complicated and constrained by the apparatus of direct regulation that has been retained. This apparatus limits the extent of control effort relaxations a source can buy, limits the circumstances in which trades can take place (both in terms of source compliance with regulatory requirements and of regional compliance with ambient quality standards) and introduces separate and to some extent inevitably *ad hoc* approval procedures for each desired trade. On the other hand, the regulatory apparatus introduces possibilities for unwanted outcomes. For example, existing permits under State Implementation Plans may allow sources far more discharges than they are using or indeed have ever used. These excess emissions are apparently available for trade and the results have been damned as "paper offsets" when used [Liroff (1980)].

An analysis of the actual cost and discharge results of operation of this system must wait on more experience. What seems likely at this point is that many proposed and approved trades have involved notional or paper offsets or their equivalent in bubbles – as when dirt roads are to be oiled to cut ground level dust in exchange for relaxation in high-level particulate emission requirements. On the other hand, the mere existence of the system and experience with its operation can give us confidence to go on into better structures.

4. Other incentive systems

4.1. Deposit–refund systems and performance bonds

As we have seen, remedies such as charges or marketable permits require that discharges be monitored. This may not be feasible in practice, i.e. when the sources of environmental degradation are numerous and/or mobile. Moreover, a system of charges or marketable permits provides incentives for concealing the volume of discharges, which may jeopardize reliable monitoring. For these reasons, such systems are not likely to work in many cases, such as releases of freons from automobile air conditioners; improper disposal of mercury batteries or waste lubrication oil and other hazardous material by individuals; or littering, be it beer cans or abandoned cars.

Similarly, the establishment of property rights through appropriate liability assignments (discussed below in this section) runs into many problems that limit its use. For example, proof of guilt is required and often difficult to establish even in cases where proof of innocence would be easy, had it been required or had there been incentives to provide such evidence. Furthermore, the exact implication of liability may be unclear, in particular concerning the size of indemnities for a given type of violation, which makes the deterrent role of this instrument unclear. In addition, if the probable size of indemnities exceeds the net worth of the violator, the incentive effect on behavior as well as compensation to the injured party (when relevant) may be insufficient.

General deposit–refund systems may be a better instrument in such situations. These systems imply that the potential injurer is subjected to a tax (deposit) in the amount of the potential damage and receives a subsidy (refund), equally large in terms of present value, if certain conditions are met, e.g. proof that a product is returned to a specified place or that a specified type of damage has not occurred. Thus, such systems introduce a price for the right to inflict detrimental effects on the environment and a (negative) price if this right is not used. As a special case, the government may not be involved at all, instead the separate tax payment is set to zero and the subsidy payment is required to be made by a non-government party engaged in damage-related transactions with the potential injurer (for example, sellers of beverages in certain types of containers). This party would typically respond by increasing prices for such transactions and by introducing a "deposit" as part of the new price. The resulting arrangement amounts to a so-called "mandatory deposit" where the sole requirement is that a refund be made (e.g. mandatory deposits on beverage containers). As another special case, the potential injurer may be allowed to transfer the liability to pay the *net* tax/deposit, i.e. when the conditions for a subsidy/refund are not met, to a trusted third party such as a bank or an insurance company. This amounts to a "performance bond" for which the potential injurer will have to pay some interest or a premium [Bohm (1981)].

Deposit–refund systems may perform better than alternative instruments in that (a) they also work when the act of environmental degradation is not directly observable or when the potential injurers are numerous and/or mobile, (b) they simplify the proof of compliance in some cases, (c) they specify the (maximum) economic consequences of noncompliance, (d) actual or expected damages are covered by actual payments, at least in principle, and (e) in certain applications they may stimulate people other than those directly involved to reduce the effects on the environment (such as scavengers in the case of refunds on littered items).

In addition, as compared to alternative economic incentive systems such as pure charges or pure subsidies, deposit–refund systems have properties that would make them more attractive from the politician's point of view. Charges have sometimes been avoided because of fears that low-income people would be found to be hit relatively hard by such measures. In contrast, taxes/deposits are balanced by the right to subsidies/refunds which would leave nominal income unaffected. Indeed, the refund incentives may be particularly strong for low-income people and allow them to make income gains on balance. Subsidies have to be financed by government revenue and are disliked for that reason. In contrast, the specific taxes/deposits cover the subsidies/refund in a deposit–refund system.

Thus, deposit–refund systems – when applicable – can be said to provide the advantages of an economic incentive system, while avoiding some of the political disadvantages of the "traditional" forms of such incentive schemes. The applicability of such systems requires that it is technically feasible and not prohibitively expensive to establish proof of absence of pollution from the potential polluter.

4.1.1. Forms of deposit–refund systems

4.1.1.1. Adjusting market-generated systems.. The fact that deposit–refund systems (or refund offers) are found in the market economy indicates that there exists empirical experience with such systems. The reasons for the emergence of market-generated systems are diverse, ranging from a reuse value (e.g. old tires, containers) or a recycling value (e.g. lead batteries) to price differentiation or the speeding up of replacement purchases by refund offers to old customers. Thus, the rationale for voluntary refund offers may be that the reuse or recycling value (V) is positive or simply that a refund prospect (R) stimulates demand; in the latter case, V may be negative.

As some monopoly element is likely to be present when an individual firm makes a refund offer, we may write the profit function as

$$\Pi = p(Q, R)Q - c(Q) + r(R)(V - R)Q,$$

where Q is output;[40] $p(Q, R)$ the inverted demand function; $c(Q)$ the cost function; and $r(R)$ the return rate. The return rate will be determined by the individual consumer's (i) disposal options, where c_d^i is the total unit disposal cost without a return alternative and c_R^i the corresponding cost of returning the product. Consumers whose $c_R^i - c_d^i$ falls short of R will be assumed to choose the return alternative.

---

[40] To fix ideas, the output may be considered as a quantity of bottled beverages or mercury batteries. Later when we deal with government-initiated deposit–refund systems, a better illustration may be provided by the production of freons; here, freons (chlorofluorocarbons) could be returned for a refund (instead of being released into the atmosphere) when cooling equipment is being serviced or scrapped.

The introduction of a refund offer can normally be expected to raise prices. However, for a given demand effect $\partial p/\partial R > 0$, and a given effect on the return rate, $dr/dR > 0$, a sufficiently high V value will cause equilibrium prices to fall [see Bohm (1981, ch. 2)]. Regardless of this outcome it is up to the firm to announce that part of the price now is a "deposit" $D = R$.

If non-returns typically create negative external effects in the amount of E (expected environmental hazards or extra waste treatment costs), the firm's optimal $R(R_F)$ may not give rise to a socially optimal return rate. Assuming for simplicity that V also equals the social reuse value and that second best complications from the monopolistic behavior of the firm can be disregarded, the socially optimal $R(R_S)$ would equal either $E + V$ (where $V \gtrless 0$), if the return rate is less than 100 percent, or the lowest level $R < E + V$ at which a 100 percent return rate is attained. Thus, if $R_F < R_S$, an adjustment of the market refund rate may be called for. A "mandatory deposit" in the amount of R_S may, however, create problems, as the firm would lose when refunds are set at a level other than R_F. Hence, the firm might want to obstruct the system by making returns from consumers more cumbersome (increasing c_R^i). If so, either measures specifying the obligations of the firm would have to be taken or the government would have to become financially involved in the administration of the system. The latter alternative could be designed as a full-fledged deposit–refund system with a tax imposed on output in the amount of $D = R_G = R_S - V = E$ and a subsidy per unit returned in the amount of R_G.

4.1.1.2. Government-initiated systems. If no market-generated return system is in operation, but the disposal of used products gives rise to negative marginal external effects (E), which would be avoided if the used products were returned, a deposit–refund system of the type just mentioned could be introduced by the government. Assuming that the industry is competitive, $V \gtrless 0$ would be the market price, equal to the firms' value, of a returned product, whereas the socially optimal payment (R_S) for a returned unit equals (at most) $E + V$. If so, a tax/subsidy in the amount of $D = R_G = R$ would be appropriate.

As consumers whose disposal cost difference $c_R^i - c_d^i$ exceeds the total payment, $R_S = R_G + V$ will continue to use the traditional disposal option, then, at the margin, social costs of traditional disposal equal social costs incurred by the return alternative, i.e. $E + V = c_R^i - c_d^i = R_S$. In the general case, the shift to this optimum will give rise to various distribution effects, where the losers will be (a) the producers, as producer price net of D is likely to go down (by $\Delta p < 0$) and (b) those consumers whose $c_R^i - c_d^i > R_S + \Delta p$. The winners include the remaining consumers, scavengers (who now may pick up discarded units for a refund), and taxpayers, to the extent that total deposits exceed total refunds.

So far we have discussed deposit–refund systems for *consumers* of products which may create environmental effects when disposed of (mercury and cadmium batteries, beverage containers, tires, junked cars, used "white goods", lubrication oil, freons in air conditioners and refrigerators, etc.). Similarly, deposit–refund systems may be designed for *producers* to check hazardous emissions of chemicals into the air and waterways or dumping of toxic wastes, in particular when proper treatment of such releases or wastes is expensive and improper disposal is easy to conceal. If the potential emissions or wastes are related to certain inputs in a straightforward fashion (such as potential sulphur emissions to the input of high-sulphur fuel oil), a tax/deposit could be levied on these inputs and a subsidy/refund paid for the quantity of chemicals (e.g. sulphur) or toxic material transferred to a specified type of processing firms. Here, as well as for other deposit–refund systems, a precondition for a well-functioning application is that there are sufficient safeguards against abuses, e.g. that ordinary sulphur cannot be bought and passed off as sulphur extracted from stack gases.

4.1.1.3. Performance bonds. Producer-oriented deposit–refund systems can be used to control other kinds of detrimental effects on the environment than those explicitly discussed so far [Solow (1971)]. First, restoration of production sites after shut-down may be required to avoid unwarranted permanent eyesores or accident risks (strip mining sites, junk yards, etc.) Second, we have the vast problem of safeguarding against *a priori* unknown environmental effects of new products, in particular new chemicals, or new production processes. When applying the principle of deposit–refund to such cases, the producer could be required to pay a deposit, determined by a court estimate of the likely maximum restoration costs or the maximum damages (in general or specific respects), to be refunded if certain conditions are met. In this way, society is protected against incomplete restoration because of intentional or unintentional bankruptcies. Moreover, the firm's operation will now be planned with respect to future restoration costs as well. And in the case of potential risks of innovation, this creates an alternative to awaiting the results of a test administered or supervised by the government. In this way, the introduction of the new products or processes would not be delayed. This alternative may be attractive to the innovating firm because the firm may have gathered information – and now definitely has an incentive to gather such information from the beginning of its R & D activities – implying that no harm is likely to result. Therefore, the firm may be willing to market the product or start using the new process with the specified financial responsibility, and both the firm and its customers may be better off [Bohm (1981, ch. 4)].

Although we take it for granted that the government will not trust a firm to meet its obligations without a financial commitment, in either of our two cases, it is conceivable that other parties which *are* trusted by the government would like to assume the financial responsibility involved. Thus, for example, the firm may convince a bank or an insurance company that the new product is safe. Or the firm may reveal its product secrets only to such a party but not to a public authority. If so, banks or insurance companies may assume the liability at a price. Thus, by using the risk-shifting mechanisms of the credit or insurance markets, the deposit–refund system can be transformed from a cash deposit version to a performance bond version, or firms could be allowed to choose either of these two versions. In other words, whenever the environmental effects potentially attributable to an individual decision-maker, and hence that individual's deposit, become sufficiently large and the transaction costs of the credit or insurance markets are no longer prohibitive, deposit–refund systems are likely to take the form of a performance bond system.

4.2. Liability

Another possibility for providing incentives to polluters or potential polluters is to make them liable for the actual damage they cause but without demanding a deposit or performance bond. To some extent, of course, they have been liable right along, at least in common-law countries; and remain liable even after the enactment of regulatory legislation aimed at pollution control. This liability arises under the common law of private and public nuisance and is enforceable through the courts; by damaged parties in the former case and, for the most part, by governments in the latter case [Boger (1975)]. The "natural" occurrence of this instrument and thus its apparent independence of government regulatory activity have made it attractive to those who favor minimal government interferences with the functioning of the market system.

The theoretical literature dealing with liability as a policy instrument for the most part descends from the important and challenging theorem of Coase on the irrelevance of property rights to efficiency outcomes in environmental conflicts [Coase (1960)]. This line of descent is hardly surprising, since the right to enjoy property free from external interference and the entitlement to liability for interferences that do occur are closely related though distinct possibilities for dealing with conflicts over the use of property generally [Calabresi and Melamed (1972), Bromley (1978)].

This literature is interested in the efficiency properties of these alternative principles and in their comparison with explicit government intervention of the classical Pigouvian sort (e.g. Brown (1973), Polinsky (1979)]. For the most part it confines itself to the case of small numbers of both polluters and damaged parties, though alternative assumptions about the availability of information and the behavior of those parties in bargaining (cooperative or not) are explored. In addition, the costs of enforcement through the courts and the problems of proof of damage for liability purposes are generally ignored. In these circumstances property and liability approaches have been shown to be roughly equivalent in efficiency properties and in terms of protection of the entitlement at issue and both have been shown superior to Pigouvian taxes when behavior is not cooperative [Polinsky (1979)].

Unfortunately, the restriction to small numbers, which frees one from the internal information and decision problems that would be faced by, say, a river basin's population if it tried to act collectively to stop a polluter of the river, and the ignoring of real costs of enforcement make these results of limited interest. Moreover, writers on liability seem, rather surprisingly, to have ignored the problem of incentives for damage-seeking behavior created by the liability payments to damaged parties. As we noted above in Section 2, in discussing the possibility of using emission-charge revenues to indemify pollutees, the conclusion of writers in that literature has been that such a policy would be incorrect. The largest difference between this conventional charge-payment idea and a legislated liability system would be that arising from uncertainty about whether damage would occur or not and whether if occurring they would be compensated. It would still seem to be the case that the more successful a liability system were in guaranteeing compensation, the stronger the incentives it would provide to potential damaged parties. Finally, the problems raised by the uncertainty itself have been disregarded in this literature's comparisons of liability rules and Pigouvian taxes. If discovery and ultimate proof of responsibility are uncertain, the polluter must face a potential payment adjusted to provide the socially correct signal, given that no payment at all may be required even if an incident occurs and damages result. [For a discussion of a related situation, see Shavell (1982).]

Somewhat more to the point is work such as that of Wittman (1977), focusing on the role of monitoring costs in choosing between prior regulation and expost liability for attacking public problems. This points the way to some interesting considerations relevant to choosing liability as a policy instrument. It also emphasizes the close relation between a system of expost liability and some of the deposit–refund arrangements just discussed.

Thus, a liability system, despite its drawbacks, may be a desirable way to approach problems for which information, in any of several senses, is scarce and expensive. For example, take a case in which the prospective damages of some contemplated action (introduction of a new drug or construction and use of a hazardous waste dump site) cannot be estimated even in a meaningful probabilistic sense. This might be true if the experts' prior subjective probability density function were uniform over a very wide range from zero to some catastrophic loss. This provides a weak basis for choosing a particular set of regulations (deciding on a drug ban or on a landfill design requirement) or for setting a fee (for wastes dumped at the site). In such circumstances a designation of strict liability could be appealing. The liability payment might be guaranteed by a performance bond or insurance policy as described in the preceding subsection. It would provide incentives for the active party to engage in information gathering and to take some actions aimed at prevention, at least those where the costs are small and the information or prevention effects are likely to be substantial.

If monitoring of actions to avoid causing damage (e.g. discharge reduction or spill prevention activities) is expensive or technically very difficult, but the sources of actual discharges or spills could be identified expost, a liability rule might usefully substitute for a regulatory rule. If monitoring the quantity of discharge, as opposed to the mere existence of some discharge, is expensive, or if the problem is with spills seen as stochastic discharges, so that fixed fees per unit discharge are difficult to apply, liability may again hold promise.

Notice that even in these rather special situations, the choice of a liability approach is not without serious disadvantages, however. Unless some special process of enforcement were set up, damaged parties would still: suffer real and possibly very serious damage; have to hire lawyers and go to court to claim their entitlements; and have to prove the connection between their damages and the act of the active party. The first of these three requirements must be seen as a political strike against the liability instrument. Policies that appear to prevent damages are surely easier to sell to an electorate than policies that depend for their working on a more or less ironclad guarantee that damage will be compensated by the polluter.

The third requirement, that a connection between action and damage be proved, also looms large as a potential difficulty. If the drug we originally hypothesized could only have one type of ill-effect or if the landfill were completely isolated from other sources of ground-water pollution, the position of the damaged party would be most clear cut. But, if the drug might produce long-delayed symptoms that could also be attributable to naturally occurring disease, or if the landfill site is surrounded by other industrial and commercial establishments (and perhaps even old landfills) proof of the cause–effect relation may be very difficult or even impossible. Special standards of proof (one or another version of a "rebuttable presumption" of causality) may be established to get around this obstacle in particular circumstances, but this course is circumscribed. If every case of X arising within T years among residents of area Y is by fiat to be attributed to our landfill, we must be quite sure that X arises only rarely without *any* obvious cause. Furthermore, we cannot thereafter similarly attribute X to another competing cause should we wish to use the liability instrument in other contexts near Y. This limitation has its most obvious meaning where some ubiquitous cause, such as sulfate air pollution of a metropolitan area is to be attacked by a compensation scheme amounting to the imposition at joint liability on the polluters of the region.

Where these difficulties of proof can be overcome, and where the political objection to a damage-accepting policy can also be overcome, liability as an instrument of policy does offer some dynamic advantages. It is self-adjusting in the face of exogenous change. For example, as technology changes, the polluters can adjust their actions to reflect the new balance between avoidance cost and expected damages. And it provides a continuing incentive to seek new technologies reducing expected damages.

An actual strict liability system, where damages are hard to estimate and preventive action hard to monitor, has been established in the United States Outer Continental shelf oil tract leasing program. Liability for damage from spills attaches to lease owners, and some information is available on the likelihood that a spill in a particular block would affect either fishing grounds or beaches. For a brief description and some preliminary evidence that the value of leases reflects an estimate of potential liability costs (or the costs of their avoidance) see Opaluch and Grigalunas (1983).

For a brief discussion of the problems of liability law in the context of damages from toxic substances, and for suggestions on moving away from that law toward "no-fault" victim compensation funds, see Trauberman (1983). It would appear that the desire to make compensation easy to obtain conflicts with the desire to impose incentives for improving disposal systems on individual generators of hazards. An attempt to make the two goals more compatible is the proposal to fund the U.S. Superfund (for the restoration of hazardous waste disposal sites and other compensation-type activities) from a tax on hazardous waste disposal rather than chemical feedstock use [AWPR (1983)].

5. Regulation

By regulation we mean essentially "a directive to *individual* decision-makers requiring them to set one or more output or input quantities at some specified levels or prohibiting them from exceeding (or falling short of) some specified levels" [Baumol and Oates (1975)]. As pointed out earlier, regulation has been the form of environmental policy preferred by politicians throughout the industrial world. We begin by presenting what appears to be the main arguments for this choice (Section 5.1). The different forms of regulation and their efficiency effects are then discussed (Sections 5.2 and 5.3). Finally, we analyze how the drawbacks of regulations in some applications can be mitigated or eliminated by certain modifications and, in particular, by introducing some complementary element of economic incentive systems (Section 5.4).

5.1. Why politicians prefer regulation

As we shall see in the next section, in some situations regulation emerges as an efficient instrument of environmental policy. However, efficiency aspects alone do not explain why governments in most countries have relied mainly on regulatory instruments in this field. It is hardly an easy undertaking to pin down what these other considerations have been. Different reasons seem to have been invoked in different nations and in different policy situations as well as at different points in time. In addition, important reasons may not have been explicitly invoked at all, implying that their identification becomes guesswork and possibly subject to tendentious interpretations. An attempt to identify the factors which influence the choice of policy instruments is nevertheless central to a discussion of environmental policy alternatives in the real world. This statement is partly due to the fact that not all – perhaps not even one – of these factors are irrelevant from the point of view of the complete set of policy goals and the policy constraints existing in a democratic political environment.

In passing, it should be pointed out that the dominance of direct command and control instruments can be observed not only in environmental but also in other policy areas such as occupational health and safety, consumer protection and transportation. It appears that taxes and charges have rarely been introduced as instruments to control specific activities; and even more rarely have they been designed to achieve a specified goal with respect to such activities. The principal long-term function of these "economic incentive" systems has been to withdraw purchasing power from consumers and firms in order to finance the activities of the public sector. (The economic incentive system of subsidies, on the other hand, seems to have been used as an intentional control instrument, although the transfer of purchasing power may have been an important complementary reason for such a policy.) But this principal function of taxes and charges only increases economists' doubts about why governments "avoid" the use of charges in environmental policy when these charges, in contrast to those instruments now in force would provide revenue to the government without, in principle, any deadweight loss or excess burden.

We now try to identify some of the main reasons why politicians have taken the regulatory approach to environmental policy; most of the reasons that originate in the technical characteristics of environmental problems are left to the next subsection.

(1) In many countries, economists play a minor part, if any, in the administrative groundwork of environmental policy. If the administrators have a background in science, technology or law, the economic aspects will not always be taken into account for obvious reasons. And especially when members of the legal profession dominate the higher echelons of the executive agencies, instruments of the law and of traditional law enforcement are more likely to have the upper hand.

(2) Still, economists have made their voices heard and have confronted politicians with efficiency arguments in favor of economic incentive instruments. One reason why the impact has been small seems to be that these arguments are "sophisticated" and rely on an understanding of the market mechanism and of

the "indirect" effects of prices. In contrast, bans and other forms of regulation are often geared precisely to the activity which is to be controlled. Even when politicians grasp the implications of the alternative policy solutions, they may feel that their constituents would not and that they have to settle for the policy which will receive broad support from the general public.

(3) Financial considerations can prompt the government to prefer regulation to economic incentive instruments. This is obvious for the case of subsidies, but it may concern the case of charges as well. The fact that the effects of effluent charges on ambient quality are uncertain means that government revenue from such charges is also uncertain. This is a drawback from the point of view of budget administration.

(4) Taking other specific policy goals into account can favor the regulatory alternative. Thus, charges will add to inflation, whereas regulation may not do so to the same extent.

(5) Charges can have clearcut distribution effects, which the government may be hesitant to accept. This is so, for example, when low-income groups are in a position where reductions in real income are judged to be unacceptable and when a charge system would hit the consumption of this group. The fact that the distribution effects of regulation are less conspicuous of course does not mean that they are unimportant or even that they are less objectionable than those of a corresponding system of charges.[41] As the time profile of the price effects of charges and regulation, respectively, may be quite different – say, higher prices in the short run with charges than with direct control measures, and vice versa in the long run – an adequate consideration of the distribution aspects becomes quite difficult. But from a political point of view, the short-term distribution effects may be judged to be the most important ones, and here regulation is likely to perform better.

(6) Moving into the sphere of environmental policy proper, it is important to note that, if successful, regulation of discharges or the production processes of polluters will, in general, result in a more certain effect on ambient quality than charges levied on pollutants. As we saw in Section 2, unless the cost function for the reduction of discharges is known, directly or after a trial-and-error process, the effect of a given effluent charge is uncertain. We return to this important aspect in what follows.

(7) Regulation, even when it is less direct that we just suggested, has the aura of being a "no-nonsense" instrument, adequate for the control of serious environmental problems. In contrast, charges have often been viewed as an imperfect obstacle to continued environmental degradation and even as a "license to pollute".

[41] See, for example, White (1982, pp. 88, 89), where he estimates that both costs and benefits of the regulation of automobile exhaust emissions in the United States have been regressive. See also Pearce (1983).

(8) It may have come as a surprise to those who hold the view that charges provide a "license to pollute" that the polluting firms and their trade associations seem to prefer regulation to charges. This, in itself, may be enough to make the government choose a regulatory approach. There are at least three reasons for polluters to take a position in favor of regulation:

(a) If charges were to be set at levels which would produce the same reduction of discharges as a regulation in the long run as well as in the short run, it is of course worse for the polluters if they, in addition, would have to pay fees.[42]

(b) As regulation in general can be said to be more uncompromising for the polluters than charges, government is more inclined to listen to the views of the polluters or their representatives before any action is taken. In this process, the polluters may expect to have some influence on the design and stringency of the regulation.[43]

(c) In certain countries, the legal process of introducing new regulations implies drawnout negotiations and provides ample opportunity for appeals. In this way, government intervention may be delayed for a considerable period of time to the benefit of the polluters.

5.2. Forms of regulation: Static efficiency and information

In what follows we take the polluter to be a producer. (This terminology is formally adequate even for a polluting household which obviously not only consumes but also produces effects on others.) The main reason for this choice is a practical one; more often than charges or subsidies, regulation has been and, on administrative grounds, must be aimed at firms.

If a set of effluent charges can be determined so that given ambient standards are met, it is obvious that the same result can be achieved by regulating individual sources of pollution, provided the necessary information is available.[44] Thus, if such charges would make producer A reduce his discharges by 90 percent next year and producer B by 1 percent (due to higher removal costs), effluent standards for the two sources could be so specified.[45] If it were known that the charges would lead to the introduction of a new abatement technology in firm A five years from now and in firm B two years from now, design standards for the two firms

---

[42] On this point, and the possibility that cost savings would more than make up for the added out of the pocket cost of charge payments, see the discussion of Spofford's study above.

[43] For a discussion of the influence of business on regulation in the United States see Quirk (1981). For a different view, see Linder and McBride (1984).

[44] For a simple presentation see, for example, Tresch (1981, pp. 164–168).

[45] However, the *optimal* volume of pollution will, in general, vary with the policy instrument used. See Harford and Ogura (1983).

could be so specified. What may differ between the two alternative policies are the costs of administration, monitoring and enforcement. Once we observe that the necessary information is not *freely* available, however, an even more important difference between the two policies is seen to be the information cost or the availability of the necessary information at any cost. If the necessary information is not attainable, the two alternatives are no longer comparable on a cost-effectiveness basis; policy benefits as well as compliance costs may differ as well. To complicate matters further, given the information constraint, these differences cannot be known in complete detail.

This sets the stage for evaluating the static efficiency of regulation. What are its benefits, compliance costs, information costs, and administrative, monitoring and enforcement costs? Space does not allow us to cover all these aspects, nor does the literature or at least our knowledge of it. Instead we observe the different principal forms of environmental regulation, essentially in the order of decreasing degrees of freedom for the regulated parties, commenting on that appears to be the characteristic differences in the dimensions just referred to.

5.2.1. Forcing the polluter and the pollutee to negotiate

This regulatory approach obviously requires that the parties involved be either few in number or organized in such a way that they emerge as only a few negotiating parties. The two-party case is probably the only one pertinent for this kind of mild regulation. At the one extreme, negotiations would develop similar to those within a merger and lead to an efficient solution. Such an outcome would imply that both parties have free access to relevant information about one another. This outcome is likely only for parties engaged in activities about which there is common knowledge. At the other extreme, information and bargaining strength are unevenly distributed between the parties so that the outcome may be far from a first-best optimum, say close to status quo but with significant negotiating costs being incurred.

Thus, legislation that forces a polluter and a pollutee to negotiate a settlement can be an efficient policy under certain conditions. These conditions would include, in addition to complete information about relevant costs on both sides, sufficiently small monitoring costs, small compliance costs for the polluter, and the threat of alternative measures if a settlement satisfactory to the pollutee is not reached. One important case where this kind of regulation is not likely to be an efficient policy should be mentioned. If the information as specified is far from complete, while the authorities can extract the necessary information at low costs, other solutions, such as a more interventionist form of regulation, may be preferable.

5.2.2. Performance standards

A form of regulation that provides the polluter with maximum freedom of compliance is the establishment of effluent standards for pollutants. Assuming that monitoring does not cause any significant problems and that information about compliance costs is available to the regulator at low costs, this kind of performance standard is likely to qualify as an efficient instrument. It should be noted, however, that the determination of *optimal* effluent standards requires at least as much information as the determination of optimal effluent charges [Mäler (1974b)].

Even when little is known about compliance costs, effluent standards may be more efficient than alternative instruments such as effluent charges.[46] One reason is that the costs of the trial-and-error process of adjusting charges to meet the given standard may be high (see Section 2). Another reason arises when, in a given air- or watershed, there are several polluters, whose discharges have different "transfer coefficients" (the α_i in Section 2.1). As the optimal charges must be source specific in this case, effluent standards would perform at least equally well. Temporary fluctuations in the assimilative capacity of the environment, giving rise to occasional environmental crises, would call for either "unrealistically" frequent changes in charge levels or more constant and occasionally too high charge levels. In such cases, a flexible effluent standard has been suggested as a feasible and more efficient solution [Baumol and Oates (1975, ch. 11), Baumol and Oates (1979, ch. 20) and Howe and Lee (1983)].

Another instance when performance standards can be an efficient instrument has been discussed above in the context of marketable permits (Section 3). In the simplest version of such a system, pollutants released from all members of a given set of sources are taken to have the same environmental impact. Although the initial distribution of pollution rights is specified according to source, the transferability of these rights makes the regulation area-specific instead of source-specific.

Turning to applications of performance standards where inefficiency is likely to result even in the short run, we should note at least the following three cases. First, we have the traditional showcase of inefficient standards, where different polluters with the same environmental effect per unit of pollutant discharged have different marginal removal costs at the individual standards assigned to them (e.g. a 50 percent reduction of discharges for all polluters). Here, a given reduction of pollution is achieved at a higher total costs than would be the case for a uniform charge per pollutant which would equalize marginal removal costs for all polluters.

---

[46] For a pathbreaking analysis of charges vs. standards in the presence of uncertainty about, *inter alia*, compliance costs, see Weitzman (1974). See also the survey article by Yohe (1977). And for a recent extension to more general functional forms and error structures, see Watson and Ridker (1984).

Second, effluent standards are often differentiated between old and new sources of pollution. For example, a producer who operates an existing plant is exempted from pollution control, whereas new or remodeled plants are subjected to emission limits. This application of performance standards provides an incentive to keep old plants for a longer period of time than would be the case, for example, under a system of effluent charges. Obviously, this is a special case of the problem discussed in the preceding paragraph, with effluent standards allocated to polluters regardless of marginal removal costs.

Finally, when monitoring the discharges of pollutants is costly, neither effluent charges nor effluent standards may be the optimal policy choice. The special difficulty of the monitoring problem should be elaborated at this point. This difficulty may be ascribed to five features and applies, as already observed, to charges and marketable permits as well as performance standards.

(1) All emissions are fugitive in the sense that once outside the source's stack or wastewater pipe they are lost to measurement. They leave no trail unless some human agency intervenes.[47] Thus, we cannot monitor at our leisure if we really wish to know what is and has been going on.

(2) Discharges very randomly because of random equipment breakdowns, shifts in product mix or input quality, and changes in production levels at the source. These variations, it must be stressed, are separate from any intention the discharger might have to cheat; even the best corporate citizen can suffer a breakdown of a precipitator in vastly increased emissions. This randomness has itself two implications. First, we cannot usefully think of emission standards as simple fixed numbers. The appropriate orders for a region must take into account source variations and the probability of ambient standard violations. In addition, the orders must recognize in one way or another that in adjusting to the order (or to an economic incentive) the source must balance probability of violation against cost of controlling or narrowing its range of variation.[48] Second, the rules for

---

[47] This statement must be qualified in two ways. Remote monitoring equipment makes it possible to measure concentrations of certain residuals in a stack plume, though these methods are neither simple nor precise. [See Williamson (1981)]. Somewhat more tenuous is the technique of using ambient quality levels and discharge composition to infer discharges, though it might in some cases provide a defensible check on self monitored data. See Courtney, Frank and Powell (1981) and Gordon, (1980). More generally, some residuals are disposed of in "packages" – for example, drums of hazardous pollutants.

[48] At its simplest this means that if the agency orders a source to hold its dischargers below D at all times, the source must actually aim at a target or mean discharge value far enough below D that random occurrences of excess emissions will be so infrequent as to be ignored. How far below D the target emission must be depends on the width of possible swings in discharge, the costs of control, and the penalties for detected violations. If the regulatory agency wants to see the source emit D on average, it must redefine a violation. For example, if it knew the distribution of actual discharges around the source's target, it might define a violation as any discharge greater than $D + K$. K would reflect how closely the source could control its emissions and would be matched to an appropriate penalty reflecting the costs of this control and the acceptable probability of really high emissions (greater than $D + K$).

identifying violations must be consistent with the statement of the discharge limitation orders [e.g. Beavis and Walker (1983)].

(3) Some pollutants are measured using "batch" or discrete sampling techniques.[49] This means that the choice of discharge limitation order and the source's optimal reaction to it should both be complicated by the choice of sampling regime (how often to sample and how many individual samples to draw at a time).[50]

(4) Monitoring instruments are inevitably imprecise – that is, they measure with some error. This further complicates the task of defining and finding real violations.

(5) All the above features of the monitoring problem take on a different cast when we drop the implicit assumption that sources *will* try to obey their discharge limitation orders. Cheating will be worthwhile if the probability of detection and the penalty for a detected violation do not together provide a strong enough incentive. Where intermittent agency monitoring visits are involved, we further have to reckon with legal problems of access to sample, whether (and how much) advance notice is required, and how hard it is for the source to adjust discharges up and down – to avoid being caught cheating. Given these monitoring problems, regulatory orders other than simple discharge limits may be preferable.

5.2.3. Regulating decision variables correlated with emissions

If certain inputs or outputs are perfectly correlated with the volume of pollutants discharged and less costly for the government to monitor, indirect control is more efficient than direct control. This may be true even when correlation is less than perfect, but the advantages of indirect regulation may be limited to the short term and may not even hold for the period during which the firm's basic production process remains unchanged. The correlation between emissions of pollutants and the variable monitored may be based on the inspection of a plant or a piece of equipment when new (see, for example, standards for noise and exhaust emissions from new vehicles) or when carefully maintained with respect to releases of pollutants. This performance may not be representative at later stages of operation or when it is no longer worthwhile for the firm to undertake maintenance. Thus, if the government is forced to rely on information provided by the polluters, the reduction in monitoring costs from making control indirect may be outweighed by the imperfections of such information.

---

[49] It appears that continuous sampling methods with automatic recording are being developed for more and more pollution types, so this difficulty may tend to disappear as time goes on [APCA (1981)].

[50] Sampling size and frequency, given the source's distribution of discharges and the characteristics of the tests performed, define the probabilities of missing the violations and of finding false violations [Vaughan and Russell (1983)].

5.2.4. Design standards

When direct as well as indirect monitoring of releases of pollutants is unreliable, expensive or technically infeasible, requirements that producers use a specific technology become an obvious candidate for optimal policy. Such a policy has been used in practice in a large number of cases. For example, it is often difficult to monitor the source of air or noise pollution. Measuring emissions of BOD in waste water has proved expensive. In such cases, producers can be required to use particular production processes or input qualities (e.g. low-sulphur fuel). Alternatively, they can be required to install a specific kind of abatement or purification process or be forced to reprocess certain kinds of wastes. Or they can be required to transfer certain wastes to publicly owned purification plants, without (as it often happens) being charged the full costs of waste treatment.[51] As a less specific kind of design standard (at the time of the regulatory decision), dischargers may be required to apply the "best practicable technology" (BPT) or "best available technology" (BAT) at some given future date.

Design standards can be efficient policy not only for reasons of low monitoring costs. They also provide a way to save information costs among polluters. When there is no doubt about the most efficient solution to meeting a certain performance standard, a design standard is the obvious policy choice [Crandall (1979)].

But, when there are doubts about the most efficient approach to meeting a performance standard, the requirement that a specific technology be used is likely to cause misallocation of resources. For all firms in an industry, a series of small adjustments of the existing production processes or simply reduced output may turn out to be less costly alternatives to the required production process or abatement technology. More often perhaps, different firms in an industry have different least-cost solutions to the reduction of discharges accomplished by a certain design standard [see, for example, OECD (1982a, 1982b)].

Many of the political aspects discussed in the preceding subsection may explain why politicians often prefer the design standard solution. Installation of purification equipment is the "natural" policy if you want wastes to contain a smaller volume of pollutants; moreover, it may appear as an effective instrument if you want to satisfy the environmentally conscious general public, etc. Above all, perhaps, design standards are believed to contribute to protection of the environment with a high degree of certainty. However, there is evidence that the security provided by design standards in environmental policy is false or exaggerated in a number of cases. Thus, as touched upon earlier, the amount of actual discharges for which the required process was designed may be exceeded dramatically [see,

---

[51] This may be seen as a combination of a design standard and a subsidy. It is a subsidy in the sense that all costs of the regulation are not borne by the regulated party. Combinations of this kind have been quite popular with policy-makers, involving either lump-sum subsidies or subsidizing a part (or percentage) of the costs incurred, e.g. a percentage of the installation costs for the equipment required.

for example, Mäler (1974b)]. And equipment which meets certain standards when leaving the producer may be tampered with by the user; although peripheral to the case of design standards, the difference between emission levels for new cars and actual in-use emissions is a good illustration [White (1982)]. There are also indications that stricter standards for new equipment are circumvented by increasingly frequent modification of the equipment when in use.[52]

In many cases where design standards have not proved effective in practice, the problem has not so much been the standards themselves as the way they are enforced or checked. Thus, inspection of plants or equipment when in use can improve the results of design standards. However, the advantages in terms of low administrative costs that this kind of regulation was credited with may be lost in the process.

5.2.5. Bans on products or processes

Outright bans may appear to be the strictest form of regulation. Banning the production (or use) of a product which has no close substitutes is a case that supports this view. But close substitutes are often available at low extra costs (as is illustrated, for example, by the appearance of other propellants for aerosol sprays when chlorofluorocarbons were banned in certain countries). And this may be true when bans are imposed on certain inputs, such as high-sulphur fuel in certain areas. Moreover, when bans take the form of zoning or curfews, compliance costs may be small, because alternatives remain open to the regulated party. This is so in particular when bans are announced well in advance. In this perspective, design standards rather than bans represent the most severe type of regulatory constraint.

It follows from what we just said that bans on products or processes may be an efficient policy instrument when there are close substitutes at low additional costs. Moreover, bans – and even more, design standards – may make economies of scale in the production of the substitutes (the required or nonbanned equipment) materialize faster than through the market mechanism by itself. In fact, nonconvexities in production may prevent the market mechanism from ever reaching a point which is less harmful for the environment, and, at the same time, less costly; in such a case, regulation may be the obvious way to eliminate, as it were, the two market failures.

A similar case of non-convexities appears when the pollution problem is only latent, but still the source of inefficient resource allocation. This is the case, for example, where an existing plant pollutes the environment so that certain other activities sensitive to the pollution have never been established in the vicinity, although the social surplus would be higher if they were than if the existing firm

---

[52] See Broder (1982, ch. 5) for the case of noise emissions from motorcycles.

were kept there.[53] Charges are not likely to work in this situation, especially not if they should reflect the value of the latent externalities; an arrangement along such lines might incite blackmail or at least create insurmountable information problems. A ban on pollution, e.g. in the form of zoning, is perhaps the obvious choice of policy in this "no-pollutee case", given that the optimum form of land use has been identified.

The traditional case for bans is, of course, when environmental standards call for the elimination of a certain kind of discharges, such as highly toxic substances. In addition, even though zero pollution from a particular type of activity is not called for, a ban may be chosen for administrative reasons, e.g. because it is immediately apparent when the ban has been broken.

5.2.6. Collective facilities – a digression

Government investments in facilities for environmental protection (sewers, waste treatment plants, walls for protection against motorway noise, etc) or government restoration activities (cleaning up, reforestation, reaeration of lakes, etc.) bear some resemblance to the regulatory solution and may be discussed at this point.

The analytical background for government protection and restoration activities can be briefly outlined as follows. If costs of protection/restoration fall short of the value of the corresponding environmental damages, there is a case for protection/restoration. Furthermore, if collective protection/restoration activities are less costly than environmental protection administered by the polluters individually, the collective alternative is favored. To implement this kind of policy, it may be sufficient for the government to ban certain kinds of discharges into the environment, provided that this ban actually institutes voluntary actions leading to the emergence of the optimal, collective arrangement. An illustrative example here could be the emergence of privately owned refuse collection activities as a consequence of such a ban.

Privately owned facilities of this kind may not materialize for reasons of administrative complexity or when the protection involved is a pure public good, instigating free-rider behavior among individual members of the common-interest group. Or organization costs may simply be believed to be too high, e.g. due to fears that several competing units may be established (at least temporarily) for a private-good kind of activity subjected to large economies of scale. Or a privately owned natural monopoly, once established, may charge monopoly prices. For

---

[53] For example, the existing firm A runs at a profit of $1 million per year. The "other activities", if firm A were absent, would run at an aggregate profit of $2 million per year. However, when A is present, they would not be able to make a profit due to pollution from A. Moreover, costs of organizing these other activities or lack of available funds bar the formation of an interest group which could buy firm A and shut it down. Or, there may be space for a new firm A' to locate in the area once firm A is shut down. Hence, for several reasons, the market cannot make the optimum allocation materialize.

reasons such as these, the government may prefer to give the protection activities a public-utility status with the government control accompanying such a status; or the activities may be operated directly by the government. To implement such a choice, the government may want to complement the ban with, or have it replaced by, a design standard requiring the polluters to be connected to a central waste treatment plant.[54]

In other instances of government provision of collective facilities, no act of regulation may be involved. This is the case, for example, with most forms of restoration campaigns as well as with all improvements of existing waste treatment plants. To evaluate whether such activities are worthwhile it is only required that they meet the relevant cost–benefit criterion.

5.3. Regulation and dynamic efficiency

In the preceding section, our primary objective was to describe the principal forms of regulation and their static or short-term efficiency characteristics. In this section, we discuss regulatory instruments with respect to efficiency over time. Economists' evaluations of environmental regulation have to a large extent concentrated on this aspect. Here we discuss the following three issues: adaption to changes in exogenous variables, incentives to develop new forms of pollution-abatement technology, and effects on market structure and competition.

5.3.1. Environmental regulation in the presence of exogenous changes

Efficiency over time requires, in principle, that policy be adapted to exogenous changes in environmental costs as well as compliance or removal costs, subject to administrative and other specific costs associated with policy change. As mentioned above these costs of policy change may be lower for regulatory instruments than for economic incentive systems in the context of short-term fluctuations in the assimilative capacity of the environment. This might extend to the case of exogenous long-term fluctuations as well. In practice, however, regulation may not be administered with sufficient flexibility to take advantage of this potential. This is likely to be true at least for certain forms of regulation such as design standards, for which the regulatory process may be very slow.

If it turns out that regulation and economic incentive systems in fact tend to be equally inflexible over time, we may investigate the relative merits of the two policy approaches when confronted by exogenous changes. Assume a situation where a system of effluent charges and a system of effluent standards would be

---

[54] For a discussion of the choice between pollution charges leading to individually administered protection and forcing or simply allowing polluters to connect to centralized waste treatment activities, see Bohm (1972).

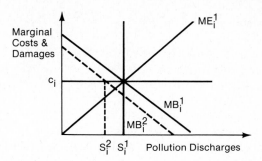

Figure 10.1. Charges, standards, and change in the marginal costs of reducing pollution discharges.

equally efficient and successful in guiding the economy to a short-term optimum position. See the standard S_i^1 for firm i and the uniform charge per unit of pollutant c_i in Figure 10.1. Emissions are brought to the point where the initial marginal benefit curve of the polluter (MB_i^1), also the reverse of the marginal compliance cost curve, intersects the curve for the marginal environmental effects (ME_i^1). Now, we should note first of all that neither the inflexible charge system (with unit charges independent of emission volume) nor the inflexible standard would allow any adjustments when the estimated marginal environmental effects (ME_i) change. On the other hand, when external factors influence the marginal compliance costs (MB_i), some adjustment will automatically take place in the charges case. $(MB_i^2$ produces discharges equal to S_i^2 when a charge is applied.) But as long as the charges do not change to perfectly reflect the marginal environmental effects, these adjustments may not be preferable to the absence of adjustments in the standard case. It is clearly seen that the outcome will depend on the extent to which both the marginal environmental effects and the marginal compliance costs change in the relevant interval. The charge system will tend to perform better than the standard if the marginal environmental effects are sufficiently close to being constant around the initial optimum point. Conversely, if these effects rise at a sufficiently high rate at this point, the inflexible standard will be the least imperfect instrument of the two [see Weitzman (1974) and Yohe (1977)].

5.3.2. Endogenous adjustments of compliance costs

When subjected to a given policy, the polluter has, in principle, a larger number of adjustment options open to him, the longer the adjustment period. Furthermore, if there are incentives for the polluter to develop new forms of adjustments – something which may be influenced by policy design – additional options may emerge over time. For these two reasons, compliance costs of a given policy will in general be lower in the long run than in the short run. This also means that compliance costs at the time the policy takes effect will be lower if advance notice of the policy is given [see Kneese and Schultze (1975, pp. 79–80)]. And this may be increasingly important the fewer the options allowed by the policy. For example, compliance with a design standard introduced on short notice may be very costly to the firm; say if the plant has just been remodeled. In contrast, an effluent standard – and even more an effluent charge – may allow the firm to make a much less costly temporary adjustment and introduce the technology implied by the design standard at a later stage, assuming this standard is the most efficient form of long-term adjustment.

Incentives to develop new options diminish the smaller the scope of adjustment allowed by the policy, *ceteris paribus*. Thus, with effluent charges, a maximum number of compliance alternatives are acceptable and hence, technological R&D may be pursued in any direction. At the other extreme, a design standard leaves no room for innovation. Or this is so at least if policy cannot easily be redesigned should new and superior ways to meet a given ambient standard happen to be developed. The important aspect from the incentive point of view is, of course, to what extent the firm believes it to be possible to influence policy by developing new and more efficient technology.

Moreover, once the polluter has adjusted to the new piece of regulation, there is no longer any incentive for him to attempt reaching a lower level of pollution than that implied by the regulation (be it a performance or a design standard), even when such a reduction would be valuable to society. Charges, on the other hand, provide such an incentive although its size may be nonoptimal (e.g. too large in the situation portrayed in footnote 22). Certain forms of regulation may even actually discourage the development or introduction of innovations. Thus, establishing shifting BAT standards for an industry creates perverse incentives for innovation.[55]

Although no real-world policy instrument can be expected to send correct signals to guide the long-term adjustment of pollution abatement and the development of new abatement technology, regulation and especially design standards are likely to perform much worse than economic incentive systems in these

---

[55] For example, in the U.S. Clean Water Act explicitly, and at least in the rhetoric surrounding the Clean Air Act, improvements in technology are supposed to trigger tightening of the standards [Clean Water Act, Section 302d in Government Institute (1980)]. This reduces the incentive to seek cost-reducing technical improvements in production process or treatment equipment, and under some circumstances may eliminate the incentive altogether. A very simple way of looking at this process uses the figure in footnote 22. When technology is improved, and marginal cost falls to MC_1, the ratchetting-down requirement implies a new lower discharge standard. Let us say that the rule for choosing this level is to maintain equal marginal costs (e_0) before and after. Then, after technical change, the standard would be D_1, and the net savings to the firm would be C-F. In this figure, area F will always be greater than area C, so there is a *disincentive* to innovate. More generally, the existence of the additional cost, F, will at least reduce the positive incentive to innovate.

respects. Thus, a policy that relies on regulatory intervention tends to make the long-term costs of attaining a given ambient quality unnecessarily high. This does not mean, however, that environmental regulation must lead to a reduction in productivity as commonly measured. In fact, there are some indications that increasingly stringent effluent standards have operated as a challenge to industry and spurred an innovation response whereby both pollution has been diminished and productivity has increased [OECD (1982a, 1982b)]. This is not to say, of course, that policy instruments, which allow a still larger freedom of adjustment and provide stronger incentives for developing new ways of reducing pollution, would not have performed even better.

5.3.3. *The effects of regulation on market structure*

If industry has an influence on the design of environmental regulation and the larger firms play a prominent role in this process, the result may be unfavorable for the smaller competitors in the industry. Moreover, the use of design standards requiring new production processes or the installation of expensive pollution-abatement technology may hit small firms particularly hard.[56]

If regulation tends to disfavor certain types of firms in an industry, the effect may be that competition is reduced [see Buchanan and Tullock (1975) and Dewees (1983)]. This effect may be particularly serious if mainly innovative firms (e.g. small growing firms) are hit hard by regulation. Moreover, if control is tighter for new firms, competition and innovation in the industry may be reduced still further [OECD (1982b)]. All this would contribute to maintaining a high level of direct as well as indirect compliance costs of regulation in the long run.

5.4. *Modifying the performance of regulatory instruments*

Some ways to improve the efficiency of the regulatory approach follow from our discussion in the preceding section. First of all, we saw that adding dynamic efficiency aspects to the static ones presented in Section 5.2 suggests that regulatory design be shifted towards forms which allow more freedom of adjustment. Second, advance notice of a given piece of regulation tends to reduce compliance costs. Third, design standards and other inflexible forms of regulation may be less costly to society if government shows a willingness to redesign its rulemaking when new solutions for protecting the environment emerge. In this way, the regulated party may be given an incentive to undertake R&D of new pollution-abatement technologies. In contrast, the use of BAT standards and a tendency to introduce stricter standards for industries that have developed less

---

[56] See Grabowski and Vernon (1978) for examples from the field of consumer product safety regulation.

harmful production processes are likely to impede innovation. Hence, compliance costs for a given ambient quality are increased or political ambitions with respect to ambient quality may have to be lowered.

In addition to modifications of the type suggested above, the regulatory system may be improved by introducing elements from economic incentive schemes. In this way, the high degree of certainty as to the effects of regulation, which – right or wrong – seems to be decisive for policy choice in the real world, can be obtained along with a stimulus towards efficiency that otherwise may be absent.

First, it should be noted that an economic incentive element is in fact already incorporated into most forms of regulation. If a polluter fails to comply with the directive given to him, he may be fined for doing so. A disadvantage of this regulatory design is, however, that the exact penalty level often is not known beforehand.

The problem of uncertain penalties would be eliminated if regulated parties were confronted with explicit, punitive *non-compliance fees* [see, for example, Viscusi (1979)]. That is, the polluter is formally allowed to exceed the standard given to him and will do so if his compliance costs are high.[57] Although regulation might seem less stringent as a consequence of such a system, it should be noted that this kind of legalized non-compliance allows standards to be set at a more demanding level than otherwise.

In practice, the application of noncompliance fees is often subject to severe imperfections. Thus, the fee is frequently calculated to equal the regulated party's gain from non-compliance; in other words, the fee is not punitive. Given that non-compliance is not always detected and that the regulated party's gain is likely to be underestimated by an outside party such as the government, this kind of policy can hardly be conceived of as rational. For example, it is difficult to see why the polluter would pay any attention to the standard imposed under these circumstances, unless, of course, there were additional and diffuse costs of stigmatization embedded in non-compliance.

As another form of incentive element, effluent charges could be levied on the polluter along with an effluent standard.[58] Assuming that the standard is binding when initially introduced, the effect of the charge would be to promote a future reduction in pollution below the level of the standard. This would increase long-run efficiency, provided, of course, that the value of further reductions in pollution were sufficiently high. Alternatively, reduction in pollution below the

---

[57] This idea, which in the United States originated as a practical policy in Connecticut and came to Washington with Douglas Costle, former Administrator of EPA, is now part of the Clean Air Act. (Section 120 of the Clean Air Act is devoted to a noncompliance penalty system.) See also, Drayton (1980). It allows EPA administratively to assess, on a source not complying with discharge regulations, a penalty equal to what the agency calculates the source would save through its noncompliance.

[58] For a version of an optimal mixed program of this kind see Baumol and Oates (1975, pp. 162–171).

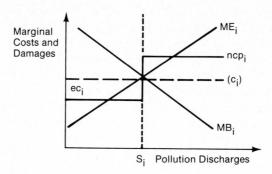

Figure 10.2. Combination of charge, standard, and non-compliance penalty.

level of the standard could be subsidized. The overall effects of a subsidy would differ from those of an equally large effluent charge, unless the income effect of the charge/subsidy could be disregarded and the shadow price of a dollar of government revenue equalled a dollar.

In principle, such a combination of standards and charges (subsidies) would provide the advantages of both systems, i.e. the relative certainty of a maximum limit to pollution and an incentive for the polluter to seek ways to reduce pollution still further in the short as well as in the long run. Furthermore, the standard could be combined with both (a subsidy or) an effluent charge (*ec*) and a noncompliance penalty (*ncp*), exceeding the level of the effluent charge.[59] Given sufficient information about the (nonconstant) marginal environmental effects of discharges and about the frequency distribution of the curve displaying the polluter's marginal benefits of discharges, such a system could be more efficient than a pure system of uniform effluent charges (see Figure 10.2). However, a prerequisite for such an outcome is that discharges from one polluter do not significantly alter the marginal environmental effects of discharges from another.

To sum up: although the actual use of environmental regulation appears to be based largely on factors unrelated to efficiency, there are as we have seen a number of instances in which efficiency aspects call for regulation instead of economic incentive schemes. But when emphasis is placed on long term efficiency and on the strength of the profit motive for seeking innovations in pollution abatement, economic incentives become more important. How much more im-

---

[59] See Roberts and Spence (1976). A fee-subsidy system was developed by James Smith and his colleagues at the City of Philadelphia Air Management Services and is reported in *Feasibility Study: A Fee/Subsidy System for Controlling Sulfur Dioxide Emissions*; a multiple-volume set of working papers by various authors [Philadelphia Air Management Services (1981)]. The aim here is zero net revenue raising (zero net transfer cost to polluters) and the mechanism is a combination of a specified emission level for each source, a fee for emissions over that level, and a subsidy for reductions in emissions below the chosen level.

portant is a matter of belief in the innovating capacity of the polluters and special firms developing pollution abatement equipment. However, combining standards and economic incentive schemes opens up a possibility to extract some of the best from both approaches. Such a combination can be obtained with a system of marketable permits, as discussed in Section 3. Or, a set of charges or subsidies and/or noncompliance penalties can be added to the set of standards. But for this to be meaningful, the standards must be of a type that allows some freedom of adjustment.

6. Moral suasion

As we saw in the preceding section, the choice of environmental policy instruments may be influenced by a number of "non-economic" factors. As a special but probably not unusual case, the policy-maker is confronted with a situation where there are definite constraints on the set of policy instruments. The origin of such constraints may be found in the political interpretations of public opinion. Thus, for example, it may become clear or interpreted as clear that charges on polluters are out-of-bounds, politically speaking, whereas subsidies are not or vice versa.

Estimates of compliance costs, employment effects, etc. made by interest groups often play a prominent role in the formation of such constraints. Typically, these estimates are based on insights that outsiders, and among them the government, cannot check. In particular, the effect of pollution charges on employment and the volume of exports of an industry may be greatly exaggerated by industry representatives without anyone else being able to prove that these estimates are biased and even less, of course, to ascertain the extent of which they are biased. [See Sonstelie and Portney (1983) for possible solutions to some of these problems.]

Thus, political constraints on environmental policy (to be distinguished from observing other goals of economic policy such as distribution goals) may be in force and turn the choice of optimal policy into a second best problem. In the limiting case, all stringent political actions to meet certain government policy goals may be blocked by such constraints. In that case, only actions that are voluntary on the part of the polluters are open to government influence. We now turn to a brief discussion of this "policy of moral suasion", which has occasionally been used and, in some cases, has proved to be effective.

Government initiatives to influence behavior on a voluntary basis can hardly be expected to be effective in all instances of environmental protection. If the environmental hazards are not conspicuous or dramatic enough, moral pressure may not materialize among any significant number of people. Similarly, when it is generally felt that the formal or moral responsibility rests with an identifiable party, others may not be easily convinced to take action. But many cases of environmental degradation are characterized by a lack of well-defined property rights and hence by unclear responsibility. In such cases, protection of the environment may be seen as a moral concern for people in general.

Attempts to influence the behavior of *individuals and households* can gain support from existing attitudes and social valuations related to the environmental issue involved. Thus, an attempt to make people abstain from buying fur coats to protect endangered species may receive firm backing from people who cannot afford to buy them. In other cases, where voluntary actions to protect the environment are conspicuous, such actions may be supported by feelings of cooperation and shared interests. This is probably more true for non-government initiatives than for the government-initiated attempts to influence behavior, which we are concerned with here. But this distinction may be less relevant for certain countries or local areas with a tradition of consensus on a large number of social issues. Thus, for example, attempts to make people voluntarily return used mercury and nickel-cadmium batteries to sellers have been fairly successful in some countries [see, for example, OECD (1981)]. A more general problem is that, unless new habits have had time to be formed, moral suasion may be effective only for a short period – as long as the arguments seem new and compelling.[60]

The likelihood of persuading *firms* to take voluntary action of reduce pollution (without the backing of a threat of harsher measures) is even smaller. Firms under the pressure of competition can be assumed to pay attention to arguments without a legal or economic content only when their costs of reducing pollution are negligible. Exceptions will be found when a conspicuous attempt to take moral arguments into account would serve the purpose of sales promotion, as when consumers have been building up a demand for new products with less negative effects on the environment (such as low phosphate detergents). But in such cases, unless the new product happens to be as effective, attractive and inexpensive as the original one, it is the consumers who pay the costs.

It should be noted in this connection that the relation between voluntary actions and constraints on policy may be the opposite of the one assumed here. Thus, firms may support voluntary programs among consumers or take voluntary actions on their own as an offensive measure to block the government from using more stringent and more effective policy instruments in the future.

So far we have discussed whether it is worthwhile for the government to undertake moral suasion when other instruments are blocked. But as pointed out by Baumol and Oates (1979), there are instances when such a policy is in fact more efficient than other instruments. First, this may occur when the monitoring required for economic incentive schemes or regulation is ruled out as being

---

[60] See, however, Baumol and Oates (1979, ch. 19) for examples where voluntary actions have remained in effect for longer periods of time.

technically infeasible or prohibitively expensive. For example, improper disposal of hazardous material into the sewage system is difficult to control by such methods, as is littering or careless use of open fire in wilderness areas. Here, moral suasion may be more efficient than realistic versions of other instruments. That this approach can also be quite effective is supported to some extent by experience from campaigns against littering in Scandinavia and "Smokey the Bear" forest-fire prevention campaigns in the United States.

Second, in certain cases of environmental catastrophies or immediate risks of such catastrophies (e.g. extremely hazardous smog levels), ordinary policy instruments may be too cumbersome or simply too slow. Again, there are examples which show that government appeals for voluntary actions can work fast and have an important impact in such voluntary situations.

To sum up, there are indications that, in certain cases, it may be worthwhile for the government to rely on moral suasion when alternative measures are blocked for political reasons. In addition, even when more sophisticated policy alternatives are available, there are cases when moral suasion emerges as an efficient policy instrument.

7. Concluding remarks

The message of this chapter may be seen as either negative or positive, depending on the perspective of the reader. The negative version is that no general statements can be made about the relative desirability of alternative policy instruments once we consider such practical complications as that location matters, that monitoring is costly, and that exogenous change occurs in technology, regional economies, and natural environmental systems. The positive way of stating this result is to stress that all the alternatives are promising in some situations. Even design standards have a place in the armamentarium of the environmental policy-maker. If the classic case for the absolute superiority of effluent charges is flawed by the simplicity of the necessary assumptions, the arguments for the superiority of rigid forms of regulations suffer equally from unstated assumptions and static views of the world. There is no substitute for careful analysis of the available alternatives in the specific policy context at issue.

That said, however, we are still tempted to stress the advantages of economic incentive systems in the long-run context, at least as a complement to a regulatory approach. The extra push toward the development of new production and discharge reduction technology provided by these instruments seems likely to dwarf in importance the short-run, and to some extent illusory, advantages to be gained by specifying actions or stigmatizing pollution at any non-zero level. Furthermore, we believe it worthwhile expanding the fields of application contemplated for such relatively unexplored instruments as deposit–refund systems.

Some exploration and experimentation can be done in real policy problems, but in many instances realistically complicated models will, we anticipate, provide insights currently lacking because of the simplicity of available theoretical models and the narrowness of actual experience.

References

Adar, Z. and J.M. Griffin (1976) "Uncertainty and Choice of Pollution Control Instruments", *Journal of Environmental Economics and Management* 3, no. 3, 178–188.

APCA (1981) *Continuous Emission Monitoring: Design, Operation, and Experience* (Air Pollution Control Association, Pittsburgh).

Atkinson, Scott E. and Donald H. Lewis (1974a) *A Cost Evaluation of Alternative Air Quality Control Strategies*, Report No. EPA 600/5-74-003, (USEPA, Washington Environmental Research Center, Washington).

Atkinson, Scott E. and Donald H. Lewis (1974b) "A Cost-Effective Analysis of Alternative Air Quality Control Strategies", *Journal of Environmental Economics and Management* 1, 237–250.

Atkinson, Scott E. and T.H. Tietenberg (1982) "The Empirical Properties of Two Classes of Designs for Transferable Discharge Permit Markets", *Journal of Environmental Economics and Management* 9, no. 2.

AWPR (Air/Water Pollution Report) (1983) *Chemical Industry, Environmentalists Support Tax on Waste Disposers to Finance Superfund* (May) p. 202.

Baumol, William J. and Wallace E. Oates (1971) "The Use of Standards and Prices for Protection of the Environment", *Swedish Journal of Economics*, 73, no. 1.

Baumol, William J. and Wallace E. Oates (1975) *The Theory of Environmental Policy* (Prentice-Hall, Englewood Cliffs).

Baumol, William J. and Wallace E. Oates (1979) *Economics, Environmental Policy, and the Quality of Life* (Prentice-Hall, Englewood Cliffs).

Beavis, Brian and Martin Walker (1983) "Achieving Environmental Standards with Stochastic Discharges", *Journal of Environmental Economics and Management*, 10, no. 2, 103–111.

Boger, Kenneth S. (1975) "The Common Law of Public Nuisance in State Environmental Litigation", *Environmental Affairs* 4, no. 2, 367–392.

Bohm, Peter (1972) "Pollution: Taxation or Purification?", *Kyklos*, Vol. XXV, no. 3, pp. 501–517.

Bohm, Peter (1981) *Deposit–Refund Systems: Theory and Applications to Environmental, Conservation, and Consumer Policy* (Baltimore: Johns Hopkins University Press for Resources for the Future).

Bower, B.T., Remi Barre, Jochen Kuhner and Clifford S. Russell (1981) *Incentives in Water Quality Management: France and the Ruhr Area* (Resources for the Future, Washington).

Brady, Gordon L. and Richard E. Morrison (1982) *Emissions Trading: An Overview of the EPA Policy Statement.* (Washington, D.C., National Science Foundation) Policy and Research Analysis Rep. 82-2 (May).

Broder, Ivy E. (1982) "Regulation of Transportation Noise", Working Paper no. 18, American Enterprise Institute, Washington, mimeo.

Bromley, Daniel W. (1978) "Property Rules, Liability Rules and Environmental Economics", *Journal of Economic Issues* 12, 43–60.

Brown, Gardner (1982) "The Effluent Charge System in the Federal Republic of Germany", unpublished report, University of Washington, Department of Economics, Seattle.

Brown, John Prather (1973) "Toward an Economic Theory of Liability", *Journal of Legal Studies* 2 no. 2, 323–349.

Buchanan, James M. and G. Tullock (1975) "Pollutors' Profits and Political Response: Direct Control versus Taxes", *American Economic Review* 65, no. 1, 139–147.

Burrows, Paul (1981) "Controlling the Monopolistic Polluter: Nihilism or Eclecticism", *Journal of Environmental Economics and Management* 8, no. 4, 372–380.

Calabresi, Giudo and A. Douglas Melamed (1972) "Property Rules, Liability Rules, and Inalienability: One View of the Cathedral", *Harvard Law Review* 85, 1089–1128.

Case, Charles D. (1982) "Problems in Judicial Review Arising from the Use of Computer Models and Other Quantitative Methodologies in Environmental Decisionmaking", *Boston College Environmental Affairs Law Review* 10, no. 2, 251–363.

Cass, Glen et al. (1980) "Implementing Tradeable Emissions Licenses: Sulfur in the Los Angeles Air Shed", Environmental Quality Laboratory, California Institute of Technology, for the National Commission on Air Quality.

Coase, Ronald H. (1960) "The Problem of Social Cost", *Journal of Law and Economics* 3, no. 1, 1–44.

Collinge, Robert A. and Martin J. Bailey (1983) "Optimal Quasi-Market Choice in the Presence of Pollution Externalities", *Journal of Environmental Economics and Management* 10, no. 3, 221–232.

Courant, Carl (1980) "Emission Reductions From Shutdowns: Their Role in Banking and Trading Systems", U.S.E.P.A., unpublished.

Courtney, F.E., C.W. Frank and J.M. Powell (1981) "Integration of Modelling, Monitoring, and Laboratory Observation to Determine Reasons for Air Quality Violations", *Environmental Monitoring and Assessment* 1, no. 2, 107–118.

Crandall, Robert W. (1979) "Reforming Social Regulation," The Brookings Institution, Washington, mimeo.

Crocker, Thomas D. (1966) "The Structuring of Atmospheric Pollution Control Systems", in: H. Wolozin (ed.), *The Economics of Air Pollution* (W.W. Norton, New York).

Crone, Theodore M. (1983) "Transferable Discharge Permits and the Control of Stationary Air Pollution: Comments", *Land Economics* 59, no. 1, 123–125.

Dales, J.H. (1968a) "Land, Water and Ownership", *Canadian Journal of Economics* 1, 797–804.

Dales, J.H. (1968b) *Pollution, Property and Prices* (Toronto: University Press).

David, Martin, W. Eheart, E. Joeres and E. David (1980) "Marketable Permits for the Control of Phosphorous Effluent into Lake Michigan", *Water Resources Research* 16, no. 2, 263–270.

deLucia, R.J. (1974) *Evaluation of Marketable Effluent Permit Systems*, Office of Research and Development, U.S. Environmental Protection Agency (Government Printing Office, Washington).

Dewees, Donald N. (1983) "Instrument Choice in Environmental Policy", *Economic Inquiry* 21, no. 1, 53–71.

Drayton, William (1980) "Economic Law Enforcement", *The Harvard Environmental Law Review* 4, no. 1, 1–40.

Eheart, J. Wayland (1980) "Cost-Efficiency of Transferable Discharge Permits for the Control of BOD Discharges", *Water Resources Research* 16, 980–986.

Elliott, Ralph D. (1973) "Economic Study of the Effect of Municipal Sewer Surcharges on Industrial Wastes and Water Usage", *Water Resources Research* 9, no. 5, 1121–1131.

Fisher, Anthony C. (1981) *Resource and Environmental Economics* (Cambridge University Press, Cambridge).

Førsund, Finn R. (1972) "Allocation in Space and Environmental Pollution", *Swedish Journal of Economics* 74, 19–34.

Førsund, Finn R. (1973) "Externalities, Environmental Pollution, and Allocation in Space: A General Equilibrium Approach", *Regional and Urban Economics* 3, no. 1, 3–32.

Freeman, A. Myrick III (1970a) "Should Maine Polluters Pay "By the Pound?", Maine *Times*, 27 (February).

Freeman, A. Myrick III (1970b) "An Amendment of Title 38 of the Maine Revised Statutes to Institute a System of Effluent Charges to Abate Water Pollution", unpublished.

Freeman, A. Myrick III (1978) "Air and Water Pollution Policy", in: Paul Portney (ed.), *Current Issues in U.S. Environmental Policy* (Johns Hopkins University Press for Resources for the Future, Baltimore).

Ginberg, P. and Grant W. Schaumberg, Jr. (1979) *Economic Incentive Systems for the Control of Hydrocarbon Emissions from Stationary Sources*, Report by Meta Systems, Cambridge, Massachusetts, to U.S. Council on Environmental Quality (September).

Gordon, Glen E. (1980) "Receptor Models", *Environmental Science and Technology* 14, no. 1, 792–800.

Government Institute (1980) *Environmental Statutes: 1980 Edition*, (Government Institutes, Washington).

Grabowski, Henry G. and John M. Vernon (1978) "Consumer Product Safety Regulation", *American Economic Review* 68, no. 2, 284–289.

Gulick, Luther (1958) "The City's Challenge in Resource Use", in: H Jarrett (ed.), *Perspectives on Conservation*, (Johns Hopkins University Press for Resources for the Future, Baltimore).

Hahn, Robert W. (1980) "On the Applicability of Market Solutions to Environmental Problems", unpublished. EQL paper 314-40 (California Institute of Technology, Pasadena) (February).

Hahn, Robert W. and Roger Noll (1981) "Implementing Tradable Emissions Permits", a paper prepared for the Conference on Reforming Government Regulation: Alternative Strategies to Social Regulatory Policy. (California Institute of Technology, EQL, Pasadena) (February).

Harford, J. and S. Ogura (1983) "Pollution Taxes and Standards: A Continuum of Quasi-optimal Solutions", *Journal of Environmental Economics and Management* 10, no. 1, 1-17.

Howe, Charles W. and Dwight R. Lee (1983) "Priority Pollution Rights: Adapting Pollution Control to a Variable Environment", *Land Economics* 59, no. 2, 141-149.

Inside EPA (1983) "Durenberger May Draft Acid Rain Bill to Tax SO_2 Emissions Across Nation", 20, 4.

Jacobs, J.J. and G.L. Casler (1979) "Internalizing Externalities of Phosphorus Discharges from Crop Production to Surface Water: Effluent Taxes versus Uniform Restrictions", *American Journal of Agricultural Economics* 61, 309-312.

Johnson, Edwin (1967) "A Study in the Economics of Water Quality Management", *Water Resources Research* 3, no. 2.

Johnson, Ralph W. and Gardner M. Brown (1976) *Cleaning Up Europe's Waters*, (Praeger, N.Y.).

Kelman, Steven (1981) *What Price Incentives?* (Auburn House Publishing Company, Boston).

Klevorick, Alvin K. and Gerald H. Kramer (1973) "Social Choice on Pollution Management: The Genossenschaften", *Journal of Public Economics* 2, 101-146.

Kneese, Allen V. (1964) *The Economics of Regional Water Quality Management* (Johns Hopkins University Press for Resources for the Future, Baltimore).

Kneese, Allen V. and Blair T. Bower (1972) *Managing Water Quality: Economics, Technology, Institutions* (Johns Hopkins University Press for Resources for the Future, Baltimore).

Kneese, Allen V. and Charles E. Schultze (1975) *Pollution, Prices, and Public Policy* (The Brookings Institution, Washington).

Krupnick, Alan J. and Wallace E. Oates (1981) "On the Design of a Market for Air-Pollution Rights: The Spatial Problem", unpublished paper, University of Maryland, Department of Economics.

Krupnick, Alan J., Wallace E. Oates and Eric Van De Verg (1983) "On Marketable Air Pollution Permits: The Case for a System of Pollution Offsets", *Journal of Environmental Economics and Management* 10, no. 3, 233-247.

Kurtzweg, Jerry A. and Cristina J. Nelson (1980) "Clean Air and Economic Development: An Urban Initiative", *Journal of the Air Pollution Control Association* no. 11, 1187-1193.

Lave, Lester and Gilbert Omenn (1981) *Clearing the Air: Reforming the Clean Air Act* (The Brookings Institution, Washington).

Lee, Dwight (1982) "Environmental Versus Political Pollution", International Institute for Economic Research, Original Paper, no. 39, Los Angeles.

Lewis, Tracy (1981) "Markets and Environmental Management with a Storable Pollutant", *Journal of Environmental Economics and Management* 8, no. 1, 11-18.

Linder, Stephen H. and Mark E. McBride (1984) "Enforcement Costs and Regulatory Reform: The Agency and Firm Response", 11, no. 4, 327-346.

Liroff, Richard A. (1980) *Air Pollution Offsets: Trading, Selling, and Banking* (Conservation Foundation, Washington).

Magat, Wesley A. (1978) "Pollution Control and Technological Advance: A Dynamic Model of the Firm", *Journal of Environmental Economics and Management* 5, no. 1, 1-25.

Majone, Giandomenico (1976) "Choice Among Policy Instruments for Pollution Control", 2, 589-613, June.

Mäler, Karl-Goran (1974a) *Environmental Economics: A Theoretical Inquiry* (Johns Hopkins University Press for Resources for the Future, Baltimore).

Mäler, Karl-Goran (1974b) "Effluent Charges versus Effluent Standards", in: J. Rothenberg and G. Heggie (eds.), *The Management of Water Quality and the Environment* (Macmillan, London).

McGartland, Albert H. and Wallace E. Oates (1983) "Marketable Permits for the Prevention of Environmental Deterioration", University of Maryland (Department of Economics) Working Paper 83-11.

Meselman, Stuart (1982) "Production Externalities and Corrective Subsidies: A General Equilibrium Analysis", *Journal of Environmental Economics and Management* 9, no. 2, 186-193.

Mills, Edwin S. (1966) "Economic Incentives in Air-Pollution Control", in: Harold Wolozin (ed.), *The Economics of Air Pollution* (W.W. Norton, New York).

Montgomery, David (1972) "Markets in Licenses and Efficient Pollution Control Programs", *Journal of Economic Theory*, 5, 395-418.

Moore, I. Christina (1980) "Implementation of Transferable Discharge Permits When Permit Levels Vary According to Flow and Temperature: A Study of the Fox River, Wisconsin", Department of Civil and Environmental Engineering (University of Wisconsin, Madison) Masters Thesis.

OECD (1978) *Employment and Environment Policy – A State of the Art Review*, ENV/ECO77.5 (OECD, Paris).

OECD (1981) *Economic Instruments in Solid Waste Management* (OECD, Paris).

OECD (1982a) *Environmental Policy and Technical Change*, report by The Secretariat of the Environment Committee (OECD, Paris) mimeo (November).

OECD (1982b) *Impact of Environmental Policies on Technological Change: A Synthesis of the Industrial Case Studies*, ENV/ECO82.5 (OECD, Paris) mimeo.

Olsen, Mancur, Jr. and Richard Zeckhauser (1970) "The Efficient Production of External Economies", *American Economic Review* 60 512–517.

O'Neil, William (1980) "Pollution Permits and Markets for Water Quality", Unpublished Ph.d dissertation, (University of Wisconsin, Madison).

O'Neil, William, Martin David, Christina Moore and Erhard Joeres (1981) "Transferable Discharge Permits and Economic Efficiency", Workshop Sheries 8107, Madison, Wisconsin, Social Science Research Institute. (May).

Opaluch, James J. and Thomas A. Grigalunas (1983) "Controlling Stochastic Pollution Events Through Liability Rules: Some Evidence from OCS Leasing", Staff Paper 83-13, Department of Resource Economics (University of Rhode Island, Kingston).

Oppenheimer, Joe. A. and Clifford S. Russell (1983) "A Tempest in a Teapot: The Analysis and Evaluation of Environmental Groups Trading in Markets for Pollution Permits", in E. Joeres and M. David (eds.), *Buying a Better Environment*. Land Economics, Monograph #6, (University of Wisconsin Press, Madison).

Palmer, Adele R., William E. Mooz, Timothy H. Quinn and Kathleen A. Wolf (1980) *Economic Implications of Regulating Chlorofluorocarbon Emissions from Nonaerosol Applications*, Rand Corporation Report R-2524-EPA (June).

Parker, Roland (1976) *The Common Stream* (Granada Publishing, London).

Pearce, David W. (1983) *The Distribution of the Costs and Benefits of Environmental Policy*, Report from the Environmental Committee of the OECD (OECD, Paris), mimeo.

Philadelphia Air Management Services (1981) *Feasibility Study: A Fee/Subsidy System for Controlling Sulfur Dioxide Emissions in Philadelphia Air*, esp. vol. II, *Economic Theory* (Air Management Services, Philadelphia).

Polinsky, A. Mitchell (1979) "Controlling Externalities and Protecting Entitlements: Property Right, Liability Rule, and Tax-Subsidy Approaches", *Journal of Legal Studies* 8, no. 1, 1–48.

Quirk, Paul G. (1981) *Industry Influence on Federal Regulatory Agencies* (Princeton, N.J.: Princeton University Press).

Railton, Peter (1984) "Locke, Stock, and Peril: Natural Property Rights, Pollution, and Risk", *To Breathe Freely: Risk, Consent and Air*, to be published by Rowman and Allanheld (eds.), Forthcoming Fall of 1984.

Reppeto, Robert (1979) "Economic Systems for the Allocation of Entitlements to Degrade Air Quality in Clean Air Areas Under Prevention of Significant Deterioration Rules", unpublished, Harvard School of Public Health, (October).

Richardson, Genevra with Anthony Ogus and Paul Burrows (1983) *Policing Pollution*, (Oxford University Press).

Roberts, Marc. J. and Michael Spence (1976) "Effluent Charges and Licenses under Uncertainty", *Journal of Public Economics*, 5, no. 3, 4, 193–208.

Rose, Marshall (1973) "Market Problems in the Distribution of Emission Rights", *Water Resources Research* 9, no. 5, 1132–1144.

Ruff, Larry E. (1970) "The Economic Common Sense of Pollution", *The Public Interest* no. 19, 69–85.

Russell, Clifford S. (1973) *Residuals Management in Industry: A Case Study from Petroleum Refining* (Johns Hopkins University Press for Resources for the Future, Baltimore).

Russell, Clifford S. (1979) "What Can We Get from Effluent Charges?" *Policy Analysis* 5, no. 2 155–180, Spring.

Russell, Clifford S. (1981) "Controlled Trading of Pollution Permits," *Environmental Science and Technology* 15, no. 1, 24–28.

Russell, Clifford S. (1984) "Achieving Air Pollution in Three Different Settings", in: *To Breathe Freely: Risk, Consent and Air* (Rowman and Allanheld).

Russell, Clifford S. and William J. Vaughan (1976) *Steel Production: Processes, Products and Residuals* (Johns Hopkins University Press, Baltimore).

Seskin, Eugene P., Robert J. Anderson, Jr. and Robert O. Reid (1983) "An Empirical Analysis of Economic Strategies for Controlling Air Pollution", *Journal of Environmental Economics and Management* 10, no. 2, 112–124.

Shavell, Steven (1982) "The Social Versus the Private Incentive to Bring Suit in a Costly Legal System", *Journal of Legal Studies* XI 333–339.

Sims, W.A. (1981) "Note: The Short-Run Asymmetry of Pollution Subsidies and Charges", *Journal of Environmental Economics and Management* 8, no. 4, 395–399.

Solow, Robert M. (1971) "The Economist's Approach to Pollution and Its Control," *Science*, 173 (August 6).

Sonstelie, Jon C. and Paul R. Portney (1983) "Truth or Consequences: Cost Revelation and Regulation", *Journal of Policy Analysis and Management* 2, no. 2, 280–284.

Spofford, Walter O. Jr., Clifford S. Russell and Robert A. Kelly (1976) *Environmental Quality Management: An Application to the Lower Delaware Valley* (Resources for the Future, Washington).

Spofford, Walter O. Jr. (1983) "Properties of Alternative Source Control Policies: Case Study of the Lower Delaware Valley", Resources for the Future, unpublished report.

Teller, Azriel (1967) "Air Pollution Abatement: Economic Rationality and Reality", *Daedalus* 96, no. 4, 1082–1098.

Terkla, David (1984) "The Efficiency Value of Effluent Tax Revenues", *Journal of Environmental Economics and Management* 11, no. 2, 107–123.

Tietenberg, T.H. (1974) "The Design of Property Rights for Air Pollution Control", *Public Policy* 22, 275–292.

Tietenberg, T.H. (1980) "Transferable Discharge Permits and the Control of Stationary Source Air Pollution: A Survey and Synthesis", *Land Economics* 56, no. 4, 391–416.

Tietenberg, T.H. (1983) "Transferable Discharge Permits and the Control of Stationary Source Air Pollution: Reply," *Land Economics* 59, no. 1, 128–130.

Trauberman, Jeffrey (1983) "Toxic Substances and the Chemical Victim", *Environmental Law* (Summer) p. 1–3, and 8, 9.

Tresch, Richard W. (1981) *Public Finance: A Normative Theory* (Business Publications, Inc., Plano).

Urban Systems Research and Engineering, Inc. (1979) *Responses to Local Sewer Charges and Surcharges*, Report to the U.S. Council on Environmental Quality, Contract No. EQ8AC029.

Vaughan, William J. and Clifford S. Russell (1983) "Monitoring Point Sources of Pollution: Answers and More Questions from Statistical Quality Control", *The American Statistician* 37, no. 4, pt. 2, 476–487.

Viscusi, W. Kip (1979) "Impact of Occupational Safety and Health Regulation", *Bell Journal of Economics* 10, no. 1, 117–140.

Watson, William D. and Ronald G. Ridker (1984) "Losses from Effluent Taxes and Quotas Under Uncertainty", forthcoming in the *Journal of Environmental Economics and Management*.

Webb, Michael G. and Robert Woodfield (1981) "Standards and Charges in the Control of Trade Effluent Discharges to Public Sewers in England and Wales", *Journal of Environmental Economics and Management* 8, no. 3, 272–286.

Weitzman, Martin L. (1974) "Prices vs Quantities", *Review of Economic Studies* XLI (4), no. 128, 477–491.

Wenders, John T. (1975) "Methods of Pollution Control and the Rate of Change in Pollution Abatement Technology", *Water Resource Research*, 11, no. 3, 393–396.

White, Lawrence J. (1982) *The Regulation of Air Pollutant Emissions from Motor Vehicles* (American Enterprise Institute, Washington).

Williamson, M.R. (1981) "SO_2 and NO_2 Mass Emission Surveys: An Application of Remote Sensing", in: Air Pollution Control Association, *Continuous Emission Monitoring: Design, Operation, and Experience* (APCA, Pittsburgh).

Wittman, Donald (1977) "Prior Regulation Versus Post Liability: The Choice Between Input and Monitoring Cost", *Journal of Legal Studies* 6, 193–211.

Yohe, Gary W. (1976) "Substitution and the Control of Pollution: A Comparison of Effluent Charges and Quantity Standards Under Uncertainty", *Journal of Environmental Economics and Management* 3, no. 4, 312–324.

Yohe, Gary W. (1977) "Comparisons of Price and Quantity Controls: A Survey", *Journal of Comparative Economics* 1, no. 3, 213–233.

Zeckhauser, Richard (1981) "Preferred Policies When There is a Concern for Probability of Adoption", *Journal of Environmental Economics and Management* 8, no. 3, 215–237.

INDEX